CHEMISTRY FOR
LIFE SCIENCES

CHEMISTRY FOR THE LIFE SCIENCES

J. G. Dawber and A. T. Moore
Department of Chemistry and Biology
North Staffordshire Polytechnic
Stoke on Trent

SECOND EDITION

First edition published 1973 by
McGraw-Hill Book Co. (UK) Ltd

Second edition published 1980 by
THE MACMILLAN PRESS LTD
London and Basingstoke
Associated companies in Delhi Dublin
Hong Kong Johannesburg Lagos Melbourne
New York Singapore and Tokyo

Produced by offset lithography by
UNWIN BROTHERS LIMITED
The Gresham Press, Old Woking, Surrey
A member of the Staples Printing Group

British Library Cataloguing in Publication Data

Dawber, John Graham
  Chemistry for the life sciences. — 2nd ed.
  1. Chemistry, Organic
  I. Title   II. Moore, Alan Thomas
  547′.002′4574   QD251.2

  ISBN 0–333–25820–7
  ISBN 0–333–25821–5 Pbk

Contents

Preface

This book is designed for students taking BSc courses in biology, biochemistry, pharmacy, combined science, and pre-clinical medical and dental courses. It will also be useful for students on HND and HNC courses in medical laboratory subjects and applied biology. Students on courses leading to MIBiol and the MILT qualifications, and also some Open University science students, will find the book helpful. We have assumed that readers of this book will have taken an introductory course in chemistry to at least GCE O-level and thus will be familiar with the more fundamental terms and concepts.

Our aim in writing this text is to provide the student of the life sciences with a sound knowledge of the many aspects of chemistry that are required for a study of modern biology. Much emphasis is now being placed on teaching students that the functioning of living organisms can be understood at the molecular level. This trend is likely to increase rapidly with our ever-increasing knowledge of the structure and function of cell organelles and the cell systems which make up tissues. It follows that the student must understand as much as possible about the 'molecular' level, its structure, and the forces and constraints acting there.

This revolution in the teaching of biological sciences has stemmed, first, from the result of the work of chemists in the determination of the structure of proteins, nucleic acids and other compounds of complex structure and, second, from the ever-increasing degree of detail with which the chemical reactions of living organisms are being studied by biochemists. Nowhere is the impact of chemistry more keenly felt than in the sphere of microbiology and the stage is approaching where much of the activity of a microorganism can be expressed in molecular terms.

The progress in our knowledge of the molecular basis of the activity of living organisms has been paralleled by the growth of the new branch of science known as *molecular biology*. The term *molecular biology* was introduced some twenty-five years ago by W. T. Astbury and, at its outset, was associated primarily with the structure of proteins, nucleic acids and other large molecules, and also with the detailed structure of cell organelles of which these molecules are a part. Now the term is able to cover the description of the action of these molecules in cells, tissues and organs just as Astbury had predicted.

The discovery of the molecular architecture of DNA proposed in 1952 has led to the formulation of the general principles for the molecular basis of genetics and the control of cell metabolism. The techniques for the elucidation of protein structure through the pioneering chemical studies of Sanger (1955) and by the X-ray studies of Perutz and Kendrew (1960) have led to the detailed structures of many enzymes being known. As a consequence of this, it is now possible to explain in precise chemical terms the superb catalytic action of these enzymes. The last few years have shown that the avalanche of discoveries has by no means abated. The first detailed structures of DNA and RNA molecules from viral sources have been recently reported, and this, together with the structural analysis of the corresponding viral proteins, has led to the elucidation of the covalent structure of the entire organism. Furthermore, organic chemists are playing an increasing role with the supply of synthetic materials such as the first 'man-made' enzyme compounds for the precise determination of the genetic code and the first 'man-made' gene.

Today the student of the life sciences needs a deeper understanding of basic chemistry than was ever required of his predecessor. Biology is taking on a quantitative rather than the traditional qualitative outlook. Chemistry has always provided a discipline which covers both the qualitative and the quantitative approaches. We hope in this book to have shown both types of approach and, at the same time, provided a fair coverage of the many aspects of chemistry with which the life sciences student needs to be conversant.

In this new edition, several amendments have been made in response to comments from many sources. In chapter 6, small sections have been added dealing with ionophoresis, affinity chromatography and X-rays. The major changes from the first edition occur in chapters 8 and 9 which have been revised and extended considerably. The sections dealing with enzymes and nucleic acids have been revised and new advances in the latter field have been incorporated. In chapter 9, a section on the control of carbohydrate metabolism has been added and a revision made on material describing protein and nucleic acid biosynthesis.

Many colleagues and friends offered valuable advice during the preparation of the first edition of the book, and this has also been the case during the preparation of this second edition. In particular, we would like to thank our colleagues Dr C. Arme, Dr J. C. Tebby, Dr R. A. Williams, Mr E. G. Tyler and Mr R. A. Tribbeck. Finally, we again take this opportunity to thank our wives for their forebearance and understanding.

Stoke on Trent, 1979   J.G.D.
                                                                   A.T.M.

1. Atomic structure and chemical bonding

1.1 THE ELECTRONIC STRUCTURE OF ATOMS

In this chapter an outline of the more important aspects of atomic structure will be presented in order that the reader may understand, in a qualitative way, the modern theories of valency and chemical bonding. This is necessary since chemistry as a science is concerned with the properties of matter and their interpretation in terms of molecular structure. This approach is not merely confined to chemistry, as witnessed by the recent growth of the subject known as molecular biology, where the fundamental processes occurring in living systems are interpreted from a molecular level.

A model of the structure of atoms has been developed, some general features of which will be familiar to the reader from his previous study of chemistry and physics. These are based on the Rutherford and Bohr theories of atomic structure where the atom is envisaged as a minute planetary system consisting of a positively charged nucleus surrounded by a sufficient number of negatively charged electrons to confer electrical neutrality.

Although the detailed study of the fundamental particles which constitute the nuclei of atoms is of great importance in nuclear physics, of far more importance in chemistry is the behaviour of the extranuclear electrons, since it is these and their interaction with the nucleus as a whole which determines the chemical properties of the atom and the bonding in which it may participate.

A great deal of the information concerning the electronic structure of atoms has been derived from a study of their emission spectra. When elemental substances or their compounds are heated to high temperatures, for example, in an electric arc, light is emitted. The wavelengths of the light emitted are characteristic of the elements present. If the light is passed into a spectrograph and diffracted by a prism, the emission spectrum is obtained which may be recorded photographically (Fig. 1.1). If pure elements are used then an atomic spectrum is obtained. The atomic spectrum of hydrogen is relatively simple and is shown in Fig. 1.2.

For other atoms, however, the atomic spectra are considerably more complex, containing many lines. It is found that, in order to account for all the lines in atomic spectra, it is necessary to assume that there exist many discrete levels of

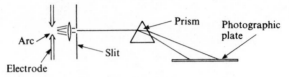

Fig. 1.1 Schematic diagram of a spectrograph

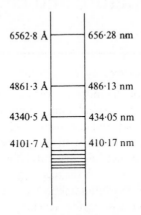

6562·8 Å	656·28 nm
4861·3 Å	486·13 nm
4340·5 Å	434·05 nm
4101·7 Å	410·17 nm

Fig. 1.2 The emission spectrum of hydrogen in the visible and near-ultraviolet region

energy for the electrons. These energy levels may be described uniquely by means of four *quantum numbers*.

The quantum numbers needed to completely characterize every energy level are shown in Table 1.1, together with their permitted values.

Consider the case when n is 1. The value of l corresponding to this is 0 and thus m is 0 also. For every value of m, the values of s are $+\frac{1}{2}$ and $-\frac{1}{2}$. Hence there is only one energy level (orbital) with n equal to 1 and it can contain a maximum of two electrons with opposite values of s— $+\frac{1}{2}$ and $-\frac{1}{2}$. When n is 2, values of $l = 0$ and also $l = 1$ are allowed. In the first case, there is only one value of m, whereas, in the second case, there are three values of m. Thus there can be a total of eight electrons which have a value of n equal to 2.

The energy levels, or '*orbitals*' as they are more frequently called, are classified according to the values of the *azimuthal quantum number* (l). When $l = 0$,

Table 1.1 Allowed values for the quantum numbers

Quantum number	Symbol	Allowed values
Principal	n	$1, 2, 3, 4, 5, \ldots, n$
Azimuthal	l	$0, 1, 2, 3, 4, \ldots, (n-1)$
Magnetic	m	$l, (l-1), \ldots, 0, \ldots, -l$
Spin	s	$\pm\frac{1}{2}$

2

the orbital is called an s orbital. When $l = 1$, the orbital is a p orbital of which there are three for every value of n; these arise from the three possible values of m. When $l = 2$, the five orbitals, from five values of m, are called d orbitals. A value of $l = 3$ gives seven orbitals and these are designated the f orbitals. The distribution of orbitals within any atom and the maximum number of electrons they can contain are summarized in Table 1.2.

Table 1.2 Quantum numbers and orbital representation

Shell	n	l	m	Name of orbital	Numbers of electrons	
K	1	0	0	$1s$	2	
L	2	0	0	$2s$	2	
		1	1, 0, −1	$2p$	6	8
		0	0	$3s$	2	
M	3	1	1, 0, −1	$3p$	6	18
		2	2, 1, 0, −1, −2	$3d$	10	
		0	0	$4s$	2	
N	4	1	1, 0, −1	$4p$	6	32
		2	2, 1, 0, −1, −2	$4d$	10	
		3	3, 2, 1, 0, −1, −2, −3	$4f$	14	

Certain conventions are followed in describing electrons. All electrons which possess the same value of the principal quantum number n are said to be in the same *shell*. The values of 1, 2, 3, and 4 for n correspond to the K, L, M, and N shells respectively. Thus, the K shell may accommodate two s-electrons in the $1s$ orbital which differ only in that they have *opposite spins*. The L shell can accommodate two electrons in the $2s$ orbital and six electrons in the three $2p$ orbitals. The M shell can contain two electrons in the $3s$ orbital, six electrons in the three $3p$ orbitals and ten electrons in the five $3d$ orbitals. In order of increasing orbital energy, the order in which the orbitals are occupied is $1s$, $2s$, $2p$, $3s$, $3p$, $4s$, $3d$, $4p$, $5s$, $4d$, $5p$, $6s$, $4f$, $5d$, $6p$, $7s$, $5f$, and $6d$.

1.2 THE PERIODIC TABLE

In the Periodic Table, the elements are arranged in order of atomic number. The atomic number is the number of protons in the nucleus and there are a corresponding number of orbital electrons to maintain electrical neutrality. Thus the position occupied by an element in the Periodic Table is directly related to its electronic structure. If we consider atomic hydrogen in its ground state, the single electron occupies the orbital of lowest energy, i.e. the $1s$ level. This is designated: $1s^1$ and may also be written as in the diagram, where the symbol ↑ represents an electron with a given spin. The next element, helium, has two

$1s$

H

3

electrons, and both of these are accommodated in the $1s$ level, and both electrons have opposed spins, i.e., spin quantum numbers of $+\frac{1}{2}$ and $-\frac{1}{2}$. This electron configuration is designated $1s^2$ and is very stable since the electrons are paired together and the quantum shell is now complete. The configuration may also be written as in the diagram, where the two arrows represent two electrons having opposite spins.

In the next two elements, electrons occupy the $2s$ energy level and the configurations are designated $1s^2$, $2s^1$ for lithium and $1s^2$, $2s^2$ for beryllium. The numbers used as superscripts in these designations, and others like them, refer to the numbers of electrons in the orbital concerned. Beryllium exhibits divalency, and for this to take place *excitation* of a $2s$ electron to a $2p$ orbital must occur, as shown in the diagram. The energy required to do this is more

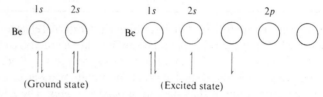

(Ground state)　　　　　　(Excited state)

than compensated for by the pairing of the two electrons with electrons of other atoms or groups when compounds are formed. A similar situation arises in the case of boron where the ground-state configuration ($1s^2$, $2s^2$, $2p^1$) is excited to $1s^2$, $2s^1$, $2p^2$ and in the case of carbon ($1s^2$, $2s^2$, $2p^2$) to $1s^2$, $2s^1$, $2p^3$. In both cases the p orbitals are singly occupied. This is an example of *Hund's rule*, which states that orbitals will be singly occupied before pairing up of the electrons in the same quantum shell takes place. In the case of nitrogen the configuration is $1s^2$, $2s^2$, $2p^3$ and only the $2p$ electrons are used in the first place in bond formation, giving nitrogen trivalency. The pair of electrons in the $2s$ orbital are termed *lone-pair* electrons and are used in bonding only in special circumstances.

The configurations of oxygen, fluorine and neon are obtained using the same principles and are as follows: $1s^2$, $2s^2$, $2p^4$; $1s^2$, $2s^2$, $2p^5$ and $1s^2$, $2s^2$, $2p^6$. The quantum shell corresponding to $n = 2$ (the L shell) is complete in neon and this fact explains the chemically inert nature of this element. All of the noble gases have electronic configurations in their outer electron shells of ns^2, np^6 and this is the reason for their chemical stability. All other elements attempt to achieve the noble gas electronic configuration by either losing, gaining or sharing electrons when they form chemical compounds. The electronic configurations of the other elements are shown in the Periodic Table (Fig. 1.3).

4

1 H $1s^1$																	2 He $1s^2$
3 Li $2s^1$	4 Be $2s^2$											5 B $2p^1$	6 C $2p^2$	7 N $2p^3$	8 O $2p^4$	9 F $2p^5$	10 Ne $2p^6$
11 Na $3s^1$	12 Mg $3s^2$											13 Al $3p^1$	14 Si $3p^2$	15 P $3p^3$	16 S $3p^4$	17 Cl $3p^5$	18 Ar $3p^6$
19 K $4s^1$	20 Ca $4s^2$	21 Sc $3d^14s^2$	22 Ti $3d^24s^2$	23 V $3d^34s^2$	24 Cr $3d^54s^1$	25 Mn $3d^54s^2$	26 Fe $3d^64s^2$	27 Co $3d^74s^2$	28 Ni $3d^84s^2$	29 Cu $3d^{10}4s^1$	30 Zn $3d^{10}4s^2$	31 Ga $4p^1$	32 Ge $4p^2$	33 As $4p^3$	34 Se $4p^4$	35 Br $4p^5$	36 Kr $4p^6$
37 Rb $5s^1$	38 Sr $5s^2$	39 Y $4d^15s^2$	40 Zr $4d^25s^2$	41 Nb $4d^45s^1$	42 Mo $4d^55s^1$	43 Tc $4d^65s^1$	44 Ru $4d^75s^1$	45 Rh $4d^85s^1$	46 Pd $4d^{10}5s^0$	47 Ag $4d^{10}5s^1$	48 Cd $4d^{10}5s^2$	49 In $5p^1$	50 Sn $5p^2$	51 Sb $5p^3$	52 Te $5p^4$	53 I $5p^5$	54 Xe $5p^6$
55 Cs $6s^1$	56 Ba $6s^2$	57 La $5d^16s^2$	72 Hf $5d^26s^2$	73 Ta $5d^36s^2$	74 W $5d^46s^2$	75 Re $5d^56s^2$	76 Os $5d^66s^2$	77 Ir $5d^76s^2$	78 Pt $5d^96s^1$	79 Au $5d^{10}6s^1$	80 Hg $5d^{10}6s^2$	81 Tl $6p^1$	82 Pb $6p^2$	83 Bi $6p^3$	84 Po $6p^4$	85 At $6p^5$	86 Rn $6p^6$
87 Fr $7s^1$	88 Ra $7s^2$	89 Ac $6d^17s^2$															

RARE-EARTH ELEMENTS (THE LANTHANIDES)

58 Ce	59 Pr	60 Nd	61 Pm	62 Sm	63 Eu	64 Gd	65 Tb	66 Dy	67 Ho	68 Er	69 Tm	70 Yb	71 Lu

THE ACTINIDES

90 Th	91 Pa	92 U	93 Np	94 Pu	95 Am	96 Cm	97 Bk	98 Cf	99 Es	100 Fm	101 Md	102 No

Fig. 1.3   The Periodic Table and electronic configuration

A fundamental theorem of modern physics is the *Heisenberg uncertainty principle*. The implication of this theorem is that it is impossible to define precisely at the same time both the position of moving objects and their momenta (and hence velocity). The uncertainty in position Δx and the uncertainty in momentum Δp are related to Planck's constant by the equation

$$\Delta p\,\Delta x \sim h \qquad (1.1)$$

This principle has important consequences for orbital electrons. It means that we cannot define precisely their position in atomic space and therefore may only speak in terms of the probability of finding electrons in certain positions. This is commonly done in two complementary ways. Firstly, by plotting radial probabilities; that is, the probabilities of finding the electrons as a function of distance from the nucleus for each orbital. The results of this for the $1s$ and $2s$ orbitals are shown in Fig. 1.4. The probability of finding the electron at the

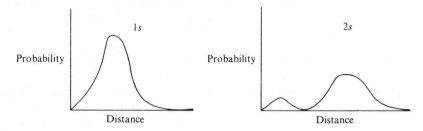

Fig. 1.4   Radial probabilities for hydrogen-like orbitals

nucleus is zero and, the higher the value of the quantum number n, the further away from the nucleus is the electron likely to be found.

In order to complete the probability picture for orbital electrons, it is necessary to consider their angular probabilities—in other words, the directional properties of orbitals. This is of extreme importance since the directional properties of the orbitals play a major role in the determination of molecular shape. The s orbitals are all spherically symmetrical about the nucleus and a cross section through the origin would appear as in Fig. 1.5. The three p orbitals in each quantum shell are not spherically symmetrical with respect to angular probability and, although they are all identical in shape, they differ with respect to orientation about the x, y and z coordinate axes. The three orbitals are designated p_x, p_y, and p_z, depending upon orientation along the coordinate axes (Fig. 1.6).

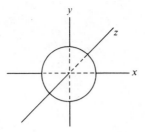

Fig. 1.5 Angular probabilities of *s* orbitals

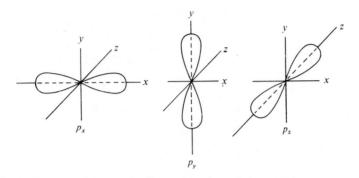

Fig. 1.6 Angular probabilities of *p* orbitals

As we have seen, there are five *d* orbitals in each quantum shell and the angular probability distributions are rather more complicated. These are illustrated in Fig. 1.7.

The angular probability distributions for the *f* orbitals are even more complicated, and since they are rarely used in chemical bonding, they will not be discussed here.

1.4 IONIC BONDING

The formation of chemical compounds takes place as a result of the interaction of the electrons in outer *shells* of different atoms or groups of atoms. There are various types of interaction covered by the generic title *chemical bonding*.

In the early stages of the electronic theory of valency, it was realized that the electronic configurations of the *noble gases*: helium, neon, argon, krypton, xenon and radon must be of special significance on account of the chemical inertness of these elements. When an *ionic bond* is formed, there is a transfer of one or more electrons from one atom to another in order to achieve a noble-gas configuration. This results in the formation of ions which have formal charges.

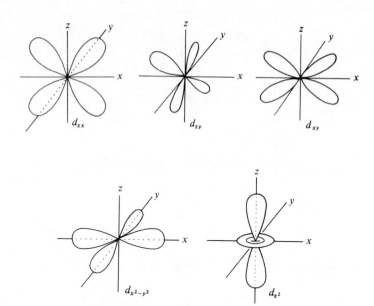

Fig. 1.7 Angular probabilities of *d* orbitals

Thus ionic compounds in the solid state are made up of positively and negatively charged ions. The forces which hold the ions together are electrical in nature and there is a balance of the attractive and repulsive forces between unlike and like ions respectively. The ions form lattices which are arranged in an orderly manner throughout the crystal. Some examples are shown in Fig. 1.8.

A simple example of electron transfer is the case of potassium chloride. The potassium atoms, by the loss of an electron, can achieve the stable configuration of a noble gas—argon.

$$\text{K} \quad 1s^2, 2s^2, 2p^6, 3s^2, 3p^6, 4s^1 \rightarrow \text{K}^+ \quad 1s^2, 2s^2, 2p^6, 3s^2, 3p^6$$

(configuration of argon)

The loss of an electron from an atom, however, is not a completely spontaneous process. The positive charge on the nucleus is attracting the single electron in the $4s$ orbital and, in order to form the positive ion (the *cation*), a certain amount of energy has to be supplied to overcome the attractive force. The energy necessary to do this is called the *ionization potential*. In the case of potassium and the other alkali metals, the value of the ionization potential is low, and this explains the readiness of these atoms to form cations.

The electron from the $4s$ orbital of the potassium atom is transferred to the chlorine atom, which is deficient of one electron in a $3p$ orbital compared with the configuration of the noble gas argon. In this way, the chloride *anion* (Cl⁻)

8

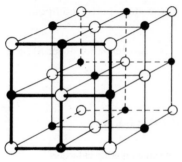
Sodium chloride structure

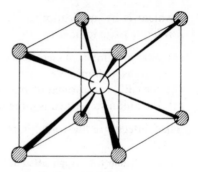
Caesium chloride structure

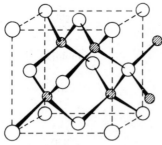
Zinc blende structure

⊘ Zn ◯ S

Fig. 1.8 Some common crystal structures

is formed. The tendency of the chlorine atom to accept this electron is expressed in the *electron affinity* and, in this case, it is high. Electron affinity is defined as the amount of energy released when an electron is added to a neutral gaseous atom in its lowest energy state.

It follows from this discussion that ionic compounds should occur most frequently between elements of low ionization potential and elements of high electron affinity, and this is found to be the case. There are some ionic compounds, however, in which the two energies are not balanced, i.e., the ionization potential far exceeds the electron affinity and yet ionic bonds arise. The reason for this is that sufficient energy results from the electrostatic attraction within the crystal to make the formation of ions favourable. The energy of the formation of the crystal lattice, the *lattice energy*, plays an important role in relation to the formation of ionic compounds. In general, a large value for the lattice energy indicates considerable crystal stability, since only processes which supply a large amount of energy can disrupt this lattice.

A qualitative method for estimating whether a compound is ionic or

9

covalent is by application of *Fajan's rules*. These state that a compound is *less likely* to be ionic if

(a) a large number of electrons would have to be transferred in order to form cations and anions,
(b) the cation so formed is small in size,
(c) the anion so formed is large in size.

These effects are illustrated in the examples in Table 1.3.

Table 1.3   Application of Fajan's rules for some metallic chlorides

Compound	Cation radius (pm†)	Melting point (°C)	
(a) Effect of cation charge			
NaCl	95	800	Decreasing ionic character
$CaCl_2$	99	772	
$MgCl_2$	65	712	
$AlCl_3$	50	Sublimes	
(b) Effect of cation size			
$BeCl_2$	31	405	
$MgCl_2$	65	712	Increasing ionic character
$CaCl_2$	95	772	
$SrCl_2$	113	872	
$BaCl_2$	135	960	
(c) Effect of anion size	Anion radius (pm)		
CaF_2	136	1392	
$CaCl_2$	181	772	Decreasing ionic character
$CaBr_2$	192	730	
CaI_2	216	565	

† pm = picometre = 10^{-12} metre = 0·01 Å.

1.5   COVALENT BONDING

1.5.1   Formation of sigma bonds

Covalent bonds are formed by the *sharing* of electrons between atoms and, for this to take place, the atoms must come very close together. Each covalent bond that is formed in this way contains two electrons which have opposite values of spin quantum number (i.e., $s = +\frac{1}{2}$ and $-\frac{1}{2}$) and the electrons are said to have *opposed spins*. Once a covalent bond is formed, the two electrons in the bond become indistinguishable. It is this property of the electrons in the bond which gives rise to the stability of the covalent bond, since each of the two atoms or groups finds its electronic requirements satisfied.

The simplest molecule is that of hydrogen. When two hydrogen atoms with electrons of opposed spins are brought together, a covalent bond is formed

10

between the atoms. This is illustrated in Fig. 1.9, where the covalent bond arises through overlap of the two 1s orbitals. The combined orbital is termed a *molecular orbital*. There are two types of molecular orbital: a *sigma* (σ) orbital and a *pi* (π) orbital. The one that arises in a single covalent bond is a σ molecular orbital. If the molecular orbital is of lower energy than the contributing atomic orbitals it is said to be a *bonding orbital* and will lead to the formation of a bond. On the other hand if the molecular orbital is of higher energy it is said to be an *antibonding orbital* (signified as σ^* or π^*) and no bond formation occurs.

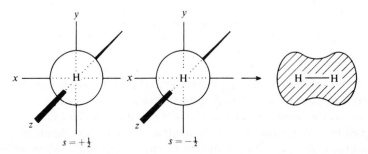

Fig. 1.9 Schematic representation of the formation of the hydrogen molecule (H_2)

The chlorine molecule is made up of two chlorine atoms each of which possesses the electronic configuration of $3s^2$, $3p^5$ in the outermost shell. Overlap of the two $3p_z$ takes place and results in the formation of a covalent bond between the two atoms.

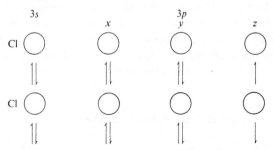

When a covalent bond is formed by overlapping of two s orbitals, an s and a p orbital or two p orbitals, the bond so formed is called a *sigma* (σ) bond. A description of the formation of *pi* (π) bonds (π-molecular orbitals) will be found in section 1.5.6, in connection with the formation of multiple bonds.

1.5.2 Electronegativity

When covalent bonds are formed between different atoms, there is an unequal sharing of the two electrons within the bond. This situation arises, for example, in the hydrogen halides HF, HCl, HBr and HI. In these molecules, the halogen atoms have a greater affinity for the electrons than the hydrogen atom. This causes a separation of charge within the molecule. The molecule will possess a certain amount of ionic character even though it is predominantly covalent. The percentage of ionic character in this type of bond may be calculated and, in the case of the hydrogen halides, is HF 40 per cent, HCl 17 per cent, HBr 11 per cent and HI 5 per cent.

$$\overset{\delta+}{H}\!\!-\!\!\!\div\!\!\overset{\delta-}{X} \quad \text{or} \quad \overset{\text{\Large$+\!\!\longrightarrow$}}{H\!\!-\!\!\!-\!\!X}$$
$$\quad\quad I \quad\quad\quad\quad\quad\quad II$$

Molecules of this type are referred to as having *polar covalent* bonds and they possess a *dipole* represented by II. When there are a number of dipoles within a molecule, the resultant molecular dipole and its direction of action may be obtained by vector addition of the individual moments. The dipole moment of a compound is thus a manifestation of the partial ionic character of the molecule arising from unequal sharing of electrons in the bonds. Further consideration is given to this concept with reference to bonds involving carbon atoms in chapter 4.

The tendency of atoms to have preferential affinity for electrons with respect to one another is described by the concept of *electronegativity*. The halogens are the most electronegative and the alkali metals are the least electronegative elements. An element of low electronegativity is also referred to as an *electropositive* element. The elements oxygen and nitrogen which are important in organic compounds have high values of electronegativity, comparable to the value for chlorine. If there is a large difference in electronegativity between two elements, then it is likely that an ionic bond will be formed between them.

1.5.3 Bonding and structure in polyatomic molecules

In 1940, Sidgwick and Powell pointed out that elements which have the same number or the same grouping of electrons in the outermost or *valency* shell have the same spatial arrangement of bonds or *stereochemistry*. This stereochemistry can often be deduced by making the simple assumption that electron pairs repel each other and therefore orientate themselves in such a way as to be as far apart in space as possible. The theory can be made more quantitative by assuming that the strength of the repulsions between electron pairs is in the order

lone pair–lone pair > lone pair–bond pair > bond pair–bond pair

Perfectly regular molecular shapes are achieved only if the electron pairs are all alike within the valency shell of the central atom, and they all repel each other equally. If a lone pair is present in the valency shell, then its greater repulsive power will cause the molecule to be slightly distorted from a regular shape.

Shapes of some simple molecules

(a) Two electron pairs A simple polyatomic molecule having two covalent bonds is beryllium chloride ($BeCl_2$). We have already seen that the excited configuration of Be is $1s^2$, $2s^1$, $2p^1$ and two covalent bonds are formed by the pairing of the two outer electrons with two electrons (p_z) from two chlorine atoms.

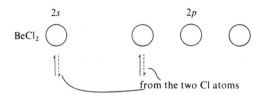

The beryllium atom is making use of its $2s$ orbital which is non-directional in character and one of its $2p$ orbitals which is strongly directional. It might be expected that the shape of the compound ($BeCl_2$) would reflect these two different covalent bonds. Both bonds are, however, entirely equivalent and, in order to overcome this apparent anomaly in the theory, we have to introduce another concept—the *scrambling* or *mixing* of orbitals. This process is called *hybridization* and results in the formation of *hybrid orbitals*. In the case of beryllium chloride, one *s* orbital and one *p* orbital have been hybridized to give two *sp* hybrid orbitals which are directed outwards from the beryllium atom at 180°, i.e., the molecule $BeCl_2$ is linear as shown in Fig. 1.10.

(b) Three electron pairs When three electron pairs are present, the hybridization of orbitals usually involves one *s* orbital and two *p* orbitals and is

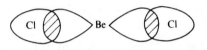

Fig. 1.10 Linear *sp* hybrid bonds in beryllium chloride ($BeCl_2$)

13

denoted as sp^2 hybridization. These orbitals have a planar trigonal distribution in space. Two cases arise with molecules having three electron pairs:

(*i*) *Three bonds* An example of this type of molecule is found in boron trichloride (BCl_3). Boron has an excited configuration: $1s^2, 2s^1, 2p^2$. Hybridization of the three unpaired electrons gives three sp^2 hybrid bonding orbitals which lie in a trigonal plane and the angles between the bonds are 120° (Fig. 1.11).

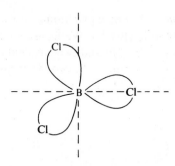

Fig. 1.11 Planar sp^2 hybrid bonds in boron trichloride (BCl_3)

(*ii*) *Two bonds* An example of a molecule with three pairs of electrons, one of which is a lone pair, is found in stannous chloride ($SnCl_2$). Although the 5s

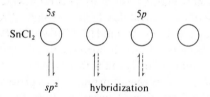

and the two $5p$ orbitals are hybridized in the usual way, the greater repulsive power of the lone pair distorts the bond angles from 120° to a slightly narrower angle (Fig. 1.12).

Fig. 1.12 The stannous chloride molecule ($SnCl_2$)

(*c*) *Four electron pairs* When four electron pairs are present, the hybridization of orbitals usually involves one s and three p orbitals and is denoted as sp^3. Three cases arise with molecules having four electron pairs:

14

(*i*) *Four bonds*   The simplest example of this type of molecule is methane (CH_4). Carbon has an excited configuration $1s^2$, $2s^1$, $2p^3$ which produces four sp^3 hybrid bonding orbitals. These four unpaired electrons are now available for sharing with the electrons from four hydrogen atoms. sp^3 hybrid orbitals have tetrahedral symmetry with respect to the central atom, and in methane a perfectly regular tetrahedral arrangement is found with bond angles of 109° 28′ (Fig. 1.13).

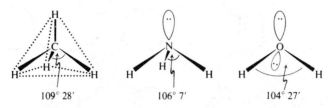

Fig. 1.13–15   Hybridization of four electron pairs

(*ii*) *Three bonds*   In this case, three of the electron pairs are used in bonding and the remaining electron pair is a lone pair. The hybridization is still sp^3, but the lone pair exerts a greater repulsive action on the bonding pairs than they do on themselves. This has the effect of distorting the molecule from the regular tetrahedral shape and the bond angles, in the case of the ammonia molecule (NH_3), are 106° 7′ (Fig. 1.14).

(*iii*) *Two bonds*   In this case, there are two sets of lone-pair electrons. A simple example of this type of molecule is water (H_2O). sp^3 hybridization of the valency electrons of oxygen takes place to give two hybrid orbitals containing the lone pairs and two which contain unshared electrons to form the two bonds with hydrogen. Again the lone pairs have a greater repulsive effect on themselves than on the bonding pairs and this causes a further distortion from the regular tetrahedral structure. The bond angle is less than the tetrahedral angle of 109° 28′ and is 104° 27′ (Fig. 1.15).

This type of treatment may be extended to cases of five and six electron pairs.

1.5.4   Rotation about single (σ) bonds

It is possible for some groups or atoms to undergo torsional rotation about single (σ) bonds. For example, in an alcohol molecule (R—OH) the hydrogen atom can be imagined as rotating with almost complete freedom around the bond between the rest of the molecule (R) and the oxygen atom (III). This relatively unrestricted rotation is due to the small size of the hydrogen atom.

$$R \longleftarrow O \diagdown {}_H$$

III

15

In other cases, the ease of torsional rotation is decreased and in some it is even completely prevented. This situation is referred to as *restricted rotation*. In the ethane molecule, restricted rotation is present and the two extreme spatial arrangements of the molecule are shown in Fig. 1.16.

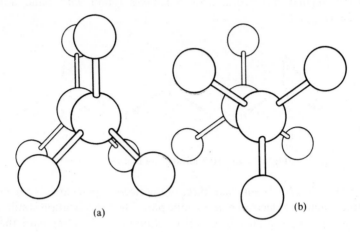

(a)   (b)

Fig. 1.16 Conformations of ethane: (a) eclipsed conformation; (b) staggered conformation

The different spatial arrangements that are found in molecules are called *conformations* and they have an important influence on the molecular shape. A *staggered* conformation, for example Fig. 1.16(b), is the most stable arrangement, since it has the lowest potential energy. The repulsive forces between the atoms are at a minimum, since every atom is as far apart as possible. In the case of ethane, other conformations are obtained by rotation of the two methyl groups rotating with respect to each other. Although the precise nature of the forces which restrict rotation about single bonds is not fully understood, energy must be expended to bring about rotation even in a molecule as simple as ethane.

A graph may be plotted of the potential energy of a molecule against the angular rotation. The result in the case of ethane is shown in Fig. 1.17. The maximum in the curve corresponds to the completely eclipsed positions and the minima to the fully staggered positions. The height of these potential-energy barriers determines the rate at which the molecule can twist from one conformation to another. In the case of ethane, this is 11 500 J mole^{-1} (2750 cal mole^{-1}).

If we now consider the molecule 1,2-dichloroethane ($ClCH_2CH_2Cl$), we find that there are three different conformations (Fig. 1.18) corresponding to the 'staggered' conformation of ethane [Fig. 1.16(b)].

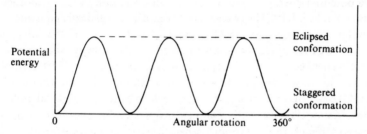

Fig. 1.17   Energy barriers to rotation in ethane

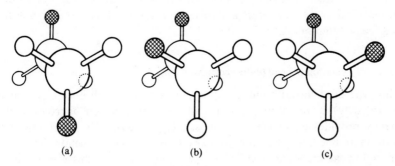

Fig. 1.18   Conformations of 1,2-dichloroethane: (a) *anti* (or *trans*); (b) *gauche*; (c) *gauche*

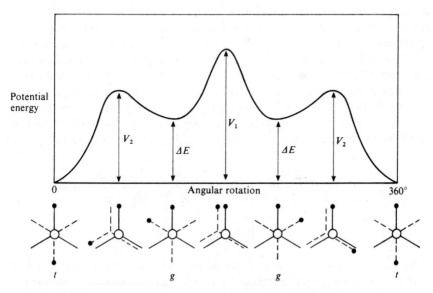

Fig. 1.19   Potential-energy curves for internal rotation in 1,2-dichloroethane

17

The potential-energy curves for the internal rotation in 1,2-dichloroethane are shown in Fig. 1.19. The two *gauche* forms are energetically equivalent. The two potential-energy maxima (V_2) are 12 760 J mole^{-1} (3050 cal mole^{-1}), while the large maximum (V_1), which corresponds to the maximum repulsive interaction between the two chlorine atoms, is 23 350 J mole^{-1} (5580 cal mole^{-1}). Both *gauche* conformations are less stable than the *anti* conformation by an amount ΔE which, in this case, amounts to 4650 J mole^{-1} (1110 cal mole^{-1}).

The interconversion of the conformations (*conformers*) in derivatives of ethane is extremely rapid at room temperature so that separate forms cannot be isolated. Nevertheless, there will be more molecules in the *anti* conformation than in any other. The study of the conformations available for a molecule is termed *conformational analysis* and this important concept in organic molecules is discussed in more detail in section 2.11.

1.5.5 The coordinate bond (dative covalent bond)

This type of chemical bond is a covalent bond in which both electrons are provided by the same atom or group, and the other atom, ion, or group involved merely provides an orbital. The most frequent examples are found in the coordination compounds (or complexes) of transition metals. The group providing the electrons is called a *ligand* and it acts in this way because it possesses one or more sets of lone-pair electrons. Once the coordinate bond is formed, it is identical in character to a normal covalent bond except that it may have a rather large dipole moment associated with it.

A familiar molecular species in which coordination occurs is the cuprammonium ion, which is the dark-blue coloured ion formed when concentrated ammonia is added to a solution of copper sulphate. It will be remembered that the ammonia molecule possesses a lone pair of electrons situated in an orbital belonging to the nitrogen atom. It is this pair of electrons that is utilized in forming a coordinate bond to a cupric ion (Cu^{2+}) to form the tetraammine copper(II) ion ([$Cu(NH_3)_4$]$^{2+}$). The formation of this ion may be considered to take place in the following manner: copper has a valency configuration of $3d^{10}$, $4s^1$ and the cupric ion $3d^9$, and this situation is illustrated in the diagram.

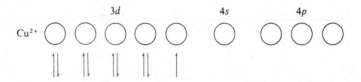

The unpaired electron in one of the 3d orbitals is excited to one of the 4p orbitals and four pairs of electrons from four ammonia molecules are used to fill the empty 3d, 4s and 4p orbitals, as shown. The bonding orbitals are then

18

[Cu(NH₃)₄]²⁺ ... $3d$ ... $4s$ ... $4p$

hybridized to make them equivalent, which gives dsp^2 hybridization. The arrangement of orbitals with dsp^2 hybridization is square planar (Fig. 1.20).

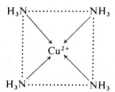

H₃N············NH₃
Cu²⁺
H₃N············NH₃

Fig. 1.20 Planar four-coordinate complexes of copper

The four-coordinate complexes of platinum are also planar and involve dsp^2 hybridization. The four-coordinate complexes of nickel on the other hand can be either planar involving dsp^2 hybridization (the ion [Ni(CN)₄]²⁻) or tetrahedral involving sp^3 hybridization of the coordinate bonds (the ion [Ni(NH₃)₄]²⁺). Some ions can form six coordinate bonds with groups or molecules possessing lone pairs. The resulting species usually have octahedral symmetry and either sp^3d^2 or d^2sp^3 hybridization of the coordinate bonds. Examples of this type of complex are the hexaammino cobaltous ion [Co(NH₃)₆]²⁺, hexafluoroferric ion [Fe(F₆)]³⁻, hexacyanoferrate ion [Fe(CN₆)]³⁻, and hexacyanocobaltic ion [Co(CN₆)]³⁻.

The formation of coordination complexes can provide an important method of estimating metal ions in solution. An important reagent used in these analyses is ethylene diamine-tetraacetic acid (EDTA or 'sequestrene') (IV). EDTA forms complexes with a wide range of divalent metal ions. These complexes are often referred to as *chelates*. Another example of chelate complexes used in analysis are those formed by cupric ion (Cu²⁺) with amino acids. For example, glycine forms a neutral complex with two glycine residues coordinated to a cupric ion in a planar arrangement (V).

HOOC—CH₂—CH₂—COOH
HOOC—N: :N—COOH

IV

O=C—O   O—NH₂—CH₂
Cu
CH₂—H₂N   O—C=O

V

19

Metal chelates find extensive uses in biological systems, including the following.

(a) Carriers for iron in plant nutrition.
(b) The nutrition of microorganisms.
(c) Animal nutrition, for example, the introduction of iron in anaemia.
(d) The removal of metals from physiological systems.
(e) Inhibition of calcium-induced coagulation of blood (by EDTA).
(f) The pharmacological action of certain drugs.

The formation of metal ion complexes is of great importance to the chemistry of living systems. The metal ions which all living organisms require for their maintenance are sodium, potassium, magnesium, calcium, manganese, iron, cobalt, copper and zinc. Some organisms also require small quantities of vanadium, chromium, molybdenum, cadmium and niobium.

The behaviour of these metals in biological systems can be roughly divided into two classes. The transition metals (with the possible exception of manganese) and also zinc are strongly bound to particular chemical neighbours. The Group I metals sodium and potassium, and the Group II metals magnesium and calcium are much less strongly bound to biological molecules and therefore exhibit fairly mobile behaviour in biological systems. These differences influence to a large extent the biological function of these metals. The cations of copper, iron, cobalt and molybdenum are involved in biological oxidation–reduction reactions and the zinc ion can act as an acid-type catalyst. The catalysing action of enzymes is often dependent on metal ions, for example Zn^{2+} in the enzymes of carboxypeptidase A and carbonic anhydrase, Mn^{2+} in isocitric dehydrogenase, and Mg^{2+} in enolase.

One remarkable feature of these cations in living systems is their specificity and discriminating behaviour. This arises largely from their behaviour towards the ligands with which they may form complexes. The ligands of interest contain the donor atoms oxygen, nitrogen, or sulphur, or a combination of these.

The stability of the complexes formed between ligands and the metal ions mentioned above is in the order $Na^+ < Ca^{2+} < Mg^{2+} < Mn^{2+} < Fe^{2+} < Co^{2+} < Zn^{2+} < Ni^{2+} < Cu^{2+}$ for a given ligand. However, some of the cations have a greater affinity for ligands containing oxygen than nitrogen atoms and some vice versa. For the ions Co^{2+}, Ni^{2+}, Cu^{2+} and Zn^{2+} nitrogen is the preferred chelating atom, whereas for Ca^{2+}, Mg^{2+}, and Mn^{2+} oxygen is the preferred chelating atom, while for Fe^{2+} the stability of both types of complex is roughly equal. Thus in a mixture containing several cations and a number of different ligands (in which there may be *different* donor atoms within the same molecule) considerable competition between the ligands will occur for the metal ions.

One feature of transition metal ions is their relatively small variation in ionic size within a given period of the Periodic Table. On the other hand the ionic radii of lithium, sodium and potassium cations are 0·60 Å (60 pm),

0·95 Å (95 pm) and 1·33 Å (133 pm) respectively, which are quite different, while those for magnesium and calcium are 0·65 Å (65 pm) and 0·99 Å (99 pm) respectively. The differences in size-to-charge ratio within this group of metals greatly influences their extent of hydration and the geometrical arrangement of ligands around the cations. These properties in turn influence their specificity. Studies with enzymes and other proteins suggest that

(a) binding by nitrogenous bases is in the order $Mg^{2+} > Ca^{2+} > Na^+ > K^+$, i.e., there is preferential binding of magnesium. Usually a phosphate or a carboxylate group is also present near the basic group,
(b) binding by multidentate anions and strong acid anions is in the order $Ca^{2+} > Mg^{2+} > Na^+ > K^+$. The binding site may include phosphate, carboxylate, or sulphonate, but no nitrogenous bases.
(c) magnesium and calcium ions bind more or less equally to multi-anion sites and much more strongly than sodium and potassium ions,
(d) binding by neutral or singly charged oxygen donors is in the order $K^+ > Na^+ > Ca^{2+} > Mg^{2+}$.

Thus, one can appreciate the manner in which selectivity and specificity of metal ions arises in certain environments in biological systems.

1.5.6 Multiple bonds

In all the molecules and ions considered so far, the bonds, whether they are covalent or coordinate, have been single bonds only. A great many covalent compounds, however, contain double and triple bonds. A simple example of a molecule with a multiple bond is ethylene (C_2H_4). Each carbon atom forms three σ bonds, one with the other carbon atom and two bonds with hydrogen atoms. These three σ bonds are formed through sp^2 hybridization:

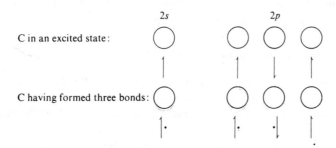

The two carbon atoms of each CH_2 group are joined by a σ bond and coplanar with this bond are the σ bonds with the hydrogen atoms. Each of the carbon atoms, however, possesses an unpaired electron in a $2p$ orbital. These can overlap (see Fig. 1.21) to form another bond between the carbon atoms. A bond formed in this way is termed a π·*bond* and the new orbital which has

21

resulted from the overlap of the two orbitals is called a π *molecular orbital*. In this case, since two *p* orbitals are involved, the bond may be referred to as *p*π–*p*π *bonding*.

Acetylene (C_2H_2) contains a triple bond where six electrons are shared between the two carbon atoms. Two *sp* hybrid orbitals are used to form σ bonds with the hydrogen atoms and the inter-carbon σ bond. Each carbon atom then has two electrons in *p* orbitals with which to form two π bonds. These are at right angles to each other and also to the σ bond between the two carbon atoms.

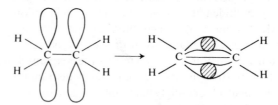

Fig. 1.21 The formation of the π bond in ethylene

One of the consequences of π bonding, in addition to increased reactivity, is a shortening of the distance between the two atoms involved. Thus the carbon–carbon internuclear distance in ethylene is 15 per cent less than the corresponding distance in ethane, i.e. 134 pm (1·34 Å) compared with 154 pm (1·54 Å). In acetylene molecules, the shortening of the distance between the carbon atoms is even more pronounced, the carbon–carbon distance being 106 pm (1·06 Å).

A further important feature of π bonding is that it does not affect the shape of the molecule in which it occurs. The shape of the molecule as judged by the directions in which the bonds point is determined by the σ bonds present, although any π bonding will produce a shortening of the interatomic distances. A final important feature is that rotation about a double bond is *not* possible due to resistance to rotation of the π bond.

1.5.7 Delocalization of π bonds and resonance

Certain molecules can be represented by more than one structural formula. For example, the nitromethane molecule can be represented by two conventional structures. In each of the formulae, the valencies of all the atoms are

$$CH_3 - \overset{+}{N} \overset{O^-}{\underset{O}{\diagup\diagdown}} \qquad\qquad CH_3 - \overset{+}{N} \overset{O}{\underset{O_-}{\diagup\diagdown}}$$

(a) (b)

satisfied, but the actual structure of the nitromethane molecule is neither of these *limiting structures*, since experiment shows that the bond lengths from the nitrogen atom to the oxygen atoms are identical. Furthermore, the length of these bonds is intermediate between those of single and double bonds. The charge cloud of a pair of electrons is distributed between each of the N—O bonds and is said to be *delocalized* and thus the true structure of the nitromethane molecule is best represented as

$$CH_3—N\overset{\displaystyle O}{\underset{\displaystyle O}{}}$$

where the dotted lines represent the delocalization of the π bond.

When the situation arises that the limiting structures have no real existence, the molecules are said to be in a state of *resonance* or *mesomerism*. The actual structure of the molecule is said to be a *resonance hybrid* of the limiting structures (*canonical forms*).

One of the important consequences of resonance is that, when it is present, it decreases the length of the bonds concerned and increases their stability. For example, the molecule of buta-1,3-diene is usually written as $CH_2=CH—CH=CH_2$, but the chemical properties of the compound and the bond lengths indicate that this cannot be the real structure. The central carbon–carbon length is 146 pm (1·46 Å) which is intermediate between the single carbon–carbon length of 154 pm (1·54 Å) and 134 pm (1·34 Å) for the isolated double bond. Buta-1,3-diene may be reduced by hydrogen and the heat change of this reaction is known as the heat of hydrogenation. The experimental heat of hydrogenation of buta-1,3-diene is less than might be expected by an amount equal to 12·2 kJ mole^{-1} (3·0 kcal mole^{-1}). The enhanced stability is due to resonance and the amount of energy by which the system is lower than that of the corresponding non-resonance system is the *resonance energy*. Resonance occurs in systems like buta-1,3-diene where double and single bonds alternate. Such a system is known as a *conjugate system*, and is explained by assuming that the π electrons are delocalized over the whole molecule and not restricted to regions between two carbon atoms (Fig. 1.22).

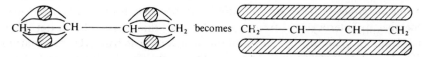

Fig. 1.22   Delocalization of π electrons in buta-1,3-diene

Resonance can be present in quite simple molecules. It has been established that the carbon dioxide molecule is linear (O=C=O) and the actual bond lengths are shorter than would have been anticipated. This may be explained if it is assumed that resonance is present in carbon dioxide and that the actual hybrid is made up from contributions from the following canonical forms:

$$\bar{O}—C\equiv\overset{+}{O} \longleftrightarrow O=C=O \longleftrightarrow \overset{+}{O}\equiv C—\bar{O}$$

(the double-headed arrow $\longleftrightarrow$ is commonly used to represent resonance).

23

One of the most important applications of the theory of resonance and delocalization of π bonds is in the benzene molecule and compounds derived from it. Although many canonical forms can be written for benzene, the two most important are the so-called Kekulé structures. All the carbon–carbon

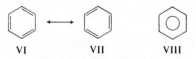

VI   VII   VIII

bond distances in the ring are identical, 140 pm (1·40 Å) a value intermediate between that for a single carbon–carbon bond and a double bond. The heat of hydrogenation shows that benzene is more stable than the hypothetical compound cyclohexatriene (VI or VII) by an amount of energy equivalent to 151 kJ mole⁻¹ (36 kcal mole⁻¹). In this book, benzene is represented by structure VIII.

An interpretation of the delocalization of the π electrons in benzene may be made using orbital theory. Each carbon atom can form three σ bonds of maximum strength by making use of sp^2 hybrid bond orbitals. These will be arranged trigonally. The angle between the orbitals is 120° and this will be uniquely preserved if the six carbon atoms are linked together in a planar six-membered ring. This structure is shown in Fig. 1.23(a). The remaining p orbitals would then project above and below the ring. They are then in an ideal position for multiple overlapping and multiple sharing of the six electrons they contain. This is shown in Fig. 1.23(b). The delocalization of the π orbitals produces a *sandwich* of electron charge distribution above and below the ring as shown in Fig. 1.23(c). This extensive delocalization of the six electrons gives rise to the large resonance energy and the characteristic properties in benzene and its derivatives which is referred to as *aromaticity* (see section 4.4).

Another important group of unsaturated cyclic molecules in which there is extensive delocalization of a sextet of π electrons is in heterocyclic compounds. Some examples of these are compared with benzene in Fig. 1.24. In the five-membered heterocycles—furan, pyrrole, and thiophene—the sextet of π electrons is made up by contribution of a lone pair from the heteroatom (O, N and S respectively). Although these compounds show many of the reactions of typical aromatic compounds, they are much more reactive, a feature consistent with their lower resonance energy. Pyridine, on the other hand, has a stability comparable to that of benzene, and in fact is generally less reactive to aromatic electrophilic substitution (see section 4.4.3). It should be noted that in this case the lone pair on nitrogen is not required to make up the sextet of π electrons.

It is the modern tendency in writing the structures of these compounds to indicate the presence of the delocalized sextet of π electrons by a circle in the same way as benzene (VIII). However, it is often desirable to use the Kekulé

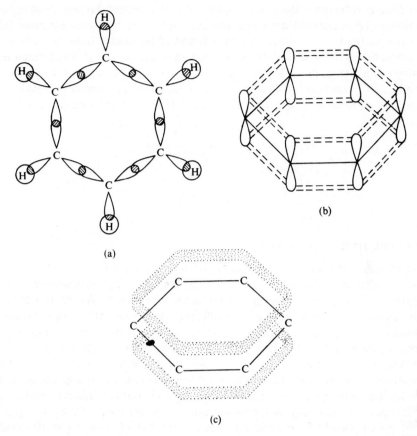

(a)

(b)

(c)

Fig. 1.23 The electronic structure of benzene: (a) σ bond formation; (b) the arrangement of p orbitals; (c) delocalization of the π electrons

structures particularly in describing the structure of reactive intermediates as a series of canonical forms. It must be emphasized that in many aromatic compounds the delocalization is not as complete as is indicated by the circle representation. Localized regions of high π electron density may be present,

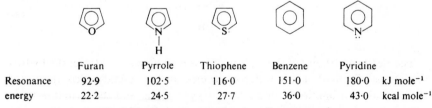

	Furan	Pyrrole	Thiophene	Benzene	Pyridine	
Resonance	92·9	102·5	116·0	151·0	180·0	kJ mole^{-1}
energy	22·2	24·5	27·7	36·0	43·0	kcal mole^{-1}

Fig. 1.24 Some common heterocyclic compounds

25

and this is reflected in the bond lengths and in the enhanced reactivity at these regions. Thus phenanthrene (IX and X) contains a high concentration of charge at the C_9—C_{10} bond, which is found to be shorter than the carbon–carbon bonds in the rest of the molecule, and is also the site at which reaction most readily takes place. Similarly in furan, pyrrole and thiophene the C_2—C_3 and C_4—C_5 bonds are shorter than the C_3—C_4 bond, a feature consistent with the conventional structures (XI; X = O, N—H and S respectively).

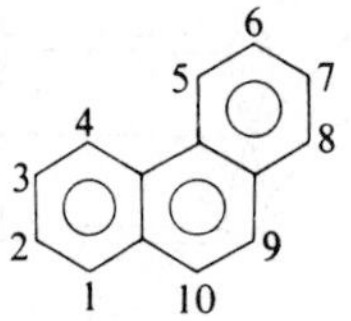

IX 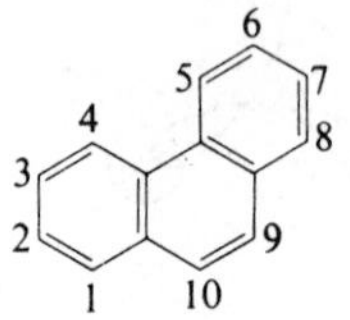   X 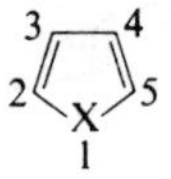   XI

1.6 THE HYDROGEN BOND

The forces that have so far been discussed in this chapter are those which hold atoms together. Other forces exist in matter, and those between molecules are particularly important. Intermolecular forces are generally known as *Van der Waals* forces, and arise from several different causes. One of the Van der Waals forces is the *hydrogen bond*, which is an example of dipole–dipole interaction, that is, the interaction of two molecules which possess dipole moments.

The hydrogen bond is a very common type of intermolecular force and involves the interaction of one or more hydrogen atoms with an electronegative atom such as oxygen, nitrogen, fluorine or chlorine. It is particularly important because of its low energy of formation and ease of disruption. Ordinary covalent bonds usually have bond energies of 200–400 kJ mole^{-1} (50–100 kcal mole^{-1}), whereas the hydrogen bond strength is about 12–29 kJ mole^{-1} (3–7 kcal mole^{-1}). The different types of hydrogen bonding may be classified as follows.

(a) Intermolecular hydrogen bonding extending over many molecules A simple example of this type occurs in water:

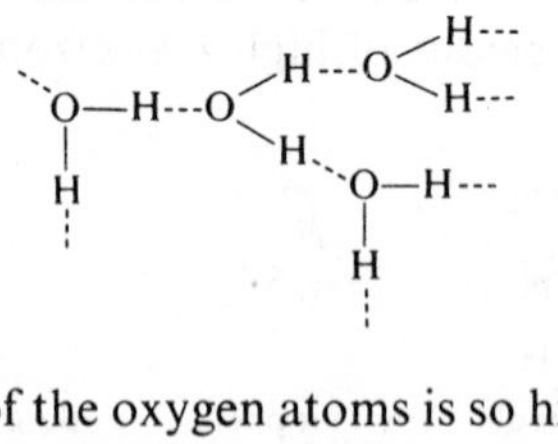

The electronegativity of the oxygen atoms is so high as to attract the hydrogen atoms of neighbouring water molecules. In the crystal of ice, there is a tetrahedral coordination around each oxygen atom, and the structure is an open one with the molecules relatively far apart. Similar extensive hydrogen

26

bonding is found in liquid ammonia, hydrogen peroxide, pure sulphuric acid, and liquid hydrogen fluoride.

(b) *Intermolecular hydrogen bonding extending over two molecules to form a dimer* Examples of this type of hydrogen bonding are common among organic carboxylic acids. In the case of acetic acid the dimer (XII) exists both in the liquid and vapour states. This demonstrates that a hydrogen-bonded structure has considerable stability.

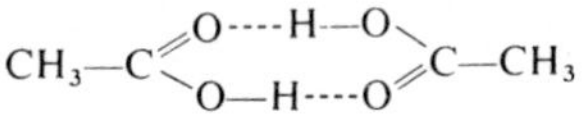

$$CH_3—C\overset{O\cdots H—O}{\underset{O—H\cdots O}{}}C—CH_3$$

XII

(c) *Intramolecular hydrogen bonding* In this case, the hydrogen atom is shared between two electronegative atoms within the same molecule. A simple example of this occurs in o-chlorophenol (XIII).

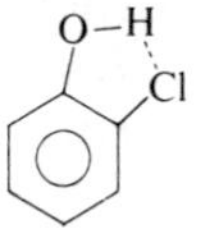

XIII

Examples of hydrogen bonding are very numerous, particularly among organic compounds, due to the prevalence of the —OH and the —NH groups. Hydrogen bonding often plays a large part in crystal formation in covalent compounds. However, because of the small energy associated with the hydrogen bond, the melting points and boiling points of covalent compounds are considerably lower than those of ionic compounds. The differences in melting points and boiling points of corresponding alkanes, alcohols and carboxylic acids—for example, ethane, ethyl alcohol and acetic acid—are due to the different extents of hydrogen bonding in these compounds, being greatest in the acids and least in the alkanes.

Association among simple inorganic hydrides is due to hydrogen bonding. The hydrides HF, H_2O and NH_3 are characterized by melting points and boiling points which are abnormally high when compared with compounds of similar molecular weight. In Fig. 1.25 the boiling points for a series of hydrides are plotted together with the corresponding values for the noble gases. The anomolous behaviour can, in all cases, be explained by hydrogen bonding in the liquid state.

There are many familiar situations in which hydrogen bonding plays an important part. These include the phenomenon of adhesion between two surfaces and the adhesion of dirt to skin and textiles. Two important examples of hydrogen bonding in biological systems are the hydrogen bonds which stabilize the ordered conformations of a polypeptide chain in proteins, and the

27

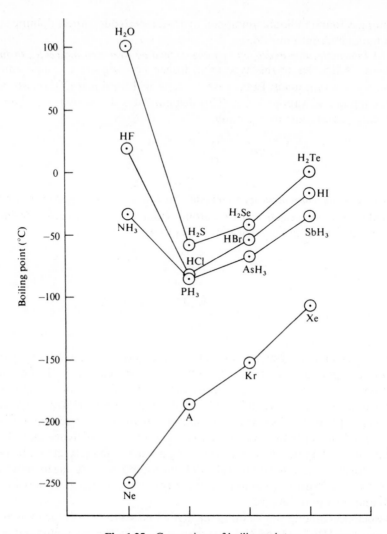

Fig. 1.25 Comparison of boiling points

interaction between heterocyclic bases in the nucleotide residues in deoxy-ribonucleic acid molecules, which stabilizes the double helix structure (see chapter 8).

1.7 RADIOACTIVITY

1.7.1 Radioactive disintegration

The stabilities of atomic nuclei depend on the number of protons in the nuclei and the ratio of neutrons to protons. Some nuclei exhibit instability and disintegrate to form new elements, the process being accompanied by the emission of radiation. This radiation is termed radioactivity. The terminology used to describe elements in nuclear chemistry is as follows.

(a) Nuclide This is a species of atom which is characterized by its mass number, atomic number, and nuclear energy state. The atomic number (the number of protons in the nucleus) is written as a subscript, and the atomic weight (mass number) as a superscript, e.g. $^{12}_{6}C$. If the atom is radioactive it is called a *radionuclide*.

(b) Isotopes These are nuclides of an atom which have the same atomic number but different mass numbers. Since the atomic number is the same, the number of protons in the nucleus is identical for each isotope, and hence the total nuclear charge is the same for each isotope. This means that they also possess the same number of orbital electrons, and hence have identical chemical and biochemical properties.

Nuclear instability, although more often associated with elements of high atomic weight, may also be found with some nuclides of low atomic weight. For example, the nuclides $^{3}_{1}H$, $^{14}_{6}C$, $^{15}_{8}O$, $^{19}_{8}O$, and $^{35}_{16}S$, and many others, are all radioactive.

For the heavier elements, more neutrons are required for nuclear stability, for example, $^{208}_{82}Pb$ contains 126 neutrons and 82 protons. For the heaviest elements, with atomic number greater than 84, all of the nuclides are radioactive, regardless of the number of neutrons. These are the *natural radioelements*. However, radioactive nuclides of any element may be produced artificially.

Often a nucleus produced in a radioactive disintegration is itself radioactive. This gives a *parent–daughter* relationship. The *daughter* of the *daughter* may again be radioactive and so on. It is thus possible to have chains of disintegrating nuclides in a *radioactive equilibrium*. The best-known radioactive series occur among the natural radioelements. There are three main series. One of these starts with uranium-238 ($^{238}_{92}U$) and ends with lead-206 ($^{206}_{82}Pb$) with radium-226, radium emanation (Rn-226; radon), radium D ($^{210}_{82}Pb$), radium E ($^{210}_{83}Bi$) and radium F ($^{210}_{84}Po$) as members of the chain. The other two naturally occurring chains start with uranium-235 and thorium-232 ($^{232}_{90}Th$).

The unit of radioactivity is the *curie* (Ci) and this is defined as that activity in which the number of disintegrations per second is $3 \cdot 7 \times 10^{10}$. Thus, for example, $0 \cdot 224$ mg of carbon-14 produces $3 \cdot 7 \times 10^{7}$ disintegrations per second and hence has an activity of a *millicurie* (mCi). Other submultiples of the curie are the *microcurie* (μCi) which is equivalent to $3 \cdot 7 \times 10^{4}$ disintegrations per second and the *nanocurie* (nCi) which is equivalent to 37 disintegrations per second*. Table 1.4 contains a list of levels of activity and the purposes for which they are used.

The measurement for *absorbed* radiation is the *rad*. This is the amount of radiation which results in the dissipation of 100 ergs of energy per gram of

*It has been agreed internationally that 1 disintegration per second be termed a *becquerel* (Bq). Thus 1mCi = 37 MBq. Both units are currently in use.

Table 1.4   Uses of radioactive sources

Activity	Use
100 00 Ci	High-energy source for industrial processing such as sterilization
1000 Ci	Source used in teletherapy
10 Ci	Source used in industrial radiography
1–100 mCi	Administration to patients in clinical radioisotope therapy
10 μCi–10 mCi	Patient administration for organ-scanning techniques
0·01–10 μCi	Activity of samples from patients undergoing radio-isotope therapy
10 nCi	Approximate level of background radioactivity in the body

material. This unit is of great importance in the specification of levels of radiological protection.

Each radioactive species is characterized by a constant known as its *half-life* (cf. section 3.9.4). This is the time for a given quantity of a radionuclide to have disintegrated to half its original amount. The value for radium-226 ($^{226}_{88}$Ra) is 1622 years, that of uranium-238 ($^{238}_{92}$U) is $4·5 \times 10^9$ years, while that of polonium-226 ($^{226}_{84}$Po) is $1·6 \times 10^{-4}$ sec. The radioisotopes used in clinical practice have a more restricted range of half-lives; for example, iodine-132 ($^{132}_{53}$I) has a half-life of 2·3 hours and hydrogen-3 ($^{3}_{1}$H; tritium) has a half-life of 12·26 years.

The decay processes of artificially produced radionuclides are no different in character from those of the naturally occurring radionuclides. The disintegration process for a given radionuclide follows first-order kinetics (cf. section 3.9.2) where the rate of decay at time t is proportional to the number, N, of atoms of the radionuclide remaining at time t. This may be expressed by the equation:

$$\text{Rate} = -\frac{dN}{dt} = \lambda N, \tag{1.2}$$

where λ is a constant for the radionuclide called the *decay constant*. Integration of eq. (1.2) gives

$$N = N_0 e^{-\lambda t}, \tag{1.3}$$

where N_0 is the number of atoms of parent radionuclide present initially, i.e., when $t = 0$. The half-life ($t_{1/2}$) is when N is equal to $N_0/2$ and using eq. (1.3), we have

$$t_{1/2} = \frac{0·693}{\lambda}. \tag{1.4}$$

There are three types of emission from radionuclides. For each type there may be a range of energies of the radiation and it is usual to express this in terms of *electron-volts* (eV). An electron-volt is the energy of one electron accelerated through a potential of 1 volt.

$$1 \text{ eV} = 1 \cdot 6 \times 10^{-12} \text{ erg} = 3 \cdot 82 \times 10^{-20} \text{ cal} = 16 \times 10^{-20} \text{ J}.$$

The electron-volt is an atomic unit of energy. When expressed per gram mole (i.e., multiplied by the Avogadro number, $6 \cdot 02 \times 10^{23}$), 1 eV mole^{-1} is equal to 96·6 kJ mole^{-1} (23 kcal mole^{-1}). The most frequently used multiples of the electron-volt are the mega-electron-volt (MeV), which is 1 eV $\times 10^6$ and the kilo-electron-volt (keV), which is 1 eV $\times 10^3$.

(*i*) *Alpha radiation* (α)   Alpha radiation consists of particles containing two protons and two neutrons, that is helium nuclei (He^{2+}). The energies of α particles are usually in the region 1–10 MeV depending on the particular radionuclide from which they originate. They have rather limited penetrating power (about 35 mm in air) and they would usually be absorbed by a sheet of paper. The reason for the limited penetrating power, in spite of their high energy, is their relatively high mass. As α particles pass through air they produce ionization of the air. For example, 5 MeV α radiation produces about 25 000 ion pairs per centimetre.

(*ii*) *Beta radiation* (β)   Beta radiation consists of high-speed electrons. Most β radiation consists of negatively charged electrons but the β radiation from neutron-deficient radionuclides is often positively charged electrons (positrons). The penetrating power of β radiation is higher than that of α radiation and has energies in the range 15 keV to 15 MeV. Passage of β radiation through air and other materials produces ionization in the material.

(*iii*) *Gamma radiation* (γ)   Gamma radiation does not consist of particles, but is high-energy electromagnetic radiation of short wavelength. It produces less ionization than α or β radiation; on the other hand it has great penetrating power.

Radionuclides usually emit β and γ radiation simultaneously. A few emit β radiation only, and of these phosphorus-32 ($^{32}_{15}$P), carbon-14 ($^{14}_{6}$C), tritium ($^{3}_{1}$H) and sulphur-35 ($^{35}_{16}$S) have been used in clinical applications. Some radionuclides emit only γ or X radiation, for example, iodine-125 ($^{125}_{53}$I), mercury-197 ($^{197}_{80}$Hg) and technetium-99 ($^{99}_{43}$Tc). When a radionuclide emits more than one type of radiation it may be important to know the amount of each type. This is termed the *branching ratio*. Table 1.5 gives a selection of radioactive nuclides together with their half-lives and the radiation they emit.

1.7.2   Detection, measurement and applications of radioactivity

The radiation from radioactive materials leaves a trail of ionization in its path. It is the production of ions that provides the most common methods for the detection and measurement of radioactivity. A number of detectors are based upon the electrical conductivity of a gas which has been ionized to a small

Table 1.5 Some radioactive nuclides

Radionuclide	Half-life	Radiation emitted
^{3}H	12·26 years	β^-
^{14}C	5720 years	β^-
^{32}P	14·3 days	β^-
^{35}S	87 days	β^-
^{59}Fe	45 days	β^-, γ
^{60}Co	5·26 years	β^-, γ
^{90}Sr	29 years	β^-
^{131}I	8·06 days	β^-, γ
^{226}Ra	1622 years	α
^{232}Th	10^{10} years	α
^{235}U	7×10^8 years	α, γ

extent by the passage of radiation. They usually contain two electrodes across which a high voltage is applied. As an emitted particle passes through the gas, there is transient increase in the conductivity of the gas, and a pulse of electricity flows from the electrodes into the external circuit. This pulse may then be registered by electronic devices. Systems which are designed to detect radiation in this way are called *ionization chambers.*

If the voltage applied to the electrodes in the ionization chamber is increased, the size of the pulse during an ionization event also increases. There are regions of voltage, however, where the counting rate (number of pulses per minute) is almost constant, and this is called the *counter plateau* (see Fig. 1.26). Outside these regions the pulse height (size) is proportional to the initial ionization produced, and, since α and β radiation produce different amounts of ionization, they will each produce a different pulse height. A further characteristic is that both types of radiation have separate plateaux. Such counting devices are called *proportional counters.*

If the voltage applied to the electrodes is very high, then the electrons produced in the ionization chamber, as a result of radiation, are accelerated so much that when they strike the anode they produce emission of photons. This, in turn, produces an avalanche of electrons due to further ionization, and these

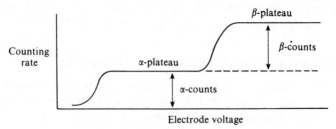

Fig. 1.26 Counter plateaux

also travel to the anode. Thus every particle which produces primary ionization within the chamber triggers off a very large pulse into the external circuit. This is the principle of the *Geiger counter*. The interior of the ionization chamber is usually filled with a mixture of argon (the ionizable gas) and gases such as methane or halogens (avalanche quenchers).

An alternative method of detection and measurement of radioactivity is by means of *scintillation counters*. In this method the radiation falls upon a material—the *phosphor*—which produces a flash of light for each particle. In the case of β radiation, the phosphor is an aromatic compound such as anthracene or stilbene. The photons of light produced are detected by photomultiplier tubes placed close to the phosphor. For γ radiation, sodium iodide crystals containing 1% thallium iodide are used as the phosphor material. The pulse size from the photomultiplier is proportional to the energy of radiation.

A modification of this technique, known as *internal sample liquid scintillation counting* is used for weak β-emitters. This is particularly useful for samples containing carbon-14 or tritium. The radioactive sample is dissolved in a *scintillating solution*, which contains the following components.

(a) A bulk solvent which absorbs most of the energy of the β-radiation and transfers the energy to a solute acting as the primary scintillator. Solvents used for this purpose include dioxan, toluene and xylene.
(b) A primary scintillator soluble in one of these solvents. Such compounds are: *p*-terphenyl, 2,5-diphenyloxazole (PPO) and 2-(4-diphenyl)-5-phenyl-1,3,4-oxadiazole (PBD).
(c) A secondary scintillator used to shift the wavelength of the radiation emitted by the primary scintillator to a longer wavelength to which the photomultiplier is more sensitive. Such compounds are: 1,4-di[2-(5-phenyloxazolyl)]-benzene (POPOP) and 2,5-di(diphenylyloxazole) (BBO).

If the radioactive sample is insoluble a gel is made which includes the scintillating liquids.

One of the main uses of radioisotopes in chemistry and biochemistry is the elucidation of reaction mechanisms and pathways. Two outstanding examples of this use are the tracing of the pathways for the fixation of carbon dioxide in photosynthesis and the biosynthesis of steroids. In both cases simple radioactive starting materials containing carbon-14 were used, which led to final reaction products containing carbon-14. From the positions of these radioactive carbon atoms found in the products and reaction intermediates, the complete pathways were traced.

Radioactive tracers have also been used extensively in physiology and medicine. Studies in membrane permeability, absorption of nutrients and distribution of metabolites have been possible by this technique. For example, studies on the absorption of vitamin B_{12} in patients suffering from pernicious anaemia is now possible, using cyanocobalamin labelled with radioisotopes of cobalt. Cell permeability studies have been made possible with radioisotopes. The permeability of red blood cells to various substances have been made with labelled compounds. The determination of intracellular and extracellular space may be measured using tritium-labelled water.

There are many applications of radioactivity in clinical research. These include:

(a) determination of blood circulation time,
(b) measurement of total blood volume,
(c) studies in uptake, retention and excretion of radioactive compounds in relation to radiotherapeutic procedures (especially the use of $^{32}_{15}P$),
(d) diagnosis of thyroid disorders using radioactive iodine,
(e) immunological studies and the fate of drugs and antibodies,
(f) studies on lung function in relation to lung ventilation and blood flow using radioactive gases such as ^{133}Xe, ^{13}N, ^{15}O and aerosols labelled with ^{131}I and ^{51}Cr,
(g) the location of venous thrombi using labelled fibrinogen which is converted to fibrin in forming the thrombus,
(h) the measurement of individual kidney function with ^{131}I.

Bibliography

1. E. Cartmell and G. W. A. Fowles, *Valency and Molecular Structure*, Butterworths, 1966.
2. L. Pauling and R. Hayward, *Architecture of Molecules*, Freeman, 1970.
3. J. Barrett, *Introduction to Atomic and Molecular Structure*, Wiley, 1970.
4. W. E. Addison, *Structural Principles in Inorganic Chemistry*, Longmans, 1963.
5. R. J. P. Williams, 'The Biochemistry of Sodium, Potassium and Calcium', *Chemical Society Quarterly Reviews*, **3**, 331, 1970.
6. D. B. McCormick and H. Sigel, 'Discriminating behaviour of metal ions and ligands with regard to their biological significance', *Accounts of Chemical Research*, **3**, 201, 1970.
7. C. A. Coulson, *The Shape and Structure of Molecules*, Clarendon Press, 1973.

2. The structural theory of organic chemistry

2.1 INTRODUCTION

It is the purpose of this chapter to present an outline of the main structural facets of organic chemistry, particularly those which concern spatial relationships within molecules. The number of organic compounds known is so large that a systematic study of the structure and reactions (see chapter 4) is essential. In this book, we shall be mainly concerned with organic compounds of natural origin which are of interest in biology and medicine. It is for this reason that certain aspects of structural theory—notably stereochemistry—will be emphasized. Structural theory is at the heart of a study of organic chemistry, for it is on this basis that facts about millions of different compounds are collected and arranged in a systematic way.

In organic molecules, the most important binding force between atoms is a covalent bond. In chapter 1, examples of small molecules produced by a few covalent bonds were described; these ideas have now to be extended to molecules containing many carbon atoms. The large number of organic compounds arises through the ability of carbon atoms to form very stable covalent (σ) bonds with themselves—a property unique to carbon. Apart from carbon and hydrogen, a number of atoms of other elements—*additional elements*—notably oxygen, nitrogen, phosphorus, sulphur, and halogens also occur.

In the elucidation of the structure of an organic molecule, the order in which the atoms are attached to each other and the positions they occupy in space must be determined. The molecule can then be represented by means of a diagram or, better, by the construction of a three-dimensional model where the individual atoms may be represented by spheres and the covalent bonds by rods. The reader is strongly recommended to obtain one of the many types of molecular model kit in order to be able to understand fully the three-dimensional aspects of the structure of organic compounds.

2.2 EMPIRICAL, MOLECULAR, AND CONSTITUTIONAL FORMULAE

Before any structural investigation is undertaken, it is necessary to obtain the compound in a high state of purity. For the purification of the complex molecules of interest to the biologist, many new techniques have been devised, and some of these are described in chapter 6. The introduction of accurate quantitative elemental analysis early in the history of organic chemistry afforded a means of determining the *empirical formula* for an organic compound—that is, the simplest ratio of the constituent atoms by which the composition of the substance can be described. These ratios must, of course, be written as integers, since a single molecule cannot contain fractional numbers of atoms. Today instruments are available for the accurate and automatic determination of the percentages of carbon and hydrogen through the combustion of very small amounts (1 mg) of the compound. Methods are also available for the determination of the additional elements on a micro-scale.

The next stage is to determine the exact number of each type of atom present in the molecule. For this, the molecular weight of the compound must be measured. Many methods are available for this, and the physical principles of the methods are described in chapter 8. A modern instrumental method based on vapour-pressure phenomena gives molecular weight values to an accuracy of one or two per cent. Even more precise values may be obtained from a mass spectrum. In fact, values obtained by the latter method may be used directly to calculate the molecular formula without elemental analysis data.

However, the traditional method for the calculation of molecular formula is still used. In this, the sum of the atomic weights as given by the empirical formula is compared with the molecular weight. In some cases they are approximately equal, and thus the empirical formula is in fact the molecular formula—that is, it gives the actual number of each type of atom in a molecule of the compound. In other cases, the molecular weight is a multiple of the empirical formula weight. For example: the elemental analysis of a typical carbohydrate like glucose gives an empirical formula CH_2O (formula weight 30). The molecular weight of glucose is 180, hence the molecular formula is $(CH_2O)_6$, or $C_6H_{12}O_6$.

One of the main problems in the structural determination is the elucidation of the *constitutional formula*—sometimes called the structural formula—which tells us the bonding arrangement of the atoms in the molecule. To do this, the valency of the atoms present must be taken into account. Carbon is invariably tetravalent, hydrogen and halogens univalent, oxygen and sulphur divalent, while nitrogen normally forms three covalent bonds and a fourth bond by the donation of an unshared electron pair. The chemical reactions of the compound are studied, particularly those which involve the additional elements present, and also reactions which indicate the presence of multiple bonds ($>C=C<$; $-C\equiv C-$; $>C=O$; $-N=N-$). Today, much time is saved in this part of the structural investigation by the use of physical instrumental methods, particularly spectroscopic methods (see chapter 6). These methods give direct information regarding the position and arrangement of small groups of atoms within the molecule.

Since, apart from hydrogen, the majority of atoms in most organic compounds are carbon atoms, it is important to decide what is the arrangement of the carbon atoms. For such a study, it is possible to divide organic compounds into a number of major groups.

(a) Open-chain compounds (aliphatic compounds)

In this group, the carbon atoms are joined together in a linear manner. These compounds may contain only carbon–carbon σ bonds—saturated compounds—or carbon–carbon multiple bonds—unsaturated compounds. The saturated hydrocarbons, known as *alkanes*, have the general formula C_nH_{2n+2}. These form a closely related family or *homologous series*, with similar chemical properties and a gradation of physical properties ranging from gaseous members methane $(n = 1)$, ethane $(n = 2)$, and propane $(n = 3)$, through volatile liquids like pentane $(n = 5)$ to waxy solids like eicosane $(n = 20)$. The carbon chain may be completely linear as in *n*-butane (I) or branched as in 2-methyl propane (*iso*-butane, II).

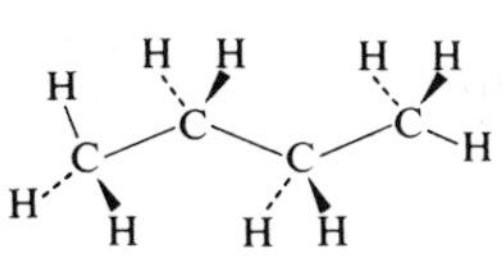

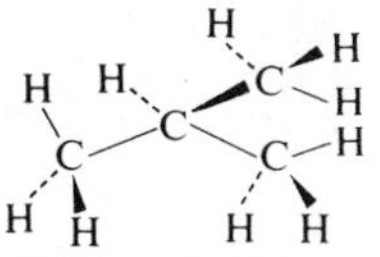

There are similar series of unsaturated hydrocarbons which may contain either double or triple bonds. The *alkenes* contain carbon–carbon double bonds. The structurally simpler members contain one double bond (III) while more complex alkenes contain several double bonds which are often found to alternate with single bonds to give an arrangement (IV) known as a *conjugated system*. The *alkynes* contain a triple bond; on the whole, these are less common among naturally occurring compounds, but examples of both isolated (V) and conjugated (VI) systems are known.

$$CH_3(CH_2)_nCH{=}CH(CH_2)_mCH_3$$
III

$$CH_2{=}CH{-}CH{=}CH{-}CH{=}CH{-}CH{=}CH{-}$$
IV

$$CH_3(CH_2)_nC{\equiv}C(CH_2)_mCH_3$$
V

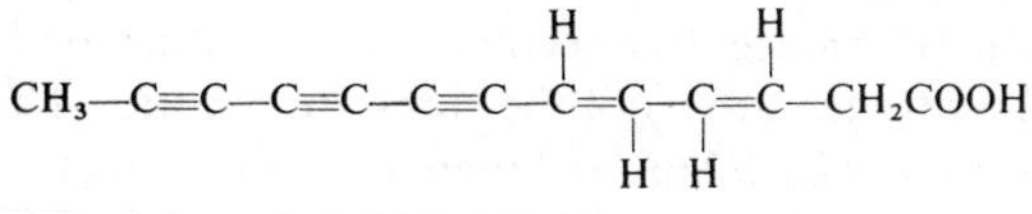

Isomycomycin   VI

37

(b) Cyclic non-aromatic compounds

The members of this group are often referred to as the *alicyclic* compounds; they have a ring of carbon atoms joined mainly through σ bonds. The smallest ring is a three-membered ring found in cyclopropane (VII). Six-membered rings (VIII) are the most common, and compounds with two or more fused together (IX) are found. This latter type of structure is found in the carbon skeleton of steroids. When diagrams of ring systems are drawn, the carbon atoms are omitted and may be assumed to be at the intersection of each line. Hydrogen atoms are also omitted except at ring junctions. Although six-membered rings are conventionally shown as flat hexagons as in VIII and IX, these rings are not in fact planar. The actual shape is discussed in detail in section 2.11.

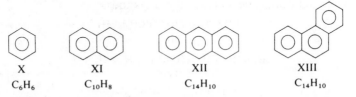

C_3H_6 C_6H_{12}
VII   VIII   IX

(c) Aromatic compounds

While open-chain and alicyclic compounds have fairly similar properties, aromatic compounds on the other hand have special properties. Aromatic compounds have a fundamental skeleton of a carbon ring system and can be considered as derivatives of a number of unsaturated hydrocarbons of which benzene (X), naphthalene (XI), anthracene (XII) and phenanthrene (XIII) are the most common.

X	XI	XII	XIII
C_6H_6	$C_{10}H_8$	$C_{14}H_{10}$	$C_{14}H_{10}$

These molecules' structures have been represented in the modern way to show the delocalized π sextet (see section 1.5.7). In drawing these structures, the carbon and hydrogen atoms of the rings are omitted. The carbon atoms lie at the intersection of each line, and there is a hydrogen atom joined to each carbon except at the ring junctions. It is quite in order to represent these molecules by flat hexagonal rings since, in order to get efficient delocalization of π electrons to take place, the molecules must be planar. Once again it must be emphasized that it is always useful to consider Kekulé-type structures for aromatic molecules, particularly when any electron-pair movements are being considered (see section 4.4).

(d) Heterocyclic compounds

The common feature of this group of organic compounds is the presence of at least one of the additional elements: oxygen, nitrogen and sulphur. One or more of these atoms, together with carbon atoms, make up a ring system. The rings are usually five- or six-membered. Rings of this size have bond angles consistent with the hetero-atom's normal valency angles. The ring system may be unsaturated in such a way as to give rise to aromatic properties. Some simple examples of heterocyclic compounds were given in section 1.5.7. Some others which are of interest in biological chemistry which include both mono-cyclic and polycyclic rings are as follows:

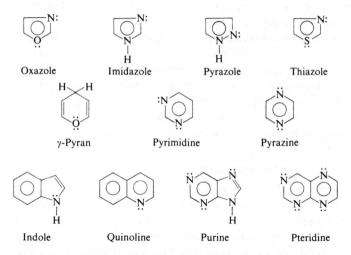

| Oxazole | Imidazole | Pyrazole | Thiazole |

| γ-Pyran | Pyrimidine | Pyrazine |

| Indole | Quinoline | Purine | Pteridine |

On the other hand, saturated heterocyclic systems are known, in which the molecules resemble alicyclic molecules in shape and properties. Common examples of this type of heterocycle are:

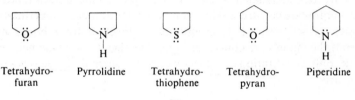

| Tetrahydro-furan | Pyrrolidine | Tetrahydro-thiophene | Tetrahydro-pyran | Piperidine |

39

2.4 FUNCTIONAL GROUPS IN ORGANIC COMPOUNDS

In general, carbon–carbon or carbon–hydrogen σ bonds are stable and un-reactive, because the two electrons are evenly distributed between the atoms of the bond, and each atom has a very stable electron configuration. Chemical reactions in organic compounds take place, for the most part, at regions of the molecule which contain the additional elements. A group of atoms which gives rise to a particular set of reactions is called a *functional group*. Other reactive sites in an organic molecule include multiple bonds ($>C=C<$; —C≡C—) where the high electron density due to the π bond causes reaction. Other reactions arise through the activation of a carbon–carbon or carbon–hydrogen σ bond through the presence of a neighbouring functional group or multiple bond. A knowledge of the behaviour of functional groups is essential to the understanding of the properties of organic compounds. A discussion of the way in which organic reactions occur will be the subject of chapter 4; at the moment, only the structural significance of functional groups will be considered. A list of the more common functional groups is given in Table 2.1.

By studying the properties of each group in a representative member of a homologous series—for example, ethane for the alkanes, cyclohexane (VIII) for the alicyclic compounds, and benzene (X) for aromatic compounds—a number of generalizations can be made regarding the properties of that group in any other member of the series. In this way, we have another method of collecting information regarding the properties of organic compounds. It is, of course, quite usual to find more than one functional group in a molecule, and, if these are structurally different groups, the compound can be expected to show properties characteristic of the groups and also new properties due to modification by one group of the properties of another.

2.5 CONSTITUTIONAL ISOMERISM

The comparison of the molecular formula of a large number of organic compounds reveals that there are usually a number of compounds that have exactly the same molecular formula. The term *isomerism* is used to denote the relationship in which two or more compounds differing in structure and properties have the same molecular formula. Isomers may have different arrangements of atoms either in the way they are covalently bonded together (constitutional or structural isomers) or in the way the atoms are arranged spatially (stereoisomers). When two compounds with the same molecular formula are to be designated as isomers, three-dimensional models representing their structures are constructed and compared. One model is superimposed on the other, remembering that groups joined together by σ bonds may be rotated. If the models are non-superimposable, then they are isomers. For the moment, only constitutional isomers will be considered. Three types of such isomers arise.

40

Table 2.1 Common functional groups

Group structure	Group name	Occurrence in compounds
—O—H	Hydroxy	Alcohols and phenols
—S—H	Thiol	Thiols (mercaptans)
—N$\big\langle^H_H$	Amino	Amines
—C—O—C—	Ether	Ethers
—C—S—C—	Thio-ether	Thio-ethers
—X (X = Cl, Br, I)	Halo	Halides and halogen substituted
—CN	Cyano	Cyanides (nitriles)
—NC	*Iso*-cyano	*Iso*-cyanides (*iso*-nitrile)
—N$\big\langle^{\nearrow O}_{\searrow O}$	Nitro	Nitro-compounds
$\overset{\text{O}}{\underset{\text{O}}{\overset{\|}{\underset{\|}{-S}}}}$—O—H	Sulphonyl	Sulphonic acid
—S—S—	Disulphide	Disulphides
$>$C=O	Carbonyl	Compounds listed below:
—C$\big\langle^{O}_{H}$	Aldehydo (formyl)	Aldehydes
$\begin{array}{c}-\overset{\|}{C}\\ \quad\diagdown\\ \quad\quad C=O\\ \quad\diagup\\ -\overset{\|}{C}\end{array}$	Keto	Ketones
—C$\big\langle^{O}_{OH}$	Carboxyl	Carboxylic acid
—C$\big\langle^{O}_{O-C-}$	Ester	Ester
—C$\big\langle^{O}_{S-C-}$	Thio-ester	Thio-ester
—C$\big\langle^{O}_{NH_2}$	Amido	Amides
—C$\big\langle^{O}_{Cl}$	Acid chloride	Acid chlorides
$\begin{array}{c}-C\diagup^{O}\\ \quad\diagdown O\\ -C\diagdown_{O}\end{array}$	Anhydride	Acid anhydride

(a) **Chain isomerism** Isomers of this type differ only in the arrangement of the carbon chain. Thus the two hydrocarbons *n*-butane and *iso*-butane (I and II, section 2.3) are chain isomers. Chain isomers have fairly similar chemical properties but sufficiently different physical properties to be separated and characterized. A special form of chain isomerism, known as *metamerism*, occurs, for example, in ethers, where isomers may arise through different numbers of carbon atoms on either side of the ether group. Thus, diethyl ether (I), methyl propyl ether (II) and methyl *sec*-propyl ether (III) are isomers.

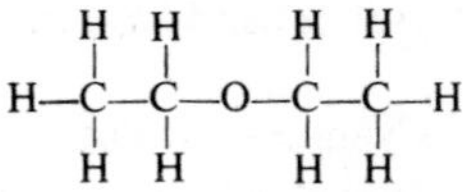

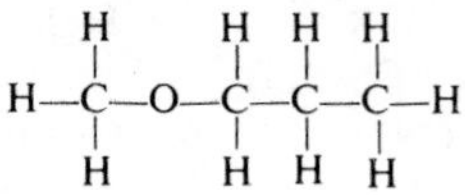

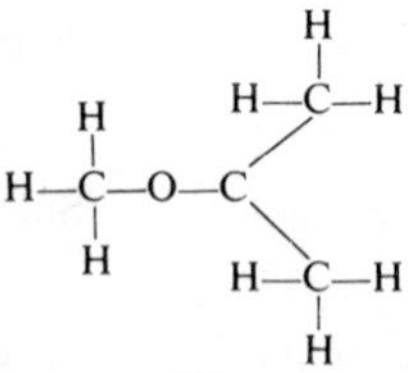

(b) **Positional isomerism** In this type of isomerism, compounds are found with the same arrangement of the carbon skeleton but differing in the position of the functional group. For example, there are two alcohols (IV and V) which are derived from propane, and four alcohols of the butanes—two from each of the parent hydrocarbons (I and II, section 2.3).

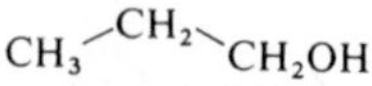

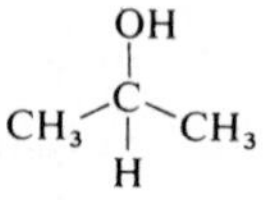

In cyclic compounds, positional isomerism arises through the different positions a functional group may have on the ring. Thus there are three di-hydroxy derivatives of benzene (VI, VII and VIII). Positional isomers have

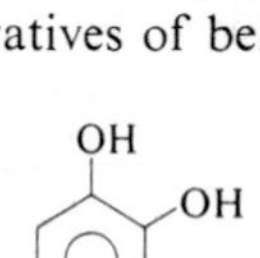

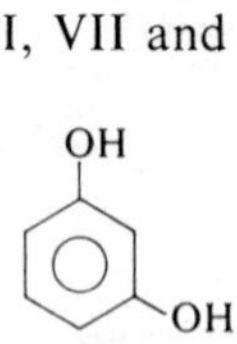

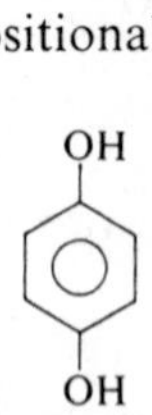

quite different physical properties and there are often significant differences in chemical properties making them easy to separate and to identify.

(c) Functional group isomerism   In a number of cases, a molecular formula can fit two or more compounds having completely different functional groups. One of the simplest examples of this is that of ethanol (IX) and dimethyl ether (X). These compounds have the molecular formula C_2H_6O. In this type

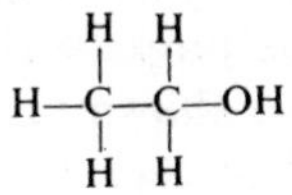

$$
\begin{array}{cc}
\text{H—C—C—OH} & \text{H—C—O—C—H} \\
\text{IX} & \text{X}
\end{array}
$$

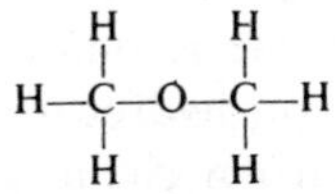

of isomerism, the two isomers have completely different properties, and are very easily separated and identified. A more important example of this is found among the carbonyl compounds, aldehydes and ketones. Thus propion-aldehyde (XI) and acetone (XII) are isomers having molecular formula C_3H_6O.

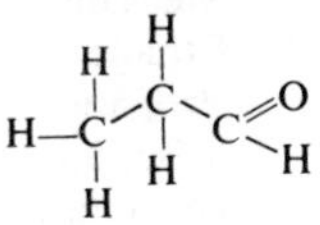

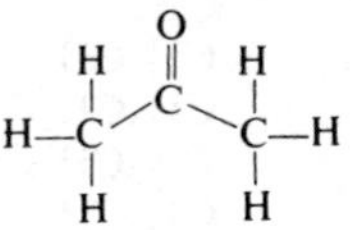

$$
\begin{array}{cc}
\text{XI} & \text{XII}
\end{array}
$$

The same situation arises in carbohydrates where, for example, glucose, an *aldehydo-sugar*, and fructose, a *keto-sugar*, have the same molecular formula, $C_6H_{12}O_6$.

2.6   THE NOMENCLATURE OF ORGANIC COMPOUNDS

One of the most confusing aspects of organic chemistry that confronts a student is the fact that an organic compound may have several different names. This situation has arisen because, as these compounds were isolated during the development of this branch of chemistry, they were given names which were not necessarily related to their structures but rather to the source of the compound. For example, formic acid was isolated from ants, and the Latin word for 'ants' is 'formica'. Many trivial names like that of formic acid are still in common usage and probably always will be, but a systematic method for the naming of organic compounds has been developed. In its present form the scheme is known as the IUPAC system and was devised by the International Union of Pure and Applied Chemistry. This system is primarily used in open-chain compounds but many of its rules can be applied with advantage to other types of compound.

(a) Nomenclature in open-chain compounds   The name of the compound is derived directly from the parent hydrocarbon. The alkanes are named according to the number of carbon atoms they contain. Up to C_4, the trivial names are used where the prefix *n*- indicates the straight-chain isomer; above C_4, a more systematic scheme is followed, where the first part of the name

indicates the number of carbon atoms followed by the suffix *-ane*. Some of the lower members of this series are listed in Table 2.2.

In branched-chain hydrocarbons, the name is obtained from the longest carbon chain present. Thus, the systematic name for *iso*-butane (II, section 2.3) is 2-methyl propane; this is obtained from the fact that there is a methyl group ($-CH_3$) on the second carbon of the propane chain. The names of some branched-chain hydrocarbons are also shown in Table 2.2. In these compounds the carbon chain is numbered in such a way that the lowest possible numbers are used to indicate the position of the alkyl *branches*.

Table 2.2   Structure and nomenclature of some alkanes (general formula C_nH_{2n+2})

Number of carbons (n)	Number of isomers	Structure	Trivial name	IUPAC name
1	1	CH_4	Methane	Methane
2	1	CH_3CH_3	Ethane	Ethane
3	1	$CH_3CH_2CH_3$	Propane	Propane
4	2	$CH_3CH_2CH_2CH_3$	*n*-Butane	Butane

		CH_3CH-CH_3
		   |
		   CH_3
			iso-Butane	2-Methyl propane

5	3	$CH_3CH_2CH_2CH_2CH_3$	*n*-Pentane	Pentane

		$CH_3CH_2CH-CH_3$
		   |
		   CH_3
			iso-Pentane	2-Methyl butane

		CH_3
		   |
		CH_3-C-CH_3
		   |
		   CH_3
			neo-Pentane	2,2-Dimethyl propane

For unsaturated hydrocarbons, the suffix '-ene' is used for alkenes and '-yne' for alkynes. The first part of the name indicates the number of carbons present in the longest chain. The position of the multiple bond is indicated by means of a number. This number is chosen in such a way that one of the carbon atoms in the multiple bond has the lowest possible number. Thus structure I is named pent-2-ene (or 2-pentene) and not pent-3-ene.

$$\underset{1}{CH_3}-\underset{2}{CH}=\underset{3}{CH}-\underset{4}{CH_2}-\underset{5}{CH_3}$$

I

When a functional group is present, the position of the group on the carbon chain is indicated by a number. Thus, the two isomeric alcohols of propane (IV and V, section 2.5) are called 1-propanol and 2-propanol respectively. There are four isomeric saturated alcohols with four carbon atoms; two are named as derivatives of butane, and two, with branched chains, are derivatives of propane.

$$CH_3CH_2CH_2CH_2-OH$$
1-Butanol
(n-Butanol)

$$CH_3CH_2\overset{\displaystyle OH}{\overset{|}{CH}}-CH_3$$
2-Butanol
(sec-Butanol)

$$\begin{array}{c} CH_3 \\ {\diagdown} \\ {}^{}C \\ {\diagup} \quad {\diagdown} \\ CH_3 \quad CH_2OH \end{array} \overset{H}{}$$
2-Methyl-1-propanol
(iso-Butanol)

$$CH_3-\overset{\displaystyle CH_3}{\overset{|}{\underset{\displaystyle OH}{\underset{|}{C}}}}-CH_3$$
2-Methyl-2-propanol
($tert$-Butanol)

When a functional group is present which would naturally end a chain such as a carboxyl or aldehyde group, the chain is numbered counting the carbon of the functional group as number one. If two or more functional groups are present, then the compound is named after the most dominant group in reactivity, and the others are regarded as substituents. For example, if a carboxyl group is present, the compound is always called an acid; such a situation arises in amino acids, keto acids or hydroxy acids.

An alternative system of indicating the position of substituents or multiple bonds still in common usage is that making use of Greek letters (α, β, γ, δ, ..., ω). It is particularly common among substituted and unsaturated carboxylic acids. For example, α-amino acids (II), $\alpha\beta$-unsaturated acids (III) and γ-hydroxy acids (IV). In this system, the carboxyl carbon is not given a letter

$$NH_2\overset{\displaystyle R}{\overset{|}{CH}}-COOH$$
$$\alpha$$
II

$$R-CH\!=\!CH-COOH$$
$$\beta \quad \alpha$$
III

$$R-\overset{\displaystyle OH}{\overset{|}{CH}}-CH_2CH_2COOH$$
$$\gamma \quad \beta \quad \alpha$$
IV

since it contains no hydrogen atom and no substitution can take place on it.

(b) Nomenclature in cyclic aromatics The positions of substituents on the ring carbon atoms are indicated by numbers. The ring is numbered in a consecutive manner, starting at one of the substituents in order to use the lowest possible numbers. If, however, there is only one substituent, and all the carbons in the ring are equivalent, a number is not necessary [for example, the monosubstituted benzenes (V)]. On the other hand, when two substituents are present, there are three possible isomers: VI, VII and VIII. The trivial naming system for these disubstituted benzene derivatives is still in common use: *ortho* (*o*) for the 1,2-compound (VI), *meta* (*m*) for the 1,3-compound (VII) and *para* (*p*) for the 1,4-compound (VIII). In the trisubstituted derivatives a numbering system is used: 1, 2, 3 (IX), 1, 2, 4 (X) and 1, 3, 5 (XI).

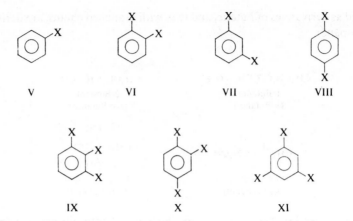

V	VI	VII	VIII

IX	X	XI

The naming of the alicyclic compounds follows the same pattern, but the matter is complicated by the need to designate stereoisomers as well (see section 2.10).

In heterocyclic compounds the systematic name consists of a prefix denoting the heteroatoms present, and a suffix indicating the ring size. The common heteroatoms nitrogen, sulphur, and oxygen are given prefixes 'aza', 'thia' and 'oxa' and five- and six-membered rings the suffixes '-ole' and '-ine' respectively. When a single heteroatom is present, the ring is numbered with this atom as position 1. With different heteroatoms the preference in numbering is given first to the highest periodic group (i.e., O before N), and second to the lowest atomic number (i.e., O before S). Thus pyridine has the systematic name *azine*, pyrimidine is 1,3-*diazine* and pyrazine is 1,4-*diazine*.

2.7 FURTHER TYPES OF ISOMERISM

2.7.1 Tautomerism

There have been found, among organic substances, a number which exist as two or more isomeric forms in a dynamic equilibrium. This phenomenon is called *tautomerism*. The isomeric structures differ from each other in the distribution of electrons and in the position of a *mobile atom*—usually hydrogen. This latter feature makes tautomerism quite distinct from resonance. The best-known examples of this phenomenon are found in compounds containing a 1,3-dicarbonyl arrangement. For example, β-diketones and β-keto acids and their esters.

2,4-Pentadione (acetylacetone) exists as an equilibrium mixture of a structure with two carbonyl groups (the keto form, I) and a structure containing an unsaturated alcohol group (the enol, II). In the liquid state at normal temperatures, the latter predominates.

$$
\underset{\substack{\text{(20 per cent)} \\ \text{I}}}{CH_3\overset{\overset{\displaystyle O}{\|}}{C}-CH_2-\overset{\overset{\displaystyle O}{\|}}{C}-CH_3} \quad\rightleftharpoons\quad \underset{\substack{\text{(80 per cent)} \\ \text{II}}}{CH_3-\overset{\overset{\displaystyle OH}{|}}{C}=CH-\overset{\overset{\displaystyle O}{\|}}{C}-CH_3}
$$

$$
\underset{\substack{\text{Keto-form} \\ \text{(93 per cent)} \\ \text{III}}}{CH_3-\overset{\overset{\displaystyle O}{\|}}{C}-CH_2-\overset{\overset{\displaystyle O}{\|}}{C}-O-C_2H_5} \quad\rightleftharpoons\quad \underset{\substack{\text{Enol-form} \\ \text{(7 per cent)} \\ \text{IV}}}{CH_3-\overset{\overset{\displaystyle OH}{|}}{C}=CH-\overset{\overset{\displaystyle O}{\|}}{C}-O-C_2H_5}
$$

The equilibrium in ethyl acetoacetate, a β-keto ester (III and IV), has been the subject of detailed investigation, and at normal temperatures the major part is in the keto-form (see also section 4.7.1).

Of great importance in biological chemistry are the various tautomeric structures for heterocyclic bases. Some simple pyridine derivatives are normally obtained as a tautomeric mixture. For example, 2- and 4-hydroxy-pyridines (V and VII) exist partly, in both the solid state and neutral solution, as the corresponding pyridones (VI and VIII). The tautomeric structures for the nitrogen heterocycles that occur in nucleic acids is discussed later (see section 7.4.1). Another group of compounds where complex tautomeric equilibria arise is in carbohydrate solutions, where as many as five isomeric forms may coexist at the same time (see section 7.3.1).

V	VI	VII	VIII

2.7.2 Stereoisomerism

In chapter 1, it was shown how the four covalent bonds around a carbon atom are directed tetrahedrally in space. Consequently, an important aspect of the structure of organic molecules is the spatial arrangement of the constituent atoms. That part of the subject which deals with the structure in three dimensions is called *stereochemistry*. One aspect of stereochemistry is *stereoisomerism*. The types of isomerism so far considered have involved isomers which are constitutionally different. Stereoisomers may be distinguished from constitutional isomers in that the difference between isomers does not lie in the order in which the atoms are linked together, but in the positions in space occupied by the atoms. Thus stereoisomeric compounds have identical constitutional formulae but different spatial arrangements of the component atoms. This is termed a difference in *configuration*.

Stereoisomers are conveniently classified under two broad groups: geometrical isomers and optical isomers. Both types of stereoisomerism are found extensively among natural organic compounds. In geometrical isomers, the isomerism does not depend on dissymmetry of the molecule; optical isomers, on the other hand, possess a dissymmetric molecular structure which endows them with the property of optical activity.

2.8 OPTICAL ISOMERISM AND MOLECULAR DISSYMMETRY

2.8.1 Dissymmetry, asymmetric carbon atoms and enantiomorphs

If an object is such that it contains no plane of symmetry, it may exist in forms which are mirror images of each other but are otherwise identical. Such an object is said to be *dissymmetric†*. The reader will see a simple example of dissymmetry if he looks at his hands. There is no plane that can be drawn through either hand such that a part on one side of the plane is matched by an identical part on the other. Furthermore, if the hands are placed directly opposite each other, each part of one hand may be placed opposite the same part of the other hand. This is the *mirror-image* relationship, since one hand is the mirror image of the other.

Similarly, an organic molecule which is dissymmetric may exist in two forms which are mirror images of each other. Two molecules related in this way constitute a specific type of optical isomer and are known as a pair of *enantiomorphs*. The most common cause of dissymmetry in an organic molecule is the presence of one or more asymmetric carbon atoms†. An asymmetric carbon atom is one to which four different groups are joined. The spatial relationships involved are best described by the use of molecular models. The four different groups A, B, C and D shown in Fig. 2.1 may be represented in the models by four differently coloured balls. When model I is

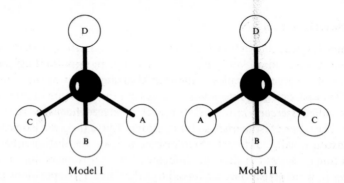

Model I   Model II

Fig. 2.1 Spatial relationships at an asymmetric carbon atom using molecular models

†The term *chiral* is now also used to describe a dissymmetric molecule and *achiral* for a symmetric one. An asymmetric carbon atom is referred to as a *chiral centre*.

48

held in front of a mirror, model II can be constructed to resemble the mirror image of model I. Furthermore, it will be found that these two models are not superimposable. This fact may be ascertained by trying to superimpose model I on model II. It will be found that it is not possible to get more than two of the groups to coincide.

There are many examples of molecules with one asymmetric carbon atom among natural organic compounds, and these can exist as a pair of enantiomorphs. For example, the α-substituted carboxylic acids such as hydroxy (I) and amino (II).

I   II

Since enantiomorphs are identical to each other in all respects except their configuration, it is not surprising to find that their physical properties are identical except for a physical property dependent on molecular dissymmetry. Thus, criteria such as melting point, refractive index, etc. are of no use in identifying a particular enantiomorph. The property that affords a method of distinguishing between enantiomorphs is their power to rotate the plane of polarized light, and this phenomenon is known as *optical activity*.

Optical activity is observed when a beam of plane-polarized light is passed through a solution of a dissymmetric compound. The plane of the polarized light is rotated, and the magnitude and direction of the rotation are measured by an instrument known as a *polarimeter*. It has been found that each of a pair of enantiomorphs rotates the plane of the polarized light by an equal amount in opposite directions. If the direction of rotation of the beam of light is clockwise, the rotation is designated as positive (or +). Conversely, an anti-clockwise rotation is termed negative (or −). The value of the rotation for a particular compound is constant under specified conditions, and is quoted in terms of specific rotation $[\alpha]_\lambda^t$ (section 6.2.8).

2.8.2 Relative and absolute configuration

Each particular enantiomorph has its own characteristic arrangement of atoms which is termed its *configuration*. Thus, the two enantiomorphic forms of lactic acid (α-hydroxypropionic acid), III, each has its own configuration and, using the test of superimposability, they can be shown to be different molecular species.

III   IV   V

49

In order to distinguish the two forms diagrammatically, it is necessary to draw them as three-dimensional formulae—IV and V. This is rather time consuming and a more simple type of diagram can be used. Most of the spatial relationships may be visualized by the use of *projection formulae*. Thus, when a single asymmetric carbon atom is present, as in the case of lactic acid, the two enantiomorphs IV and V may be represented by the semi-projection diagrams VI and VII or by *Fischer* projections VIII and IX respectively. The

	COOH		COOH		COOH		COOH

HO⟍ ⟋H   H⟍ ⟋OH   HO—C—H   H—C—OH
    CH₃   CH₃   CH₃   CH₃

       VI   VII   VIII   IX

two-dimensional Fischer diagram is obtained by orientating the three-dimensional model so that the carbon chain is vertical and projecting to the rear, while the hydrogen and hydroxyl groups stand out in front; the model is then imagined to be flattened and the groups are laid out on the plane of the paper in the order they appear in the model.

The two enantiomorphic forms of lactic acid have been isolated from natural sources; for example, lactic acid isolated during metabolism in muscle has a positive rotatory power. But how do we know which configuration (IV or V) this isomer possesses? This is the problem of assigning to a stereoisomer an *absolute configuration*. It is only recently, using X-ray diffraction studies, that it has become possible to determine in a fundamental way which configurational formula should be assigned to the compound with the positive rotation, and which to that with the negative rotation.

It should be remembered that measurement of specific rotation affords only a method of identifying a particular stereoisomer; it does *not* tell us directly what the configuration of that isomer is. In fact, the rotatory power of a particular enantiomorph may be changed both in magnitude and direction by small constitutional changes in groups two or three atoms distant from the asymmetric carbon atom. For example, the values of the specific rotation of various derivatives of (+)-lactic acid are:

	OH		OH		OH		OCH₃

CH₃CH—COOH   (CH₃CH—COO⁻)₂ Zn⁺⁺   CH₃CH—COOCH₃   CH₃CH—COOH
$[\alpha]_D^{20°}$ +3·3°   −6·0°   −8·2°   −75·5°

Salts of (+)-lactic acid and the methyl ester are readily reconverted to the free acid with the positive rotation. In these interconversions, none of the bonds from the asymmetric carbon atom is broken, hence the configurations of all these molecules are the same. Thus changes in the sign of rotation during a

50

reaction do not necessarily reflect a change in the configuration within the molecules.

These compounds illustrate a very important principle: that it is possible to assign a *relative configuration* by converting one compound to another with the same absolute configuration, provided, of course, that the reactions involved do not bring about changes at the asymmetric centre or, if they do, that these changes are fully understood, i.e., the reaction mechanism is known. Thus, by synthesis, it could be shown that all these derivatives of lactic acid are obtained only from (+)-lactic acid and not (−)-lactic acid. Thus, if the configuration of (+)-lactic acid is known, the same configuration may be inferred for the derivatives.

At the end of the nineteenth century, Emil Fischer proposed that glyceraldehyde—a *triose*, and the simplest of sugars—be used as a reference point for establishing the relative configuration of carbohydrates and many other important naturally occurring organic compounds. Fischer proposed that configuration X be arbitrarily assigned to the enantiomorph with the positive rotatory power. All compounds which can be related to this enantiomorph through degradation or synthesis are then said to belong to the *dextro* series and are designated as 'D' compounds, regardless of the direction of their rotatory power. Similarly, compounds related to (−)-glyceraldehyde— assigned configuration XI—belong to the *laevo* series and are designated as

CHO
C
H   OH
CH$_2$OH
X
D(+)-Glyceraldehyde

CHO
C
HO   H
CH$_2$OH
XI
L(−)-Glyceraldehyde

CHO
H   OH
CH$_2$OH
X'

CHO
HO   H
CH$_2$OH
XI'

CHO
H—C—OH
CH$_2$OH
X''

CHO
HO—C—H
CH$_2$OH
XI''

'L' compounds. The semi-projection and Fischer projection diagrams, X' and XI', X'' and XI'' respectively, are normally used for representing (+)- and (−)-glyceraldehyde.

These assignments by Fischer were purely arbitrary, since at that time, there was no method for the determination of absolute configuration. The application of the X-ray diffraction technique to this problem has established

51

that Fischer's choice was correct, and thus all configurations established relative to the glyceraldehydes are in fact the absolute configurations.

In order to have a uniform system of classifying compounds as belonging to the D or L series, certain rules are necessary: the dissymmetric molecule is drawn so that an aldehyde or closely related group, such as a carboxyl group, is directed vertically with the hydrogens and hydroxyl groups extended forward. When the hydroxyl group is on the right-hand side with the viewer facing the molecule, then the isomer is a member of the D series whose parent

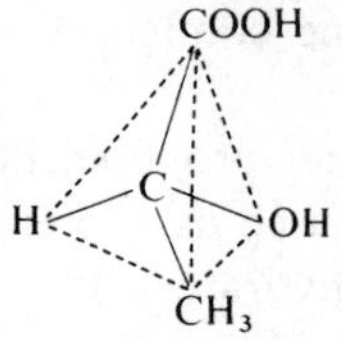

XII	XII'	XII"

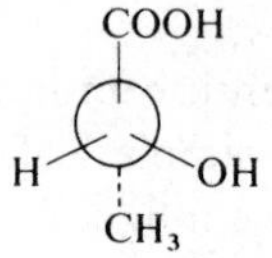

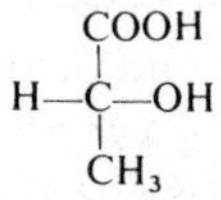

compound is (+)-glyceraldehyde (X, X' and X"). Thus D-lactic acid has configuration XII (also represented by XII' and XII") and is, incidentally, the (−)-enantiomorph.

In order to accommodate a number of other important compounds within the D/L convention, further rules are necessary. For example, if an amino group is present, instead of a hydroxyl group, as in the case of α-amino acids, the amino group is considered to have replaced the hydroxyl group. While nearly all the naturally occurring carbohydrates belong to the D series, most α-amino acids belong to the L series. Thus L-alanine has the configuration XIII (also represented by XIII' and XIII") and is the (+)-enantiomorph.

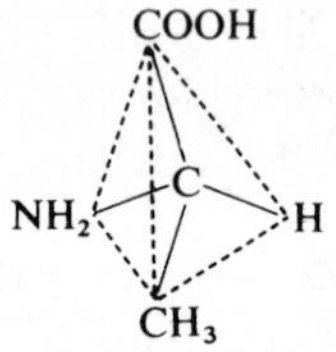

XIII	XIII'	XIII"

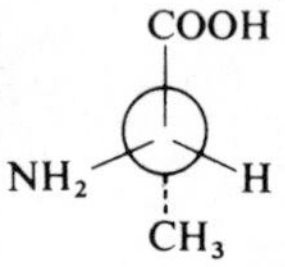

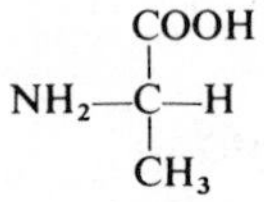

2.8.3 Correlations using the D/L convention

The system for correlating the configuration of a stereoisomer with the configuration of D- or L-glyceraldehyde has been widely applied, particularly in the carbohydrates and α-amino acids. Before proceeding with these compounds a simpler case will first be considered—the assignment of configuration to (−)-lactic acid. Oxidation of the aldehyde group of (+)-glyceraldehyde affords (−)-glyceric acid (XIV). Hence the latter compound is a member of

52

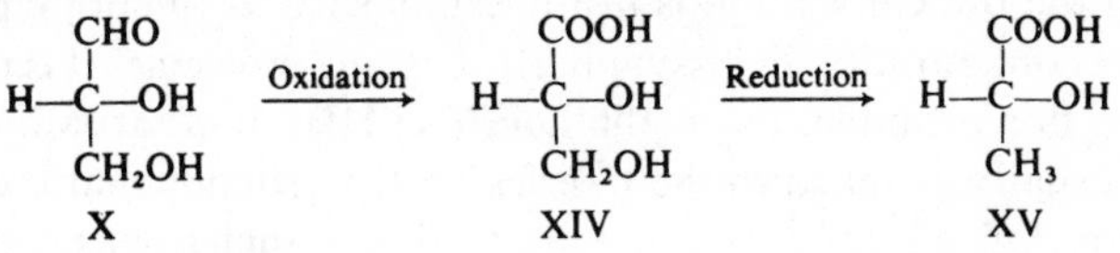

$$
\begin{array}{ccccc}
\underset{\text{X}}{\begin{array}{c}\text{CHO}\\|\\ \text{H—C—OH}\\|\\ \text{CH}_2\text{OH}\end{array}}
& \xrightarrow{\text{Oxidation}} &
\underset{\text{XIV}}{\begin{array}{c}\text{COOH}\\|\\ \text{H—C—OH}\\|\\ \text{CH}_2\text{OH}\end{array}}
& \xrightarrow{\text{Reduction}} &
\underset{\text{XV}}{\begin{array}{c}\text{COOH}\\|\\ \text{H—C—OH}\\|\\ \text{CH}_3\end{array}}
\end{array}
$$

the D series. Selective reduction of the primary alcohol group of (−)-glyceric acid yields (−)-lactic acid (XV) which is thus a D compound.

With the exception of glycine, the common naturally occurring α-amino acids (Table 7.1) are dissymmetric and most of them have a single asymmetric carbon atom (for example L-alanine, XIII). In the correlation with (−)-glyceraldehyde the two key amino acids are (+)-alanine and (+)-serine. These two compounds can be related to (−)-glyceraldehyde by the sequence of reactions shown in Fig. 2.2. These reactions involve the enantiomorphs of those in the sequence (+)-glyceraldehyde, (−)-glyceric acid and (−)-lactic acid, i.e. (−)-glyceraldehyde, (+)-glyceric acid (XVI) and (+)-lactic acid (XVII). The conversion of (+)-lactic acid to (+)-alanine involves two stages in each of which reaction occurs at the asymmetric carbon atom. Both these reactions are bimolecular nucleophilic substitutions (S_N2) and the mechanism is fully understood (see section 4.3.2). During each reaction, inversion of configuration occurs and thus the relative positions of the —NH$_2$ in (+)-alanine is the same as the —OH group of (−)-glyceraldehyde. The correlation of the other α-amino acids shown in Fig. 2.2 involves changes in the structure of parts of the molecule not directly bonded to the asymmetric centre.

Carbohydrates, apart from the glyceraldehydes, contain more than one asymmetric carbon atom, and the consideration of correlation in these molecules must await a discussion of the number of stereoisomers in molecules with a number of asymmetric centres.

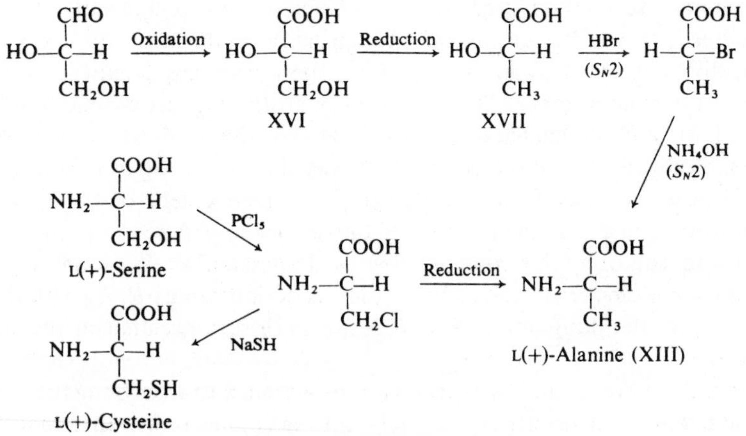

Fig. 2.2 Correlation pathways for α-amino acid configuration

Although the D/L convention is firmly established as the principal method of specifying configuration in dissymmetric organic molecules it is not without ambiguities. For example, (−)-malic acid (XVIII)—the naturally occurring isomer—is usually assigned to the L series on the grounds that the reduction of the carboxyl group (attached directly to the asymmetric carbon atom) to an aldehyde group, followed by degradation of the —CH₂COOH group to a primary alcohol group, yields (−)-glyceraldehyde:

$$\underset{\text{XVIII}}{\text{HO}\!\!-\!\!\overset{\displaystyle\text{COOH}}{\underset{\displaystyle\text{CH}_2\text{COOH}}{\text{C}}}\!\!-\!\!\text{H}} \equiv \text{HO}\!\!-\!\!\overset{\displaystyle\text{COOH}}{\underset{\displaystyle\text{CH}_2\text{COOH}}{\text{C}}}\!\!-\!\!\text{H} \longrightarrow \text{HO}\!\!-\!\!\overset{\displaystyle\text{CHO}}{\underset{\displaystyle\text{CH}_2\text{OH}}{\text{C}}}\!\!-\!\!\text{H}$$

On the other hand, there is an alternative multi-stage process by which the opposite conversions could be affected and the carboxyl group on the asymmetric carbon atom is converted to the primary alcohol group and the —CH₂COOH degraded to an aldehyde group:

$$\underset{\displaystyle\text{CH}_2\text{COOH}}{\overset{\displaystyle\text{COOH}}{\text{HO}\diagdown\!\!\diagup\text{H}}} \xrightarrow[\text{thro' }180°]{\text{Rotation}} \underset{\displaystyle\text{COOH}}{\overset{\displaystyle\text{CH}_2\text{COOH}}{\text{H}\diagdown\!\!\diagup\text{OH}}} \equiv \text{H}\!\!-\!\!\overset{\displaystyle\text{CH}_2\text{COOH}}{\underset{\displaystyle\text{COOH}}{\text{C}}}\!\!-\!\!\text{OH} \longrightarrow \text{H}\!\!-\!\!\overset{\displaystyle\text{CHO}}{\underset{\displaystyle\text{CH}_2\text{OH}}{\text{C}}}\!\!-\!\!\text{OH}$$

This sequence of reactions yields (+)-glyceraldehyde, showing that (−)-malic acid is a D compound.

2.8.4   The sequence rule

An alternative method used in the specification of configuration has been developed, called the *sequence rule*. The principle in this convention is that the four atoms attached to an asymmetric carbon atom are assigned priority in order of atomic number. Thus the atom with the highest atomic number is placed first and designated *a*, the next highest *b*, the third *c*, and the lowest *d*. The molecule is then observed in such a way that the group of lowest priority (*d*) is directed away from the viewer. The arrangement of the remaining groups *a*, *b*, and *c* is then noted. If the sequence *a* → *b* → *c* is in an anti-clockwise rotation, the configuration is designated as *S*. If the sequence *a* → *b* → *c* is clockwise, the configuration is designated as *R*. As with the D/L convention, the designation *S* or *R* is not necessarily related to the sign of rotation.

Since there are usually two carbon atoms attached to an asymmetric carbon, the assignment of priorities must take into account atoms other than those joined directly to the asymmetric centre. For example, in the case of lactic acid, the —OH group has the highest priority, *a*, and the hydrogen the lowest, *d*. When the atoms attached to the outer carbon atoms are examined, those on the carboxyl group have the highest atomic number, and thus this group will have priority *b*, and the methyl group will have priority *c*.

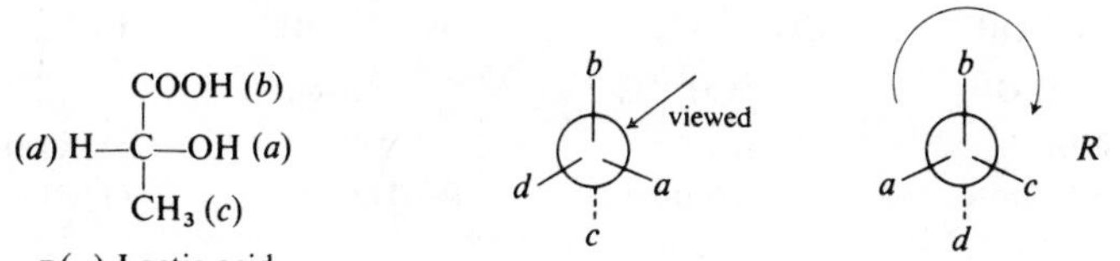

COOH (*b*)

(*d*) H—C—OH (*a*)

CH₃ (*c*)

D(−)-Lactic acid

The order of priority adopted for various functional groups containing carbonyl bonds is as follows:

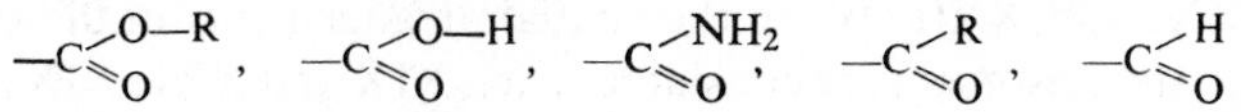

$$-C\overset{O-R}{\underset{O}{\diagdown}} \;,\quad -C\overset{O-H}{\underset{O}{\diagdown}} \;,\quad -C\overset{NH_2}{\underset{O}{\diagdown}} \;,\quad -C\overset{R}{\underset{O}{\diagdown}} \;,\quad -C\overset{H}{\underset{O}{\diagdown}}$$

and these all have priority over a group with a carbon–oxygen single bond, such as —CH₂OH. Thus, the configuration of (−)-glyceraldehyde is assigned as follows:

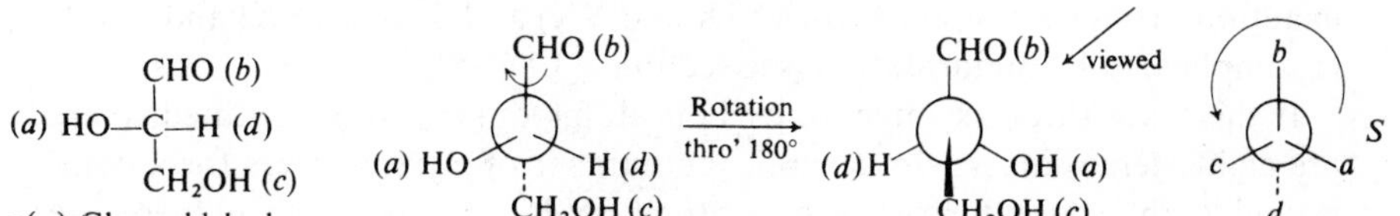

CHO (*b*)

(*a*) HO—C—H (*d*)

CH₂OH (*c*)

L(−)-Glyceraldehyde

When (−)-malic acid (XVIII) is treated by the sequence rule, there is no ambiguity in specifying its configuration. It has an *S* configuration.

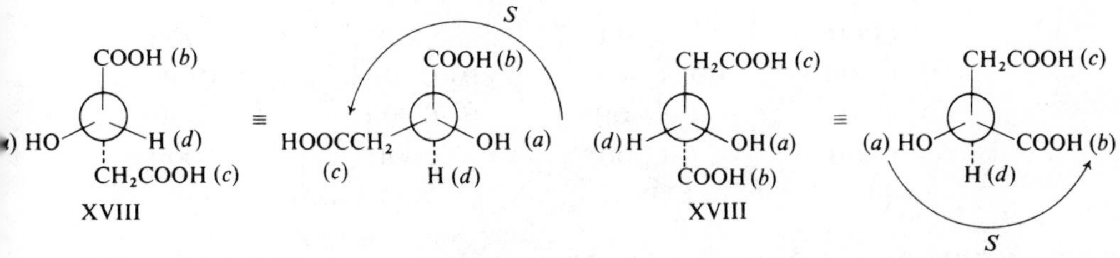

2.8.5 Compounds with two or more asymmetric carbon atoms

When there are two asymmetric carbon atoms in a molecule which are differently substituted, four spatial arrangements of the groups are possible. The

55

tetrose sugars provide a good example of this stereoisomerism. The stereoisomers are usually represented by means of Fischer projection formulae:

CHO	CHO	CHO	CHO
H—C—OH	HO—C—H	HO—C—H	H—C—OH
H—C—OH	HO—C—H	H—C—OH	HO—C—H
CH_2OH	CH_2OH	CH_2OH	CH_2OH
XIX	XX	XXI	XXII
(−)-Erythrose	(+)-Erythrose	(−)-Threose	(+)-Threose

These projection diagrams are obtained in the usual way; the asymmetric carbon atoms lie in the plane of the paper, the hydrogen and hydroxyl substituents are in front of this plane, and the primary alcohol group to the rear.

There are two pairs of enantiomorphs among these stereoisomers: XIX and XX; XXI and XXII. When the spatial arrangements in the other combinations of stereoisomers are considered, i.e., XIX and XXI; XIX and XXII; XX and XXI or XX and XXII, the molecules are no longer related as enantiomorphs, and these pairs are called *diastereoisomers*. Whereas enantiomorphs have identical physical properties apart from their rotatory power, diastereoisomers usually differ widely in physical and even in some chemical properties. It should be noted that comparison of specific rotation data for carbohydrate enantiomorphs such as erythrose (XIX and XX) and threose (XXI and XXII) is complicated by mutarotation (see section 7.3.1).

If there are three asymmetric carbon atoms differently substituted, there are eight stereoisomers. In general, the number of stereoisomers for a compound with n asymmetric carbon atoms is 2^n. However, when there are identically substituted asymmetric centres present, the number of stereoisomers is less. The classical example of this situation is found in the tartaric acids. There are two identically substituted asymmetric carbon atoms present, and three isomers are found. These consist of a pair of enantiomorphs XXIII and

COOH	COOH	COOH		COOH
H—C—OH	HO—C—H	H—C—OH		HO—C—H
HO—C—H	H—C—OH	H—C—OH	≡	HO—C—H
COOH	COOH	COOH		COOH
XXIII	XXIV		XXV	

XXIV (+)- and (−)-tartaric acids. Although there are two asymmetric atoms present in the third isomer, the molecule as a whole is symmetric and hence will not exhibit optical activity. This is called the *mesoisomer* (XXV). This isomer will have completely different physical properties, such as melting point, solubility, and density, from the pair of enantiomorphs.

56

In deducing the structure of a stereoisomer with more than one asymmetric centre, it is necessary, of course, to establish the configuration at each centre. This problem will be illustrated with reference to the structure of carbohydrate molecules. (−)-Erythrose and (−)-threose are two naturally occurring tetrose sugars. The configuration of the asymmetric carbon atom at C_3 is related in both cases to the configuration at the asymmetric carbon of (+)-glyceraldehyde, since both sugars may be synthesized from the latter compound. The configuration of the second asymmetric centre (C_2) is revealed by oxidation to an isomer of tartaric acid with known configuration (see Fig. 2.3).

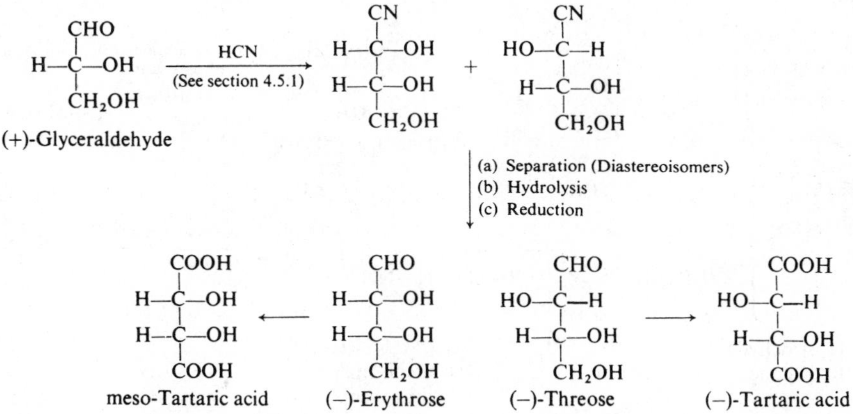

CHO
|
H—C—OH $\xrightarrow[\text{(See section 4.5.1)}]{\text{HCN}}$
|
CH$_2$OH

(+)-Glyceraldehyde

CN   CN
| |
H—C—OH   HO—C—H
| |
H—C—OH   +   H—C—OH
| |
CH$_2$OH   CH$_2$OH

(a) Separation (Diastereoisomers)
(b) Hydrolysis
(c) Reduction

COOH   CHO   CHO   COOH
| | | |
H—C—OH   H—C—OH   HO—C—H   HO—C—H
| | | |
H—C—OH   H—C—OH   H—C—OH   H—C—OH
| | | |
COOH   CH$_2$OH   CH$_2$OH   COOH
meso-Tartaric acid   (−)-Erythrose   (−)-Threose   (−)-Tartaric acid

Fig. 2.3   Correlation pathway for aldotetrose configuration

2.8.6   Separation of mixtures of enantiomorphs

A system containing equal quantities of a pair of enantiomorphs, formed in a reaction or obtained from natural sources, is termed a *racemic modification*. Since enantiomorphs possess identical solubilities and chemical properties, it is impossible to separate a mixture by fractional crystallization. Diastereoisomers, on the other hand, do have different solubility properties and thus, if a pair of enantiomorphs can be converted to a pair of diastereoisomers, it may be possible to find a solvent in which there is a sufficient difference in solubility to obtain a separation. It is fortunate that in living organisms, a single optical isomer of a dissymmetric molecule usually arises. Making use of these materials, a series of methods is available for the separation of natural and synthetic racemic modifications. Such separations are called *resolutions*.

The simplest resolutions are those of racemic acids and bases. A mixture of diastereoisomeric salts is prepared, which is then separated by fractional crystallization. In the case of racemic acids, dissymmetric alkaloid bases such as (−)-quinine, (−)-brucine, (+)-strychnine and (−)-morphine are used. After separation, the salts are converted separately back to the acid as pure enantiomorphs.

$$\left.\begin{array}{l}(+)\text{-Acid}\\(-)\text{-Acid}\end{array}\right\} + (-)\text{-Base} \longrightarrow \begin{array}{l}((+)\text{-Acid }(-)\text{-Base}) \text{ Salt}\\((-)\text{-Acid }(-)\text{-Base}) \text{ Salt}\end{array} \xrightarrow[\text{(b) Dilute HCl}]{\text{(a) Separation}} \begin{array}{l}(+)\text{-Acid}\\(-)\text{-Acid}\end{array} + \text{Base HCl}$$

Racemic bases are resolved by the corresponding process using a dissymmetric acid such as (+)-tartaric acid.

Racemic alcohols may be separated by modification of the technique used for racemic acids. The racemic alcohol is converted to a half-ester of phthalic acid and then resolved with dissymmetric base.

$$\left.\begin{array}{l}(+)\text{-Alcohol}\\(-)\text{-Alcohol}\end{array}\right\} + \text{[phthalic anhydride]} \longrightarrow \text{[acid phthalate ester]}\begin{array}{c}\text{C}-\text{O}-\text{Alcohol}\\\\\text{COOH}\end{array}$$

Racemic acid phthalate

$$\xrightarrow[\substack{\text{(b) Hydrolysis}\\\text{(i) HCl}\\\text{(ii) KOH}}]{\substack{\text{(a) Separation}\\\text{of Base salts}}} \begin{array}{c}(+)\text{-Alcohol}\\+\\(-)\text{-Alcohol}\end{array}$$

$$\left.\begin{array}{c}\text{O}\\\|\\(+)\text{R}-\text{C}-\text{X}\\(-)\text{R}-\text{C}-\text{X}\\\|\\\text{O}\end{array}\right\} + \begin{array}{c}\text{CH}_3\\\\\\\text{NH}_2\text{NH}\text{—}\\\\\text{CH}\\\text{CH}_3 \quad \text{CH}_3\\\\\text{XXVI}\end{array} \longrightarrow \begin{array}{c}\text{CH}_3\\\\\text{X}\\|\\\text{R}-\text{C}=\text{N}-\text{NH}\text{—}\\\\\text{CH}\\\text{CH}_3 \quad \text{CH}_3\end{array}$$

X = H, Aldehyde
X = R, Ketone

Diastereoisomeric
hydrazones

$$\xrightarrow[\substack{\text{(b) Heat with}\\\text{acid}}]{\substack{\text{(a) Separation}\\\text{(Crystallization)}}} \begin{array}{c}\text{O}\\\|\\(+)\text{R}-\text{C}-\text{X}\\+\\(-)\text{R}-\text{C}-\text{X}\\\|\\\text{O}\end{array}$$

Racemic aldehydes and ketones have been resolved by means of optically active hydrazines such as (−)-menthyl hydrazine (XXVI). A mixture of diastereoisomeric hydrazones is obtained (see section 4.5.1), separated and converted back to the carbonyl compound.

2.9 GEOMETRICAL ISOMERISM IN UNSATURATED COMPOUNDS

In chapter 1, the electronic arrangement in a carbon–carbon double bond was explained in terms of σ and π bonds. The presence of the π bond, formed by overlap of p atomic orbitals, prevents rotation, which would otherwise occur about the σ bond. Stereoisomerism arises in compounds containing double bonds, provided they are suitably substituted. For example, compounds of type I would exist in only one spatial arrangement; while those of type II can exist as two stereoisomers—II′ and II″.

Type I

$$\begin{array}{c}\text{A} \quad \text{A}\\\diagdown\diagup\\\text{C}\\\|\\\text{C}\\\diagup\diagdown\\\text{B} \quad \text{B}\end{array}$$

Type II

$$\begin{array}{c}\text{A} \quad \text{B}\\\diagdown\diagup\\\text{C}\\\|\\\text{C}\\\diagup\diagdown\\\text{A} \quad \text{B}\\\\\text{II}'\end{array} \qquad \begin{array}{c}\text{A} \quad \text{B}\\\diagdown\diagup\\\text{C}\\\|\\\text{C}\\\diagup\diagdown\\\text{B} \quad \text{A}\\\\\text{II}''\end{array}$$

When *like* groups are on the same side of the double bond, the stereoisomer is called the *cis* isomer; when *like* groups are on the opposite sides of the double bond, it is known as the *trans* isomer. The designation *cis* or *trans* is quite adequate for geometrical isomers where there are *two* identical substituents on the carbon atoms of the double bond (for example, maleic and fumaric acids or long-chain unsaturated fatty acids—VI). However, when *four* different substituents are present on the carbon atoms of the double bonds, a more fundamental system of specifying configuration must be used. This involves the assigning of 'sequence rule' (section 2.8.4.) priorities to each substituent. Consider, for example, the two isomers of 1-bromo-2-chloro-1-iodo-ethene (III and IV):

III   IV

In isomer III, the groups bonded to C_1 have priority $I > Br$ and those at C_2 have priority $Cl > H$. Thus isomer III has the highest priority groups (I and Cl) on the same side and is designated *seqcis* or the 'Z' isomer. In isomer IV, the groups of highest priority (I and Cl) are on opposite sides of the molecule and it is designated as the *seqtrans* or 'E' isomer.

Since the covalent bonds around the carbon atoms of a double bond have a trigonal disposition, the spatial arrangement around the central part of the molecule is planar and symmetrical. Thus, geometrical isomers do not possess rotatory power, unless there is some other centre, such as an asymmetric carbon atom in the molecule. One of the first examples of this type of isomerism was observed in the reaction products of the dehydration of malic acid:

Maleic acid (*cis*)   Fumaric acid (*trans*)
m.p. 130°   m.p. 287°

The two stereoisomers formed in this reaction—maleic and fumaric acids—clearly belong to the geometrical class and, although constitutionally identical, they show considerable differences in properties. Unlike optical isomers, there are very significant differences in chemical properties, and they differ in all their physical properties.

The configuration of geometrical isomers is deduced from a study of chemical reactions and physical constants. Thus, in the case of maleic and fumaric acids, the fact that the former loses water with the formation of a cyclic anhydride (V) much more easily than the latter suggests that both carboxyl groups are on the same side of the molecule, i.e., a *cis* configuration. Fumaric acid has to undergo rearrangement (breaking of the π bond and rotation about the σ bond) to maleic acid before dehydration can occur. These deductions are confirmed by mild hydrolysis of the anhydride, under conditions where rearrangement is impossible, which yields only maleic acid.

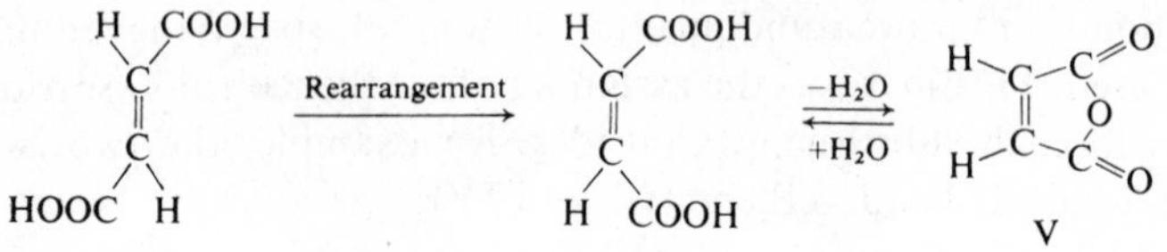

From a study of the physical properties, a number of general rules have been deduced regarding the relationship between molecular structure and the values of certain physical constants; for example, the melting point of the *cis* isomer is lower than that of the *trans*. This generalization arises from the greater symmetry of a *trans* isomer compared with a *cis* isomer so that the molecules pack more efficiently in the crystal lattice and thus produce a material with higher melting point. For other physical properties, the general relationship is that the *cis* isomer has a *higher* solubility, heat of hydrogenation, heat of combustion (section 3.4.3) and dipole moment (section 1.5.2). When the isomers are liquids, the *cis* isomer has a higher boiling point, refractive index and density than the *trans* isomer (see, for example, data in Table 2.3).

Table 2.3   Structure and physical properties of the 2-butenes

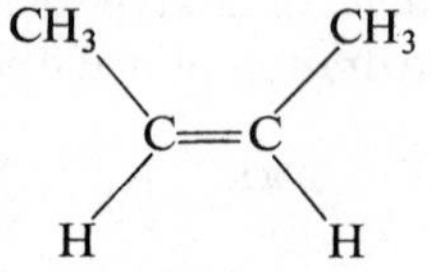

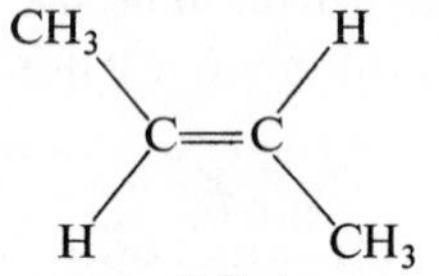

Isomer	B.p. (°C)	M.p. (°C)	Density at $-20°C$ (g cm^{-3})	Refractive index at $-13°C$	ΔH^* (kJ mole^{-1})	ΔH^{**} (kJ mole^{-1})
cis	+4	−139	0·667	1·3868	2712	120
trans	+1	−106	0·649	1·3778	2707	115

ΔH^* = Heat of combustion (section 3.4.3)

ΔH^{**} = Heat of hydrogenation for reaction:

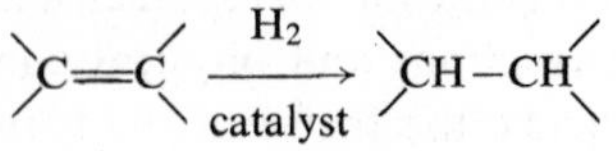

These generalizations about physical properties afford a method of deducing the configuration for a pair of geometrical isomers. Spectroscopic methods (chapter 6) such as infra-red, ultra-violet and NMR are also used for this purpose. In the case of crystalline solids, a complete X-ray crystallographic analysis, although lengthy, is the only physical method that can give directly the actual configuration of a particular stereoisomer.

An important group of natural compounds in which geometrical isomerism arises is the unsaturated fatty acids (VI). In these compounds, the double bonds may occur at various points within the long hydrocarbon chain. The presence of the double bond is denoted by the symbol Δ and a number indicating the position in the chain. At each double bond a *cis* (VI') or *trans* (VI'') configuration may be present. The designation *cis* or *trans* now refers to the two hydrogen atoms on the carbon atoms of the double bond. Most natural

$$CH_3(CH_2)_nCH=\!\!=CH(CH_2)_mCOOH$$

VI

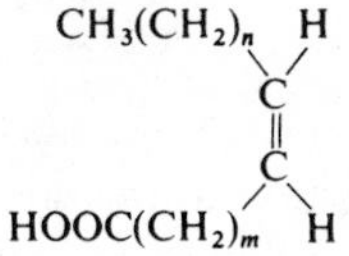

(structures VI' and VI'')

VI' 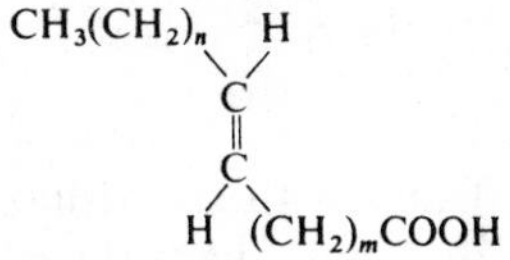   VI''

unsaturated acids have a *cis* configuration, for example oleic acid (VI'; $n = 7$, $m = 7$, i.e. Δ^9 oleic acid). The *trans* isomer elaidic acid (VI''; $n = 7$, $m = 7$, i.e. Δ^9 elaidic acid) occurs to only a small extent, but can be prepared synthetically from oleic acid. Examples of fatty acids with more than one double bond will be found in Fig. 7.4.

2.10 STEREOISOMERISM IN CYCLIC COMPOUNDS

So far in this chapter only the stereoisomerism of open-chain compounds has been considered. Both geometrical and optical isomerism can arise in cyclic compounds. One of the simplest examples arises in the disubstituted cyclopropane derivatives. When the substituents are on different carbon atoms, there are three spatial arrangements possible (I, II and III). These ring systems

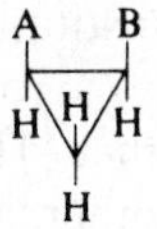

I    II 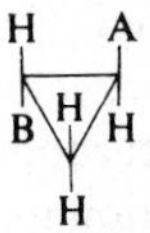   III

are planar and rigid; free rotation about the carbon–carbon single bonds is not possible. In the *cis* isomer (I), both substituents lie on the same side of the ring, while in the *trans* isomers (II and III), they are on opposite sides. Furthermore, inspection of the *trans* isomers reveals that they are dissymmetric although they have no distinct asymmetric carbon atom. These two isomers are related as a pair of enantiomorphs, and have rotatory power due to their molecular dissymmetry. The *cis* isomer, on the other hand, has a plane of symmetry and is optically inactive.

The situation in larger ring systems is similar except, of course, there may be positional isomers as well. Thus, in the disubstituted cyclobutanes, there are 1,3- as well as 1,2-derivatives to consider. There are three stereoisomers of the 1,2-disubstituted derivative, which arise in exactly the same way as those for the 1,2-disubstituted cyclopropanes. *Cis* and *trans* isomers are found in the 1,3-derivatives but the *trans* isomer (V) has a symmetric molecular arrangement and exists only as one stereoisomer, which is, of course, optically inactive.

Rings with six or more carbon atoms are not planar, except in *aromatic* compounds, nevertheless the number of stereoisomers that arise at normal temperatures may be calculated as if the ring were planar. The reason for this is considered in the next section.

2.11 CONFORMATION OF OPEN-CHAIN AND CYCLIC MOLECULES

The concept that molecules can exist in different shapes by virtue of rotation about single bonds was introduced in chapter 1. The term *conformation* is used to describe the spatial arrangement of the whole molecule, in contrast to the term *configuration*, which has been used in this chapter to describe the spatial arrangement around a particular carbon atom or group of atoms. It has already been pointed out (see section 1.5.4) that the energy barriers between different conformations are too low to allow the separation of pure conformational isomers—*conformers*. However, in some cases, rotation is completely restricted and, when the molecule is dissymmetric, optical isomers may be isolated. The best-known examples of this are the substituted diphenyls, where interaction between the *ortho* substituents prevents free rotation about the carbon–carbon bond which joins the two rings together. The two rings adopt a position in which they are at right angles to each other, and there are two possible conformations which are non-superimposable. Thus *o,o'*-dinitrophenic acid, for example, will exist as a pair of enantiomorphs (I and II).

62

There are two ways in which conformers of open-chain molecules can be represented graphically. Firstly, the *saw-horse* representation where the atoms or groups bonded to the carbon atoms are arranged trigonally at each end of a carbon–carbon bond. The different conformations are obtained by rotation about the carbon–carbon σ bond. Consider the two diastereoisomers D(–)-erythrose and D(–)-threose, the planar projection diagrams (III and IV) are first converted to *eclipsed* saw-horse diagrams (III′ and IV′) and thence to the *staggered* representation (III″ and IV″). Alternatively, these two types of conformation can be represented by the *Newman* diagrams (III‴ and IV‴) in which the molecules are viewed along the central carbon–carbon σ bond.

CHO
|
H—C—OH
|
H—C—OH
|
CH₂OH

III   III′   III″   III‴

CHO
|
HO—C—H
|
H—C—OH
|
CH₂OH

IV   IV′   IV″   IV‴

It can be seen from this *conformational analysis* of the two carbohydrates that D(–)-erythrose can adopt a staggered conformation in which the two largest groups are *anti* (section 1.5.4), and on each side of the molecule there is a medium-sized group (—OH) and a small group (H). On the other hand, D(–)-threose (IV″ and IV‴) has a conformation *anti* with respect to the largest groups, but has two medium-sized groups on the same side. Thus, D(–)-erythrose will be energetically more stable than D(–)-threose. Considerations like these play an important part in determining the rate and even the course of a chemical reaction.

The application of the principles of conformational analysis has been particularly successful when applied to cyclic compounds. In order to maintain the tetrahedral angle (109° 28′) of the covalent bonds around a carbon atom in a non-aromatic cyclic molecule with more than five carbon atoms, the ring must become *puckered*. In fact, this results in a very limited number of conformations which are energetically acceptable. For a six-membered ring there are three which are known as the *chair*, the *boat* and the *skew-boat* (*twist-boat*).

When viewed along each carbon–carbon bond in the chair conformation (VII), it is found that all the carbon–hydrogen bonds are staggered. Furthermore, there are no hydrogen atoms within the sum of the Van der Waals radii (2·5 Å, 250 pm). On the other hand, in the boat conformation, the atoms along

63

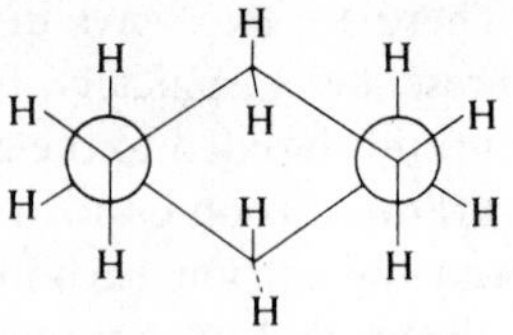

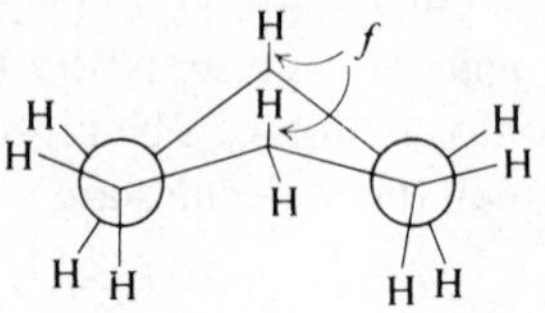

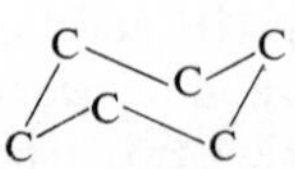

Chair conformation

V

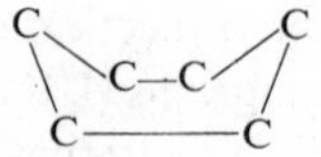

Boat conformation

VI

VII

VIII

the *sides* of the boat are eclipsed and also the hydrogen atoms on the *flag-pole* bonds (denoted by *f*—VIII) lie only 1·83 Å (183 pm) apart. This is considerably closer than the sum of their Van der Waals radii and these atoms will be subject to mutual repulsion. The energy barrier between the two conformations is estimated at 25·1 kJ mole^{-1} (6 kcal mole^{-1}). This permits interconversion at normal temperatures.

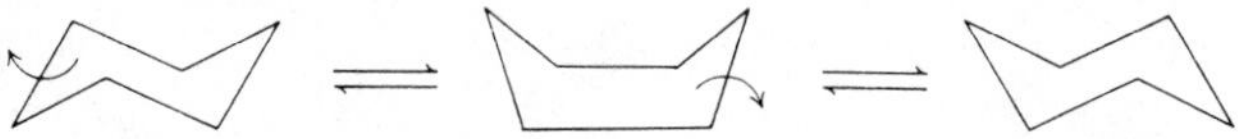

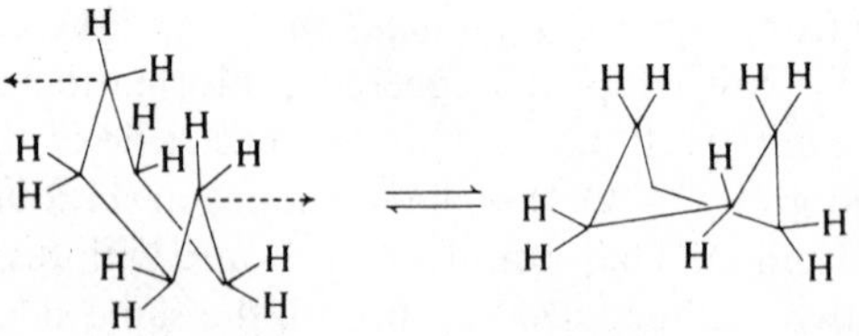

Boat conformation

Skew-boat conformation

A more stable boat conformation—the *skew boat*—is obtained by twisting the molecule so that the hydrogen atoms on the flag-pole bonds are as far apart as possible. It has been calculated that this conformation is 6·7 kJ mole^{-1} (1·6 kcal mole^{-1}) more stable than the simple boat conformation.

In the chair conformation, the bonds joining the hydrogen atoms to the ring have two spatial dispositions. There are six carbon–hydrogen bonds directed perpendicularly to the plane of the ring—three below and three above this plane—these are known as *axial* bonds. The other six hydrogens lie in the same plane as the ring, and these are in *equatorial* positions. When the hydrogen atoms are replaced by larger atoms or by groups of atoms, there is a considerable difference in the amount of interaction experienced by axial and equatorial substituents. An axial substituent lies very close to the two

64

axial hydrogens which are on the same side of the ring; an equatorial substituent does not experience such crowding. There are then two chair conformations (IX and X) for a monosubstituted cyclohexane. The lower-energy
conformation has the substituent (A) equatorial (IX), and in the higher-energy
conformation the substituent is axial (X). Once again, it is not possible to
isolate these as stable stereoisomers at normal temperatures as they are readily
interconvertable through the boat conformation (XI).

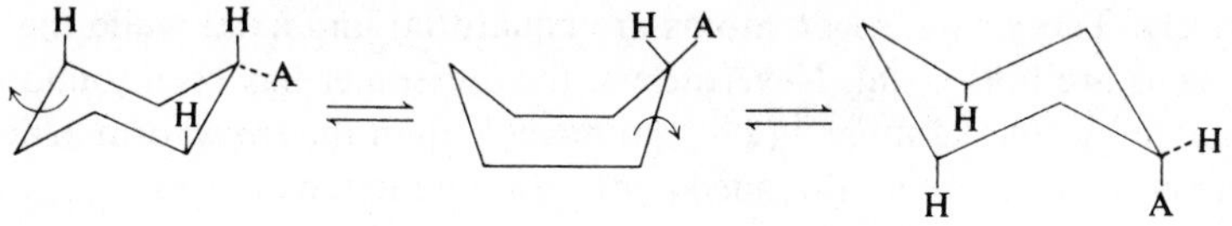

IX   XI   X

     ——— Axial bond
     ------ Equatorial bond

When two substituents are present on different carbon atoms, the problem
of geometrical isomerism arises. For each stereoisomer the spatial position,
axial or equatorial, has to be determined. For example, in the *cis* 1,2-di-
substituted derivative (XII and XIII), one substituent must be axial and
one equatorial:

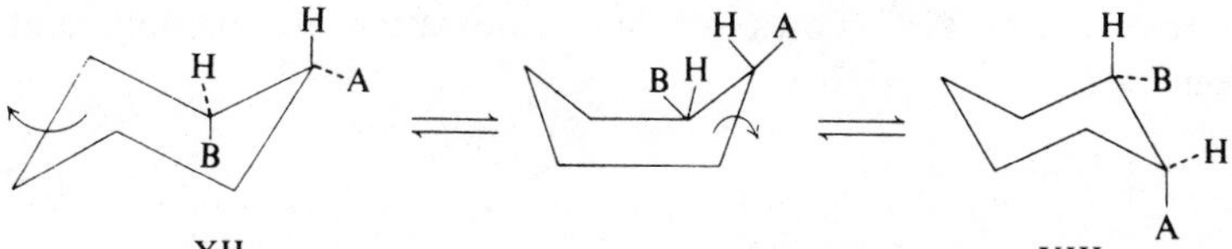

XII   XIII

The two *cis* conformers (XII and XIII) cannot, of course, be isolated at normal
temperatures. In the *trans* 1,2-disubstituted derivative the substituents are
either both axial (XIV) or both equatorial (XV), the latter is the preferred
conformation and, incidentally is of lower energy than the *cis* 1,2-isomer
where one substituent is axial. There is, of course, a pair of enantiomorphs
(XV and XVI) of the *trans* isomer.

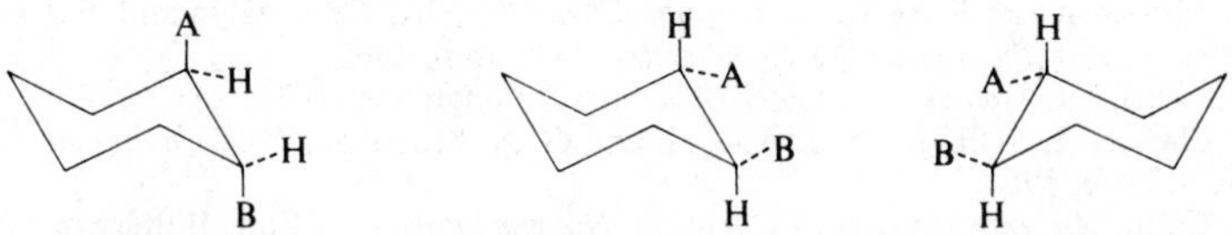

XIV   XV   XVI

Conformational analysis may also be applied to multi-ring compounds.
For example, when naphthalene is hydrogenated under different conditions,

65

two isomeric decalins are obtained (XVII and XVIII). Hydrogenation in solution with a platinum catalyst gives mainly *cis*-decalin (XVII) and hydrogenation in the gas phase gives mainly *trans*-decalin (XVIII). The isomers are easily separated by fractional distillation. Both isomers contain only *chair* conformations of the six-membered rings. In *cis*-decalin (XVII and XVII') the rings are fused together so that the hydrogens in the common C—C bond have a *cis* configuration, while in *trans*-decalin (XVIII and XVIII') they have a *trans* configuration. The rings are then said to be *cis* and *trans* fused respectively. The *cis* hydrogen atoms are equatorial and axial while the *trans* hydrogens are both axial. Nevertheless, the *cis* isomer has been found to be less stable by $10{\cdot}0$ kJ mole^{-1} ($2{\cdot}4$ kcal mole^{-1}) than the *trans* form, since the former contains more non-bonded hydrogen interactions.

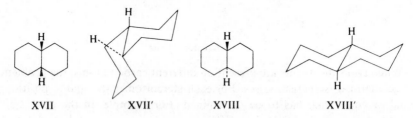

XVII   XVII'   XVIII   XVIII'

Stereoisomerism and conformation of fused six-membered ring systems is an important aspect of the structure of steroids. Examples of both *cis* and *trans* fused rings are known although the latter are predominant (see section 7.5.2).

Bibliography

1. J. D. Roberts and M. C. Caserio, *Basic Principles of Organic Chemistry*, 2nd Edn, Benjamin, 1977.
2. R. T. Morrison and R. N. Boyd, *Organic Chemistry*, 3rd Edn, Allyn and Bacon, 1973.
3. K. Mislow, *Introduction to Stereochemistry*, Benjamin, 1965.
4. F. D. Gunstone, *Guidebook to Stereochemistry*, Longmans, 1975.
5. E. L. Eliel, N. L. Allinger, S. J. Angyal, and G. A. Morrison, *Conformational Analysis*, Interscience, 1965.
6. R. S. Cahn, *An Introduction to Chemical Nomenclature*, 4th Edn, Butterworths, 1974.

3. Physical aspects of chemical reactions

THE THERMODYNAMICS (ENERGETICS) AND KINETICS OF CHEMICAL
REACTIONS

3.1 INTRODUCTION

Energy may take many forms, some of which are very familiar: heat, light, sound, chemical energy, mechanical energy, electrical energy and nuclear energy. The various forms of energy have one thing in common: the capability of doing work.

The cells of living organisms are able to accumulate chemicals which are essential for their existence and replication, and in doing so are storing energy in the form of chemical energy. This stored energy may become the driving force in many functions of the cell—for example, the biosynthesis of complex organic molecules, such as lipids, carbohydrates or proteins—or it may be used as kinetic energy in muscular contraction. The ability to convert one form of energy into another is a characteristic of all biological material.

Until recently the unit of energy was the *calorie*. In defining the calorie, use was made of the thermal properties of water. Unfortunately, this has given rise to several definitions of the calorie, all of which are different. For example, it may be quoted as the amount of heat needed to raise the temperature of 1 g of water by 1°C. This amount of heat, however, varies with initial temperature, due to the variation of the specific heat of water with temperature. The calorie may be defined as the heat required to heat 1 g of water from 15°C to 16°C or as being equal to a certain number of *joules* of work measured electrically. Clearly such variations in the definitions of the basic unit of energy are not acceptable, and the unit of energy proposed in the SI system of units is the *joule*. This amount of energy can be accurately measured electrically, and the expression of quantities of heat in joules (J) is now recommended, one calorie (cal) being equal to 4·185 J.

3.2 THE MATHEMATICAL CHARACTERIZATION OF THE FIRST LAW OF THERMODYNAMICS

After the equivalence of heat and mechanical work had been demonstrated by Joule in 1840, an important theorem was deduced by Helmholtz in 1847, called the *principle of conservation of energy*. This states that: *in all processes occurring in an isolated system, the total energy of the system remains constant.*

This principle is also the *first law of thermodynamics*. It is more usual, however, to quote the first law as a mathematical equation rather than a statement of words. Before this is done, the concept of an *isolated system* and other thermodynamic systems must be defined.

It is convenient to divide chemical systems into three types. These are isolated, closed, and open systems. An *isolated system* is one containing substances which cannot escape from the container and in which no energy can enter or leave the container. In practice, a perfect isolated system is unobtainable.

A *closed system* is one in which material is unable to escape from the container but energy can either enter the system or leave it. A closed system which approximates most closely to the behaviour of an isolated system is a closed Dewar flask ('thermos' flask).

The third type of thermodynamic system is the *open system* and is the one that is most commonly encountered in practical chemistry. In this case, not only is heat transport possible, but material transport in and out of the system can also occur. If the first law of thermodynamics is applied to open systems, the possibility of energy changes resulting from loss of material from the system to the rest of the universe must be considered.

The difference between the heat change q and the work w done by the system is equal to the difference $U_2 - U_1$ in internal energy of the system from start to finish of the process, that is,

$$q - w = U_2 - U_1$$

A difference of energy in thermodynamics is designated Δ; thus,

$$U_2 - U_1 = \Delta U \quad \text{and} \quad q - w = \Delta U \tag{3.1}$$

where ΔU is the change in internal energy.

If heat is evolved during a chemical or physical process, it is termed an *exothermic process*, and is denoted by a negative sign. Conversely, if the system absorbs heat, the process is termed *endothermic*, and is given a positive value. If the system has work done upon it by the surrounding atmosphere, the work is denoted by a negative value, and if the system does work on the atmosphere, it takes a positive value.†

Equation (3.1) is the mathematical statement of the first law of thermodynamics. It is sometimes quoted in its differential form for a very small change in the system:

$$dU = dq - dw \tag{3.2}$$

3.3 HEATS OF REACTION AT CONSTANT VOLUME AND CONSTANT PRESSURE

If the equation for the first law is rearranged thus,

$$q = \Delta U + w$$

† Some texts use the opposite sign convention, in which case equation (3.1) would be $q + w = \Delta u$.

it can be shown that the work term, w, is equal to $P(V_2 - V_1)$ or $P \varDelta V$, so that

$$q = \varDelta U + P \varDelta V$$

It can be seen that, for a chemical reaction, the heat of reaction under conditions of constant volume differs from that corresponding to conditions of constant pressure. This is because at constant volume, $\varDelta V$ equals zero and thus the heat of reaction q_v if the volume of reaction vessel is kept constant is

$$q_v = \varDelta U$$

This situation arises if the reaction is carried out in a closed vessel.

If the reaction is carried out under conditions of constant pressure, such as in a vessel open to the atmosphere, then the heat of reaction, in this case q_p, is given by

$$q_p = \varDelta U + P \varDelta V \qquad (3.3)$$

It can be seen that the two heats of reaction, q_v and q_p, for the same reaction, will differ if the reaction is accompanied by a volume change under conditions of constant pressure.

For example, the heat of reaction of carbon monoxide with hydrogen to form gaseous methyl alcohol, under conditions of constant volume, is $-141 \cdot 9$ kJ mole^{-1}:

$$CO + 2H_2 = CH_3OH \, (g), \qquad q_v = \varDelta U = -141 \cdot 9 \text{ kJ}$$

Since there is a diminution in volume accompanying the reaction when carried out at constant pressure, the atmosphere will do work on the system and the heat of reaction will be different.

The work done, w or $P \varDelta V$, is now equal to nRT, where n is the change in the number of moles during the reaction. In this reaction n equals 2, $(3-1)$. Thus

$$w = 2 \times 8 \cdot 31 T.$$

If the reaction is carried out at 300°C (573 K), then

$$w = 2 \times 8 \cdot 31 \times 573 = 9 \cdot 52 \text{ kJ}$$

Since the atmosphere does work on the system it is denoted as a negative value. Thus,

$$w = -9 \cdot 52 \text{ kJ}$$

and

$$\begin{aligned} q_p &= \varDelta U + w \\ &= -141 \cdot 9 - 9 \cdot 52 \\ &= -151 \cdot 42 \text{ kJ mole}^{-1} \ (36 \cdot 19 \text{ kcal mole}^{-1}) \end{aligned}$$

69

Thus the heat of reaction at constant pressure is $-151 \cdot 42$ kJ in comparison with $-141 \cdot 9$ kJ at constant volume.

3.4 THE ENTHALPY OR HEAT CONTENT H AND HEATS OF REACTION

3.4.1 Standard heats of formation

If the reaction:

$$A + B = C$$

is accompanied by a change in volume ΔV, the work done is $P\Delta V$:

$$w = P\Delta V = P(V_2 - V_1)$$

where V_2 is the final volume and V_1 is the initial volume. The heat of reaction q_p at constant pressure is given by

$$
\begin{aligned}
q_p &= \Delta U + w \\
&= (U_2 - U_1) + P(V_2 - V_1) \\
&= (U_2 + PV_2) - (U_1 + PV_1)
\end{aligned}
$$

The heat change at constant pressure is due to the change in the quantity $(U + PV)$ going from the initial to the final state. The quantity $(U + PV)$ is called the *enthalpy* or *heat content* and is denoted by the symbol H. Thus,

$$H = U + PV \qquad (3.4)$$

The heat of reaction q_p at constant pressure is thus $H_2 - H_1$, and is denoted by the symbol ΔH. In this book, the heats of reaction at constant pressure will be given as values of ΔH.

It is not possible to designate absolute values of enthalpy for individual substances as these values cannot be measured directly. The function that can be measured is the change ΔH in enthalpy which accompanies a chemical reaction. In order to facilitate the assignment of values of H to chemical substances, it is assumed that the enthalpy of elements at 25°C (298 K) and 1 atmosphere pressure $(101 \cdot 3$ kN m$^{-2})$ is zero. This assumption allows the molar enthalpies of chemical compounds to be quoted relative to the elements they contain. In this context, a substance such as chlorine is regarded in thermodynamic calculations as an element, even though it exists as diatomic molecules. The value of enthalpy under the standard conditions of temperature and pressure is called the *standard molar enthalpy*, $H^{\ominus}$.

The use of the concept of enthalpy may be illustrated with reference to the reaction

$$Zn + Cl_2 \rightarrow ZnCl_2$$

70

If the reaction is carried out at 1 atm pressure, then the heat of reaction is given by the symbol $\Delta H^{\ominus}$. This value arises from the differences in standard molar enthalpies of the product and reactants:

$$\Delta H_f^{\ominus} = H_{ZnCl_2}^{\ominus} - H_{Zn}^{\ominus} - H_{Cl_2}^{\ominus}$$

Since $H_{Zn}^{\ominus}$ and $H_{Cl_2}^{\ominus}$ are both zero by definition the standard molar enthalpy of zinc chloride ($H_{ZnCl_2}^{\ominus}$) is equal to the heat of the reaction in its formation from the elements under standard conditions of temperature and pressure. Some values of standard molar heats of formation ($\Delta H_f^{\ominus}$) are given in Table 3.1. A

Table 3.1   A selection of standard molar heats of formation at 25°C

Compound	$H^{\ominus}$ or $\Delta H_f^{\ominus}$ (kJ mole^{-1})	(kcal mole^{-1})	Reaction
H_2O (l)	$-285\cdot92$	$-68\cdot32$	$H_2 + \frac{1}{2}O_2 = H_2O$ (l)
H_2O (g)	$-241\cdot89$	$-57\cdot80$	$H_2 + \frac{1}{2}O_2 = H_2O$ (g)
HCl (g)	$-92\cdot32$	$-22\cdot06$	$\frac{1}{2}H_2 + \frac{1}{2}Cl_2 = HCl$ (g)
HBr (g)	$-36\cdot24$	$-8\cdot66$	$\frac{1}{2}H_2 + \frac{1}{2}Br_2 = HBr$ (g)
CO_2 (g)	$-393\cdot60$	$-94\cdot05$	$C + O_2 = CO_2$ (g)
NH_3 (g)	$-46\cdot20$	$-11\cdot04$	$\frac{1}{2}N_2 + \frac{3}{2}H_2 = NH_3$ (g)
CH_4 (g)	$-74\cdot87$	$-17\cdot89$	$C + 2H_2 = CH_4$ (g)
C_2H_6 (g)	$-84\cdot70$	$-20\cdot24$	$2C + 3H_2 = C_2H_6$ (g)
C_2H_4 (g)	$+52\cdot31$	$+12\cdot50$	$2C + 2H_2 = C_2H_4$ (g)
C_2H_2 (g)	$+226\cdot79$	$+54\cdot19$	$2C + H_2 = C_2H_2$ (g)
C_6H_6 (g)	$+49\cdot05$	$+11\cdot72$	$6C + 3H_2 = C_6H_6$ (g)
CH_3OH (l)	$-238\cdot63$	$-57\cdot02$	$C + \frac{1}{2}O_2 + 2H_2 = CH_3OH$ (l)
C_2H_5OH (l)	$-277\cdot72$	$-66\cdot36$	$2C + \frac{1}{2}O_2 + 3H_2 = C_2H_5OH$ (l)
CH_3COOH (l)	$-487\cdot13$	$-116\cdot40$	$2C + O_2 + 2H_2 = CH_3COOH$ (l)

negative value for $\Delta H_f^{\ominus}$ indicates that the reaction is *exothermic*, i.e., heat is evolved. A positive value, on the other hand, indicates an *endothermic* reaction.

With the aid of $\Delta H_f^{\ominus}$ values, it is possible to calculate heats of reaction. For example,

$$CO(g) + 3H_2(g) = CH_4(g) + H_2O(l)$$

$$\Delta H^{\ominus} = (H_{CH_4}^{\ominus} + H_{H_2O}^{\ominus}) - (H_{CO}^{\ominus} + 3H_{H_2}^{\ominus})$$

$$\text{Products} \qquad \text{Reactants}$$

$$\Delta H^{\ominus} = -74\cdot87 + (-285\cdot92) - (-110\cdot7) - 3(0)$$

$$= -250\cdot09 \text{ kJ } (-59\cdot8 \text{ kcal})$$

3.4.2   Hess's law of heat summation

From an inspection of the values for heats of formation given in Table 3.1, it can be seen that many of the values are for reactions which do not take place directly, such as the formation of methane from carbon and hydrogen. Heats of formation for these reactions are obtained by the use of *Hess's law of*

71

constant heat summation. The law is based on the fact that the heat evolved or absorbed in a given reaction is independent of the particular manner in which the reaction is carried out, and consequently depends solely on the initial and final states of the system—not on any intermediate states. This is because the heat of reaction in a multi-stage process is the algebraic sum of the heats of reaction in all the stages involved. It follows, therefore, that chemical reactions may be treated as algebraic equations. There are many applications of Hess's law in practical thermochemistry.

3.4.3 Heats of combustion

Experimental values for heats of combustion of a great many compounds are known, and it is the most important method of obtaining values for heats of formation. If an organic compound contains only atoms of carbon, hydrogen and oxygen, then the only additional data needed to calculate the heat of formation of that compound are the heats of combustion of carbon and of hydrogen. The calculation of the heat of formation can then be performed using Hess's law. The value for gaseous propane is calculated as follows:

(a) $C_3H_8(g) + 5O_2(g) = 3CO_2(g) + 4H_2O(l)$ $\quad \Delta H^\ominus = -2221 \text{ kJ}$

(b) $\qquad H_2(g) + \tfrac{1}{2}O_2(g) = H_2O(l)$ $\qquad\qquad \Delta H^\ominus = -285 \cdot 9 \text{ kJ}$

(c) $\qquad C(s) + O_2(g) = CO_2(g)$ $\qquad\qquad\qquad \Delta H^\ominus = -393 \cdot 5 \text{ kJ}$

The equation for the formation of gaseous propane may be obtained:

$$4 \times (b) + 3 \times (c) - (a)$$

i.e. $\qquad\qquad 3C(s) + 4H_2(g) = C_3H_8(g)$

Therefore, $\qquad \Delta H^\ominus = -103 \cdot 1 \text{ kJ} \,(-24 \cdot 65 \text{ kcal})$

If the combustion of a compound is incomplete, then the measured value for the heat of combustion has to be adjusted to that corresponding to the complete combustion. The heats of combustion of a selection of organic compounds are given in Table 3.2.

3.4.4 Heats of neutralization, heats of solution and heats of dilution

When dilute solutions of strong acids such as hydrochloric or nitric are neutralized with dilute solutions of strong bases such as sodium or potassium hydroxides at the same temperature, it is found that the *heat of neutralization* when calculated per mole of water formed is largely independent of the acids and bases used. This fact can be explained on the basis that the strong acids and bases are completely ionized in dilute solution and that the neutralization

Table 3.2 Heats of combustion of some organic compounds at 25°C

Substance	Heat of combustion, $\Delta H^{\ominus}$ (kJ mole^{-1})	(kcal mole^{-1})
CH_4 (g)	−890·57	−212·80
C_2H_6 (g)	−1560·16	−372·82
C_2H_4 (g)	−1299·86	−310·62
C_6H_6 (l)	−3268·49	−781·02
CH_3OH (l)	−726·93	−173·67
C_2H_5OH (l)	−1367·24	−326·70
CH_3COOH (l)	−871·74	−208·30
$C_6H_{12}O_6$ (glucose) (s)	−2815·0	−673·0

reaction is solely the reaction of hydrogen and hydroxyl ions to form water. Since this reaction will be the same for the neutralization of all strong acids by strong bases, the heat of neutralization is identical when calculated per mole of water formed in the reaction. At a temperature of 25°C and with the hydrogen and hydroxyl ion concentration at unit activity (unit *active mass*—see section 5.3.3) the heat of neutralization may be written

$$H^+_{(aq)} + OH^-_{(aq)} = H_2O_{(l)} \quad \Delta H^{\ominus}_{298} = -55 \cdot 85 \text{ kJ } (-13 \cdot 33 \text{ kcal})$$

In the case of the neutralization of weak acids by strong bases, strong acids by weak bases or weak acids by weak bases, the heat of neutralization is no longer independent of the acid and the base. The reason for this is that the measured heat of neutralization also includes the *heat of dissociation* of the weak acid or weak base in forming its ions, a process which takes place while the neutralization is proceeding. For example, the neutralization of hydrocyanic acid, a weak acid, by sodium hydroxide under the standard conditions of 25°C and unit activity is given by the equation

$$HCN_{(aq)} + OH^-_{(aq)} = H_2O_{(l)} + CN^-_{(aq)} \quad \Delta H^{\ominus}_{298} = -10 \cdot 30 \text{ kJ } (-2 \cdot 46 \text{ kcal})$$

From this value, the heat of dissociation $\Delta H^{\ominus}_d$ of the weak acid into its ions may be calculated:

$$HCN_{(aq)} = H^+_{(aq)} + CN^-_{(aq)} \quad \Delta H^{\ominus}_d = -10 \cdot 30 - (-55 \cdot 85)$$
$$= +45 \cdot 55 \text{ kJ } (+10 \cdot 88 \text{ kcal})$$

Whenever a substance (a solute) is dissolved in a solvent, there is in general a heat change. Familiar examples are the endothermic reactions when many salts are dissolved in water, and the exothermic reactions when concentrated acids are diluted with water. The endothermic nature of the process of dissolution of salts in water is the main reason for their increased solubility at higher

73

temperature. The heat liberated is called the *integral heat of solution* of the substance. When the integral heat is expressed per mole of substance dissolved, then the value varies with concentration of solute. For this reason, it is necessary to specify the number of moles of solvent per mole of solute in quoting the value for the integral heat. At very low concentrations of solute the integral heats of solution approach limiting values.

When solutions are diluted with solvent there is usually a small heat change. This heat change is related to the integral heats of solution for a particular solute. The difference between the values of the integral heat of solution at two concentrations of solute corresponds to the integral heat of dilution from one concentration to the other.

3.4.5 The temperature dependence of enthalpy and heat of reaction (the Kirchhoff equation)

In the previous sections, enthalpies and heats of reaction have been considered at one temperature, namely the standard temperature of 25°C. Heats of reaction are often measured at temperatures other than 25°C, and therefore it is important to know how to convert the values from one temperature to another. In the case of the enthalpy of a compound the equation is

$$\left[\frac{\partial H}{\partial T}\right]_p = C_p \qquad (3.5)$$

that is, the rate of change of enthalpy with respect to temperature at constant pressure is equal to the *molar heat capacity*, C_p. This is the specific heat of the substance at constant pressure multiplied by its molecular weight. The symbol ∂ (rather than d) is used to indicate the mathematical operation of partial differentiation, which means that one or more of the possible variables is being kept constant. In eq. (3.5), the pressure P is kept constant, and this is indicated by a subscript p.

Of more practical importance is the corresponding equation for the heat of reaction at constant pressure (the Kirchhoff equation)

$$\left[\frac{\partial (\Delta H)}{\partial T}\right]_p = \Delta C_p \qquad (3.6)$$

where ΔC_p is the difference in the heat capacities of the products ánd reactants in the reaction.

Integration of eq. (3.6) gives

$$\Delta H = \int \Delta C_p \, dT + constant \qquad (3.7)$$

74

The constant of integration is usually written as ΔH_0. Alternatively we can write:

$$\Delta H_2 - \Delta H_1 = \int_{T_1}^{T_2} \Delta C_p \, dT \tag{3.8}$$

where ΔH_1 and ΔH_2 are heats of reaction at temperatures T_1 and T_2. Equations (3.7) and (3.8) allow heats of reaction to be calculated at one temperature from heats of reaction at another temperature.

The actual variation in ΔH produced by a change in temperature is determined by the sensitivity of ΔC_p to temperature. In many biochemical reactions, the variation of ΔH with temperature may be neglected.

3.4.6 Bond energies

The term *bond energy* was introduced in chapter 1 in connection with hydrogen bonding, and it will be used in later chapters in the concept of *high-energy bonds* found in adenosine triphosphate (ATP) and other molecules. It is very important to make a distinction between two very similar terms: *bond energy* and *bond-dissociation energy*. The bond energy is the average dissociation energy of a given bond in a successive series of different dissociating species. The bond-dissociation energy, on the other hand, is the energy needed to break a given bond within a specific molecule. For example, the bond-dissociation energy of the C—H bond in methane is the energy of the reaction

$$CH_4(g) = CH_3(g) + H(g) \quad \Delta H_{298} = 427{\cdot}0 \text{ kJ } (102{\cdot}0 \text{ kcal})$$

The bond energy of a C--H σ bond (E_{CH}) is, however, calculated from the reaction

$$CH_4(g) = C(g) + 2H_2(g) \quad \Delta H_{298} = 1665{\cdot}6 \text{ kJ } (398{\cdot}0 \text{ kcal})$$

and is

$$1665{\cdot}6/4 = 416{\cdot}4 \text{ kJ } (99{\cdot}7 \text{ kcal})$$

To obtain the value of the heat of reaction of this process it is, of course, necessary to carry out a Hess's law calculation.

Of the two types of bond strength, the most useful is the bond energy, since it is possible to calculate approximate heats of reaction from tabulated values. Some such values are given in Table 3.3.

3.5 FREE ENERGY, AVAILABLE ENERGY AND CHEMICAL POTENTIAL

In sections 3.2 and 3.3, the relationships between energy and work are discussed. The work that can be obtained from a physical or chemical process which involves a change in volume of a substance is that which is due to the bulk expansion of the material. For example, if water is vaporized, the work obtained is that arising from the volume increase due to the production of

Table 3.3 Bond energies at 25°C

Bond	Bond energy (kJ mole^{-1})	(kcal mole^{-1})	Bond	Bond energy (kJ mole^{-1})	(kcal mole^{-1})
H—H	436·1	104·2	C—H	413·1	98·7
C—C	345·7	82·6	N—N	390·9	93·4
C=C	610·2	145·8	O—H	462·9	110·6
C≡C	835·3	199·6	Cl—H	431·5	103·1
N—N	163·2	39·0	Br—H	365·8	87·4
N≡N	945·0	225·8	I—H	298·8	71·4
F—F	154·8	37·0	S—H	347·4	83·0
Cl—Cl	242·3	57·9	C—N	304·7	72·8
Br—Br	192·9	46·1	C—O	357·8	85·5
			C=O	744·9	178·0

steam. But this is not the total energy of the system, it is merely the energy available for work. By converting water to steam, energy has been supplied to cause the water molecules to rotate and vibrate more vigorously and also to travel about the container with greater speeds. However, none of these forms of energy are available for work. This principle can be described in the equation

available energy = total energy − unavailable energy.

The total energy of the system may be taken as the internal energy U at constant volume, or the enthalpy H at constant pressure. The thermodynamic terms used for available energy are *Helmholtz free energy*, A, at constant volume, and *Gibbs free energy*, G, at constant pressure.

It was once thought that the heat of reaction was indicative of a spontaneous process and that a reaction would proceed in a given direction if ΔH was negative (*exothermic*). While this is so for many reactions such as the combustion of organic compounds, there are many well-known reactions for which the heat change ΔH is positive (*endothermic*). Thus, the dissolution of sodium chloride and many other salts in water is an endothermic reaction, and yet the reaction is spontaneous. Clearly some other thermodynamic function is needed as a criterion of spontaneity of physical and chemical processes. Such a function is the *free energy*, or more correctly the *free-energy change* which accompanies the reaction, i.e. ΔA or ΔG.

If either ΔA or ΔG is negative, then the process will occur spontaneously. This corresponds to a decrease in free energy accompanying the process. The *chemical potential energy* of a mixture of reactants decreases as the reaction proceeds to form products. Of the two forms of free energy, the most important is the Gibbs free energy, G, and the changes of free energy, ΔG, since most chemical reactions are conducted under conditions of constant pressure. Although G may be used to represent the total free energy of a system, it is often desirable to know the contributions each component in the system makes to the total free energy. This may be done by referring to the *partial molar free* energy, $\bar{G}$, of each component. The partial molar free energy is usually called the *chemical potential*, μ, and is defined by

$$\mu_i = \left[\frac{\partial G}{\partial n_i}\right]_{T,P,n_j} \tag{3.9}$$

that is, μ is the change in total free energy per mole of substance i added when temperature, pressure, and composition are kept constant. The chemical potential of a substance in a mixture is determined by its concentration or partial pressure in the mixture and the temperature. If a reaction is described by

$$\nu_A A + \nu_B B = \nu_C C + \nu_D D, \tag{3.10}$$

where there are ν_A moles of A and ν_B moles of B which produce ν_C moles of C and ν_D moles of D. As the reaction proceeds, the chemical potentials of A and B are reduced since their concentrations are lowered. On the other hand, the chemical potentials of C and D increase as more of the products are formed. The difference in chemical potentials of reactants and products at any given time is related to the maximum work available and the total free energy change at that time.

$$(\nu_C \mu_C + \nu_D \mu_D) - (\nu_A \mu_A + \nu_B \mu_B) = \Delta G \tag{3.11}$$

The reaction will continue as long as the sum of the chemical potentials of the reactants $(\nu_A \mu_A + \nu_B \mu_B)$ is greater than the sum of the chemical potentials of the products $(\nu_C \mu_C + \nu_D \mu_D)$ so that ΔG is negative. Eventually a stage will be reached where the two quantities are equal, in other words the chemical potentials of the reactants and the products are the same. When this occurs, ΔG equals zero and a state of equilibrium is reached.

The chemical potential of a gas i is given by

$$\mu_i = \mu_i^\ominus + RT \ln P_i \tag{3.12}$$

where P_i is the partial pressure of the gas and T the temperature (K). The quantity $\mu_i^\ominus$ is called the *standard chemical potential* of the substance i and is the value of its chemical potential when it has a partial pressure of one atmosphere ($101 \cdot 3$ kN m^{-2}). It can be shown that, if the reaction described in eq. (3.10) is a gas reaction, then

$$\Delta G = \Delta G^\ominus + RT \ln \frac{P_C^{\nu_C} P_D^{\nu_D}}{P_A^{\nu_A} P_B^{\nu_B}} \tag{3.13}$$

Equation (3.13) represents the value of the free-energy change ΔG going from reactants to products at any stage during the reaction. $\Delta G^\ominus$ is referred to as the *standard free-energy change*. When equilibrium has been reached, ΔG equals zero and the partial pressures in eq. (3.13) will be those corresponding to the equilibrium value. The logarithmic term can therefore be replaced by K_p, the equilibrium constant, since for this reaction

$$K_p = \frac{P_{e\,C}^{\nu_C}\ P_{e\,D}^{\nu_D}}{P_{e\,A}^{\nu_A}\ P_{e\,B}^{\nu_B}},\tag{3.14}$$

so that

$$\varDelta G^{\ominus} = -RT\ln K_p\tag{3.15}$$

Equation (3.15) is of great importance in chemical thermodynamics and is known as the *Van't Hoff isotherm* or the *reaction isotherm*. Its importance arises from the fact that the equilibrium constant for a reaction can be calculated from a value of $\varDelta G^{\ominus}$. Values of free energies of formation may be obtained from tables in a manner analogous to values of heats of formation. Since Hess's law is applicable to free-energy calculations as well as to those for heats of reaction, it is possible to calculate equilibrium constants for reactions from the values of $\mu^{\ominus}$ or $\varDelta G_f^{\ominus}$. Some values of standard free energy of formation for a selection of compounds are shown in Table 3.4. The standard free energies of formation of the elements are arbitrarily assumed to be zero. Thus for the reaction

$$CO\,(g) + 2H_2\,(g) = CH_3OH\,(l)$$

the value of $\varDelta G_{298}^{\ominus}$ for the reaction is

$$\begin{aligned}\varDelta G_{298}^{\ominus} &= \mu_{CH_3OH}^{\ominus} - \mu_{CO}^{\ominus} - 2\mu_{H_2}^{\ominus}\\ &= -166{\cdot}27 - (-137{\cdot}31) - 0\\ &= -28{\cdot}96 \text{ kJ } (-6{\cdot}92 \text{ kcal})\end{aligned}$$

Table 3.4   Selected standard free energies of formation at 25°C

Substance	$\mu_{298}^{\ominus}$ or $\varDelta G_{298}^{\ominus}$ (kJ mole^{-1})	(kcal mole^{-1})
H_2O (l)	−237·25	−56·69
HCl (g)	−95·29	−22·77
HBr (g)	−53·23	−12·72
HI (g)	+1·30	+0·31
CO (g)	−137·31	−32·81
CO_2 (g)	−394·49	−94·26
C_2H_6 (g)	−32·89	−7·86
C_2H_4 (g)	+68·13	+16·28
C_2H_2 (g)	+209·25	+50·00
C_6H_6 (g)	+129·69	+30·99
CH_3OH (l)	−166·27	−39·73
C_2H_5OH (l)	−174·81	−41·77

A negative value for $\Delta G^{\ominus}_{298}$ indicates that the reaction is spontaneous under the *standard conditions*, that is at 298 K with the reactants and products at partial pressures of 1 atm (101·3 kN m^{-2}). In normal chemical reactions, a positive value of $\Delta G^{\ominus}_{298}$ as high as 40 kJ mole^{-1} might be considered favourable for an investigation of the conditions, temperature and pressure which would give an economic yield. In biochemical processes, however, this is not possible and the sign of $\Delta G^{\ominus}$ is taken as an *indication* of the spontaneity of a given reaction.

For reactions in solution, the equation for $\Delta G^{\ominus}$ is similar. Thus, if the reaction given in eq. (3.10) occurs in solution, then the corresponding relationship to that given in eq. (3.14) is

$$K_c = \frac{a_C^{v_C} a_D^{v_D}}{a_A^{v_A} a_B^{v_B}} \tag{3.16}$$

where the *a* terms are called activities (corresponding to *active mass* in the sense of the law of mass action of Gulberg and Waage). In dilute solution the activities approximate to the concentrations of the species (see section 5.3.3) so that

$$K_c = \frac{[C]^{v_C}[D]^{v_D}}{[A]^{v_A}[B]^{v_B}} \tag{3.17}$$

where the square brackets ([]) represent the molar concentration. The standard free-energy change for the reaction will then be

$$\Delta G^{\ominus} = -RT \ln K_c \tag{3.18}$$

For ionic processes, standard free energies of formation may be obtained from values of standard electrode potential (see section 5.4.4). The standard free energies of formation of a selection of biochemically important compounds are given in Table 3.5

Table 3.5 also contains standard free energies of formation of ions and compounds in solution at unit activity. These values differ from the values for the pure compounds by the free energy of solution. From this type of data the calculation of $\Delta G^{\ominus}$ values for biochemical processes may be obtained. For example, the standard free-energy change for the hydration of fumarate ion to malate ion may be calculated using data from Tables 3.4 and 3.5 (see section 9.2.6). From the $\Delta G^{\ominus}$ obtained the equilibrium constant K_c could be calculated (eq. 3.18):

$$^-OOC-CH=CH-COO^- + H_2O = {}^-OOC-\overset{\overset{\displaystyle OH}{|}}{CH}-CH_2-COO^-$$

$$\Delta G^{\ominus} = -845·29 - (-604·36 - 237·25) = -3·68 \text{ kJ } (-0·88 \text{ kcal})$$

79

Table 3.5 Standard free energies of formation of selected compounds in the pure state at 25°C and in aqueous solution at unit activity

Substance	$\mu^{\ominus}$ or $\Delta G^{\ominus}$ in pure state (kJ mole^{-1})	(kcal mole^{-1})	$\mu^{\ominus}$ or $\Delta G^{\ominus}$ in solution at unit activity (kJ mole^{-1})	(kcal mole^{-1})
Acetate ion	—	—	−399·58	−95·48·
Acetoacetate ion	—	—	−493·83	−118·00
Ammonium ion	—	—	−79·52	−19·00
n-Butyrate ion	—	—	−352·71	−84·28
Carbon dioxide	−394·48	−94·26	−386·32	−92·31
Citrate ion	—	—	−1168·62	−279·24
Isocitrate ion	—	—	−1161·97	−277·65
Fumarate ion	—	—	−604·36	−144·41
α-D-Glucose	−910·49	−217·56	−917·44	−219·22
Glycogen (per glucose unit)	—	—	−662·49	−158·30
Hydroxide ion	—	—	−157·36	−37·60
Hydrogen ion	—	—	0·00	0·00
β-Hydroxybutyrate ion	—	—	−506·39	−121·00
α-Ketoglutarate ion	—	—	−797·74	−190·62
Malate ion	—	—	−845·29	−201·98
Nitrate ion	—	—	−110·53	−26·41
Nitrite ion	—	—	−34·53	−8·25
Oxaloacetate ion	—	—	−797·37	−190·53
Succinate ion	—	—	−690·40	−164·97
Urea	−197·20	−47·12	−203·89	−48·72

3.6 ENTROPY AND THE SECOND LAW OF THERMODYNAMICS

In the previous section, reference was made to the unavailable energy in chemical systems and accompanying chemical changes. In every chemical or physical process a certain amount of energy is inaccessible for the purposes of obtaining work. This is due to changes in vibrational, rotational and translational energies of the molecules in the system. Thus when water is vaporized to form steam, the work obtainable is that due to the gross expansion accompanying the process. But simultaneously the molecules are excited into higher vibrational and rotational energy levels and also move with greater translational velocity. The greater the extent of these latter molecular processes, the greater the amount of energy not available for doing work. This feature is commonly referred to as *dissipation of energy as heat*. The distribution of energy among molecular energy levels and the distribution of molecules in space due to translational motion is of great importance in chemical thermodynamics. The more energy levels there are available that can be occupied, the greater the possibility that they will be occupied and the larger will be the unavailable energy of the system.

This distribution of unavailable energy among quantum-mechanical energy levels and translational motion is described quantitatively by a thermodynamic function called *entropy*, *S*. It is common practice to link values of entropy for a substance with degree of order and probability. A high value of entropy for a substance is said to indicate a high degree of disorder. Consequently, entropies of gases are much higher than entropies of solids since the latter possess a much more ordered structure.

All spontaneous processes, both physical and chemical, are movements towards an equilibrium state, and they are accompanied by an overall increase in entropy. This phenomenon is described by the Second Law of Thermodynamics, which may be quoted in several ways:

(a) There is a tendency for energy to pass into less available forms.
(b) The entropy of the universe tends towards a maximum.
(c) Every spontaneous process, which in general is irreversible, leads to a dissipation of energy.

All of these may be summarized by saying that in any process in an isolated system there is an overall increase in entropy. The term *isolated system* is very important in this definition. Qualitatively it can be seen that in all spontaneous processes there is an overall increase in disorder resulting from the increase in entropy. On the other hand there are many processes where, at first sight, it appears that the natural process is accompanied by a decrease in entropy. For example, the freezing of water at 0°C and the condensation of steam below 100°C. In such cases, the actual process is accompanied by a decrease in entropy. It must be remembered that it is in an isolated system that the entropy increases. When water freezes in a normal container, the system *cannot* be classified as isolated. The water freezes simply because the heat of fusion is dissipated into the surrounding air and is lost.

Thus,

$$dS_{system} + dS_{surrounding} \geqslant 0$$

It would be impossible to freeze water in a perfect thermos flask (i.e. an isolated system) even if the water were at 0°C, because the heat of fusion could not be dissipated.

At first sight, it would appear that living systems are a contradiction of the second law of thermodynamics, since, by their very nature, they organize material into ordered units. It must be remembered that the isolated system in this case is the solar system, and that the primary source of energy is the sun. The consequences upon living systems of the light of the sun being extinguished are obvious. Thus, although in parts of a system there may be processes which bring about a decrease in entropy, there are produced in the surroundings larger increases in entropy, so that overall there is an increase in entropy.

Thus a biologist, like an engineer, must become reconciled to the fact that no process is 100 per cent efficient and that every process is accompanied by a dissipation of energy in the form of heat and an increase in molecular disorder or unavailable energy. In fact, in terms of overall efficiency, chemical reactions in living organisms compare very favourably with any process man has yet designed (see section 9.2.7).

The entropy S of a system is related to the internal energy and the Helmholtz free energy, and also to the enthalpy and the Gibbs free energy by the following equations:

$$A = U - TS \tag{3.19}$$

$$G = H - TS \tag{3.20}$$

These equations may be regarded as definitions of the functions A and G.

When chemical reactions or physical processes take place, the changes in these thermodynamic functions are related by

$$\Delta A = \Delta U - T\Delta S \tag{3.21}$$

and

$$\Delta G = \Delta H - T\Delta S \tag{3.22}$$

Of these relationships, eq. (3.22) is the most important since it contains the functions ΔG, the free-energy change, and ΔH, the heat of reaction at constant pressure. It has already been indicated that ΔG, for a spontaneous chemical reaction, must be negative. If ΔH is negative (exothermic reaction) and ΔS positive, then ΔG must be negative. For endothermic reactions (ΔH is positive), ΔG is still negative, which means that the $T\Delta S$ term must outweigh the ΔH term for the reaction to take place.

The corresponding equation for the standard free-energy change is

$$\Delta G^{\ominus} = \Delta H^{\ominus} - T\Delta S^{\ominus} \tag{3.23}$$

where $\Delta S^{\ominus}$ is the standard entropy change. Once $\Delta G^{\ominus}$ and $\Delta H^{\ominus}$ are known for a given reaction at a given temperature, then $\Delta S^{\ominus}$ can be calculated from eq. (3.23). The values of $\Delta S^{\ominus}$ for most chemical reactions lie in the range $+40$ to -20 J K^{-1} mole^{-1}. In some biochemical reactions the values of $\Delta S^{\ominus}$ may be much higher—for example, in the denaturation of proteins. The values of $\Delta S^{\ominus}$ for the thermal denaturation of α-chymotrypsin (pH 3), trypsin inhibitor and trypsin (pH 2) are respectively 1833 J K^{-1} mole^{-1} (438 cal K^{-1} mole^{-1}), 754 J K^{-1} mole^{-1} (180 cal K^{-1} mole^{-1}) and 892 J K^{-1} mole^{-1} (213 cal K^{-1} mole^{-1}). These extremely large values indicate the very high degree of structural organization that proteins have in their native state and their dramatic loss of this organization on denaturation.

3.7 ENTROPY CHANGES IN PHYSICAL PROCESSES

As a consequence of the Second Law of Thermodynamics, the entropy change of a physical process at a fixed temperature such as melting, vaporization, change of crystal form, can be calculated from the equation

$$\Delta S = q/T \tag{3.24}$$

where q is the heat change accompanying the isothermal process and T is the temperature (K) at which the process takes place. This equation is valid for processes carried out reversibly; but for non-reversible processes,

$$\Delta S > q/T$$

For example, the entropy of melting ΔS_m (melting is a reversible process), is given by

$$\Delta S_m = L_f/T_m$$

where L_f is the latent heat of fusion and T_m is the melting point (K). In the case of water, L_f is 6010 J mole^{-1} (1436 cal mole^{-1}), T is 273·15 K, and thus ΔS_m is 22·00 J K^{-1} mole^{-1} (5·257 cal K^{-1} mole^{-1}). Entropy of vaporization is calculated in a similar manner using the latent heat of vaporization. These latter values are always much greater than the corresponding values for melting (for example, the value for water is 108·98 J K^{-1} mole^{-1} (26·04 cal K^{-1} mole^{-1})). This is due to the much larger change in quantum-mechanical order on vaporization, i.e., the molecules in the gas phase are able to accommodate a great deal of energy as *unavailable energy* of vibration, rotation and translation. When a substance is heated, its entropy changes, due to the molecules occupying a larger range of quantum-mechanical energy states and hence dissipating the heat energy into less available forms.

If the process is carried out at constant pressure,

$$(\Delta S_p)_{T_1}^{T_2} = \int_{T_1}^{T_2} \frac{C_p}{T}\, dT \tag{3.25}$$

If the heat capacities for the substances are known (see section 3.4.5) then these equations may be simply integrated and the entropy change calculated.

3.8 SOME FURTHER USEFUL THERMODYNAMIC EQUATIONS

Several useful equations in thermodynamics are of the form

$$\left(\frac{\partial(\ln X)}{\partial T}\right) = \frac{\text{an energy term}}{RT^2} \tag{3.26}$$

where X is some equilibrium property of the chemical system which varies with temperature. An example of this is the *Van't Hoff Isochore*

$$\left(\frac{\partial(\ln K)}{\partial T}\right) = \frac{\Delta H}{RT^2} \tag{3.27}$$

where K is the equilibrium constant for a chemical reaction and ΔH is the heat of reaction. If ΔH is regarded as temperature independent then integration of eq. (3.27) between two temperatures T_1 and T_2 gives

83

$$\ln \left(\frac{K_1}{K_2} \right) = - \frac{\Delta H}{R} \left(\frac{1}{T_1} - \frac{1}{T_2} \right) \tag{3.28}$$

Equation (3.28) is a convenient method of obtaining mean heats of reaction over a temperature range from measurement of the equilibrium constant at various temperatures. This equation predicts that a plot of $\ln K$ versus $1/T$ should be linear and have a gradient $-\Delta H/R$; this is frequently found to be the case over narrow ranges of temperature.

The temperature variation of vapour pressure of a liquid may be represented by the equation

$$\frac{\partial (\ln p)}{\partial T} = \frac{L_v}{RT^2}, \tag{3.29}$$

where p is the vapour pressure and L_v represents the latent heat of vaporization. Thus if over a narrow temperature range L_v may be assumed to be constant, then

$$\ln \left(\frac{p_1}{p_2} \right) = \frac{-L_v}{R} \left(\frac{1}{T_1} - \frac{1}{T_2} \right) \tag{3.30}$$

This relationship predicts that a plot of $\ln p$ versus $1/T$ should be linear and have a gradient $-L_v/R$. This is often found and is a convenient method of obtaining heats of vaporization.

3.9 THE RATES OF CHEMICAL REACTIONS

3.9.1 The limitations of chemical thermodynamics and factors affecting the rate of a reaction

It has been shown in the preceding sections that chemical thermodynamics gives a valuable indication of the position of equilibrium in chemical reactions through the calculation of free-energy changes. Thermodynamic calculations will not, however, indicate the rate of attainment of the equilibrium. In other words, while thermodynamics will indicate whether or not a certain reaction is favourable, it will give no indication of the rate at which the reaction will take place. For example, gaseous mixtures of hydrogen and chlorine can be left for considerable periods of time in the dark before any appreciable reaction occurs, even though the ΔG value for the reaction is large and negative. If the mixture is subjected to a flash of light, the reaction will proceed explosively. This observation, while illustrating the limitations of thermodynamics, does not detract from the overall usefulness of the subject in giving unerring information concerning chemical equilibrium.

In chemistry today, it is common practice to speculate on the mechanism by which reactions occur, and this practice is now being extensively applied to reactions that occur in living organisms. A full understanding of the mechanism of a reaction is obtained only if the kinetics of the system are studied. The rate at which reactions proceed may be influenced by a number of factors. These include

(a) the nature of the particular reactants, e.g., the effect of substituents,
(b) the concentration of the reactants,
(c) the phase in which the reaction is carried out, i.e., gas, liquid, or solid; or if in a solution the type of solvent used,
(d) temperature,
(e) catalysis by homogeneous or heterogeneous catalysts,
(f) electromagnetic radiation.

In any normal kinetic experiment, the rate of reaction is measured by observing either the rate of disappearance of reactants or the rate of appearance of products. Implicit faith is placed in the *law of mass action*, i.e., that the rate of a single process is proportional to the concentration of the reacting species. Thus, in the process

$$A + B \rightarrow C$$

the rate of reaction is given by

$$\text{Rate } (V) \text{ is proportional to } [A] \times [B]$$

where the square-bracket terms represent the concentrations. If a constant is included in this proportionality the equation becomes

$$\frac{-d[A]}{dt} = \frac{-d[B]}{dt} = V = k[A][B] = \frac{d[C]}{dt}, \tag{3.31}$$

where the constant k is called the *specific rate constant* or simply the *rate constant*. The negative sign in eq. (3.31) indicates that the rate of the reaction decreases as the concentration of reactants becomes less. A high value of k indicates a fast reaction, whereas a small value corresponds to a slow reaction.

3.9.2 Stoichiometry, order of reaction, rate equation, and molecularity

The *stoichiometry* of a reaction is the expression of the reaction as a balanced chemical equation which shows the composition of the system. For example, the reaction between gaseous molecules of hydrogen and iodine to form hydrogen iodide may be represented by the stoichiometric equation

$$H_2(g) + I_2(g) = 2HI(g)$$

This type of representation of the reaction gives no indication of the mechanism.

The *order of reaction* is a parameter which is used to characterize the kinetic behaviour of reactions. It may be defined as the number of chemical species whose concentrations influence the rate of the reaction. The equation expressing the rate of reaction as a function of concentration of reactants is referred to as the *rate equation*. The order of reaction may also be defined as the sum of the indices of the concentration terms which appear in the rate equation.

Most chemical reactions take place by several consecutive steps and it is often found that one of these steps in the mechanism is slower than the rest and therefore dictates the overall reaction rate. This step in the mechanism is referred to as the *rate-determining step*. A further method of characterizing the kinetic behaviour of a reaction in addition to order of reaction is *molecularity*. The molecularity of a reaction is the number of species (molecules, ions or atoms) that take part in the rate-determining step. If only one species is involved in this step, the reaction is said to be *unimolecular*. If two species are involved, the reaction is *bimolecular* (examples of these two types of process will be found in section 4.3.2). Very few *termolecular* reactions exist due to the small probability of simultaneous three-body collision of species under normal experimental conditions.

Consider a reaction occurring in one step:

$$A \rightarrow B$$

The stoichiometry is

$$A = B$$

If x is the amount of A which has reacted in time t, then the rate equation is

$$V = \frac{dx}{dt} = k[A] \tag{3.32}$$

where k is the specific rate constant and $[A]$ is the concentration of A at time t. The reaction is *first order* and is also *unimolecular*.

In the reaction

$$A + B \rightarrow C$$

which also takes place in one step, the stoichiometry is

$$A + B = C$$

The rate equation is now

$$V = \frac{dx}{dt} = k[A][B] \tag{3.33}$$

and the reaction is *second order* and *bimolecular*.

If a reaction occurs in one step and can be represented by the stoichiometry

$$2A + B = C$$

the rate equation is

$$V = \frac{dx}{dt} = k[A]^2[B] \tag{3.34}$$

This reaction would be *second order* with respect to A and *first order* with respect to B, i.e., *third order* in total. If the reaction was carried out under conditions of excess B, then the rate of reaction would be effectively independent of the concentration of B since this could be regarded as constant. The rate would then be proportional to $[A]^2$ and the reaction would be said to be *pseudo-second order*. If, on the other hand, A was present in excess rather than B, then the reaction would become *pseudo-first order*. Thus, in general, the term *order of reaction* is merely a method of stating the apparent dependence of the rate of reaction on a reactant concentration in a particular experiment. By changing the conditions of an experiment, the order of reaction might be changed and yet the molecularity and mechanism remain unaltered.

In the mechanism

$$A + B \overset{\text{fast}}{\rightleftharpoons} X$$

$$X \overset{\text{slow}}{\longrightarrow} C$$

the stoichiometry is simply

$$A + B = C$$

The reaction is unimolecular, but the order may or may not be second—it must be determined. The rate equation would also have to be determined and would give a more comprehensive expression of the kinetic results than a simple determination of *order of reaction*. There is always a rate equation for a reaction, but there is not always a simple integral order of reaction. Nevertheless, of the thousands of reactions whose kinetics have been investigated, a great many of them have integral values of order of reaction under a wide variety of experimental conditions. For this reason, the concept of *order* is a useful one and, in the majority of cases, enables the value for the specific rate constant for the reaction to be evaluated from the experimental kinetic data.

3.9.3 The measurement of the rate of reaction

In most kinetic investigations, the objective is to obtain a mathematical relationship between the rate of reaction and the concentrations (or pressures) of the reactants. This involves the measurement of the concentration of the reactant or product as a function of time. There is no single experimental technique which is suitable for the measurement of the rates of all reactions. Each reaction has its own characteristics, which make a given experimental method more applicable. A detailed description of all the possible methods is outside the scope of this book, and only a brief survey of the more common methods will be given.

The simplest method of following the rate, and the one which often yields the most complete information, is the *method of sampling*. Samples are withdrawn from the reaction mixture at various intervals of time and quantitatively analysed. Unless the stoichiometry of the reaction has been established, the analysis should include the products in addition to unchanged reactants.

Immediately the samples have been taken they are *quenched*, i.e., the reaction in them is arrested either by rapid cooling or by the introduction of a chemical reagent. They are then analysed either by conventional *wet* methods or by instrumental methods.

Whenever a reaction is accompanied by the evolution or absorption of a gas, a manometric technique may be used to follow the course of the reaction. The progress of the reaction is followed by measuring the volume of gas liberated or absorbed as a function of time. Care must be taken in controlling the temperature of the system, especially if the gas is soluble in the liquid used as the solvent. Many metabolic reactions, including the complex process of cell respiration, involve liberation or absorption of gases. Manometric techniques have provided useful approaches to the study of metabolic events, and have been used in the study of rates of metabolism of

(a) cell suspensions,
(b) tissue slices,
(c) tissue homogenates,
(d) isolated sub-cellular units,
(e) isolated enzyme systems,
(f) assay of specific metabolites,
(g) small whole organisms.

Metabolic studies employing manometry (or respirometry as it is often termed) became important as a result of the work of Warburg (1919 onwards) who developed an accurate constant-volume manometer. There are three basic types of manometer used in such studies. There are the constant-volume devices (such as the Warburg apparatus), there are constant-pressure mano-meters, and also those which operate differentially by measurement of gas volume relative to a blank reaction cell. The Gilson apparatus is a modern respirometer of the latter type.

A great many of the methods available for the study of reaction rates may be classified as *indirect methods*. These involve measurement of some physical property of the system which varies in a simple manner with concentration. Invariably, the physical measurement being used has first to be calibrated against the concentration of the reactant or product prior to being used to measure the rate of the reaction. Many optical methods of analysis may be used in kinetics. Measurement of absorption spectra (see section 6.2), in all regions of the electromagnetic spectrum, may be used for following the course of a reaction. If there is an appreciable change in refractive index during the reaction, this may be used to measure the rate. For compounds exhibiting optical activity, the change in the optical rotation of plane-polarized light as the reaction proceeds may be observed in a polarimeter. Magnetic-resonance techniques such as nuclear magnetic resonance (NMR) and electron spin reson-ance (ESR) may also be used in kinetic studies. For polymeric substances, their property of scattering light may be used, and for fluorescent compounds their fluorescent emission may be measured as the reaction proceeds.

Of the many electrical methods available for measurement of reaction rates, the most commonly used are conductimetric methods and potentiometric methods. The conductimetric method is based on a change in electrolytic conduction in solution arising from a difference in ionic mobilities of reactants and products (see section 5.4.2). The potentiometric method is based upon a change in electrode potential of a reversible electrode due to a change in concentration in the solution into which the electrode is dipping. The change in pH during a reaction would also provide a suitable method for reaction-rate studies.

Since all chemical reactions are accompanied by the evolution or absorption of heat, the use of thermal methods can sometimes be used to follow the course of a reaction. Finally, the use of radioactive isotopes in kinetic investigations is common, and provides a very elegant method for the study of reaction rates and reaction mechanism.

Fast reactions in solution are often studied by means of flow methods. There are two flow methods commonly used, namely, the *continuous-flow technique* (or stirred-flow technique) and the *stopped-flow technique*. Both methods allow studies to be made of reactions which are complete within a few milliseconds.

The continuous-flow technique is illustrated schematically in Fig. 3.1. It consists in principle of two vessels A and B which contain the separate reactants. The reactants are passed, often by means of compressed air, to a reactor R which contains an efficient stirrer. The mixture of reactants and products flows out of the reactor at the same rate as the reactants entered and are monitored by some physical technique in an observation cell D. This means of detection may be a spectroscopic method using absorption of visible or ultraviolet light, fluorescence or even electron spin resonance (see chapter 6). Alternatively, the extent of reaction may be measured thermally, using thermocouples or thermistors to measure the temperature change accompanying the reaction.

The direct measurement of time is eliminated in this method and is substituted by the measurement of flow rate. There are two ways of monitoring the concentration of reactants at various times. If the observation cell D is always in a fixed position with respect to the reactor, then measurements are usually carried out at several flow rates through the instrument. Alternatively, if the position of D can be varied, then one can maintain the flow rate through the instrument at a fixed value and measure the concentration of reactant or product at various distances from the reactor.

During a given series of observations the concentrations of reactants are maintained at constant values. This means that the rate of reaction is constant while the measurements are being carried out, and this enables the rate equation in its differential form to be obtained directly. This allows fairly complex kinetics to be studied rather more easily than by normal experimental methods.

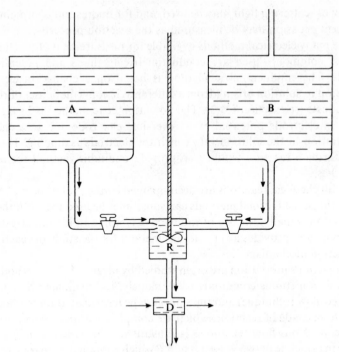

Fig. 3.1 Schematic diagram of the continuous-flow technique

Some of the types of reactions which may be investigated by the continuous-flow method include:

(a) complex consecutive reactions, that is, reactions with many successive stages,
(b) polymerization reactions,
(c) reactions of haemoglobin with oxygen and carbon monoxide,
(d) reactions involving enzymes.

In the last few years the stopped-flow technique has had great popularity as a method of studying fast reactions in solution. The reasons for this are that the method uses only small quantities of reagents and can utilize fast electronic recording techniques. Furthermore, commercial equipment is now available for this technique. In the stopped-flow technique, the flow of two reacting liquids or solutions is suddenly arrested and the progress of the reaction is then immediately followed by an optical method in conjunction with a cathode-ray oscilloscope.

A schematic arrangement for the stopped-flow method is shown in Fig. 3.2. The plungers in the syringes are very rapidly driven inwards by mechanical means, causing a rapid stream of reactants to enter the mixing chamber. The liquid passes into the observation cell, and when the plungers reach a certain point, the flow is suddenly stopped. This is usually achieved by an arresting piston on the exit side of the observation cell, which switches off the drive to the plungers and immediately activates the oscilloscope. The oscilloscope records the change in optical absorption of the contents of the observation cell and hence the changes in concentration with time occurring in the cell. The picture

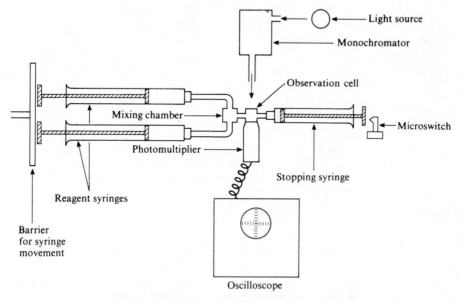

Fig. 3.2 Schematic diagram of the stopped-flow technique

produced on the oscilloscope screen may be photographed to produce a permanent record. Figure 3.3 illustrates the oscilloscope record which would be obtained in a stopped-flow study of the deoxygenation of oxyhaemoglobin (HbO_2) to haemoglobin (Hb). The decay curve is analysed mathematically from the photograph from which kinetic parameters such as rate constant and half-life may be calculated.

Typical kinetic applications of the stopped-flow technique are

(a) some proton transfer reactions,
(b) reactions of haemoglobin,
(c) oxidation–reduction reactions, including those in biological systems, e.g., oxidation of $FADH_2$,
(d) enzyme-catalysed reactions and characterization of enzymes.

For reactions that are complete in several microseconds, flow methods are too slow, and the so-called *relaxation methods* have to be used. Relaxation methods involve the measurement of the *relaxation time*. This is the time taken for a reaction to cover a certain fraction of its passage towards equilibrium. The methods basically allow the reaction to proceed to equilibrium. It is then disturbed very rapidly from equilibrium by either an increase in temperature (*temperature jump*) or an increase in pressure (*pressure jump*) or by an electric field pulse. The speed at which the system returns to equilibrium is then

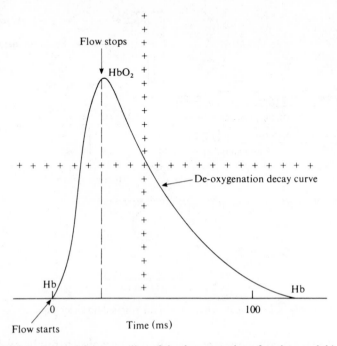

Fig. 3.3 Stopped-flow recording of the deoxygenation of oxyhaemoglobin

measured by high-speed electronic recording techniques using cathode ray oscilloscopes. Reactions which may be studied by relaxation methods include

(a) proton exchange reactions and acid–base reactions,
(b) electron transfer reactions, such as in redox reactions,
(c) biochemical reactions, such as metal–enzyme reactions, reactions of ADP and ATP with metal ions, antibody–antigen reactions, structural changes in proteins and nucleic acids.

3.9.4 The mathematical characterization of simple kinetic systems

The kinetic experiments carried out using the techniques outlined in the previous section yield values of reactant concentration or product concentration (or some related physical quantity) at various times throughout the course of the reaction. The first stage in the interpretation of these data is to see whether or not the values can be fitted by some simple mathematical relationship. This will also provide a method for the evaluation of the specific rate constant for the reaction. The equations for various kinetic processes along with various other kinetic parameters, such as *half-life*, are given in Table 3.6. The *half-life* of a reaction is the time taken for the concentration of the reactant to have fallen to half its original value.

If the reaction is following first-order kinetics under the particular experimental conditions, then a graph of the logarithm of the reactant concentration against time should be linear. This follows from the equation

$$k = \frac{1}{t} \ln \left(\frac{a}{a-x} \right),$$
(3.35)

which may be written as

$$\log_{10}(a - x) = -\frac{kt}{2 \cdot 303} + \log_{10} a$$
(3.36)

The constant $2 \cdot 303$ arises from the conversion of logarithms from the base e to the base 10.

The plot of $\log_{10}(a - x)$ against t is linear for a first-order process, and has an intercept of $\log_{10} a$ and a gradient of $-k/2 \cdot 303$, from which the specific rate constant k can be calculated.

If the reaction is following second-order kinetics, then the appropriate equation is

$$k = \frac{1}{ta} \left(\frac{x}{a-x} \right)$$
(3.37)

which may be arranged as

$$\frac{x}{a(a-x)} = kt$$
(3.38)

A plot of $x/a(a - x)$ against t will therefore be linear, passing through the origin and having a gradient equal to k.

3.9.5 The evaluation of the order of a reaction

Three general methods of evaluating the order of a reaction from the results of a kinetic study are available.

(a) The method of substitution   In this method, the kinetic data are substituted into the various expressions for the rate constant, k. The equation which yields the most constant values for k is the one corresponding to the order of the reaction under the particular experimental conditions used. Alternatively, the data may be plotted in some suitable way to indicate the appropriate order

93

Table 3.6 Characterization of simple kinetic systems

Reaction order	Kinetic process	Rate equation	Specific rate constant, k	Units of k	Half-life $t_{1/2}$
1	A → products	$\dfrac{dx}{dt} = k(a-x)$	$\dfrac{1}{t}\ln\left(\dfrac{a}{a-x}\right)$	s^{-1}	$\dfrac{1}{k}\ln 2$
2(a)	2A → products	$\dfrac{dx}{dt} = k(a-x)^2$	$\dfrac{1}{ta}\left(\dfrac{x}{a-x}\right)$	litre mole^{-1} s^{-1}	$\dfrac{1}{ka}$
2(b)	A + B → products	$\dfrac{dx}{dt} = k(a-x)(b-x)$	$\dfrac{1}{t(a-b)}\ln\left(\dfrac{b(a-x)}{a(b-x)}\right)$	litre mole^{-1} s^{-1}	$\dfrac{1}{k(a-b)}\ln\left(\dfrac{b}{2b-a}\right)$
3	3A → products	$\dfrac{dx}{dt} = k(a-x)^3$	$\dfrac{1}{2t}\left(\dfrac{1}{(a-x)^2} - \dfrac{1}{a^2}\right)$	litre^2 mole^{-2} s^{-1}	$\dfrac{3}{2ka^2}$
Opposing 1	A $\underset{k_2}{\overset{k_1}{\rightleftharpoons}}$ B	$\dfrac{dx}{dt} = k_1(a-x) - k_2(b-x)$	$k_1 = \dfrac{x_e}{ta}\ln\left(\dfrac{x_e}{x_e - x}\right)$	s^{-1}	—
1 Opposed by 2	A ⇌ B + C	$\dfrac{dx}{dt} = k_1(a-x) - k_2(b-x)(c-x)$	$k_1 = \dfrac{x_e}{t(2a-x_e)}\ln\left(\dfrac{ax_e + x(a-x_e)}{a(x_e-x)}\right)$	mole litre^{-1} s^{-1}	—

a = initial concentration of A
b = initial concentration of B
c = initial concentration of C

k = rate constant
t = time; x = moles of reactant disappeared at time t
x_e = moles of product at equilibrium

of reaction. This method is perfectly satisfactory, provided reactions of a fractional order are not encountered.

(b) The method of half-lives It may be seen from Table 3.6 that the expressions for the half-life of a reaction vary according to the order of reaction. The half-life of a first-order reaction is independent of the initial concentration of reactant, whereas, for a second- and third-order reaction, the half-life is inversely proportional to the initial concentration and inversely proportional to the square of the initial concentration respectively. This feature may be expressed as

$$t_{1/2} = \frac{K}{a^{n-1}} \quad \text{or} \quad t_{1/2} = \text{constant} \times a^{1-n} \tag{3.39}$$

where n is the order of reaction and K is the appropriate proportionality constant. By carrying out experiments with different initial concentrations of reactant and obtaining $t_{1/2}$ in each experiment, the value of n can be calculated from the results, using the following equation

$$\log_{10} t_{1/2} = -(n-1) \log_{10} a + \log_{10} K \tag{3.40}$$

A plot of $\log_{10} t_{1/2}$ against $\log_{10} a$ has a gradient of $-(n-1)$ or $(1-n)$. This method allows n to be calculated even if it is a non-integral value.

(c) The differential method For a reaction of the nth order, the rate of reaction V is related to the concentration of the reactant at any time during the reaction by the equation

$$V = kC^n, \tag{3.41}$$

where k is the specific rate constant and C the concentration of *reactant*. A graph is plotted of reactant concentration against time [Fig. 3.4(a)]. Gradients are drawn at various parts of the graph. These gradients, which are negative, will represent the rate of reaction $(-dC/dt)$ or V at these values of C. A second graph is then drawn of $\log_{10} V$ against $\log_{10} C$ [Fig. 3.4(b)], which has a gradient of n (the order of reaction) and an intercept of $\log_{10} k$. This method allows both k and n to be determined, even when the reaction has a non-integral order.

3.9.6   The effect of temperature on the rate of reaction

The rate of a chemical reaction is usually very sensitive to changes of temperature. It has been known for a long time that the variation of rate constant k with absolute temperature is given by the *Arrhenius equation*:

$$k = A e^{-E/RT} \tag{3.42}$$

95

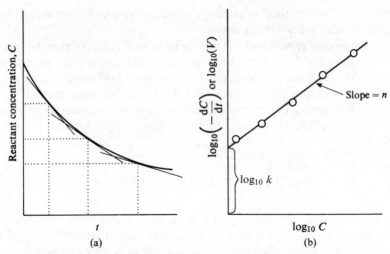

Fig. 3.4 Determination of order of reaction by the differential method

The constant A is known as the *Arrhenius frequency factor* or *pre-exponential factor*. The constant E is termed the *activation energy*. An alternative way of expressing the *Arrhenius equation* is

$$\log_{10}\left(\frac{k_1}{k_2}\right) = -\frac{E}{2\cdot 303R}\left(\frac{1}{T_1} - \frac{1}{T_2}\right) \qquad (3.43)$$

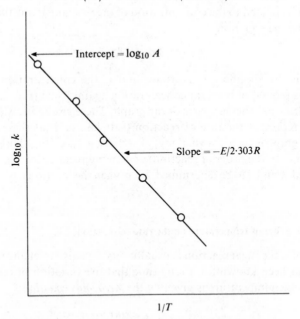

Fig. 3.5 Schematic Arrhenius plot to obtain activation energy

The value of the activation energy for a reaction is obtained by plotting $\log_{10} k$ against $1/T$ (T in K). The graph should be linear, having a gradient of $-E/2 \cdot 303R$ and intercept of $\log_{10} A$ (Fig. 3.5). The Arrhenius equation is valid for all reactions of simple mechanism. Deviation of a reaction from this equation is often indicative of a complex reaction.

3.9.7 Thermodynamic formulation of reaction rates

It is thought that during the course of a reaction the reactant molecules are activated by collisions with one another and that there is an equilibrium between the activated molecules and non-activated molecules. The activation energy is the minimum amount of energy that the molecules must acquire by collision so that they may be capable of undergoing reaction. The molecules that acquire this amount of energy are termed *activated complexes*, or said to be in a *transition state*. This process is shown diagrammatically in Fig. 3.6, together with a more complex process in which a definite reaction intermediate arises. Many examples of reactions involving both transition states and intermediates will be found in chapter 4.

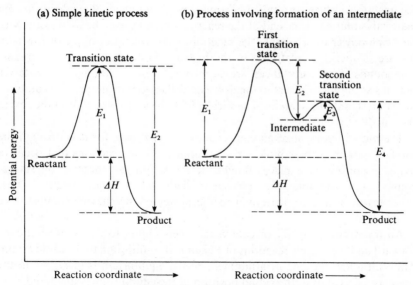

Fig. 3.6 Energy barriers in chemical systems

It can be shown that the rate constant (k) is given by the equation

$$k = v \, e^{\Delta S\ddagger/R} \, e^{-E_1/RT}. \tag{3.44}$$

Thus not only does the activation energy E_1 control the rate of reaction, but so also does the entropy of activation, $\Delta S\ddagger$. Factors such as formation of ring

97

structures, reactions of ions and solvation have important consequences for the activated complex and affect the sign and magnitude of $\Delta S\ddagger$. Catalysts affect the rate of reaction by lowering the value of the activation energy E_1. For unimolecular reactions the constant v has the value $e\bar{k}T/h$, where $\bar{k}$ is the Boltzman constant (R/N, where N is Avogadro's number) and h is Planck's constant. For bimolecular reactions, v has the value $e^2\bar{k}T/h$.

Comparison of eqs. (3.42) and (3.44) reveals the Arrhenius frequency factor A to be identical with $ve^{\Delta S\ddagger/R}$. Values of A for gas reactions are usually of the order of 10^{13} (s^{-1} for unimolecular reaction; litre mole^{-1} s^{-1} for bimolecular reaction). For reactions in solution, values of A are usually less, perhaps 10^5, due to electrostatic interactions between solute and solvent molecules which affect the value of $\Delta S\ddagger$. This is particularly true for ions, or if the reactants or transition state have large dipole moments.

3.9.8 Homogeneous chemical catalysis

It is well known that the rates of many reactions are influenced by the presence of substances other than those represented in the stoichiometric equation for the reaction. Whenever this phenomenon is observed, the added *foreign* material is unused at the end of the reaction and may even be used again with the same power to accelerate the reaction. An excellent example of this is in the use of nickel or platinum in the hydrogenation of unsaturated organic compounds. Such substances are termed *catalysts*. Although the catalyst remains at the end of the reaction, it is established that in all forms of catalysis, the catalyst molecules interact chemically with the molecules of reactant during the course of the reaction.

The most important of all catalysts are the enzymes, for it is through the catalytic power of these molecules that almost all the reactions that occur in living organisms take place. Biochemical reactions are notable on several counts, for example the efficiency with which they occur. These other features may be attributed to the power of the enzyme catalysts (see section 8.2).

An important property of catalysts is their ability to accelerate both the forward and the reverse reactions of a chemical equilibrium to the same extent. Thus, although the rate of attainment of the equilibrium is increased in the presence of a catalyst, the actual position of the equilibrium is unaltered.

Catalysis is usually divided into two broad groups: heterogeneous and homogeneous. Heterogeneous catalysis occurs when the reaction takes place at an interface or surface between two phases where one of the interfaces belongs to the catalyst. This is common in reactions in the gas phase, where the reaction might take place on the walls of the container or on the surface of some added material. In the case of homogeneous catalysis, the catalyst is present in the same phase, such as the catalysis of reactions in solution by dissolved ions. Heterogeneous catalysis is of less importance in living systems, except that certain cell components provide a surface at which enzyme and substrate can meet. Homogeneous catalysis, on the other hand, is of great importance.

Of particular importance in homogeneous catalysis are reactions catalysed by acids and bases. Chemical reactions which are catalysed solely by hydrogen ions are said to be subject to *specific hydrogen ion catalysis* or *specific acid catalysis*. Similarly, reactions catalysed only by hydroxyl ions are said to be subject to *specific hydroxyl ion catalysis*. In addition, some reactions are subject to *general acid catalysis* or *general base catalysis*. General acid catalysis occurs when the reaction is catalysed by any acidic species in solution, for example, undissociated acid, in addition to hydrogen ion. General base catalysis occurs when all basic species in solution catalyse the reaction. Reactions are also known which are catalysed by both hydrogen ion and hydroxyl ion, and said to be subject to *specific acid–base catalysis*. *General acid–base catalysis* occurs when a reaction is catalysed by all acidic and basic species in solution. Various types of acid- and base-catalysed reactions are shown in Table 3.7.

Table 3.7 Acid and base catalysis

Reaction	Catalyst
Inversion of sucrose	H^+
Hydrolysis of esters and amides	H^+
Hydrolysis of pyrophosphates	H^+
Hydrolysis of urea	H^+
Hydrolysis of adenosine triphosphate (ATP)	H^+
Decomposition of triacetone alcohol	OH^-
Conversion of acetone to triacetone alcohol	OH^-
Hydrolysis of ethyl orthocarbonate and orthoacetate	Generalized Acid
Rearrangement of N-bromoacetanilide	Generalized Acid
Decomposition of nitramide	Generalized Base
Mutarotation of glucose	General acid–base
Enolization of acetone	General acid–base

A more detailed treatment of some of these reactions will be found in later sections. It is, however, possible to describe, in a general way, the mechanism of acid–base catalysed reactions. For example, the general features of acid-catalysed reactions in aqueous solution are as shown below.

If S is the reactant (or substrate), then the first stage of the reaction is the addition of a proton to form SH^+. This may be due to a reaction with the hydroxonium ion (or higher hydrates) or other acidic species in solution represented as BH^+:

$$S + H_3O^+ \rightarrow SH^+ + H_2O \qquad \text{(a)}$$
or
$$S + BH^+ \rightarrow SH^+ + B \qquad \text{(b)}$$

Table 3.8 Some kinetic parameters for chemical and enzyme catalysis

Reaction	Catalyst	Temperature ($°C$)	k (litre mole^{-1} s^{-1})	A (litre mole^{-1} s^{-1})	E (kJ mole^{-1})	E (kcal mole^{-1})
Hydrolysis of urea	H^+	62	7.4×10^{-7}	1.8×10^{10}	103.0	24.6
	urease	21	5.0×10^{6}	1.7×10^{13}	28.5	6.8
Hydrolysis of adenosine triphosphate (ATP)	H^+	40	4.7×10^{-6}	2.4×10^{9}	88.8	21.2
	myosin	25	8.2×10^{6}	1.6×10^{22}	88.4	21.1
Decomposition of H_2O_2	Fe^{2+}	22	5.6×10^{1}	1.8×10^{9}	42.3	10.1
	catalase	22	3.5×10^{7}	6.4×10^{8}	7.1	1.7

As far as the kinetic behaviour is concerned, it is not important to know which of these two reactions takes place. The protonated species SH^+ has now the possibility of reacting either with the dissolved solute A, to form products P,

$$SH^+ + A \quad \rightarrow P \tag{c}$$

or of reacting with the solvent:

$$SH^+ + H_2O \rightarrow P + H_3O^+ \tag{d}$$

Whichever one of the reactions (c) or (d) takes place influences the kinetic behaviour of the overall reaction. If reaction (c) is involved, the mechanism is said to be *prototropic*, whereas, if reaction (d) takes place, it is *protolytic*.

The action of all catalysts in increasing the rates of reactions is by reducing the free energy of activation. This may be achieved by reducing the activation energy E, or by increasing the entropy of activation $\Delta S\ddagger$, or both. The value of the Arrhenius frequency factor A may be taken as a measure of the entropy of activation. Although acids and bases often produce large effects on the rate constants of chemical reactions, the effect of enzymes on comparable reactions is usually much greater. The values of rate constant, Arrhenius frequency factor, and activation energy for three such reactions are compared in Table 3.8.

The greater potency of urease over hydrogen ion in the catalysis of the hydrolysis of urea is apparent from the large difference in the rate constants. The enzyme augments the rate of reaction by increasing the entropy of activation and also decreasing the energy of activation. On the other hand, myosin promotes the hydrolysis of adenosine triphosphate by producing an enormous effect on the value of A, while the activation energy for the enzyme and the acid-catalysed reactions are almost the same. The decomposition of hydrogen peroxide by catalase is more efficient than the catalysis by ferrous ion, due to a considerable reduction in the activation energy by the enzyme, while the values of the frequency factor and hence the entropy of activation for the two reactions are fairly similar in magnitude.

Bibliography

1. J. G. Morris, *A Biologists Physical Chemistry*, 2nd Edn, Arnold, 1974.
2. J. H. Linford, *Introduction to Energetics with Applications to Biology*, Butterworths, 1966.
3. I. M. Klotz, *Chemical Thermodynamics*, 2nd Edn, Benjamin, 1972.
4. I. M. Klotz, *Energy Changes in Biochemical Reactions*, Academic Press, 1967.
5. V. R. Williams and H. B. Williams, *Basic Physical Chemistry for the Life Sciences*, 2nd Edn, Freeman, 1973.

6. J. L. Latham, *Elementary Reaction Kinetics*, 2nd Edn, Butterworths, 1972.
7. A. A. Frost and R. G. Pearson, *Kinetics and Mechanism*, Wiley, 1961.
8. D. N. Hague, *Fast Reactions*, Wiley, 1971.
9. A series of articles has been published in *Chemistry in Britain* concerning thermodynamics in biological systems.
   These are as follows:
   B. E. C. Banks, 'Thermodynamics and Biology', *Chemistry in Britain*, **5**, 514, 1969.
   L. Pauling, 'The Problem of Biological Energetics', *Chemistry in Britain*, **6**, 468, 1970.
   D. Wilkie, 'Thermodynamics and Biology', *Chemistry in Britain*, **6**, 472, 1970.
   A. F. Huxley, 'Energetics of Muscle', *Chemistry in Britain*, **6**, 477, 1970.
   R. A. Ross and C. A. Vernon, 'Biological Energetics—the other View', *Chemistry in Britain*, **6**, 539, 1970.
   B. E. C. Banks and C. A. Vernon, 'A reply to Linus Pauling and A. F. Huxley'. *Chemistry in Britain*, **6**, 541, 1970.

4. The reactions of organic molecules

4.1 PHYSICAL ASPECTS OF ORGANIC REACTIONS

4.1.1 Organic reaction mechanisms

The reactions that take place in organic molecules are, for the most part, concerned with the breaking and making of covalent bonds. The overall process for the breaking of a covalent bond may be visualized as taking place in three ways:

(a) $X \div Y \longrightarrow X:^- + Y^+$

(b) $X \div Y \longrightarrow X^+ + :Y^-$

(c) $X \div Y \longrightarrow X^{\cdot} + Y^{\cdot}$

In the first two cases, one of the products of the cleavage takes both bonding electrons, and this unequal division leads to the formation of ions. These types of process are called *heterolytic cleavages*. In the third case, there is an equal division of the bonding electrons, leading to neutral but still reactive species (*free radicals*). This process is referred to as a *homolytic cleavage*. Energy is required to break a bond, and the amount consumed is known as the bond-dissociation energy D (section 3.4.6). The value of this is usually quoted for the third process.

In a similar way, the formation of a single covalent (σ) bond may take place by reversal of the three processes. In the first two of these, the covalent bond arises by one of the reacting species providing both bonding electrons. In the third, the bond is formed with each component providing *one* electron. On this basis, organic reactions may be divided into two broad groups: firstly those in which bond formation proceeds via ionic species—*the polar reactions*—and secondly those involving free radicals. Both types of reaction will be described in this chapter, although the polar reactions are the more numerous. A further classification of organic reactions is possible when the nature of the *attacking reagent*, as distinct from the *organic substrate*, is considered.

If a reagent brings a pair of electrons to a substrate, it is called a *nucleophile*, and the reaction is nucleophilic. Thus species $X:^-$ or $:Y^-$ are nucleophiles, for example

$$\left[:\ddot{X}: \right]^-$$

103

where $X = Cl$, Br or I. On the other hand, if a reagent takes a pair of electrons from the substrate, it is called an *electrophile*, and the reaction is electrophilic. Thus the species X^+ and Y^+ are electrophiles, for example

$$\left[:\ddot{X}: \right]^+$$

where $X = Cl$, Br or I.

In spite of the great diversity of structure that is found in organic molecules, their reactions fall into a limited number of processes:

(a) Substitutions or displacements.
(b) Additions.
(c) Eliminations.
(d) Rearrangements.
(e) Oxidations and reductions.

In a complex reaction, there may be more than one of these reaction types taking place, but individual stages can be classified under one of the above headings. A further division of substitution and addition reactions is possible by considering the role and nature of the reagent used (electrophilic, nucleophilic or free-radical). The majority of reactions proceed through the intermediacy of ions.

The basic theory regarding the energetics of reactions has already been presented in section 3.9.7. Chemical reactions are continuous processes involving a gradual change from reactants to products. In a few cases, it is possible to isolate an intermediate stage, and in others it may be detected in the reaction mixture. The energy barrier to be overcome to reach the intermediate is the activation energy (Fig. 3.6). In most reactions, the molecular arrangement produced by the activation energy can be visualized as a *transition state* that has only momentary existence. The formation of a transition state plays a crucial role in the determination of the course of an organic reaction. When several transition states are possible, the one with the lowest energy is formed, and this is reflected in the structure of the reaction product.

The term *reaction mechanism* is used to describe a detailed study of the pathway along which the reaction proceeds. Ideally, we would like to know the exact position of the atoms in the reacting species and the energy changes that occur at every stage. Also a complete understanding of the effect of physical conditions, the role of solvent molecules, and the action of catalysts must be obtained. At the moment, we have to be content with a very limited knowledge of all these facets of a reaction. In the following discussion of the more important types of organic reaction, we shall look mainly at the structures of intermediates or transition states that are thought to arise in the reaction, and at the bearing this has on the nature of the reaction products. It will interest the biologist to know that this approach is now being applied to

104

biochemical reactions. Many of the principles deduced from ordinary organic reactions are equally valid in biochemical reactions.

4.1.2 The mechanisms of electron displacement in covalent bonds

(a) Single (σ) bonds We have seen, in chapter 1, how differences in electronegativity between atoms leads to an unequal distribution of electronic charge in covalent bonds. This gives rise to *polar* covalent bonds (see section 1.5.2). The presence of these polar bonds in an organic molecule produces centres of high and low electron density at which reaction can occur. A centre of high electron density is susceptible to attack by electrophiles, whereas a centre of low electron density is susceptible to attack by nucleophiles.

The power of atoms or groups to bring about an unequal distribution of charge in a σ bond gives rise to an *inductive effect*. For the purpose of defining more precisely the nature of inductive effects, we shall assume that a carbon–hydrogen bond in a typical saturated open-chain hydrocarbon has a uniform distribution of electronic charge. If the hydrogen atom is replaced by an atom or group X which is more electronegative than carbon, then the electron density is higher around X. The inductive effect of X is denoted by $-I$ and is indicated by a dipole in the bond (I). If the C—X bond is broken during a

$$-\overset{\displaystyle |}{\underset{\displaystyle |}{C}} \overset{\delta^+}{} \!\!\div\!\! \overset{\delta^-}{X} \quad \text{or} \quad -\overset{\displaystyle |}{\underset{\displaystyle |}{C}} \overset{\longrightarrow}{} \!\!\div\!\! X$$

I

reaction by a heterolytic process, the release of the electrons takes place in the direction of the displacement present in the reactant molecule, and such a release is indicated diagrammatically by a *curved arrow* (II)

$$-\overset{\displaystyle |}{\underset{\displaystyle |}{C}} \!\!\div\!\! X$$

II

This type of electron displacement is very important, since the great majority of functional groups present in organic molecules contain atoms which are more electronegative than carbon; for example, halo, hydroxyl, amino and nitro groups. The inductive effect exerted by a functional group is mainly confined to the carbon atom to which it is bonded, and is transmitted in a very limited way to other carbon atoms in the chain (for example, see section 4.2.1).

There are two cases in which the inductive effect causes displacement of electrons towards a particular carbon atom. Firstly, when an electropositive metal atom is present (as in organo-metallic compounds; III, M = Mg or Li); secondly, when alkyl groups themselves tend to repel electrons. The effect in both cases is designated as $+I$. In alkyl groups, the degree of chain branching increases the $+I$ effect. Thus, the effect is greatest at a tertiary carbon atom (IV)

105

and least at a primary carbon atom (VI) with a secondary carbon atom (V) intermediate.

$$-\overset{|}{\underset{|}{C}}\overset{\longleftarrow\!+}{-\!M-} \qquad R\overset{+}{\underset{\uparrow}{-}}\overset{+R}{\underset{+R}{\overset{|}{C}}}- \qquad R\overset{+}{\underset{\quad}{-}}\overset{+R}{\underset{H}{\overset{|}{C}}}- \qquad R\overset{\longleftarrow\!+}{\underset{H}{\overset{H}{\overset{|}{C}}}}-$$

$$\text{III} \qquad\qquad \text{IV} \qquad\qquad \text{V} \qquad\qquad \text{VI}$$

(b) Double bonds An unequal distribution of electronic charge can also occur in a double bond. There is a displacement of the π electron cloud in the direction of the more electronegative atom. Thus, the conventional representation of the carbonyl bond (VII), for example, is misleading, since there is a permanent dipole within the bond, oxygen being the negative end. The

$$\underset{\text{VII}}{>\!C\!=\!O} \quad\longleftrightarrow\quad \underset{\text{VIII}}{>\!\overset{+}{C}\!-\!\bar{O}}$$

electronic arrangement within the carbonyl bond can be visualized as a resonance hybrid (VII $\leftrightarrow$ VIII). In effect, there is a permanent dipole in the bond, and this explains the reactivity of the carbon atom to nucleophiles.

In a conjugated system, the unequal distribution of charge present in one double bond can be transmitted to other double bonds giving rise to a delocalized π electron system extending over several atoms. For example, in an unsaturated aldehyde (IX) the structure is best represented by the hybrid

$$\underset{\underset{\text{IX}}{3\quad 2\quad 1}}{-CH\!=\!CH\!-\!\overset{H}{\underset{|}{C}}\!=\!O} \quad\longleftrightarrow\quad \underset{\underset{\text{X}}{3\quad 2\quad 1}}{-\overset{+}{CH}\!-\!CH\!=\!\overset{H}{\underset{|}{C}}\!-\!\bar{O}}$$

IX $\leftrightarrow$ X. Thus, C_3 is also electron deficient and, like C_1, is likely to be subject to nucleophilic attack. Unlike an inductive effect, this type of electronic displacement can be transmitted very efficiently along a carbon chain, provided that it is conjugated.

Another type of electron displacement may occur in a conjugated system, notably a benzene ring, when atoms with unshared electron pairs are present. These arise in nitrogen, oxygen and halogen atoms and thus amino, hydroxy, and halo groups which, in a saturated system, produce a $-I$ effect, are electron donating (XI) in a conjugated system (see section 4.4.1).

$$\underset{\text{XI}}{-\overset{\frown}{C}\!=\!C\overset{\frown}{-}C\!=\!C\overset{\frown}{-}\ddot{X}}$$

4.2 ACIDIC AND BASIC PROPERTIES IN ORGANIC MOLECULES

4.2.1 Acidic properties

Most organic acids would be classed as *weak* acids in contrast to the *strong* mineral acids (HCl and H_2SO_4). There is, however, considerable variation in acidic strength and, in most cases, it is possible to correlate acidic strength with structural features in the molecule. In the presence of the weak base, water, an equilibrium is set up between undissociated acid (HA) and its anion (A^-):

$$HA + H_2O \rightleftharpoons H_3^+O + A^- \tag{4.1}$$

The presence of a carboxyl group endows an organic molecule with acidic properties, since the hydrogen atom of this functional group is labile and easily removed by a base. The simplest carboxylic acid, formic (I), loses a proton to produce formate ion, in which the negative charge is stabilized by delocalization (II) and is best represented by the hybrid (III). In other carboxylic acids, the acidity is increased by a structural feature which facilitates the removal of the

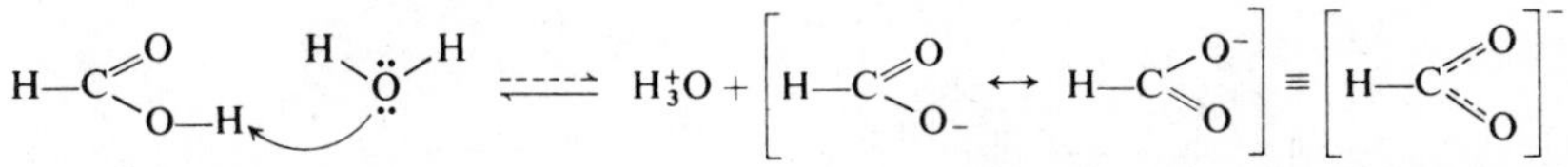

proton and discourages recombination with the anion (this latter effect could also be interpreted as decreasing the basicity of the anion). Alkyl groups exerting a $+I$ effect will reduce acidity by reducing the electron-withdrawing influence of the carbonyl group. The O—H bond is not weakened to the same extent, nor the charge so efficiently delocalized compared with formic acid. Since an inductive effect is not relayed very far, the higher aliphatic carboxylic acids have similar acid strengths (see Table 4.1). Benzoic acid is a slightly

Table 4.1   Acidity of some carboxylic acids

Acid	pK_a†	Acid	pK_a†	Acid	pK_a†
HCOOH	3·77	ClCH₂COOH	2·86	C₆H₅COOH	4·20

CH₃COOH	4·76	CH₃CH₂CHCOOH
		  |
		  Cl
			2·84	o-NO₂C₆H₄COOH	2·17

CH₃CH₂COOH	4·88	CH₃CH—CH₂COOH
		  |
		  Cl
			4·06	m-NO₂C₆H₄COOH	3·45

CH₃(CH₂)ₙCOOH	~4·86	CH₂CH₂CH₂COOH	4·52	p-NO₂C₆H₄COOH	3·43

† Values of the equilibrium constant (K_a) for eq. (4.1) are usually quoted as pK_a values (section 5.6.1).

stronger acid than the corresponding saturated acid (cyclohexanoic) but weaker than formic acid. The implication is that the benzene ring exerts a weak electron-withdrawing effect.

When electron-withdrawing groups $(-I)$ are present as substituents of alkyl or aryl groups, an increase in acidity is found. The presence of these groups supplements the electron-withdrawing effect of the carbonyl group in producing a labile hydrogen atom, and also assists in stabilizing the anion. In alkyl groups, the substituent must be attached to the carbon atom adjacent to the carboxyl group to exert its full effect. On the other hand, electronic influences are relayed much more efficiently in an aromatic ring, so that the position of the substituent is not so important (for example, o-, m-, p-nitrobenzoic acids).

Alcohols (RO—H) are very much weaker acids than carboxylic acids as there is no electron-withdrawing group to make the hydrogen labile, nor is there any way of delocalizing the charge of the anion (RO⁻). When the —OH group is attached to an aromatic ring, greater acidic properties are found. The main factor here is the stabilization of the anion by delocalization of the charge in the ring. In the presence of two or more electron-withdrawing

groups, the acidity of the phenol becomes comparable with that of carboxylic acids. For example, 2,4-dinitrophenol has a pK_a of 4·01 and 2,4,6-trinitrophenol (picric acid) has a pK_a of 1·02.

4.2.2 Basic properties

The nitrogen atom of an organic molecule may provide a pair of electrons to bind a proton, and hence gives the molecule basic properties. Organic bases are *weak* bases comparable with ammonia.

$$NH_3 + H_2O \rightleftharpoons NH_4^+ + {}^-OH \qquad (4.2)$$

Not all nitrogen-containing molecules behave as bases; structural features within the molecule can reduce the availability of the unshared pair of electrons on the nitrogen atom. The basicity of an organic molecule is governed by two factors; in the first place there is the availability of the unshared electron pair, and secondly there is the stability of the cation once formed compared with the neutral molecule. The presence of alkyl groups increases the basic strength of primary and secondary amines relative to ammonia. However, the inclusion of a third alkyl group reduces the basic strength in aqueous solution (see Table 4.2). This apparent anomaly may be explained by considering the way in which

108

Table 4.2 Basicity of some organic nitrogen compounds

Base	pK$_b$†	Base	pK$_b$†	Base	pK$_b$†
NH$_3$	4·75	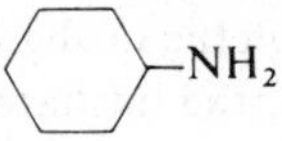 (C$_6$H$_{11}$)—NH$_2$	3·32	 (pyridine)	8·96
CH$_3$NH$_2$	3·36	C$_6$H$_5$NH$_2$	9·38	 (piperidine, N—H)	13·6
(CH$_3$)$_2$NH	3·23	(C$_6$H$_5$)(CH$_3$)$_2$N	9·62	 (piperazine, N···N)	12·7
(CH$_3$)$_3$N	4·20	o-NO$_2$C$_6$H$_4$NH$_2$	14·3	 (pyrrolidine, N—H)	2·73

† Values of the equilibrium constant (K_b) for equations of type (4.2) are usually quoted as pK_b values (section 5.6.1).

the cations formed on protonation are stabilized. The positive charge on the nitrogen atom is reduced by hydrogen bonding with water molecules.

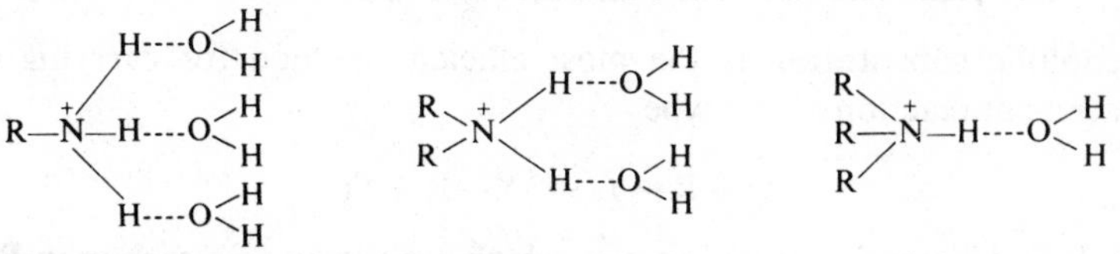

As the substitution on the nitrogen atom increases, so there will be fewer hydrogens through which hydrogen bonding can occur. Thus the cation becomes less stable with increasing alkyl substitution.

Most aromatic amines are extremely weak bases. This is because the unshared pair of electrons becomes involved in the ring π electron system. This involvement is best represented by a series of resonance structures (IV → VII). When the amino group in aniline becomes protonated (VIII), there is no longer an unshared electron pair to participate in the π electron system. This makes the cation (VIII) relatively unstable compared with the resonance-stabilized neutral molecule (IV → VII).

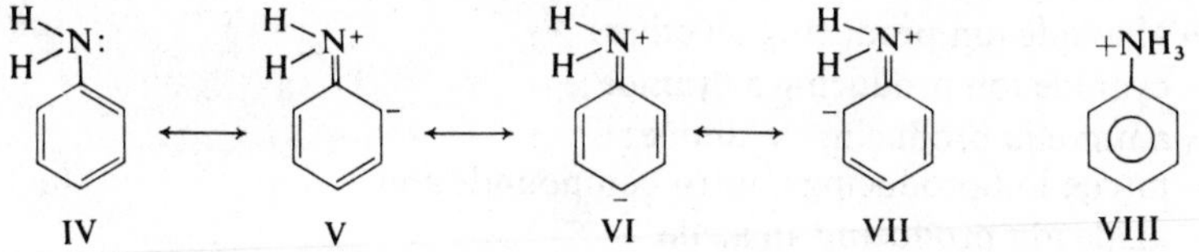

Incorporation of alkyl groups does very little to increase the basic strength, while the presence of electron-withdrawing substituents in the ring reduces the basic strength (for example o-nitroaniline).

Pyridine is also a weak base although the unshared electron pair is available for protonation. However, in pyrrole, the unshared electron pair is part of a π electron system which gives the molecule aromatic character, and thus is not available for protonation. On the other hand, the saturated nitrogen hetero-cycles such as tetrahydropyrrole have basic strengths comparable with open-chain amines.

Electron-withdrawing groups bring about a reduction in basic strength, the most important of these being a carbonyl group adjacent to a nitrogen atom. This situation arises in simple amides and peptides, and results in almost neutral properties. The structure of a simple amide is best represented by structure (XI) or by the two resonance forms IX and X.

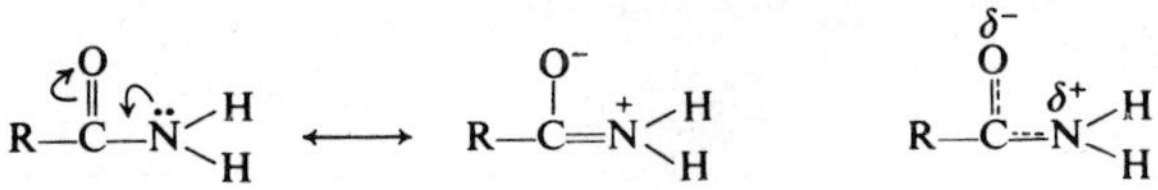

IX   X   XI

4.3   NUCLEOPHILIC SUBSTITUTION

4.3.1   Nucleophilic substitution at a saturated carbon atom

Nucleophilic substitution is the most efficient method for carrying out a displacement reaction of the type

$$X: + R\!-\!Y \rightarrow X\!-\!R + :Y$$

where X and Y are functional groups which are bound to a carbon in R. The attacking group (X:) arising from the reagent is a nucleophile and carries a pair of electrons which are used to establish a new covalent bond at a positive centre in the substrate molecule (R—Y). The group Y is displaced and departs with the electrons that previously bonded Y to the rest of the substrate. The simplest examples of nucleophilic substitution are found in the reactions of alkyl halides:

$$\text{R-Halogen} + :X \rightarrow R\!-\!X + \text{halide ion} \quad (R = \text{alkyl group})$$

Some examples of this general reaction are as follows:

X: = hydroxyl ion or water producing an alcohol;
X: = alkoxide ion producing an ether;
X: = cyanide ion producing a cyanide;
X: = ammonia producing an amine;
X: = nitrite ion producing a nitro compound; and
X: = azide ion producing an azide.

110

The displacement of the —OH group takes place in an acid catalysed reaction. For example, —OH may be replaced by a halogen atom (X: = halide ion) to give an alkyl halide:

$$\text{R—O—H} + \text{H}^+ \rightleftharpoons \text{R—}\overset{+}{\underset{\underset{\text{H}}{|}}{\text{O}}}\text{—H} + :\text{X} \longrightarrow \text{R—X} + \text{H}_2\text{O}.$$

Displacement of an —OH group frequently occurs in biochemical reactions. Phosphate ion is usually the nucleophile and the product a phosphate ester. The enzyme catalyst in such reactions probably acts by polarizing the —OH group and thus assisting its departure.

The most efficient nucleophilic reagents are those where a pair of electrons is most readily available for use in the formation of a covalent bond. This is nearly the same criterion as that used in the comparison of *basic strength* (see section 4.2.2). However, nucleophilic efficiency (*nucleophilicity*) refers to attack at a carbon atom, whereas basicity involves attack on a proton. The nucleophilic reagent does not necessarily have to be an anion such as

$$\text{OH}^-, \text{RO}^-, \text{RC}\overset{\displaystyle \text{O}}{\underset{\displaystyle \text{O}^-}{\diagup\!\!\!\diagdown}}, \text{CN}^-$$

or halide ion, but can be a species with an atom present with an unshared electron pair such as —N̈—, —Ö—, or —S̈—. Thus, groups such as —NH$_2$, —OH, or —SH have nucleophilic properties.

4.3.2 Mechanism of nucleophilic substitution

Nucleophilic substitution can take place in the following two ways.

(a) A single-stage reaction in which a new covalent bond is formed simultaneously as the old one is broken. The transition state in this process is the point at which the new bond is partially formed and the old bond is partially broken.

| X:⁀R÷Y | ⟶ | X----R----Y | ⟶ | X÷R + :Y |
| Reactants | | Transition state | | Products |

This mechanism has been designated S_N2—S for substitution, N for nucleophilic attack, and 2 indicating that it is a bimolecular process (see section 3.9.2). The formation of the transition state is the rate-determining step, and any change in the concentration of the reagent (X) and substrate (RY) brings about a change in the rate of formation of the transition state and hence of the overall reaction rate.

(b) There is an alternative but less common process in which inductive effects within the substrate are so great that, given a suitable environment, a slow bond cleavage (heterolysis) occurs before bond formation begins. This rate-determining step is followed by a rapid reaction of the intermediate (R⁺) with the nucleophile (X:).

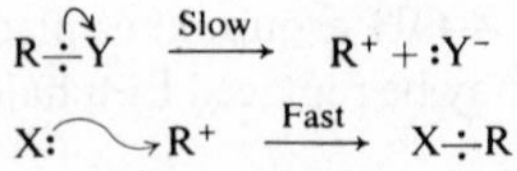

$$R \overset{\curvearrowright}{\div} Y \xrightarrow{\text{Slow}} R^+ + :Y^-$$

$$X:\searrow R^+ \xrightarrow{\text{Fast}} X \div R$$

This two-stage process has been designated S_N1, and is unimolecular, since the formation of the intermediate (R^+) is dependent only on the concentration of the substrate (RY), and is independent of the concentration of the other reagents. The intermediate is a carbon cation and is referred to as a *carbonium ion*.

There are important stereochemical implications of these two mechanisms for nucleophilic substitution. In the S_N2 process, attack by the nucleophile takes place on the side of the molecule opposite from that where the group which is to be displaced is positioned. In the transition state, five groups are momentarily bound to the central carbon atom and the configuration changes

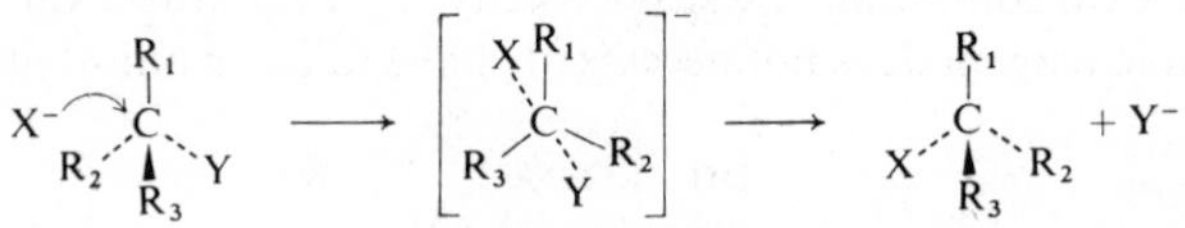

Transition state

from tetrahedral to an arrangement where the groups R_1, R_2 and R_3 lie in a trigonal plane and the groups X and Y lie at right angles to this plane. Then, as Y is displaced, the bond between C and X is fully formed and the configuration returns to tetrahedral. However, the new group X is in a different spatial position from the displaced group Y. If the carbon atom undergoing nucleophilic attack is asymmetric, then the operation of an S_N2 mechanism produces a product with the opposite absolute configuration to that of the substrate. This is referred to as an *inversion of configuration* (for examples of this see Fig. 2.4).

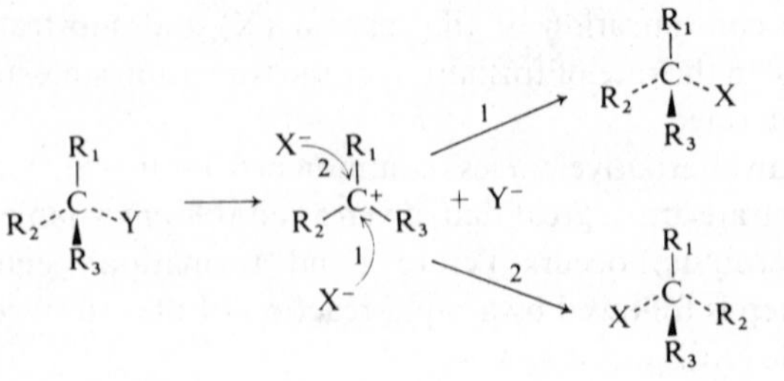

The carbonium ion intermediate in the S_N1 mechanism adopts a symmetrical trigonal arrangement, and attack by the nucleophile can then occur from two possible directions. If the carbon atom undergoing reaction is asymmetric, then the product has two configurations; one having the same spatial arrangement as the substrate, with X replacing Y, and the other having the opposite configuration. If the carbonium ion intermediate exists for long enough, then the two products are formed in equal amounts, and thus the reaction product is a racemate. However, carbonium ions are so reactive that nucleophilic attack may well start before the leaving group (Y) has departed, in which case the major part of the product has an inverted configuration.

In some cases, it is found that the whole of the product of a nucleophilic substitution has the same absolute configuration as the substrate. This fact requires a special mechanism, since neither the S_N1 nor the S_N2 mechanism can explain this possibility. The cases where retention of configuration occurs are explained either on the basis that there is some structural feature in the substrate which preserves the configuration during the reaction (*neighbouring-group participation*), or that the nucleophilic reagent preserves the configuration. An example of the former case is when there is an adjacent carboxylate anion to the carbon atom undergoing substitution. The configuration in the transition state is held by the formation of an α-*lactone* (I), which allows the leaving group (Y) to depart before nucleophilic attack occurs.

I

In enymze-catalysed reactions, both inversion and retention of configuration are observed during nucleophilic substitution. Racemization is comparatively rare.

Structural features in the substrate and reaction conditions play an important part in deciding whether the reaction proceeds by a uni- or bimolecular process and in deciding the rate at which it takes place. The S_N1 process requires prior heterolysis of a covalent bond with the formation of a pair of ions. This process takes place only in a polar medium, which must include a high proportion of water, and also it normally occurs at a tertiary carbon atom (tertiary carbonium ions are stabilized by the $+I$ effect of alkyl groups). An interesting exception is thought to occur during steroid biosynthesis, where a primary carbonium ion is stabilized by delocalization of charge through an adjacent double bond (Fig. 9.21). In most cases, however, primary and secondary carbon atoms in a non-polar solvent react by the S_N2 mechanism.

4.4 SUBSTITUTION IN AROMATIC COMPOUNDS

4.4.1 The mechanism of some common substitution reactions of benzene

Substitution in aromatic compounds usually proceeds through attack by an electrophile. Nucleophilic substitution occurs only in special circumstances. At the moment, there are relatively few electrophilic substitution reactions

113

which are known to occur in biochemical processes. On the other hand, aromatic properties are found in a large number of heterocyclic compounds, many of which play a very important part in living organisms.

In these electrophilic substitution reactions a pair of π electrons of the aromatic ring is used to establish a covalent bond between a carbon atom of the ring and the attacking electrophile. In doing so, the stable (*aromatic*) π electron system is disrupted. The transition state (I) then passes back to a stable aromatic system by loss of a proton. The electronic structure of the transition state can be represented by the resonance hybrid (I', I'', I''').

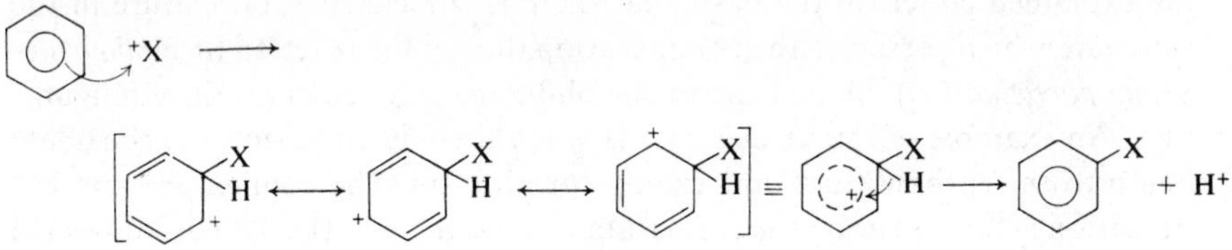

All the common aromatic substitution reactions can be shown to involve electrophilic attack, the actual electrophile depending on the reagent system. A few well known reactions will serve to illustrate this.

The nitration of benzene requires a mixture of concentrated nitric and sulphuric acids, which produce the nitronium ion (NO_2^+) which is the electrophile. In aromatic compounds which are more susceptible to substitution, a milder nitrating system is used, for example, with phenol.

$$HNO_3 + 2H_2SO_4 \rightleftharpoons H_3O + 2HSO_4^- + {}^+NO_2$$

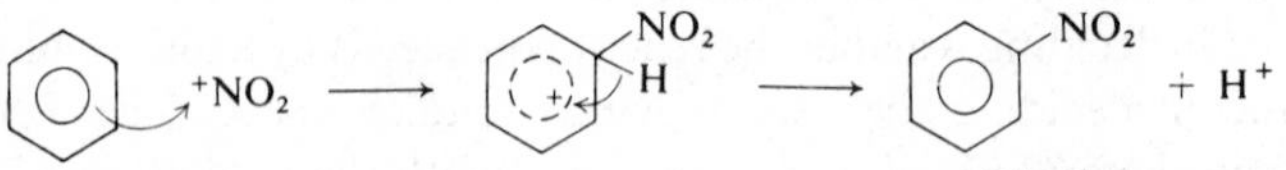

Nitrobenzene

Aromatic compounds may be converted directly into halogen-substituted derivatives. In order to ensure sufficient electrophile, iron is used as a co-reagent which reacts with the halogen molecule giving the halogen cation.

$$2Fe + 3Cl_2 \longrightarrow 2FeCl_3$$

$$FeCl_3 + Cl_2 \longrightarrow [FeCl_4]^- Cl^+$$

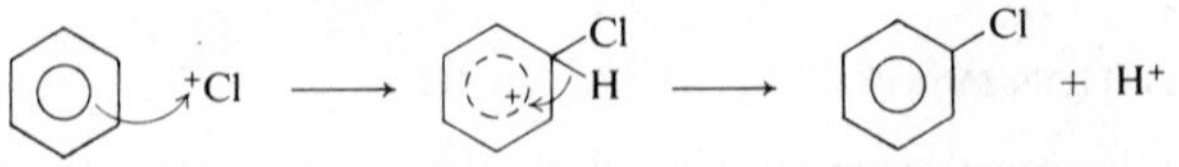

Chlorobenzene

A similar type of mechanism has been proposed for sulphonation, where sulphur trioxide acts as electrophile producing an aromatic sulphonic acid.

114

Alkylation and acylation, using an alkyl chloride and acyl chloride respectively, require the use of aluminium chloride as co-reagent. The role of this is to produce the alkyl or acyl carbonium ions which are the electrophiles.

When there is a substituent present in an aromatic compound, it greatly influences the reactivity of the ring to further substitution. If benzene is taken as a reference compound, it is found that some functional groups make the ring more reactive, and these are called *activating groups*; on the other hand, some substituents make the ring less reactive than benzene; these are known as *deactivating groups*.

Apart from influencing the reactivity of the ring, a substituent will also determine the position of further substitution. This is termed the *orientation effect*. The differences in reactivity and orientation may be explained by considering the formation of the possible transition states. The key factor in this analysis will be to see what effect the substituent has on the energy and hence the stability of the transition state. If the substituent (A) is electron withdrawing $(-I)$—for example, a halogen atom, nitro or sulphonic group—the positive charge of the transition state (II) remains localized within the ring. On the other hand, if the substituent (B) is electron donating, such as an alkyl group, the positive charge of the transition state (III) can be delocalized more efficiently and the energy of the transition state is correspondingly less. It is found that —OH and —NH$_2$ groups, which possess an electron-withdrawing effect $(-I)$ due to the presence of electronegative atoms O and N, exert an electron-donating effect in aromatic compounds, and hence strongly activate the ring to further substitution (IV; D = —OH or —NH$_2$). This is due to the interaction of an unshared electron pair with the π electron system.

In a monosubstituted benzene derivative, there are five sites for further substitution—two *ortho*, two *meta* and one *para*. The orientation effect of a substituent is broadly of two types. First, there are groups which cause further substitution to take place at positions *ortho* and *para* to them. These are called *ortho–para directors*. Second, there are groups which cause further substitution to take place at positions *meta* to them. These are the *meta directors*.

On the basis of activating and orientating effects of a substituent, it is possible to classify some of the common functional groups found in aromatic compounds as follows.

(a) Deactivating groups Two types may be distinguished, those that are *ortho–para* directors, for example, halogen substituents (Cl, Br, I) and those that are *meta* directors, for example, nitro, carboxyl, ester, aldehyde, ketone, sulphonic, and cyano substituents.

115

(b) Activating groups   These groups all direct to *ortho* and *para* positions. There is, however, a variation in the degree to which the substituent activates these sites. Alkyl and aryl groups are weak activators, ether and amide are more strongly activating and hydroxyl and amino are very strongly activating.

4.4.2   Electrophilic substitution in heterocyclic compounds

Certain unsaturated heterocyclic compounds display aromatic properties, the extent varying with the molecular structure. The values for the resonance energy provide a good guide to reactivity of the heterocyclic compound (see section 1.5.7). Pyridine is in fact more stable and less reactive to electrophilic substitution than benzene. The additional stability of pyridine may be explained by the possibility of extra canonical forms which involve the loss of π electrons from the ring. Thus, in addition to the two benzenoid structures V and VI, there are three further resonance forms (VII–IX) in which the electron-attracting nitrogen atom participates.

| V | VI | VII | VIII | IX |

Pyridine undergoes electrophilic substitution slowly and only at high temperatures. For example, nitration and sulphonation require temperatures of at least 300°C with concentrated reagents, while bromination takes place at 200°C. In all cases, substitution occurs at the 3 or β position. The lack of reactivity of pyridine to electrophiles is due to the electron-withdrawing properties of the nitrogen atom. Similar properties arise in other six-membered nitrogen heterocycles such as pyrimidine, pyrazine and purine (for structures, see section 2.3). By contrast, the five-membered ring compounds with one heteroatom, pyrrole, furan, and thiophene are much more reactive towards electrophiles. Their reactivity approximates to that of an activated benzenoid ring such as that of phenol or aniline. For example, tetraiodopyrrole is formed when an aqueous solution of potassium iodide containing iodine is added to pyrrole. When a single substituent is introduced, it invariably enters the position adjacent to the heteroatom (i.e., the 2 or α position).

When there are several heteroatoms present in a five-membered ring, the properties become more complex. Thus imidazole contains a *pyrrole-like* nitrogen atom and a *pyridine-like* nitrogen atom. Similar problems arise in other five-membered heterocycles—pyrazole, oxazole, and thiazole (for structures, see section 2.3).

4.4.3 Nucleophilic substitution in aromatic compounds

The carbon atoms of a benzene ring are extremely resistant to nucleophilic attack, except under extreme reaction conditions or when there are several electron-withdrawing groups present. Thus, chlorobenzene can be converted to phenol by sodium hydroxide solution at 350°C under pressure, whereas 1-chloro-2,4,6-trinitrobenzene is hydrolysed by hot water to give 2,4,6-trinitrophenol (picric acid). Nucleophilic substitution under these conditions proceeds by a bimolecular process (i.e., S_N2). The transition state is a negatively charged species—a *carbanion* (X) in which the negative charge is more efficiently dispersed by the electron-withdrawing groups present. An S_N1 mechanism

$$C_6H_5-X + {}^-N \xrightarrow{\text{Slow}} \left[C_6H_5{\overset{X}{\underset{N}{\diagdown}}} \right]^- \xrightarrow{\text{Fast}} C_6H_5-N + X^-$$

$$X$$

arises in the reaction of diazonium salts. In these reactions, the $-N_2^+$ group is lost with the formation of a carbonium ion intermediate. Some examples of reactions of diazonium salts are shown in Fig. 4.1. It should be noted that some of the displacement reactions proceed by a free-radical mechanism; these are

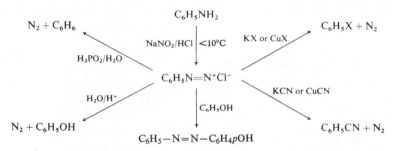

Fig. 4.1 Reactions of benzene diazonium chloride

the reactions involving CuCl, CuBr and CuCN. The use of the corresponding potassium salts is a nucleophilic process. The $-N_2^+$ group has also electrophilic properties, for example, the coupling reaction to phenols to produce an *azo-dye*.

Nucleophilic substitution also occurs in heterocycles and, in some cases, is a more important process than electrophilic substitution. The heteroatom, being electronegative, makes even an unsubstituted ring capable of stabilizing the negative charge of the transition state. For example, pyridine is substituted at positions 2 and 4 by strong nucleophiles. Thus 2-amino-pyridine is formed with sodamide and pyridine. The introduction of an activating group such as $-NH_2$ allows further substitution to be made by electrophilic reagents. In the heterocycles which are more reactive to electrophilic substitution, such as pyrrole, furan and thiophene, nucleophilic substitution is more difficult.

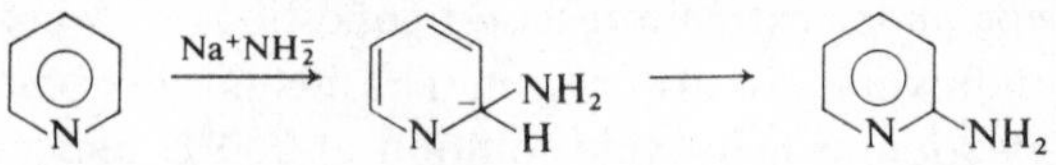

4.4.4 Aromatic substitution in biochemical reactions

So far, the studies on substitution in aromatic compounds in biochemical reactions have centred on the metabolism of the aromatic amino acids phenylalanine, tyrosine and tryptophan. Phenylalanine is converted to tyrosine in living organisms and further substitution produces 3,4-dihydroxyphenylalanine (*Dopa*). These are intermediate stages in the biosynthesis of the pigment melanin and the hormone adrenalin.

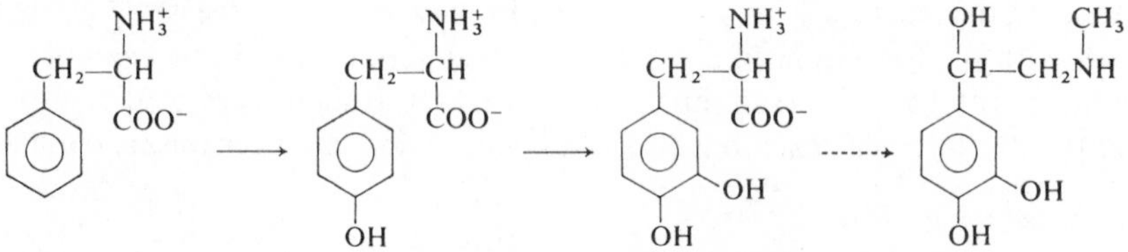

Phenylalanine   Tyrosine   3,4-Dihydroxy-   Adrenalin
                           phenylalanine

In thyroid metabolism, iodination of the aromatic ring of a protein tyrosyl residue takes place to give thyroglobulin. Tyrosine iodinase catalyses this iodination, the reaction taking place in two stages.

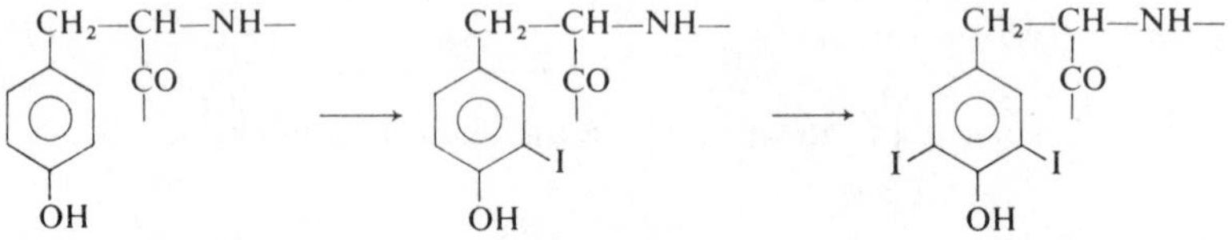

Tyrosyl residue   3-Monoiodotyrosyl   3,5-Diiodotyrosyl

Nucleophilic substitution, by hydride ion (H^-), of a pyridine ring takes place during the reversible conversion of oxidized pyridine adenine dinucleotide (NAD^+) to the reduced form (NADH). This important process is considered in section 7.4.2.

4.5 ADDITION REACTIONS

Addition reactions occur in unsaturated compounds other than aromatic compounds. The reagent *adds* to a substrate containing a multiple bond, and such reactions are found to be initiated by nucleophiles, electrophiles and free radicals. The latter will be considered separately with other free-radical reactions. Nucleophilic and electrophilic reagents do not usually act on the same type of multiple bond, but are restricted in their action. Nucleophiles bring about reactions at carbonyl bonds, while electrophiles initiate reaction at olefinic bonds.

4.5.1 Nucleophilic addition

The most common examples of this type of reaction mechanism occur in compounds containing a carbonyl bond. As we have already seen (section 4.1.2), the carbonyl bond is polarized, and the carbon atom, being the positive pole, will be susceptible to nucleophilic attack. This attack allows complete displacement of the π electrons onto the oxygen atom, and is the real cause of the reactivity of the carbonyl bond towards nucleophiles. The negatively charged oxygen binds an electrophile, usually a proton, to complete the addition reaction. In some cases, the addition product may itself be unstable, and further reaction occurs, usually by elimination.

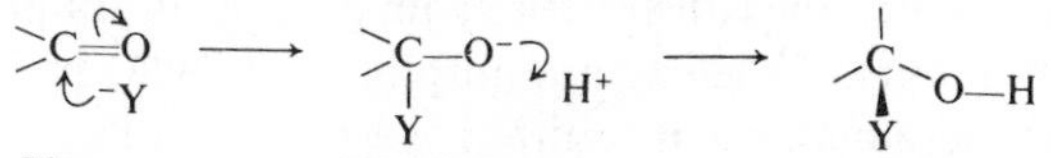

| Planar | Transition state becoming tetrahedral | Tetrahedral |

(a) Formation of hydrates and hemi-acetals The simplest reaction involving nucleophilic addition to a carbonyl bond is the reaction which occurs when aldehydes and ketones are dissolved in water. The *diol* (II; X = —H) is not usually stable except in solution, and the extent of the reaction depends on the

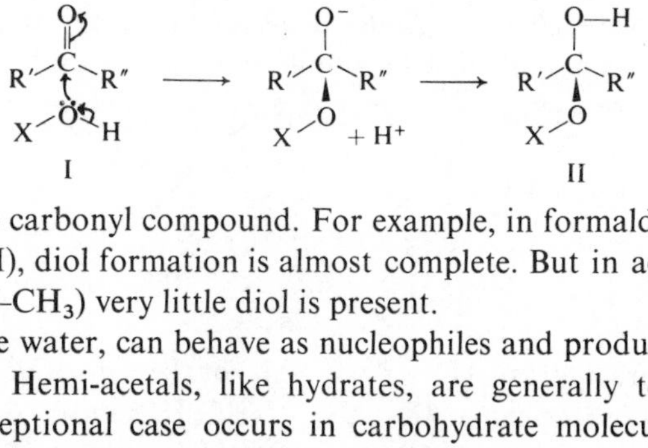

structure of the carbonyl compound. For example, in formaldehyde solution (I; R' = R'' = H), diol formation is almost complete. But in acetone solution (I; R' = R'' = —CH$_3$) very little diol is present.

Alcohols, like water, can behave as nucleophiles and produce hemi-acetals (II; X = —R). Hemi-acetals, like hydrates, are generally too unstable to isolate; an exceptional case occurs in carbohydrate molecules, where the carbonyl and hydroxyl groups are present in the same molecule (III).

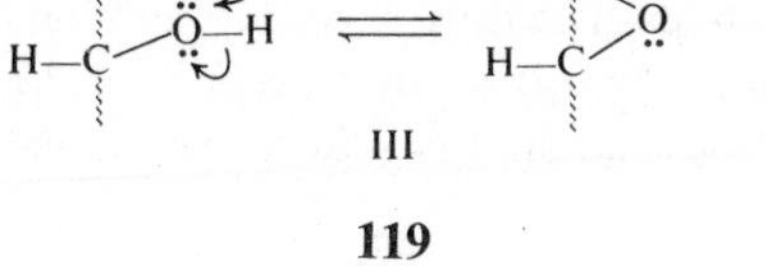

III

119

(b) Formation of cyanohydrins In this reaction, the nucleophile is a cyanide ion formed by the heterolysis of hydrogen cyanide. This reaction is

$$
\underset{\text{IV}}{\underset{\underset{HO}{|}}{\overset{R'}{\underset{\big|}{CN\diagup\overset{\displaystyle C}{}\diagdown R}}}}
\quad \longleftarrow \quad
\underset{H^+}{\overset{R\diagdown\;\diagup R'}{CN^-\!\diagup\!\!\overset{\displaystyle C}{\diagdown\!\!O}}}
\qquad
\underset{H^+}{\overset{R\diagdown\;\diagup R'}{\overset{\displaystyle C}{\underset{O}{}}\!\!\diagdown CN}}
\quad \longrightarrow \quad
\underset{V}{\underset{\underset{OH}{|}}{\overset{R'}{\underset{\big|}{R\diagdown\overset{\displaystyle C}{}\diagdown CN}}}}
$$

of importance in organic synthesis, since it provides a method of extending a carbon chain by one carbon atom. Acidic hydrolysis of a cyanohydrin (VI) yields an α-hydroxy acid (VII) and reduction yields an α-hydroxy aldehyde (VIII). In these reactions the carbon atom, undergoing nucleophilic attack by

$$
\underset{\text{VIII}}{\underset{\underset{CHO}{|}}{\overset{R}{\underset{R'}{\diagdown\,\diagup}}C-OH}}
\quad\xleftarrow{\text{Reduction}}\quad
\underset{\text{VI}}{\underset{\underset{CN}{|}}{\overset{R}{\underset{R'}{\diagdown\,\diagup}}C-OH}}
\quad\xrightarrow{H^+/H_2O}\quad
\underset{\text{VII}}{\underset{\underset{COOH}{|}}{\overset{R}{\underset{R'}{\diagdown\,\diagup}}C-OH}}
$$

cyanide ion, becomes asymmetric, and it can be expected that two stereo-isomers will arise. When the substrate is symmetric, as in simple aldehydes or ketones, equal amounts of the enantiomorphic cyanohydrins (IV and V) are formed. On the other hand, when addition occurs in a molecule which already contains an asymmetric centre, the two stereoisomers are formed in unequal amounts. Such a synthesis is termed asymmetric, for example, the reaction of HCN with D or L glyceraldehyde (see Fig. 2.2).

(c) Complex addition reactions These reactions are often referred to as *condensation reactions*, since the initial addition is followed by the elimination of water. The most common example of this type of process involves reagents which can be considered as *substituted ammonia* molecules. It should be noted that in the case of ammonia itself a simple addition occurs (IX). Three of the reagents which are used to characterize carbonyl compounds react by this

$$
\underset{\text{IX}}{\underset{\underset{O\diagdown H}{|}}{\overset{}{\underset{}{\diagdown C\diagup}}N\overset{H}{\underset{H}{\diagup}}}}
\quad\xleftarrow{NH_3}\quad
\underset{\text{X}}{\overset{H}{\underset{}{\diagdown C\diagup\; :N\!-\!Y}}}
\quad\longrightarrow\quad
\underset{H^+}{\overset{H}{\underset{O}{\diagup C\diagdown N\!-\!Y}}}
\quad\longrightarrow\quad
\underset{+\;H_2O}{>C\!=\!N\!-\!Y}
$$

pathway. They are hydrazine (X; $Y = -NH_2$) or the substituted hydrazines— phenyl or 2,4-dinitrophenyl (X; $Y = -NHC_6H_5$ and $-NHC_6H_3(NO_2)_2$ respectively); hydroxylamine (X; $Y = -OH$) and semi-carbazide (X; $Y = -NHCONH_2$). These reagents yield crystalline derivatives known as hydrazones, oximes and semi-carbazones respectively.

By a similar reaction pathway, carbonyl compounds react with amines (X; $Y = R$—alkyl or aryl group) to form a *Schiff's base* (XI). These condensation products are less stable than those mentioned previously and the reaction is reversible. Equilibria of this type provide the probable mechanism for *transamination* in amino-acid metabolism (see section 9.4.2) where the aldehyde (XII) is pyridoxal phosphate, a coenzyme derived from vitamin B_6.

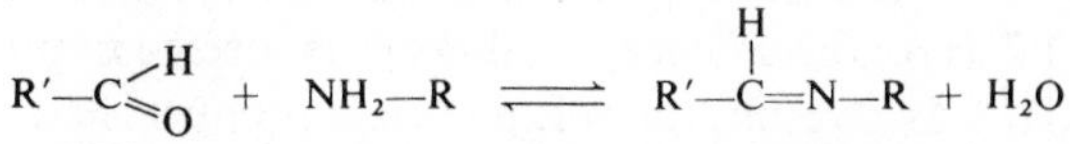

$$R'-C{\overset{H}{\underset{O}{\lessgtr}}} \; + \; NH_2-R \; \rightleftharpoons \; R'-\overset{\overset{\displaystyle H}{|}}{C}{=}N-R \; + \; H_2O$$

$$\text{XII} \qquad\qquad\qquad\qquad \text{XI}$$

Another biochemical example of nucleophilic addition to a carbonyl bond occurs in reactions where the thiazole ring of thiamine, vitamin B_1, acts as a nucleophile. (For the full structures of vitamins B_1 and B_6 see section 7.4.2.)

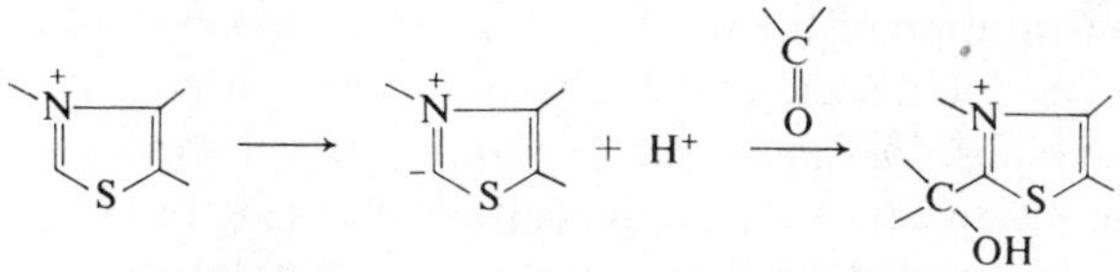

4.5.2 Electrophilic addition

Unlike the carbonyl bond, the carbon–carbon double bond is not polarized unless there is a powerful electron-withdrawing group adjacent to it. Nevertheless, the π electrons are particularly labile and attract electrophiles. Addition to a carbon–carbon double bond occurs in a stepwise manner: the initial electrophilic attack is followed by that of nucleophile. There is a wide variety of reagents which react in this way with alkenes, and they can be divided into

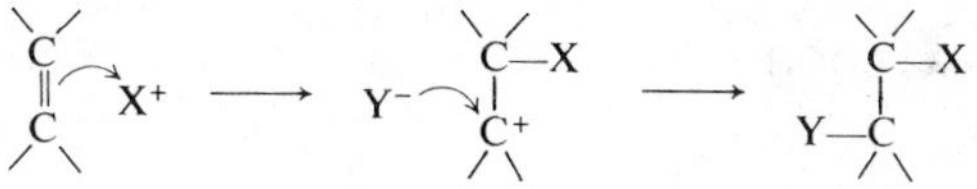

those with a symmetrical structure like the halogens (Cl_2, Br_2 and I_2) and an unsymmetrical structure like the hydrogen halides (HCl, HBr and HI). When addition of an unsymmetrical reagent to an unsymmetrical alkene such as propylene occurs, it is not at first apparent which way the addition will take place. There are two possible products: 1-bromopropane (XIII) and 2-bromopropane (XIV).

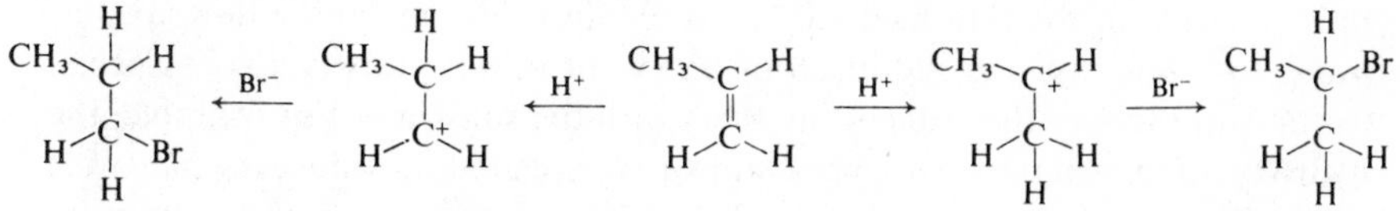

XIII   XIII′   XIV′   XIV

The experimental and empirical *Markownikoff rule* predicts that the nucleophilic group (e.g., Br^-) becomes attached to the more highly substituted

121

carbon atom of the double bond (or the carbon with the least number of hydrogens). This rule can be easily justified by examining the stability of the carbonium ion intermediate in the two reactions (XIII' and XIV'). The order of stability of carbonium ions is tertiary > secondary > primary. Thus, the intermediate XIV' is of lower energy, and hence is formed in preference to the intermediate XIII'. As a result, the sole addition product is 2-bromopropane. Exceptions to the Markownikoff rule are found, and can often be attributed to the operation of a free-radical mechanism (section 4.8).

One very important feature of addition to carbon–carbon double bonds is the high degree of stereospecificity. The simple two-stage reaction so far discussed cannot explain the stereospecificity, since any particular stereochemical configuration of the substrate (i.e., cis or trans) would be lost in the free rotation that could occur in the carbonium ion intermediate. This problem has been overcome by assuming that the configuration present in the substrate is held in the intermediate by the formation of a ring involving the carbon atoms originally joined by the double bond. For example, consider the addition of bromine to maleic acid. Electrophilic attack by a bromine cation leads to the formation of a bromonium ion intermediate (XV) which may then be attacked in two ways by the nucleophile–bromide ion to give the two reaction products in equal amounts (XVI and XVII).

Thus, the addition of bromine to maleic acid yields racemic ($\pm$)-2,3-dibromosuccinic acid, while a similar reaction with fumaric acid gives only meso-dibromosuccinic acid. It should be noted that the nucleophile can attack from only one side of the intermediate, and thus the addition can be described as trans. In a few cases, cis addition of a reagent occurs; this is due to special features in the way the reagent interacts with the substrate. For example, the hydroxylation reaction with potassium permanganate produces a diol with two —OH groups on the same side of the molecule (i.e., an erythro configuration). Another reaction in which cis addition occurs is catalytic hydrogenation. The substrate is bound to the surface of the catalyst, and only one side is then available for the reaction with hydrogen.

$$CH_3(CH_2)_7C{\equiv}C(CH_2)_7COOH \xrightarrow{H_2/Pd} \begin{array}{c} CH_3(CH_2)_7 \\ H \end{array}{>}C{=}C{<}\begin{array}{c} (CH_2)_7COOH \\ H \end{array}$$

Octadec-9-ynoic acid

Oleic acid

(*cis*-octadec-9-enoic acid)

In biochemical reactions, the addition of water to a double bond frequently takes place. These hydration reactions are under enzymic control and result in a stereospecific reaction product. For example, the addition of water to fumarate (the anion of fumaric acid) produces one enantiomorph of malate (the anion of malic acid)—the L(−)-isomer (section 9.2.6).

The structure of the substrate, particularly with regard to the double bond, plays a large part in determining the reactivity in addition reactions. The presence of alkyl groups adjacent to the double bond brings increased reactivity. This increase can be attributed to the greater stability and ease of formation of the positively charged intermediate due to the $+I$ effect of alkyl groups. Thus, propylene adds bromine twice as fast as ethylene and 2,3-dimethyl-2-butene fourteen times as fast. When there is an electron-withdrawing group adjacent to the double bond, the reactivity of the substrate is diminished. For example, vinyl halides ($CH_2{=}CH{-}X$) are very much less reactive than ethylene. When a carbonyl bond is conjugated with the double bond, addition is more complex, and this aspect is considered in the next section.

4.5.3 Addition reactions in more complex molecules

(a) *Addition to conjugate dienes*   The delocalized π electron system in a conjugated system leads to complications in electrophilic addition reactions. In the reaction between equimolar quantities of bromine and 1,3-butadiene, two products are formed; while in a similar reaction with a non-conjugated diene, such as 1,4-pentadiene, only one addition product is formed.

The possibility of 1,4-addition in the case of conjugate dienes arises because the positive charge on the intermediate can be delocalized throughout the

$$CH_2{=}CH{-}\underset{\underset{Br}{|}}{CH}{-}\underset{\underset{Br}{|}}{CH_2} \quad (1,2\text{-addition})$$

$$CH_2{=}CH{-}CH{=}CH_2 \xrightarrow{Br_2}$$

1,3-Butadiene

[ΔH of hydrogenation = 239 kJ mole^{-1} (57·1 kcal mole^{-1})] (see section 1.5.7)

$$+$$

$$\begin{array}{c} H \\ BrCH_2 \end{array}{>}C{=}C{<}\begin{array}{c} CH_2Br \\ H \end{array} \quad (1,4\text{-addition})$$

$$CH_2{=}CH{-}CH_2{-}CH{=}CH_2 \xrightarrow{Br_2} \underset{\underset{Br}{|}}{CH_2}{-}\underset{\underset{Br}{|}}{CH}{-}CH_2{-}CH{=}CH_2 \quad (1,2\text{-addition})$$

1,4-Pentadiene

[ΔH of hydrogenation = 254·5 kJ mole^{-1} (60·8 kcal mole^{-1})]

123

conjugate system. This is possible only if the electrophile attacks an 'outer' carbon atom.

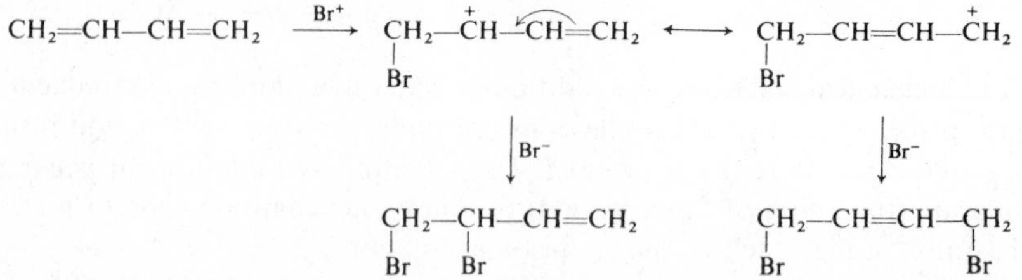

$$CH_2{=}CH{-}CH{=}CH_2 \xrightarrow{Br^+} CH_2{-}\overset{+}{CH}{-}CH{=}CH_2 \longleftrightarrow CH_2{-}CH{=}CH{-}\overset{+}{CH}_2$$

with Br substituent below on left carbon and below on left carbon respectively

$$\downarrow Br^- \qquad\qquad \downarrow Br^-$$

$$CH_2{-}CH{-}CH{=}CH_2 \qquad\qquad CH_2{-}CH{=}CH{-}CH_2$$

In an unsymmetrical but conjugate diene, the point of initial attack is determined by electronic effects within the molecule.

(b) Addition to αβ unsaturated carbonyl compounds Like conjugate dienes, αβ unsaturated carbonyl compounds have a delocalized electronic system which leads to a different mechanism for the addition compared with an isolated double bond. The electron-withdrawing power of the carbonyl bond not only lowers the reactivity of the carbon–carbon double bond but also directs the orientation. For example, the first stage of the addition of hydrogen halides with acrylic acid (**XVIII**) is protonation of the carbonyl oxygen; this electrophilic attack at the oxygen end of the conjugated system leads to a more stable intermediate. Attack by the nucleophile (halide ion) then takes place at the β carbon atom. Thus 1,4-addition has taken place. The enol (**XIX**) is unstable and tautomerizes to the keto-form (**XX**). Incidentally, this produces a product contrary to the Markownikoff rule.

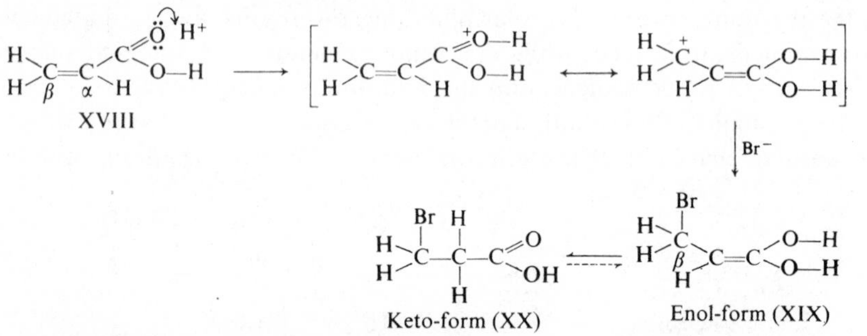

Keto-form (**XX**)   Enol-form (**XIX**)

1,4-Addition initiated by a nucleophile may also take place in αβ unsaturated ketones. In this case initial protonation of the carbonyl oxygen is not required, since the π electron displacement is already sufficient to allow nucleophilic attack at the β carbon atom. This type of reaction takes place not only with simple ions like CN⁻ but also with 'nucleophilic carbon atoms' (carbanions). Many of these reactions are used extensively in organic synthesis, for example, carboxylic acid syntheses with the anion derived from diethyl malonate (malonic ester).

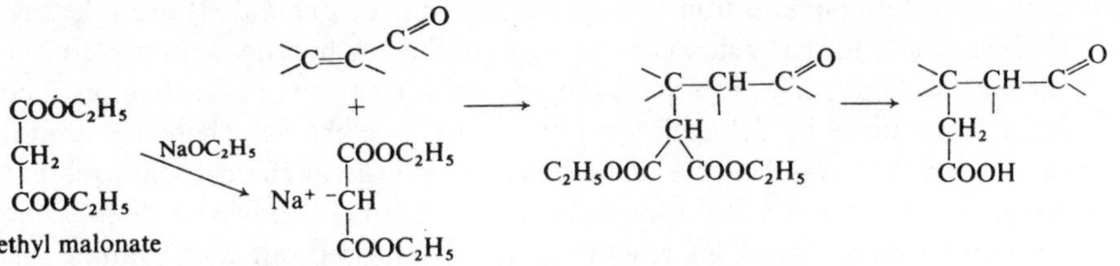

$$
\begin{array}{c}
\text{COOC}_2\text{H}_5 \\
| \\
\text{CH}_2 \\
| \\
\text{COOC}_2\text{H}_5
\end{array}
\xrightarrow{\text{NaOC}_2\text{H}_5}
\begin{array}{c}
\text{COOC}_2\text{H}_5 \\
| \\
\text{Na}^+ \ {}^-\text{CH} \\
| \\
\text{COOC}_2\text{H}_5
\end{array}
$$

Diethyl malonate

4.5.4 Carbon–carbon bond formation with aldehydes and ketones

The formation of carbon–carbon single bonds is a process of primary importance in both organic synthesis and in biosynthesis. Many of the reactions which lead to the formation of a new carbon–carbon bond make use of carbanion attack at a carbonyl bond. In organic synthesis reactions, carbanions derived from malonic ester (see previous section), Grignard reagents (R—Mg—X), anhydrides, and acetylenes are frequently used. Carbanions in biochemical reactions arise mainly from aldehydes, ketones and esters (see also section 4.7.3).

In the presence of dilute base, aldehydes possessing α-hydrogens react to form condensation products called *aldols*. The simplest example of this type of reaction occurs with acetaldehyde (formaldehyde has no α-*carbon atom*).

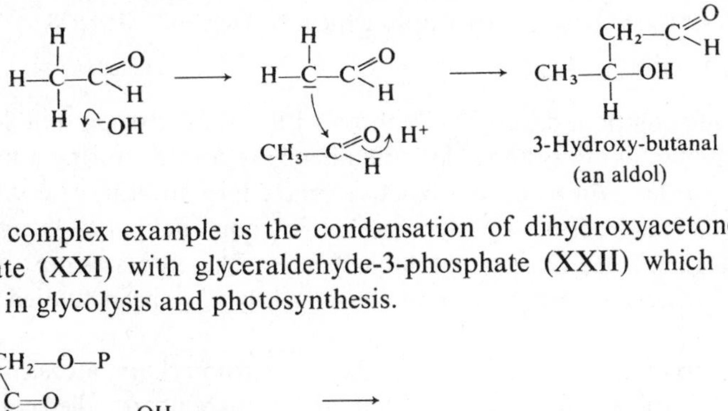

3-Hydroxy-butanal
(an aldol)

A more complex example is the condensation of dihydroxyacetone monophosphate (XXI) with glyceraldehyde-3-phosphate (XXII) which is a key reaction in glycolysis and photosynthesis.

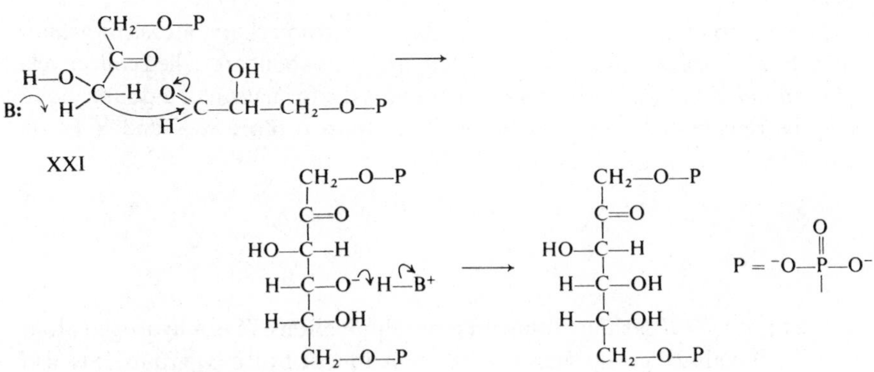

XXI

XXII

Fructose-1,6-diphosphate

$$P = {}^-\text{O}-\overset{\overset{\displaystyle O}{\|}}{\text{P}}-\text{O}^-$$

125

In an aldol condensation, the α-carbon atom of one aldehyde or ketone molecule adds to the carboxyl carbon of another. A hydrogen atom α to one carbonyl group is lost, to a base (B:), in the formation of a carbanion. The latter is stabilized by delocalization of the negative charge. There are several cases where the stabilization of the negative charge of the carbanion is not possible and yet a condensation takes place. The best known of these is the benzoin condensation. This reaction is usually carried out with cyanide ion and probably proceeds via an intermediate cyanohydrin. It is interesting to note that the carbanion derived from thiamine (vitamin B_1) also catalyses this reaction.

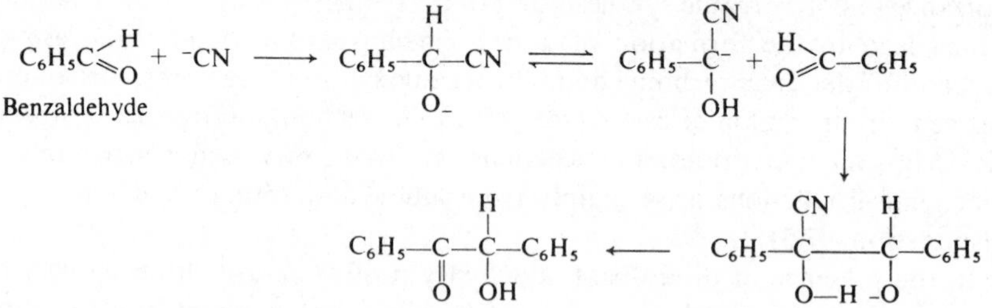

$$C_6H_5C{\overset{H}{\underset{O}{}}} + {}^-CN \longrightarrow C_6H_5{-}\overset{H}{\underset{O_-}{C}}{-}CN \rightleftharpoons C_6H_5{-}\overset{CN}{\underset{OH}{C^-}} + \overset{H}{\underset{O}{}}{>}C{-}C_6H_5$$

Benzaldehyde

$$C_6H_5{-}\overset{H}{\underset{O}{C}}{-}\overset{}{\underset{OH}{C}}{-}C_6H_5 \longleftarrow C_6H_5{-}\overset{CN}{\underset{O-H}{C}}{-}\overset{H}{\underset{-O}{C}}{-}C_6H_5$$

Benzoin

4.6 THE FORMATION OF CARBON–CARBON DOUBLE BONDS

4.6.1 Elimination reactions

Unsaturated compounds, especially those with carbon–carbon double bonds, occur widely in living systems. Double bonds are formed during a metabolic process in order to introduce a reactive centre into an otherwise unreactive compound. The processes by which carbon–carbon double bonds are formed are therefore of some interest to the biochemist. The processes are, of course, important in organic synthesis, and consequently have been studied in some detail.

In order to introduce a multiple bond into a carbon chain, atoms or groups must be *eliminated* and the reactions that bring this about are called collectively *elimination reactions*. The general reaction for the formation of a double bond may be represented as shown below. The atoms or groups X and Y lie on

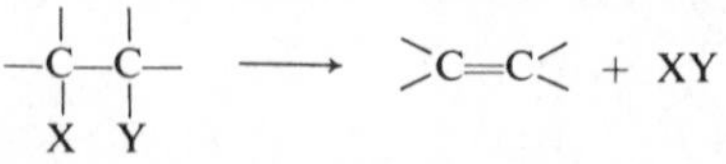

$$-\overset{|}{\underset{X}{C}}{-}\overset{|}{\underset{Y}{C}}{-} \longrightarrow {>}C{=}C{<} + XY$$

I

adjacent or *vicinal* carbon atoms. In most eliminations, X is a hydrogen atom and Y a functional group such as a halogen atom or hydroxyl group. It is also possible to eliminate two hydrogen atoms from vicinal carbons (i.e.

$X = Y = H$). This reaction is of importance in the petroleum industry and is known as *petroleum cracking*. The use of high temperatures and catalysts is necessary to bring about such eliminations. It is interesting to note that the same result can be achieved in a biochemical elimination at 37°C.

$$^-OOC-CH_2-CH_2-COO^- \xrightarrow[\substack{\text{dehydrogenase} \\ \text{(coenzyme FAD)}}]{\text{Succinate}} \ ^-OOC-CH=CH-COO^-$$

Succinate   Fumarate

There are also cases in which two functional groups may be eliminated (for example, I; $X = Y = $ halogen), and this type of process is thought to be a method of aromatic ring formation in biochemical reactions.

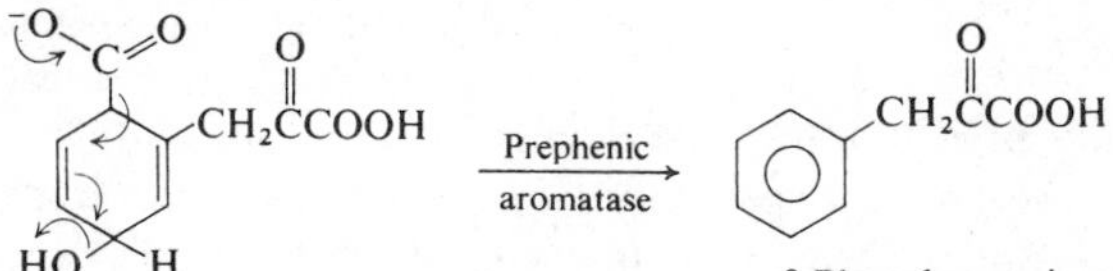

β-Phenyl pyruvic acid

4.6.2 The mechanism of common elimination reactions

The discussion in this section will be confined to two common types of elimination reaction: *dehydrohalogenation*, where a hydrogen and a halogen atom are eliminated, and *dehydration*, where a hydrogen atom and a hydroxyl group are eliminated.

(a) Bimolecular elimination (E.2) Most dehydrohalogenations are of this type. The reaction is base-catalysed and the reaction is bimolecular, since the rate of formation of the transition state (II) depends upon the concentration of the base and the substrate. This is a *concerted* process, the hydrogen atom

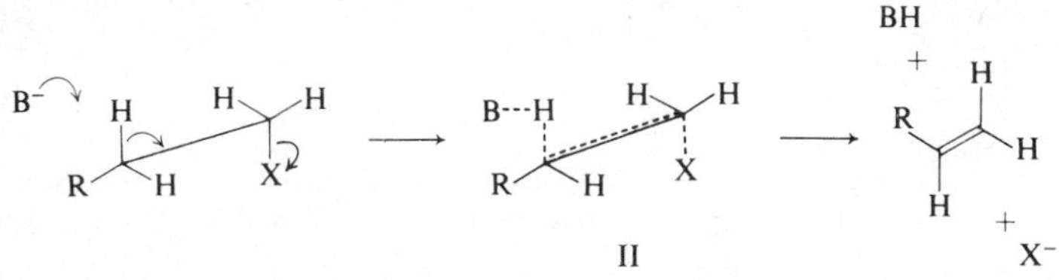

II

being removed by the base (B^-) at the same time as the bond is being formed between the two carbon atoms and the halogen anion is departing. In order for this process to take place efficiently, the atoms to be eliminated must lie in the same plane, so that the vacant orbital left after the halogen anion departs is in the same plane as the orbital containing the two electrons left after the loss of the proton. Thus the substrate adopts an *anti* conformation with respect to the groups being eliminated.

This type of reaction is competitive with the bimolecular substitution

127

reaction (S_N2) and, in most cases, both alkene and substitution product are formed, the relative amounts depending upon the reaction conditions and the

$$CH_3CH_2CH_2-Br \xrightarrow{Na^+ \ ^-OC_2H_5} CH_3CH_2CH_2-O-C_2H_5 \ + \ CH_3CH=CH_2$$
$$\sim 90 \text{ per cent} \qquad \sim 10 \text{ per cent}$$

structure of the substrate. A further possible complication is that mixtures of isomeric alkenes may arise in certain eliminations. When this does occur, one

$$CH_3CH_2\underset{\underset{Cl}{|}}{CH}-CH_3 \xrightarrow[C_2H_5OH]{KOH} CH_3CH=CHCH_3 \ + \ CH_3CH_2CH=CH_2$$
$$\text{III} \qquad\qquad \text{IV}$$
$$\sim 80 \text{ per cent} \qquad \sim 20 \text{ per cent}$$
$$\text{(Percentage of the alkene product formed)}$$

of them usually predominates. Saytzeff elucidated an empirical and experimental rule, whereby the predominant product could be predicted. The major alkene product formed in this type of elimination is the most highly substituted alkene. Thus, in the previous example, the major product is 2-butene (III) and not 1-butene (IV). The more highly branched the $E.2$ transition state, the more thermodynamically stable it is.

Another feature of these eliminations is that they are, for the most part, stereospecific. This fact provides justification for thinking that the $E.2$ mechanism is a concerted process, where the double bond is set up before either the proton or the *leaving group* departs. The stereospecificity of an $E.2$ reaction is well illustrated by considering the dehydrobromination of *meso*-1,2-dibromodiphenyl ethane (V), which gives specifically *cis* α-bromo-stilbene (VI).

Reacting conformation
(*anti* with respect to H and Br)

cis α-Bromo-stilbene
VI

(b) Unimolecular eliminations (E.1) The intermediate in this process is a carbonium ion formed by loss of the electron-withdrawing group (for example, the halogen atom). This is exactly the same type of intermediate that arises during unimolecular nucleophilic substitution (S_N1). There is competition in the second stage of the reaction between a direct attack on the carbonium ion by the base, now acting as a nucleophile, and removal by the base of a proton from a carbon atom adjacent to the positive charge. Like the S_N1 mechanism, an $E.1$ elimination operates only in special circumstances, namely, when a stable carbonium ion (usually a tertiary ion) arises, and in the presence of a polar solvent. Substitution always occurs, often as the main reaction, and, as in the $E.2$ process, isomeric alkenes may be produced.

$$CH_3-\underset{\underset{X}{|}}{\overset{\overset{CH_3}{|}}{C}}-CH_2CH_3 \xrightarrow[\text{H}_2\text{O in C}_2\text{H}_5\text{OH}]{80\text{ per cent}} CH_3-\underset{+}{\overset{\overset{CH_3}{|}}{C}}-CH_2CH_3$$

40 per cent $E.1$ S_N1 60 per cent

$$CH_3-\underset{}{\overset{\overset{CH_3}{|}}{C}}=CHCH_3 \qquad CH_3-\underset{}{\overset{\overset{CH_2}{\|}}{C}}-CH_2CH_3 \qquad CH_3-\underset{\underset{OH}{|}}{\overset{\overset{CH_3}{|}}{C}}-CH_2CH_3$$

32 per cent   8 per cent   60 per cent

(c) Dehydration of alcohols Carbon–carbon double bonds usually arise in biochemical reactions by elimination (dehydration) from alcohols. This is also a common reaction in organic chemistry; although the conditions used to bring about the two reactions are completely different the mechanisms may be similar. Dehydration of alcohols is a standard method of preparing alkenes, and it is carried out in acidic conditions (the —OH group must be protonated before it will *leave*). The formation of an alkene from a primary alcohol requires concentrated sulphuric acid at high temperature, while the dehydration of secondary and tertiary alcohols proceeds with more dilute acid at a lower temperature.

A good example of a biochemical elimination from an alcohol is the reversible dehydration of malate to fumarate. It has been found that the rate-determining step is the cleavage of the C—O bond, indicating an $E.1$ type of mechanism.

$$^-OOC-\underset{\underset{H}{|}}{\overset{\overset{H}{|}}{C}}-\underset{\underset{H}{|}}{\overset{\overset{OH}{|}}{C}}-COO^- \;\rightleftharpoons\; \overset{H^+}{}\; ^-OOC-\underset{\underset{H}{|}}{\overset{\overset{H}{|}}{C}}-\underset{\underset{H}{|}}{\overset{\overset{\overset{+}{O}H_2}{|}}{C}}-COO^- \;\rightleftharpoons\;$$

Malate

$$^-OOC-\underset{\underset{H}{|}}{\overset{\overset{H}{|}}{C}}-\underset{\underset{H}{|}}{\overset{\overset{+}{C}}{}}-COO^- \;\rightleftharpoons\; \underset{^-OOC}{\overset{H}{>}}C=C\underset{H}{\overset{COO^-}{<}} + H_2O$$

ENZ   Fumarate

4.7 SOME REACTIONS OF CARBOXYLIC ACIDS AND THEIR ESTERS

Molecules with carboxyl and ester groupings occupy an important place in biological chemistry. In this section, some of the relevant reactions and properties of these compounds will be considered. Both substituted and unsubstituted carboxylic acids are found in living organisms. The latter are

129

usually associated with the chemistry of lipids, and their properties are described in chapter 7. Esters of biochemical interest include not only oxygen esters (I), but also thioesters (II) and esters of phosphoric acid (III), both of which play an important role in metabolic reactions.

I   II   III

4.7.1 Reactions of substituted acids

The main types of substituted acid found in living organisms are hydroxy, keto and amino. Owing to their structural role in proteins, the structure and properties of amino acids are described separately later (section 7.1).

   (a) Hydroxy acids   Compounds of this type are known in which the —OH group is α, β, γ and δ with respect to the carboxyl group. α- and β-hydroxy acids may arise through the reduction of the corresponding keto acids, while γ- and δ-hydroxy acids are found in compounds derived from carbohydrates. Hydration of a double bond in an unsaturated acid provides another method for generating a hydroxy acid. In general, these compounds show properties associated with both alcohols and simple carboxylic acids. On the other hand, there are some reactions in which both functional groups participate, for example, dehydration and lactone formation. The reaction product obtained from the dehydration of a hydroxy acid depends on the position of the hydroxyl group. When an α-hydroxy acid is heated, two molecules condense together to give a *lactide* (IV) containing two intramolecular ester bonds. β-Hydroxy acids usually dehydrate by simple elimination to give an $\alpha\beta$ unsaturated acid (V). γ- and δ-hydroxy acids dehydrate with the formation of one intramolecular ester bond. These cyclic esters are called *lactones* (VI and VII).

IV   V   VI   VII

   (b) Keto acids α- and β-keto acids are extremely important intermediates in metabolism. They arise through the oxidation of the corresponding hydroxy acids. β-Keto acids may also be formed in certain ester condensations. One of the most important phenomenon associated with keto acids and related compounds is tautomerism. The attainment of the equilibrium between *keto* and *enol* forms is catalysed by acids and bases. In the acid-catalysed reaction,

130

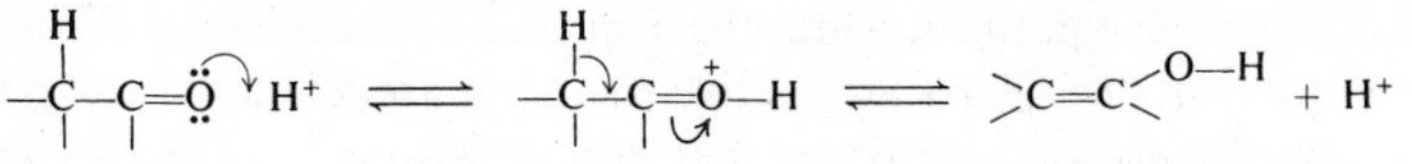

Keto form   Enol form

protonation of the carbonyl group takes place followed by an electron re-distribution. In the base-catalysed reaction, a proton is abstracted, leaving a resonance-stabilized carbanion which recombines with a proton.

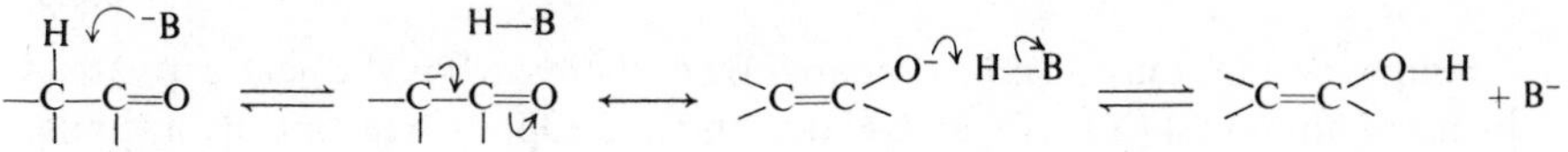

Keto form   Enol form

The amount of *enol* present varies with the structure of the carbonyl compound. In the case of acetone, there is only 0·00025 per cent enol present, while in 1,3-dicarbonyl compounds (VIII) significant amounts of enol are present. For example, in ethyl acetoacetate a β-keto ester (VIII–X: $R = CH_3$, $R' = O—C_2H_5$) there is 7·5 per cent enol. Stabilization of the enol form (IX and X) is attributed to delocalization of the π electrons and the formation of intramolecular hydrogen bonds.

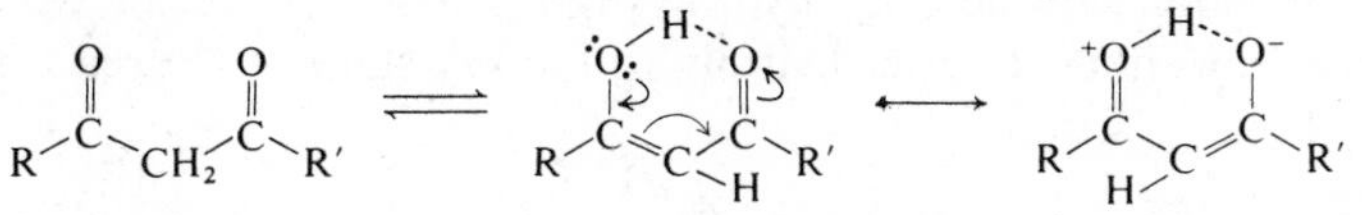

VIII   IX   X

Keto form   Enol forms

The decarboxylation of certain α- and β-keto acids provides the mechanism for the release of carbon dioxide in metabolic processes, and consequent degradation of a carbon chain. β-Keto acids undergo decarboxylation very easily, often spontaneously, while α-keto acids are more stable. The anions of β-keto acids decarboxylate giving an *enol* which tautomerizes to the more stable ketone.

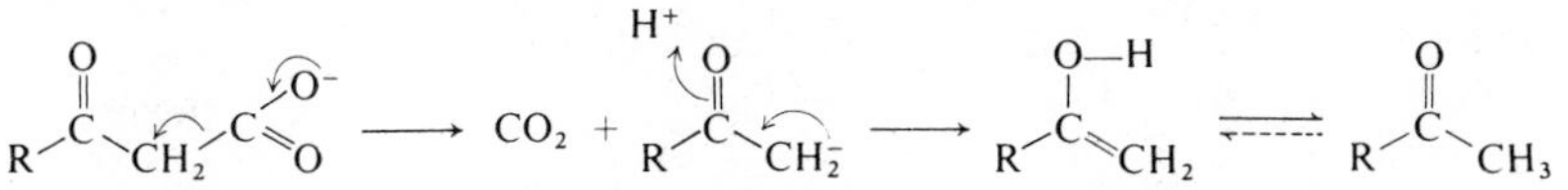

4.7.2 Esters and amides

(a) Oxygen esters and amides   The acid-catalysed reaction of a carboxylic acid with an alcohol gives rise to an equilibrium. In order to obtain satisfactory

yields of ester, the equilibrium must be displaced by the removal of water from the reaction mixture. Two alternative methods are available for preparing esters, making use of carboxylic acid derivatives—acid chlorides and acid anhydrides. In all these reactions, the alcohol (XI; X = —OR′) is acting as a nucleophilic reagent attacking the carboxyl carbon atom.

$$R-C\overset{O}{\underset{Cl}{<}} + X-H \longrightarrow R-C\overset{O}{\underset{X}{<}} + HCl$$
$$XI$$

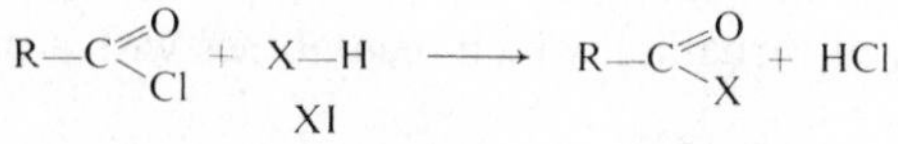

Simple amides may also be prepared from these carboxylic acid derivatives by using ammonia (XI; X = —NH$_2$) as the nucleophilic reagent. By a similar process, a *peptide bond* between two amino acids is established by nucleophilic attack at the carboxyl carbon atom of one amino acid by the amino group of another.

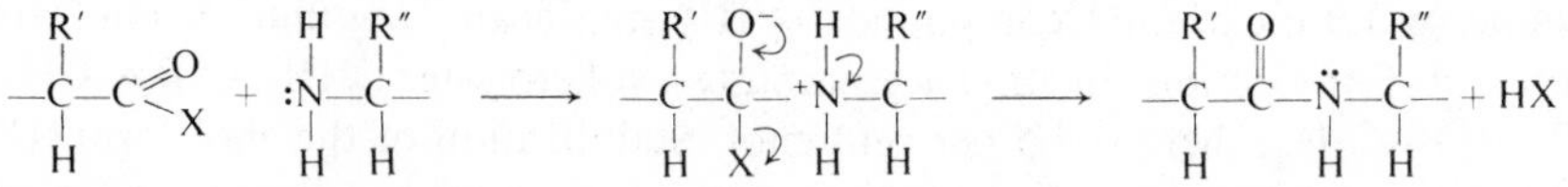

Esters and amides are hydrolysed by mineral acids and bases. In general, esters are more satisfactorily hydrolysed by bases, while amides can be hydrolysed by either. In ester hydrolysis, the key stage of the reaction is the

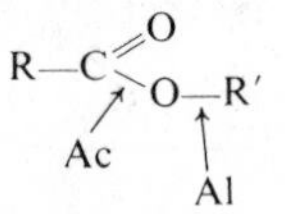

$$R-C\overset{O}{\underset{\underset{Al}{\uparrow}}{\overset{/}{\underset{Ac}{O}}-R'}}$$

cleavage of either the *acyl* (Ac) or the *alkyl* (Al) oxygen bond. It has been shown that base-catalysed ester hydrolysis proceeds by acyl oxygen fission in

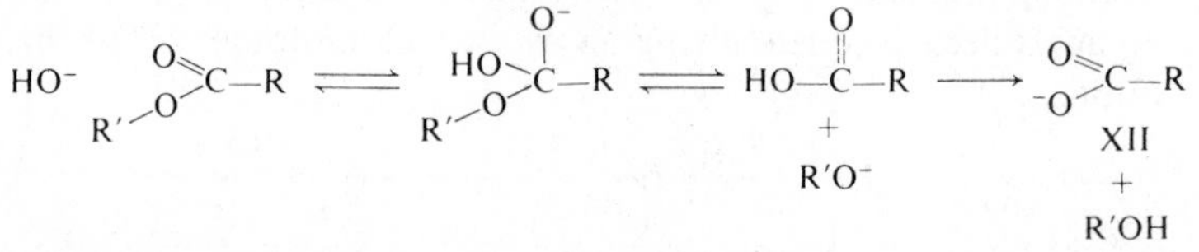

a bimolecular process. The overall reaction, unlike the acid-catalysed process, is irreversible, since the carboxylate anion (XII), formed under basic conditions, is not susceptible to nucleophilic attack by the alcohol (R′OH).

Amide hydrolysis by base involves a very similar process. The acid-catalysed reaction proceeds with protonation of the carbonyl group, nucleophilic attack by water, proton exchange and cleavage of the carbon–nitrogen bond. This reaction takes place in mono- (XIII; X = H) and di- (XIII; X = R″) substituted amides and also during the acid hydrolysis of peptide bonds.

132

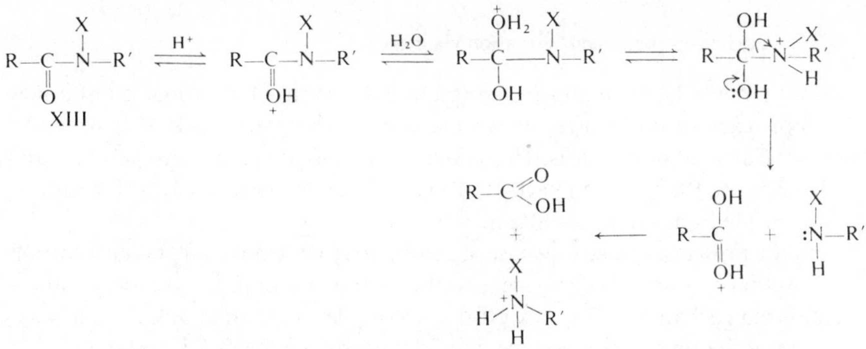

The formation and reactions of these esters

(b) Thio- and phosphate esters The formation and reactions of these esters are of great importance in biochemistry. Carbohydrate phosphates occur as components of nucleic acids and coenzymes and also as intermediates in many metabolic processes. Phosphate esters are generally produced in nature by a phosphorylation reaction with adenosine triphosphate (ATP); in a few cases they may be formed directly from phosphate ion (see the phosphorolysis process—section 9.2.1).

The most well known of the thioesters found in nature are those of coenzyme A (for the structure, see section 7.4.2). One of the most important properties of a thioester is that the carbonyl bond is much more reactive than that in an oxygen ester. This is because, in the latter, there is extensive delocalization of the π electrons (XIV and XV). This delocalization is not possible in a thioester,

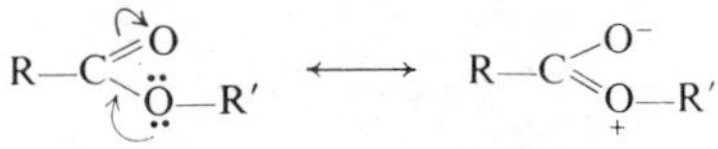

since sulphur shows less tendency to form multiple bonds than oxygen. This has two important consequences. Firstly, thioesters have a higher free energy of hydrolysis than oxygen esters. For example, acetyl coenzyme A has a free energy of hydrolysis of $-33\cdot3$ kJ mole^{-1} ($-8\cdot2$ kcal mole^{-1}) compared with a value of $-3\cdot0$ kJ mole^{-1} for ethyl acetate and $-12\cdot4$ kJ mole^{-1} for glucose-6-

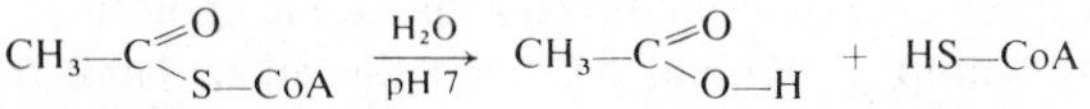

Acetyl coenzyme A   Coenzyme A

phosphate. Secondly, the carbonyl bond in thioesters reacts in a similar way to that in an aldehyde; the importance of this in the formation of carbon–carbon bonds is discussed in the next section.

133

4.7.3 Carbon–carbon bond formation via esters

It has already been demonstrated (section 4.5.4) that the formation of a new carbon–carbon bond often takes place by carbanion attack at a carbonyl bond. Carbanions may arise from esters as well as aldehydes and ketones, and furthermore the carbonyl carbon atom of an ester, particularly a thioester, is susceptible to nucleophilic attack.

In the presence of a strong base, a proton may be removed from the α carbon atom, that is, the carbon adjacent to the carbonyl group, to give a resonance-stabilized carbanion. This powerful nucleophile can then attack the carbonyl group of another ester molecule, the final product being a β-keto ester.

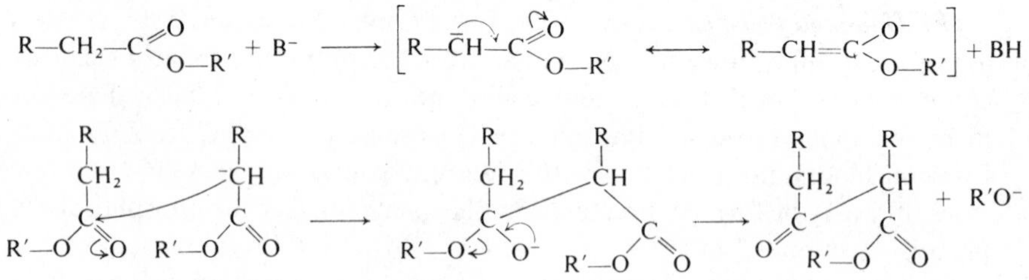

This reaction, known as a *Claisen condensation*, is used in organic synthesis; in biochemical reactions, thioesters, being more reactive, are used to bring about carbon–carbon bond formation. For example, the self-condensation of

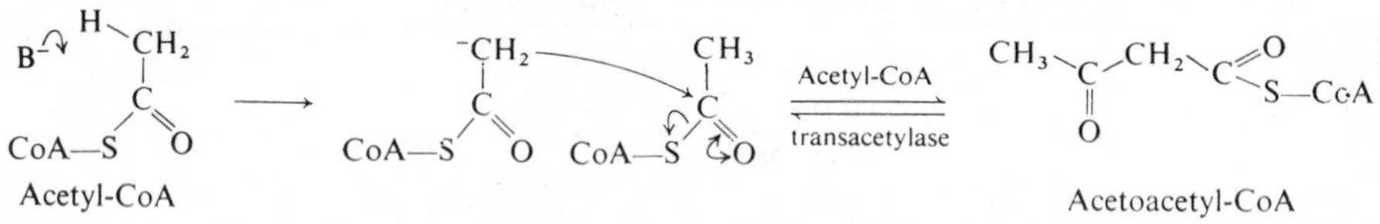

Acetyl-CoA

Acetoacetyl-CoA

acetyl-coenzyme A proceeds by a similar mechanism. Another example is the reaction between oxaloacetate and acetyl-CoA which leads to the formation of citrate at the start of the TCA cycle (see section 9.2.6).

4.8 FREE-RADICAL REACTIONS

Free radicals are formed by the homolytic cleavage of a covalent bond (see section 4.1.1). A few compounds exist as stable molecules with unpaired electrons: for example, NO and NO_2; on the other hand, free radicals are usually reactive species, and bring about both substitution and addition reactions in organic molecules.

The halogenation of alkanes, under the influence of radiation or high temperatures, proceeds by a free-radical mechanism. The generation of a halogen atom by homolytic cleavage (1) produces a reactive species which abstracts a hydrogen atom from an alkane molecule (2) and in turn releases an even more reactive alkyl radical. The alkyl radical reacts with a halogen molecule to produce alkyl halide and another halogen atom (3). Stages (2) and

(1) $\quad$ X—X $\xrightarrow{hv}$ 2X$^{\cdot}$ (Initiation)

(2) $\;$ X$^{\cdot}$ + R—H $\longrightarrow$ H—X + R$^{\cdot}$ $\left.\rule{0pt}{22pt}\right\}$ (Propagation)

(3) $\qquad$ R$^{\cdot}$ + X$_2$ $\longrightarrow$ R—X + X$^{\cdot}$

(3) continue until the reaction is complete. Numerous *termination* reactions may also take place.

(4) $\;$ R$^{\cdot}$ + R$^{\cdot}$ $\longrightarrow$ R—R $\left.\rule{0pt}{30pt}\right\}$ (Termination)

(5) $\;$ X$^{\cdot}$ + R$^{\cdot}$ $\longrightarrow$ R—X

(6) $\;$ X$^{\cdot}$ + X$^{\cdot}$ $\longrightarrow$ X—X

In an alkane containing a number of carbon atoms, different alkyl radicals may be formed, each of which would give a different alkyl halide.

$$CH_3CH_2CH_3 \underset{X^{\cdot}}{\overset{X^{\cdot}}{\Big<}}$$

$$CH_3CH_2CH_2^{\cdot} + HX \xrightarrow{X_2} CH_3CH_2CH_2X + X^{\cdot}$$

$$CH_3\overset{\cdot}{C}HCH_3 + HX \xrightarrow{X_2} CH_3\underset{X}{\overset{|}{C}HCH_3} + X^{\cdot}$$

Studies on the relative amounts of each alkyl halide formed have revealed that the ease of abstraction of hydrogen atoms follows the order: tertiary (3°), secondary (2°), primary (1°); this sequence is also the order of decreasing stability of alkyl radicals.

Free-radical-initiated addition provides an alternative mechanism for the addition to carbon–carbon double bonds to that already described (see section 4.5.2). Once again, the generation of free radicals is promoted by radiation and also, in this case, by the action of air on the alkene which produces peroxides (I) which are the potent source of free radicals.

$$\underset{I}{R—O—O—R} \longrightarrow 2R—O^{\cdot}$$

$$R—O^{\cdot} + HX \longrightarrow R—O—H + X^{\cdot}$$

$$X^{\cdot} + R—CH{=}CH—R \longrightarrow R—\underset{X}{\overset{|}{C}H}—\overset{\cdot}{C}H—R$$

$$R—\underset{X}{\overset{|}{C}H}—\overset{\cdot}{C}H—R + HX \longrightarrow R—\underset{X}{\overset{|}{C}H}—CH_2—R + X^{\cdot}$$

135

In the case of an unsymmetrical alkene, two possible alkyl radical intermediates could be formed. Since there is a considerable difference in stability

$$
R-CH=CH_2 \quad\begin{array}{c} \overset{X^{\cdot}}{\underset{1}{\searrow}} \\ \overset{2}{\underset{X^{\cdot}}{\searrow}} \end{array}\quad
\begin{array}{l}
R-\overset{\cdot}{C}H-CH_2X \xrightarrow{\text{HX}} R-CH_2-CH_2X + X^{\cdot} \\
\qquad\qquad\text{II} \\
\\
R-CH-\overset{\cdot}{C}H_2 \xrightarrow{\text{HX}} R-CH-CH_3 + X^{\cdot} \\
\quad\ \ | \qquad\qquad\qquad\quad\ | \\
\quad\ \ X \qquad\qquad\qquad\quad\ X \\
\qquad\ \text{III}
\end{array}
$$

between 1° free radical (III) and the 2° free radical (II), it would be expected that the addition would proceed through the latter. This is the case, and free-radical addition results in the formation of different products compared to those produced by electrophilic addition.

The participation of free-radical intermediates in biochemical reactions has been investigated extensively in recent years. This work has been greatly stimulated by modern methods of detecting free radicals in solution (see ESR technique, section 6.2.7). Probably the most fully investigated biochemical free radicals are the *semiquinones* formed by the flavin coenzymes (section 7.4.2). The oxidation and reduction of quinones is another vital process in all aerobic metabolism, and once again intermediate free-radical species have been detected (section 7.5.1).

4.9 REARRÁNGEMENTS

In the vast majority of reactions among organic molecules, the basic carbon skeleton remains unchanged and structural changes take place in the functional groups. There are, however, a number of exceptions to this principle. Reactions are known where changes in the position of alkyl and aryl groups as well as those of hydrogen atoms and double bonds occur. Also, in certain reactions, the migration of a functional group takes place. These reactions are grouped together and designated *rearrangement reactions*. Rearrangement reactions are known to take place during biochemical reactions but, as yet, little information is available regarding the mechanism of such reactions.

It is convenient to divide rearrangement reactions into two broad groups: those which involve a migrating group having nucleophilic character, causing it to move to an electron-deficient centre, and those with an electrophilic migrating group which moves to an electron-rich centre. There are also a small number in which no radical or ion is formed as an intermediate and a concerted mechanism has been proposed.

4.9.1 Nucleophilic rearrangements

This is by far the most usual mechanism through which a rearrangement may take place. The migrating group moves from a carbon atom to an adjacent

136

atom which is electron deficient. This deficiency arises by loss of some electro-negative group (Y) during the reaction. These rearrangements are referred to as 1,2 *shifts* and the nucleophilic species migrating may be carbon, hydrogen, a heteroatom (O, N, S) or halogen. The migrating group (X) remains partially bonded to the molecule during the migration and forms a cyclic intermediate (I).

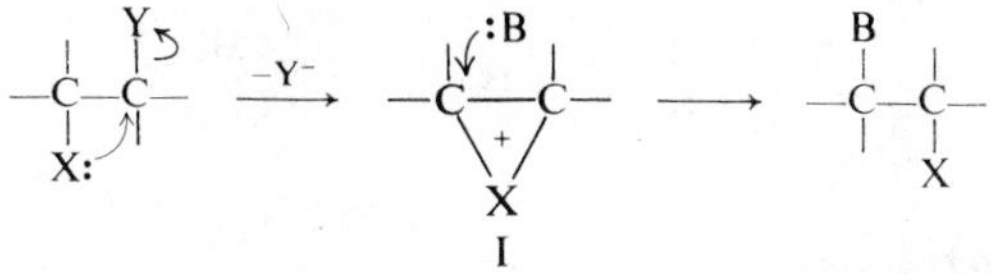

I

In some cases, there is a pair of unshared electrons on the migrating group which facilitates the formation of the intermediate. In other cases, such as

carbon or hydrogen (I; $X = -\overset{|}{\underset{}{C}}-$ or H), one pair of electrons suffices to bind three atoms momentarily together.

The rearrangements in this group are of the two following types:

(a) Those reactions in which there is a 1,2-shift of an alkyl, aryl or hydrogen, together with the pair of bonding electrons from one carbon to an adjacent atom.

(b) Those reactions in which there is a 1,2-shift to a heteroatom (e.g., N).

Carbonium ion rearrangements

The rearrangements of a carbon skeleton are known collectively as Wagner–Meerwein rearrangements. A typical example of these is the rearrangement of the neopentyl carbonium ion. When neopentyl bromide (II) is hydrolysed under conditions where an S_N1 process occurs, rearrangement of the inter-mediate carbonium ion takes place to yield 2-methyl-butan-2-ol (III) as the sole substitution product. It is interesting to note that the product produced in the concurrent elimination process—2-methyl-but-2-ene (IV)—also arises from the rearranged carbonium ion via an *E*.1 process.

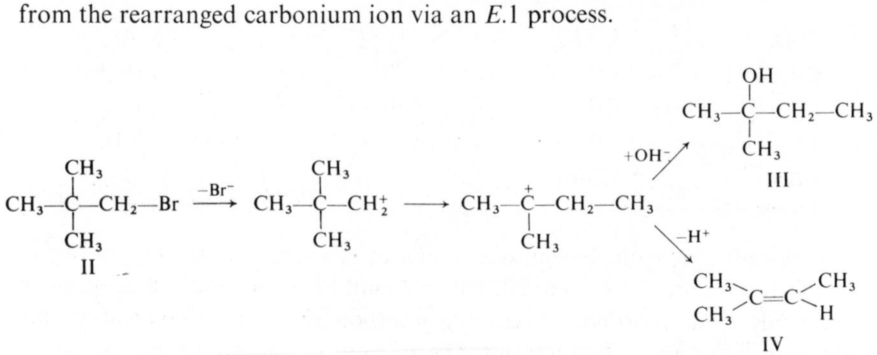

Hydrogen migration

Rearrangements involving the shift of a hydrogen atom are numerous. A simple example is in the carbonium ion reactions of isobutyl compounds, which result in the formation of products with a tertiary butyl group.

$$\underset{CH_3}{\overset{CH_3}{>}}\overset{H}{\underset{}{C}}{-}CH_2{-}X \xrightarrow{-X^-} \underset{CH_3}{\overset{CH_3}{>}}\overset{H}{\underset{}{C}}\cdots CH_2 \longrightarrow \underset{CH_3}{\overset{CH_3}{>}}\overset{+}{C}{-}CH_3 \longrightarrow \text{Products}$$

Migration to heteroatoms

A well known example of this type of rearrangement is the *Beckmann rearrangement*. In this reaction a ketoxime (see section 4.5.1) is converted to an amide. The reaction is acid catalysed and is highly stereospecific, since the group that migrates to nitrogen is *trans* (also termed *anti*) to the hydroxy group.

$$\underset{CH_3}{\overset{C_6H_5}{>}}C{=}N_{\diagdown O{-}H} \xrightarrow[\text{Ether}]{H_2SO_4} \underset{CH_3}{\overset{C_6H_5}{>}}C{=}\overset{+}{N}\underset{\underset{H}{|}}{\diagdown}O{-}H \longrightarrow CH_3{-}\overset{+}{C}{=}N^{\diagup C_6H_5} + H_2O$$

Benzophenone oxime

$$\underset{\text{Acetanilide}}{CH_3\overset{\overset{O}{\|}}{C}{-}NHC_6H_5} \rightleftharpoons CH_3{-}\overset{\overset{OH}{|}}{C}{=}N^{\diagup C_6H_5}$$

4.9.2 Electrophilic and free-radical rearrangements

These processes are not so numerous as the migration of nucleophilic groups. However, a number of rearrangements occur in which migration to carbanions is observed. One such reaction has been proposed in enzyme systems containing vitamin B_{12} involving the conversion of glutamic acid to β-methyl aspartic acid.

$$\underset{\text{Glutamic acid}}{\begin{array}{c} COO^- \\ | \\ CH{-}NH_3^+ \\ | \\ CH_2 \\ | \\ CH_2 \\ | \\ COOH \end{array}} \longrightarrow \begin{array}{c} COO^- \\ | \\ CH{\curvearrowright}NH_3^+ \\ | \\ CH_2 \\ | \\ ^-CH \\ | \\ COOH \end{array} \xrightarrow{-NH_3} \begin{array}{c} COO^- \\ | \\ CH \\ \diagup \\ CH{-}CH_2 \\ | \\ COOH \end{array} \xrightarrow{+NH_3} \underset{\beta\text{-Methyl aspartic acid}}{\begin{array}{c} COO^- \\ | \\ CH{-}NH_3^+ \\ | \\ CH \\ \diagup \diagdown \\ HOOC \quad CH_3 \end{array}}$$

Free-radical rearrangements are comparatively rare, and the first examples of this type of process were not discovered until 1944. Generally, there is much less tendency for a primary or secondary carbon free radical to rearrange than the corresponding carbonium ion. The 1,2-shift of an aryl group may sometimes proceed through a free-radical intermediate, and the aryl group migrates as a free radical. For example, the triphenylethyl radical (V) formed by the decomposition of the aldehyde (VI) in the presence of peroxide rearranges completely to give 1,1,2-triphenylethane (VII).

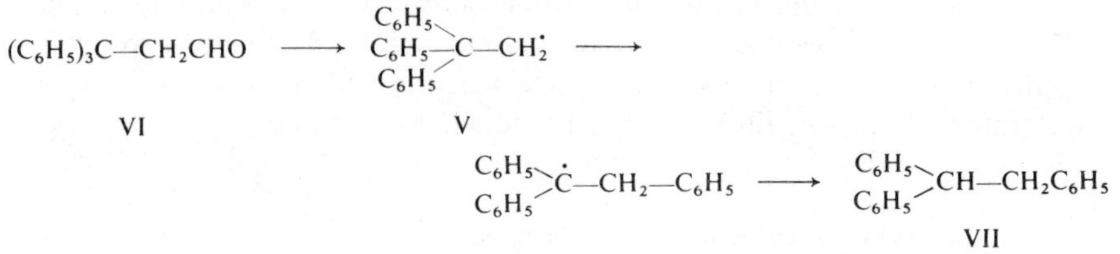

$$(C_6H_5)_3C-CH_2CHO \longrightarrow \begin{matrix} C_6H_5 \\ C_6H_5-\overset{\cdot}{C}-CH_2^{\cdot} \\ C_6H_5 \end{matrix} \longrightarrow$$

$$\text{VI} \qquad\qquad\qquad \text{V}$$

$$\begin{matrix} C_6H_5 \\ C_6H_5 \end{matrix}\overset{\cdot}{C}-CH_2-C_6H_5 \longrightarrow \begin{matrix} C_6H_5 \\ C_6H_5 \end{matrix}CH-CH_2C_6H_5$$

$$\text{VII}$$

4.10 OXIDATION AND REDUCTION REACTIONS

4.10.1 Introduction

The modern understanding of oxidation and reduction (redox) reactions is achieved by a consideration of the gain or loss of electrons. In this way it is relatively easy to obtain a complete understanding of redox reactions of inorganic ions. Thus, for example, the conversion of ferrous ion to ferric ion—an oxidation process—involves the loss of an electron from the ferrous ion.

$$Fe^{2+} \rightarrow Fe^{3+} + e^-$$

Conversely, the reduction of ferric ion involves the gain of an electron by the ion.

$$Fe^{3+} + e^- \rightarrow Fe^{2+}$$

In these reactions, only one part of the process has been considered, for, in an oxidation, a concurrent reduction must occur in which the electrons are taken up by the oxidizing reagent, which is itself reduced. Similarly, in a reduction process, the reducing reagent supplies the necessary electrons and is itself oxidized. Thus, the interaction of ferrous ions and ceric ions (Ce^{4+}) can be described either as a process for the oxidation of ferrous ion or for the reduction of ceric ion.

$$Fe^{2+} + Ce^{4+} \rightarrow Fe^{3+} + Ce^{3+}$$

The fact that this reaction proceeds quantitatively only in the direction indicated depends on the electrode potentials of the system, and this aspect is discussed in section 5.4.4.

While electrons are directly transferred in some organic and biochemical redox reactions, these considerations are not, generally, so easy to apply. The functional groups of organic molecules may be arranged in a qualitative way in order of increasing oxidation state. An oxidation process is then defined as any process leading to the conversion of one functional group to a higher one in this series. Conversely, a reduction process would be defined as one leading to descent of the series. Such a series is shown in Fig. 4.2 for some common types of organic molecule.

In this section it is possible to consider only some of the more versatile oxidizing and reducing agents. These reagents oxidize or reduce a wide range of substrates. On the other hand, there are numerous oxidizing and reducing agents which have a more specific action reacting with a particular type of substrate and occasionally even with an individual substrate.

Hydrocarbons	Unsaturated hydrocarbons	Unsaturated hydrocarbons		
	$(>C=C<)$	$(-C\equiv C-)$		
	Alcohols	Aldehydes	Acids	
		Ketones		CO_2
	Amines	Nitro-compounds	Amides	

$\longrightarrow$ Oxidation $\longrightarrow$

$\longleftarrow$ Reduction $\longrightarrow$

Fig. 4.2   Qualitative redox relationships in organic molecules

4.10.2   Some oxidizing agents used in organic chemistry

The salts of certain inorganic *oxyanions* provide the most common and versatile oxidizing agents. The reactions of these oxyanions proceed via the formation of intermediate inorganic esters (I) which decompose by an elimination to give the oxidation product (II). The best-known examples are the

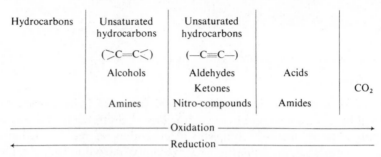

oxidizing agents potassium permanganate and potassium dichromate. Both reagents rely on the oxidizing power of the anions. Potassium dichromate is used in acid solutions, while potassium permanganate can be used in either

$$Cr_2O_7^{2-} + 14H^+ + 6e^- \longrightarrow 2Cr^{3+} + 7H_2O$$

$$MnO_4^- + e^- \xrightarrow{\;OH^-\;} MnO_4^{2-}$$

acidic or alkaline solutions. Both reagents oxidize primary alcohols (III) to carboxylic acids (V) and it is difficult to stop the reaction at the intermediate aldehyde stage (IV). Secondary alcohols (VI) are oxidized to ketones (VII) which are generally stable to further oxidation. When further oxidation does

140

occur, loss of carbon atoms as carbon dioxide takes place. An exception to this is the case of cyclic ketones (e.g., VIII) where the carbocyclic ring is opened.

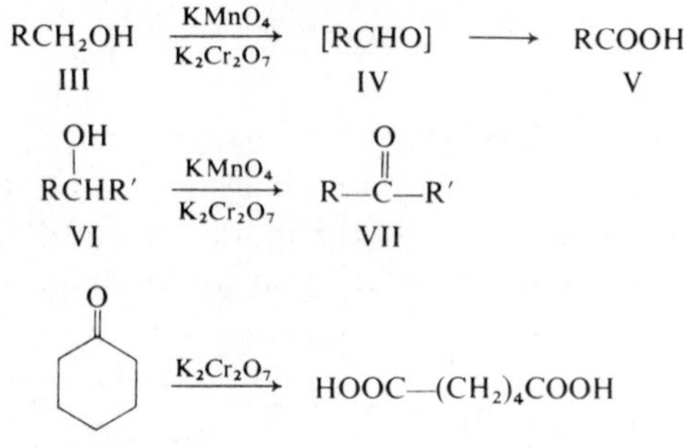

$$RCH_2OH \xrightarrow[K_2Cr_2O_7]{KMnO_4} [RCHO] \longrightarrow RCOOH$$
$$\text{III} \qquad\qquad\qquad \text{IV} \qquad\qquad \text{V}$$

$$\underset{\text{VI}}{\overset{\overset{\textstyle OH}{|}}{RCHR'}} \xrightarrow[K_2Cr_2O_7]{KMnO_4} \underset{\text{VII}}{R\overset{\overset{\textstyle O}{\|}}{-}C-R'}$$

$$\xrightarrow{K_2Cr_2O_7} HOOC-(CH_2)_4COOH$$

VIII
Cyclohexanone   Adipic acid

Phenols and aromatic amines are oxidized to quinones. *Ortho* and *para* (IX) diphenols are most easily oxidized (see also section 7.5.1). The alkyl side chain of aromatic compounds is also oxidized by these reagents.

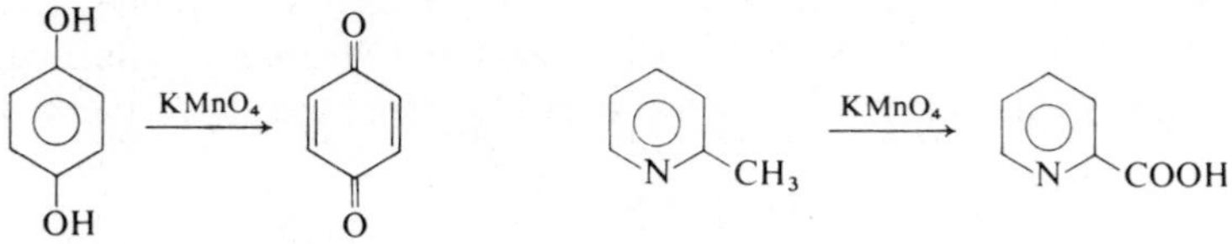

IX

Periodates and persulphates are also used as oxidizing agents. Of particular interest is the cleavage of 1,2-diols by periodate ion to give carbonyl compounds and, in certain circumstances formic acid. A similar reaction also occurs with lead tetraacetate. This type of reaction is of great value in the structural analysis of carbohydrates.

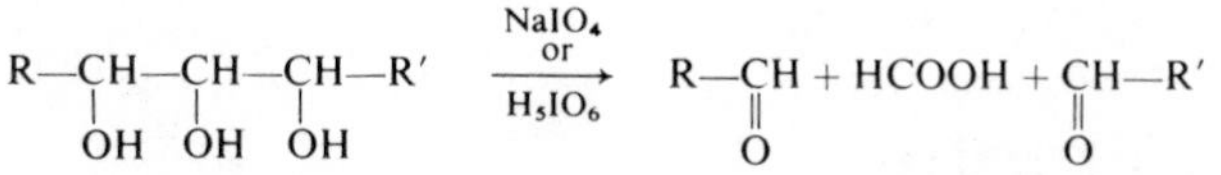

$$\underset{\overset{|}{OH}\ \overset{|}{OH}\ \overset{|}{OH}}{R-CH-CH-CH-R'} \xrightarrow[H_5IO_6]{\overset{NaIO_4}{\text{or}}} R-\underset{O}{\overset{\|}{C}}H + HCOOH + \underset{O}{\overset{\|}{C}}H-R'$$

4.10.3 Some common reducing agents used in organic chemistry

The reduction of organic compounds with hydrogen is a much more important process than the corresponding oxidation with elemental oxygen. This is because the reductions can be carefully controlled by the use of catalysts and reaction conditions. In some reduction reactions, hydrogen is generated in the reaction medium. Examples of this are the *Clemmensen reduction*, which uses zinc amalgam and hydrochloric acid, and is used for reducing carbonyl

141

compounds to hydrocarbons. Tin and hydrochloric acid are used to reduce nitro-compounds to amines.

$$R—\overset{\overset{\displaystyle O}{\|}}{C}—R' \xrightarrow[\text{HCl}]{\text{Zn/Hg}} R—CH_2—R'$$

Many reductions are carried out by the use of catalytic hydrogenation, a process known as *hydrogenolysis*. The catalysts used are mainly transition metals such as nickel, palladium and platinum. Unsaturated hydrocarbons may be reduced in a stepwise manner by hydrogenolysis, by controlling the amount of hydrogen present.

$$R—C{\equiv}C—R' \xrightarrow[\text{catalyst}]{H_2} R—CH{=}CH—R' \xrightarrow[\text{catalyst}]{H_2} R—CH_2—CH_2—R'$$

In some reductions, the reduction is effected by hydride ion (H^-) transfer. The best-known examples of this type of reaction are those using metallic hydrides. The most versatile of these reagents is lithium aluminium hydride, which reduces esters and carboxylic acids to alcohols, amides to amines and acid chlorides to alcohols.

Direct electron transfer is found in only a few cases. An example of such a reaction is the *Birch reduction*, where 1,4-addition of hydrogen to an aromatic ring occurs. In this case, sodium transfers electrons directly to the benzene

$$\bigcirc \xrightarrow[\text{NH}_3]{\text{Na}} \bigcirc$$

ring, and is itself oxidized to sodium ion.

One of the most vigorous of all reducing reagents used in organic chemistry is hot hydriodic acid and red phosphorus. Most functional groups are reduced and hydrocarbons result. An example of such a reduction will be found in section 7.3.1, where a carbohydrate is converted to an alkyl iodide. The purpose of the phosphorus is to remove all or part of the iodine from the system.

Bibliography

References 1 and 2 from chapter 2.
1. E. S. Gould, *Mechanism and Structure in Organic Chemistry*, 2nd Edn, Holt, Rinehart and Winston, 1973.
2. R. Breslow, *Organic Reaction Mechanisms*, 2nd Edn, Benjamin, 1969.
3. P. Sykes, *A Guidebook to Mechanism in Organic Chemistry*, 4th Edn, Longmans, 1975.
4. J. A. Joule and C. F. Smith, *Heterocyclic Chemistry*, 2nd Edn, Van Nostrand Reinhold, 1978.
5. J. March, *Advanced Organic Chemistry, Reactions, Mechanism, and Structure*, McGraw-Hill, 1968.
6. J. N. Lowe and L. L. Ingraham, *An Introduction to Biochemical Reaction Mechanisms*, Prentice Hall, 1974.

5. The physical chemistry of liquids and solutions

5.1 INTRODUCTION TO THE PROPERTIES OF THE LIQUID STATE

For most gases and vapours their molecules are largely free to move about the vessel containing them, and they do so with great speed. In liquids, however, the molecules are still moving about but with much reduced speed. The molecular movement is much more restricted in the liquid state than in the gaseous state. Individual molecules are continually under the influence of attractive and repulsive forces of neighbouring molecules.

The close proximity of the molecules in liquids is responsible for their densities being similar in magnitude to those of solids and the fact that they are virtually incompressible. The densities of liquids are approximately related to molecular size. Because of the restricted movement of the molecules, liquids possess a certain amount of structure. The results of X-ray diffraction measurements on liquids indicate some degree of regularity which decreases as the temperature is raised.

5.2 PHYSICAL PROPERTIES OF LIQUIDS

5.2.1 Density

The densities of liquids decrease with increasing temperature. Water, however, demonstrates anomalous density which does not decrease regularly with increasing temperature but has a maximum value at 4°C. This is attributed to two opposing effects. Ice has a rather open structure and therefore between the melting point at 0°C and 4°C there is a gradual breakdown of this open structure to a more closely packed structure. As the temperature is raised further, there is imposed upon this effect the thermal agitation of the molecules, which tends to increase the volume of the liquid and hence decrease its density. These two opposing effects cause the maximum density at 4°C.

5.2.2 The viscosities of liquids and suspensions

Whenever a liquid flows, there is frictional resistance to movement of one layer of liquid over another. In the case of liquids flowing past a stationary wall, the layer of liquid next to the wall is motionless for medium rates of flow. When the flow of liquid is down a tube and the flow is uniformly parallel to the axis of the tube, the velocity profile of the liquid is often parabolic (Fig. 5.1). Under these conditions the flow of liquid is said to be *streamlined* or *laminar*. At high flow rates, the liquid no longer travels strictly parallel to the axis of the tube, and the flow is then said to be *turbulent*.

The viscosity of a liquid is measured by its coefficient of viscosity, η. It is defined as the force per unit area which is necessary to maintain unit difference of velocity between two parallel layers of liquid one unit of distance apart. Liquids with small values of η are said to be mobile; viscous liquids have large

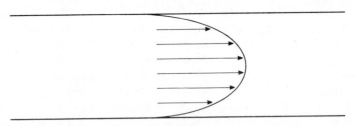

Fig. 5.1   Velocity profile in a tube for streamline flow

values of η. One unit of viscosity in common usage is the *poise* (P), a sub-unit of which is the *centipoise* (cP). The viscosity of water at 20°C is 1·008 cP. An alternative unit of viscosity is the *centistoke* (cS) (used for the *kinematic viscosity*) which is related to the centipoise by η/d, where η is the viscosity in centipoises and d is density. The unit of viscosity in SI units is the *poiseuille* (Pl) which is related to the centipoise by 1 cP = 0·001 Pl (1 millipoiseuille, mPl). This may be defined as 1 Pl = 1 N s m^{-2} (Newton seconds metre^{-2}).

For most pure liquids and for many solutions, the coefficient of viscosity, η, is constant, regardless of the rate of shear applied to the liquid. Such liquids are known as *Newtonian* liquids and are said to possess *Newtonian* or *normal* viscosity. Some solutions, especially those of long-chain polymeric substances and some suspensions, have viscosities which decrease with an increased rate of shear applied to the liquid. These systems are referred to as *non-Newtonian* or *shear-thinning*, and are said to possess anomalous viscosity.

A further class of liquids consists of those which have an initial resistance to flow up to a certain value of shear. Beyond this value the liquid will then flow, usually in a non-Newtonian manner. Systems such as these are called *Bingham* fluids. Figure 5.2 illustrates the various types of behaviour discussed above. When the system gives a loop as in curve D it is referred to as *thixotropic*.

The effect of temperature on the viscosities of gases and liquids is surprisingly different. The viscosity of a gas increases as the temperature is

144

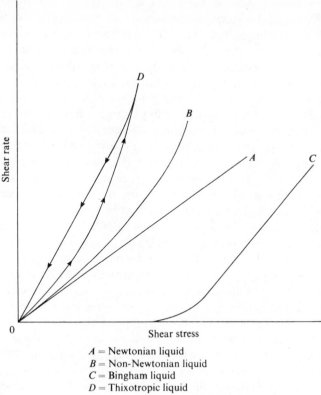

Fig. 5.2 Viscosity behaviour in liquids

A = Newtonian liquid
B = Non-Newtonian liquid
C = Bingham liquid
D = Thixotropic liquid

raised. With liquids, however, the intermolecular forces which are responsible for the viscosity are overcome at higher temperature by increased molecular agitation, and hence the viscosity decreases.

The viscosities of suspensions

Suspended particles in a liquid cause an increase in viscosity proportional to the amount of suspended material. For an ideal case, the viscosity of the suspension is given by the *Einstein equation*,

$$\eta = \eta_0(1 + kc) \qquad (5.1)$$

where η_0 is the viscosity of the pure liquid, c is the volume concentration of the particles in the liquid and k is a constant often given the value 2·5. Provided that the suspension is not too concentrated and that the particles in the

145

suspension do not interact, the Einstein equation is often obeyed by real systems. Many real systems of suspensions are non-Newtonian and deviate from the Einstein equation. There are over fifty extensions of the Einstein equation which attempt to describe the viscosity behaviour of real systems.

Concentrated suspensions often possess non-Newtonian viscosity and this can give rise to unusual behaviour when the suspension flows down a tube. The shear dependence of η of flowing suspensions can produce changes in concentration of the suspension as it flows down a tube. There is a tendency for the particles to move to the centre of the tube and leave a particle-depleted layer near the walls of the tube. This effect is often referred to as the *tubular-pinch* effect or the *Vand effect*. Not only is this observed in steady flow down a tube, but also in pulsatile flow. This hyperconcentration of particles which is developed in the axial part of the tube can, under some conditions, be very high and lead to the formation of thrombi of particles.

The most important biological suspension is blood. The particles in this case are red cells (*erythrocytes*), white cells (*leukocytes*) and platelets. The very large number of red cells (about 5×10^6 per mm^3) make the largest contribution to the viscosity of whole blood. The viscosity of whole blood is of great importance in that it provides the resistance to the heart in circulating the blood round the vascular system. The larger viscosity of plasma as compared with water is due to the dissolved proteins it contains.

Blood has properties which resemble those of a Bingham fluid. At very low rates of shear, human blood may exhibit viscosities which are 100 to 10 000 times that of water, whereas at higher shear rates it may only be 2 to 10 times as viscous as water. Blood still flows even at a haematocrit of 95 per cent, whereas other suspensions at this high concentration are solid. The reason for this remarkable property of blood is that the red cells are easily deformed and hence must have low internal viscosities. It can be calculated that the apparent internal viscosity of the red cell (that is the contribution of the cell membrane and the cell interior) is in the region 1–6 cP (1–6 mPl).

5.2.3 Surface tension of liquids

In the interior of a liquid, the molecules are completely surrounded by other molecules, and on average each molecule is attracted equally in all directions. At the surface, however, the molecules do not experience the same attractive forces from the vapour above the liquid, as there are fewer molecules in the vapour phase. This produces a resultant attractive force on the molecules at the surface of the liquid, which tends to pull them inwards. This results in the surface of the liquid tending to contract to the smallest possible area and appearing to possess a surface tension.

Surface-tension phenomena also exist between liquids and solids and between immiscible liquids. It is usual to refer to these surface tensions as *interfacial tensions.* A selection of surface-tension values is given in Table 5.1. The dimensions of surface tension are force per unit distance, and hence the appropriate units are dyne cm^{-1} or N m^{-1}, the latter being the SI unit.

Table 5.1   Surface tensions of some liquids

Liquid	Surface tension at 20°C (dyne cm^{-1})	(N m^{-1})
Water	72·8	72·8 × 10^{-3}
Glycerol	65·2	65·2 × 10^{-3}
Benzene	27·9	27·9 × 10^{-3}
Ethyl alcohol	21·7	21·7 × 10^{-3}
Ether	16·5	16·5 × 10^{-3}
Mercury	465	465 × 10^{-3}

5.3   PROPERTIES OF SOLUTIONS OF NON-ELECTROLYTES

5.3.1   Solubility of gases in liquids

The solubility of a gas in a liquid is dependent on the chemical nature of the gas and the liquid, and also the temperature of the liquid and the pressure of the gas. In the case of water as the solvent the most soluble gas is ammonia (1300 ml at NTP in 1 ml of water) and the least soluble gas is helium (0·01 ml at NTP in 1 ml of water). The solubilities of all other gases in water lie between these limits. When solubilities are quoted in this form they are called absorption coefficients.

When a gas dissolves in water there is an *evolution* of heat. Because of this the solubility of gases decreases with rising temperature. A collection of absorption coefficients at 0°C and 30°C is given in Table 5.2.

Table 5.2   Absorption coefficients in water
(ml of gas per ml of water)

Gas	Absorption coefficient 0°C	30°C
Helium	0·0094	0·0081
Nitrogen	0·0235	0·0134
Oxygen	0·0489	0·0261
Carbon dioxide	1·713	0·665

Pressure has a greater influence on the solubility of a gas than temperature. Solubility and gas pressure are quantitatively related by *Henry's law*. This states that the solubility of a gas at a given temperature in a given volume of liquid is directly proportional to the pressure of the gas, P,

$$m = kP \tag{5.2}$$

147

where m is the weight of gas dissolved per unit volume of liquid and k is a constant for the gas and the liquid. For gases of low solubility and provided the pressure is not too high or the temperature too low, Henry's law is obeyed by gases exhibiting ideal behaviour. If the gas reacts with the solvent, e.g., ammonia, hydrogen chloride, and to some extent carbon dioxide in the solvent water, then marked deviations from Henry's law occur.

For mixtures of gases, the solubilities of the individual gases are proportional to their partial pressures and their individual absorption coefficients. In general, gases are less soluble in solutions of electrolytes than they are in water at the same temperature and pressure. This is known as a *salting-out effect*.

The solubilities of gases are important in connection with the physical chemistry of blood gases. The solubility of oxygen in blood may be expressed as the percentage of oxyhaemoglobin. If this is plotted against the partial pressure of oxygen, the graph is not linear but S-shaped, indicating deviation from Henry's law. This is illustrated in Fig. 5.3. The characteristic-shaped curve has physiological advantages in that above a pressure of 9 kN m^{-2} (about 70 mm Hg) the curve is very flat. If the arterial oxygen pressure falls to 10·5 kN m^{-2} (80 mm Hg), then the arterial blood is still quite high in oxyhaemoglobin. On passing into the capillaries of tissue, where there is a low

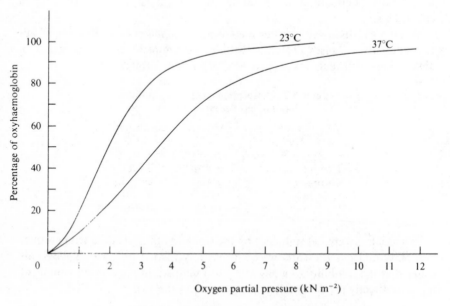

Fig. 5.3   Solubility of oxygen in blood

148

oxygen content and high carbon-dioxide content, the blood is still able to supply the necessary oxygen, in spite of the decreased oxygen partial pressure.

The solubility curve of carbon dioxide rises much more steeply than that of oxygen and this is particularly apparent in the normal physiological range of blood carbon dioxide (P_{CO_2} of 2·6 to 8 kN m^{-2} or 20 to 60 mm Hg). This property enables blood to have a considerable reserve for reaction with further CO_2. If the blood CO_2 falls below the normal value, there is a condition of alkali deficit (*metabolic acidosis*). If the blood CO_2 is too high, then a state of metabolic *alkalosis* exists, as occurs with prolonged vomiting.

5.3.2 Colligative properties of solutions

The liquid which is present in excess in a solution is referred to as the *solvent*, and the dissolved substance referred to as the *solute*. Many methods are available for expressing the concentration of the solute. The more important concentration scales are as follows.

(*a*) *Molarity (M or c)* This concentration scale is often relative to chemical reactions involving the solute in connection with quantitative analysis. The molarity of the solution is defined as the number of gram moles of solute per litre of solution. Since a volume of solution is implied in the definition, the molarity of a given solution is temperature dependent. Thus a one molar solution at 20°C is certainly not one molar at any other temperature since the volume will be different.

(*b*) *Molality (m)* The molality of a solution is the number of gram moles of solute per 1000 g of solvent. Unlike the normality and molarity concentration scales the molality of a solution is not temperature dependent.

(*c*) *Mole fraction (N or x)* It is often convenient to express the concentrations of components of a solution as fractions of the total material present including the solvent. If a binary solution (two components, solute and solvent) contains n_1 moles of component 1 and n_2 moles of component 2, then the mole fractions of the two components are

$$N_1 = n_1/(n_1 + n_2) \quad \text{and} \quad N_2 = n_2/(n_1 + n_2).$$

As long ago as 1858, Wüllner discovered that, when an involatile solute is added to a volatile solvent, the vapour pressure of the solvent is lowered, and that the lowering of the vapour pressure is proportional to the concentration of dissolved solute. If p_1^0 is the vapour pressure of the pure solvent and p_1 is the vapour pressure of the solution, then the fractional lowering of the vapour pressure is given by $(p_1^0 - p_1)/p_1^0$. In 1886, Raoult showed that this quantity was equal to the mole fraction of dissolved solute,

$$\frac{p_1^0 - p_1}{p_1^0} = N_2 = \frac{n_2}{n_1 + n_2} \tag{5.3}$$

It is then relatively easy to show that

$$p_1 = N_1 p_1^0 \tag{5.4}$$

Equation (5.4) is the mathematical characterization of *Raoult's law*. It can be seen that the vapour pressure of the solvent is directly proportional to the mole fraction of solvent. In the case of two volatile liquids forming a solution an additional equation exists for the second component:

$$p_2 = N_2 p_2^0 \tag{5.5}$$

Raoult's law is of great significance in the physical chemistry of solutions. It represents the basis of ideal-solution behaviour in the same way that the simple gas laws represent the behaviour of ideal gases. An ideal solution, by definition, is one which obeys Raoult's law over the whole range of composition possible and at all temperatures. Such solutions are formed only from components which (a) mix in the liquid state without heat change, i.e., zero heat of dilution, and (b) mix without change in volume, i.e., the *partial molar volumes* (section 5.3.3) of the components of the solution are constant at all concentrations.

Consequences of obeying Raoult's law

The colligative properties of a solution are those physico-chemical properties which are affected by the concentration of the dissolved solute. One such property has been discussed above, namely, the lowering of the vapour pressure of a solvent by a dissolved solute. Several other colligative properties will now be discussed for the ideal case, which means that the solutions obey Raoult's law.

(a) Elevation of the boiling point of a solution   The presence of a dissolved involatile solute increases the boiling point of a liquid. It can be shown that the elevation of the boiling point, ΔT_b is given by

$$\Delta T_b = K_b N_2 \tag{5.6}$$

where K_b is called the ebullioscopic constant and is given by RT_b^2/L_v, where R is the gas constant, T_b is the boiling point of the pure solvent, L_v is the molar heat of vaporization of the solvent, and N_2 is the mole fraction of the solute. An alternative to eq. (5.6) in dilute solutions is

$$\Delta T_b = K_b m_2 M_1/1000 \tag{5.7}$$

where m_2 is the molality of the solute and M_1 is the molecular weight of the solvent.

(b) Depression of the freezing point   The lowering of the freezing point ΔT_f by a solute is given by

$$\Delta T_f = K_f N_2 \tag{5.8}$$

150

where K_f is the cryoscopic constant and is given by RT_f^2/L_f, where T_f is the freezing point of the pure solvent and L_f is the molar heat of fusion of the solvent. The corresponding equation to eq. (5.7) in the case of freezing-point depression of dilute solutions is

$$\Delta T_f = K_f m_2 M_1/1000 \qquad (5.9)$$

The above equations are applicable only to non-electrolytes which provide one particle in solution per dissolved molecule. In the general case of the solute giving i particles in solution, the concentration of solute in the above equations would have to be multiplied by the factor i (the Van't Hoff i-factor) to make them applicable.

5.3.3 Non-ideal solutions, partial molar quantities and activity

An ideal solution is one which obeys Raoult's law over the whole range of composition available and at all temperatures. While for some dilute solutions the departure from ideal behaviour is often negligible, the behaviour of concentrated solutions is nearly always far from ideal. In general, the higher the temperature, the less any deviation from ideality becomes. Non-ideal behaviour of solutions may be due to several causes. If the intermolecular forces of each constituent are altered by the presence of the other constituents, then deviations from ideality will occur. Similarly, if compounds are formed between the solute and the solvent, or even if the solute is strongly solvated, or if complex molecules are formed, then Raoult's law will not be obeyed.

In Figs. 5.4(a) and (b) are plotted the vapour pressure–composition graphs for mixtures of two liquids and a solution of an involatile solute. Figure 5.4(a)

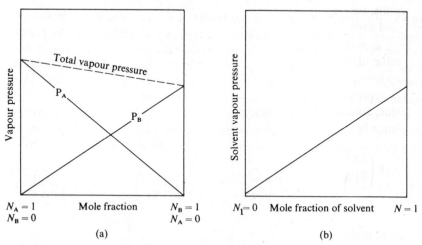

Fig. 5.4 (a) Vapour pressures for mixtures of two volatile liquids. (b) Vapour pressure of a solution with an involatile solute

shows the ideal case for liquid mixtures where the partial vapour pressure of each component is a linear function of its mole fraction. This is the ideal case, and corresponds to the heats of mixing and volume changes of mixing being zero. The converse, that if these quantities are zero the solution is necessarily ideal, is not always true (see *athermal solutions*, below).

Figure 5.4(b) shows the corresponding graph for an involatile solute. In this case, the heat of solution is equal to the heat of fusion of the solute.

Deviations from Raoult's law can be classified as follows.

(a) Positive deviations   Positive deviations from Raoult's law occur when, for mixtures of volatile liquids, the partial vapour pressures of the constituents are greater than the values predicted by Raoult's law. For an involatile solute at a certain temperature, the solubility is lower than that predicted by Raoult's law.

(b) Negative deviations   In this case the partial vapour pressures of the constituents in a mixture of volatile liquids are less than those predicted by Raoult's law. For involatile solutes, the concentration needed to produce a given lowering of the solvent vapour pressure is greater than in the ideal case.

(c) Regular solutions   These are solutions which give large deviations from ideality, and have large heats of mixing but low entropies of mixing or dilution.

(d) Athermal solutions   In this case the heat of mixing is either small or zero, but the solutions have finite entropies of mixing. They always give negative deviations from Raoult's law, but the deviations are usually small, except in the case of solutions of high-molecular-weight polymers.

Partial molar quantities

In a solution containing several constituents, the total value of thermodynamic functions, such as internal energy (U), enthalpy (H), free energy (G), entropy (S), and even volume (V), is dependent on the amounts of the constituents present as well as temperature and pressure. In the case of non-ideal systems the value also depends on the extent of the departure from ideality. These factors have to be considered in the thermodynamics of solutions.

If X represents any of the above properties, then for a small change dX in its value, contributions from changes in temperature, pressure, and composition must be considered. For a binary mixture this may be represented by

$$dX = dT \left(\frac{\partial X}{\partial T}\right)_{P, n_1, n_2} + dP \left(\frac{\partial X}{\partial P}\right)_{T, n_1, n_2} + dn_1 \left(\frac{\partial X}{\partial n_1}\right)_{P, T, n_2} + dn_2 \left(\frac{\partial X}{\partial n_2}\right)_{P, T, n_1}$$

(5.10)

where n_1 and n_2 are the numbers of gram moles of constituents 1 and 2. The quantities $\partial X/\partial n$ are called *partial molar quantities* and are written as

152

$$\left(\frac{\partial X}{\partial n_1}\right)_{P,T,n_2} = \bar{X}_1$$

$$\left(\frac{\partial X}{\partial n_2}\right)_{P,T,n_1} = \bar{X}_2.$$

(5.11)

Each partial molar quantity can be regarded as the contribution per mole of each constituent to the total value of the property X. The two values in a binary mixture are related by the important *Gibbs–Duhem equation*,

$$n_1 \, d\bar{X}_1 = -n_2 \, d\bar{X}_2 \qquad \text{(at constant } P \text{ and } T) \tag{5.12}$$

This allows $\bar{X}_1$ to be calculated from values of $\bar{X}_2$, if these are known, by graphical integration of a plot of n_2/n_1 against $\bar{X}_2$, since

$$X_1 = -\int \frac{n_2}{n_1} \, d\bar{X}_2 \tag{5.13}$$

Some common partial molar quantities are partial molar volume, partial molar enthalpy, partial molar heat of mixing. A very important partial molar quantity is *partial molar free energy*,

$$\left(\frac{\partial G}{\partial n}\right)_{P,T} = \bar{G} \tag{5.14}$$

Partial molar free energy, $\bar{G}$, is identical to chemical potential, μ (section 3.5).

Activity

Even though the qualitative reasons for the departure from ideality may be known, it is usually difficult to calculate from first principles the exact extent of the departure. Equations are available, however, for non-ideal solutions which express the departure from ideal behaviour in a form which is independent of the precise factors responsible.

For an ideal solution formed from two liquids, the chemical potentials of each constituent are of the form

$$\mu_1 = \mu_1^{\ominus} + RT \ln N_1 \tag{5.15}$$

$$\mu_2 = \mu_2^{\ominus} + RT \ln N_2 \tag{5.16}$$

where the $\mu^{\ominus}$ terms are *standard chemical potentials*, and are chemical potentials corresponding to the values for the pure components at 1 atm pressure. For a non-ideal solution of two liquids, eqs. (5.15) and (5.16) have to be modified. The reason for this is that each constituent, due to the presence of the other component, does not exert its influence on the properties of the solution to

153

an extent proportional to its concentration. In place of the mole fraction terms in eqs. (5.15) and (5.16), it is customary to use a term called *activity* for non-ideal solutions. This means that the above equations would read

$$\mu_1 = \mu_1^\ominus + RT \ln a_1 \qquad (5.17)$$

$$\mu_2 = \mu_2^\ominus + RT \ln a_2 \qquad (5.18)$$

where a_1 and a_2 are the activities of the two components. The activities are related to the mole fractions by

$$a_1 = N_1 f_1 \quad \text{and} \quad a_2 = N_2 f_2 \qquad (5.19)$$

where the f terms are called *activity coefficients*. As the properties of the solution approach those of ideal behaviour, the value of activity approaches the value of mole fraction and the activity coefficients approach values of unity, so that eqs. (5.17) and (5.18) become identical with eqs. (5.15) and (5.16) respectively.

For non-ideal solutions of an involatile solute there are three appropriate equations for the chemical potential corresponding to the mole fraction (N), molarity (c), and molality (m) concentration scales,

$$\mu = \mu_N^\ominus + RT \ln N f_N = \mu_N^\ominus + RT \ln a_N \qquad (5.20)$$

$$\mu = \mu_c^\ominus + RT \ln c f_c = \mu_c^\ominus + RT \ln a_c \qquad (5.21)$$

$$\mu = \mu_m^\ominus + RT \ln m f_m = \mu_m^\ominus + RT \ln a_m \qquad (5.22)$$

(the subscript 2 has been omitted for clarity). In dilute solutions, the activity coefficients f_N, f_c, f_m tend to unity. Although they will have different values for a particular solute in a given solution, they are in fact related to each other. The activity coefficients f_N, f_c and f_m are often designated by the symbols f, y and γ respectively.

5.4 PROPERTIES OF THE SOLUTIONS OF ELECTROLYTES

5.4.1 Electrolytic dissociation, activity, and ionic strength

A large number of compounds, when they are dissolved in water, dissociate into sub-molecular species known as ions. Many such solids are already composed of positively and negatively charged ions in the solid state (ionic compounds), and when they dissolve, the ionic lattice falls apart to give discrete ions in the solution. The ions have considerable affinity for water, and the energetics of their hydration by the solvent favours their formation in solution.

The solutions of these compounds are able to conduct electricity and they are referred to as *electrolyte solutions*. The positively charged ions migrate towards a negatively charged electrode (a cathode) and are termed *cations*, while the negatively charged ions migrate towards a positively charged electrode (an anode) and are termed *anions*. Since an electrolyte molecule is in total an electrically neutral species, it must provide equal numbers of positive and negative charges when the cations and anions are formed in solution. For example, sodium chloride (NaCl) provides equal numbers of Na^+ and Cl^- ions, sodium sulphate (Na_2SO_4) provides two sodium ions, Na^+, for every sulphate ion, SO_4^{2-}, and barium chloride, $BaCl_2$, provides two chloride ions, Cl^-, for every barium ion, Ba^{2+}.

Some covalent compounds behave as electrolytes in solution, but usually they dissociate only partly into ions in solution, in contrast to ionic compounds which are largely dissociated into ions in solution. Thus it is common to classify electrolytes into two types: namely, *strong* electrolytes and *weak* electrolytes. Strong electrolytes are completely dissociated into ions in *dilute* solution. Weak electrolytes, on the other hand, are only partially dissociated into ions even in very dilute solution. Common examples of weak electrolytes are the organic carboxylic acids.

Solutions of electrolytes are even more non-ideal than those of non-electrolytes. This means that the activity of an electrolyte cannot be identified with its concentration even in dilute solution. The ratio of a/m or a/c for an electrolyte does not tend to unity at low concentrations. It is necessary therefore to define new quantities to describe the non-ideality of electrolytes. This may be illustrated with sodium chloride;

$$\text{Mean ionic activity} = a^{\pm} = \sqrt{a_{Na^+} \times a_{Cl^-}} \qquad (5.23)$$

$$\text{Mean ionic molality} = m^{\pm} = \sqrt{m_{Na^+} \times m_{Cl^-}} \qquad (5.24)$$

$$\text{Mean ionic (molal) activity coefficient} = \gamma^{\pm} = \gamma_{Na^+} \times \gamma_{Cl^-} = \frac{a^{\pm}}{m^{\pm}} \quad (5.25)$$

Thus, for sodium chloride the mean ionic activity is

$$a^{\pm} = \sqrt{a_{Na^+} \times a_{Cl^-}} = \sqrt{a_{NaCl}} \qquad (5.26)$$

In general, if an electrolyte produces v ions per molecule, v^+ of them being cations and v^- of them being anions, then the mean ionic activity is

$$a^{\pm} = a^{1/v} = (a_+^{v^+} \times a_-^{v^-})^{1/v} \qquad (5.27)$$

Analogous equations are available for the other concentration scales. The departure from ideal behaviour of an electrolyte solution is indicated by the amount the mean ionic activity differs from the mean ionic molality, and the amount the mean ionic activity coefficient, $\gamma^{\pm}$, differs from unity.

For dilute solutions of electrolytes, it is possible to calculate mean ionic activity coefficients using the *Debye–Huckel equation*. For aqueous solutions (less than about 1×10^{-2} molal) at 25°C the equation may be written in the form

$$\log \gamma^{\pm} = -0.509 z_i^2 \sqrt{I} \qquad (5.28)$$

where z_i is the sum of the charges carried by the ions, and I is called the ionic strength of the solution, and is defined by the equation

$$I = \tfrac{1}{2} \sum m_i z_i^2 \qquad (5.29)$$

The applicability of eq. (5.28) to aqueous solutions is limited to those whose ionic strengths are less than 0·01. For solutions normally encountered in the laboratory there is no simple general theory which allows the activity coefficients to be calculated. They are more frequently measured by the normal colligative properties discussed in section 5.3.2.

5.4.2 Applications of cryoscopy in biology and medicine

The depression of the freezing point of water by a dissolved solute may be used as a method of quantitative analysis. This has become possible in recent years due to the development of accurate temperature-measuring devices. Several commercial instruments make use of the marked change in resistance of thermistors as a function of temperature, and temperature changes of 1×10^{-4} °C are commonly measured by this method.

Due to the importance of osmotic pressure in biology, it is unfortunate that several instruments which measure other colligative properties have been called osmometers, whereas they do not measure osmotic pressure at all. (They are really cryoscopes and measure freezing-point depression.) The reason for this *apparent* misuse of terminology is that a common unit of concentration in biology is the *osmol per litre*, one osmol per litre producing an osmotic pressure of 22·4 atmospheres. It is also the same concentration, which in an ideal solution, would produce a lowering of the freezing point of water by 1·857 °C (i.e., 1 mole of non-electrolyte per 1000 g of water). The measurement of the osmolality of body fluids such as plasma or urine is of considerable importance in the measurement of body electrolyte balance. A sub-unit of the osmol is the *milliosmol* (0·001 osmol). Normal human serum contains about 290 milliosmols of total dissolved solute per kg of water or litre of serum.

Since cryoscopy is now such a precise technique, it is often used for the determination of the osmolality of biological fluids, and the method is preferable to measurements of electrical conductivity, specific gravity or refractive index. The osmolality (O) is related to molality by

$$O = \phi i m \qquad (5.30)$$

156

where ϕ is the *osmotic coefficient* (analogous to activity coefficient, and equal to 1·00 for non-electrolytes such as glucose and urea, and to 0·93 for sodium chloride), i is the number of species produced in solution from 1 mole of solute, and m is molality.

When used in conjunction with other physiological data such as glucose, urea, and sodium analyses, the measurement of solute osmolality in urine, serum and other biological fluids can provide useful diagnostic information. The measurement of urine osmolality by the freezing-point technique can be used in the following clinical situations.

(a) As an alternative for less adequate methods in the evaluation of the concentrating ability of the kidney.
(b) As a monitor in following the development of intrinsic renal disease.
(c) In conjunction with plasma osmolality in the differential diagnosis of diabetes insipidus and compulsive water drinking.
(d) In conjunction with density measurements as a method of observing changes in the molecular-weight distribution of metabolites excreted in urine.

Other applications of freezing-point measurements in the determination of osmolality include the following.

(a) The testing of blood and other transfusion liquids, and biological liquids generally.
(b) The testing of isotonic solutions.
(c) The measurement of fluid balance and dehydration in cases of severe burns and also in glucose administration following abdominal surgery.
(d) The monitoring and control of dialysis procedures with artificial kidney machines.

5.4.3 Measurement and interpretation of electrolytic conductance

The ions formed in solution by electrolytes are capable of conducting electricity through the solution. If a voltage is applied to two electrodes placed in an electrolyte solution, the ions move to the electrode of opposite polarity. The basic requirements for the measurement of the conductances of electrolyte solutions are a conductivity cell which contains two electrodes and a Wheatstone bridge arrangement having the cell as one of its arms. The electrodes are usually *platinized* platinum electrodes. The measurements are usually made with an alternating current whose frequency is in the range 1000 to 10 000 Hz.

The unit of conductance is the *reciprocal ohm*, or the *mho*. For solutions, however, the measured conductance of a solution is a function of the size of the electrodes and their distance apart. Thus, it is necessary to introduce special definitions for the conductances of electrolyte solutions. The first of

157

these is *specific conductance*, κ, which is defined as the conductance of a solution in a cell having electrodes of 1 m² area and placed 1 m apart in the solution.

Since no conductivity cell is made with exactly such dimensions, it is necessary to convert all measured conductances with a given cell to correspond to the value required by the above definition. This is achieved by

$$\kappa = ks$$

where s is the measured conductance and k is called the cell constant. The value of k for a particular cell is determined by using it to measure the conductivity of a solution of accurately known specific conductance, such as potassium chloride solutions.

A further definition of electrolytic conductance is *molar conductance*, Λ. This is the product of the specific conductance and the volume in m³ containing 1 gram mole of electrolyte, and hence

$$\Lambda = \kappa V, \tag{5.31}$$

where V (the *dilution*) is the volume in m³ containing 1 gram mole of electrolyte. It follows therefore that

$$\Lambda = \kappa/c \tag{5.32}$$

where c is the electrolyte concentration in gram mole per m³. In SI units the specific conductance should refer to electrode areas of 1 m² and a distance of 1 m apart and hence have dimensions of ohm^{-1} m^{-1}. Similarly, eqs. (5.31) and (5.32) should refer to volumes of 1 m³ and hence molar conductance should have the dimensions of ohm^{-1} m² mol^{-1}.

The molar conductances of strong electrolytes change only slowly at low concentrations, which is in marked contrast to the values for weak electrolytes. This is shown schematically in Fig. 5.5. For strong electrolytes a limiting value of molar conductance is obtained at low concentrations (high dilution) of electrolyte, and this is designated Λ_0. Theoretically, Λ_0 may be interpreted as the conductance of 1 gram mole of electrolyte when it is completely dissociated and when the ions are so far apart as to have no influence on each other. A graph of Λ against $\sqrt{c}$ should be linear, and from such a graph Λ_0 values for strong electrolytes may be obtained by extrapolation of the graph to zero concentration. For weak electrolytes, a non-linear plot is obtained, and Λ_0 has to be obtained by an indirect method using Kohlrausch's *law of independent migration of ions*. This law demonstrates that Λ_0 is made up of specific contributions from each ion present, so that for an electrolyte MA one can write

$$\Lambda_{0_{MA}} = \lambda_{0_{M^+}} + \lambda_{0_{A^-}}$$

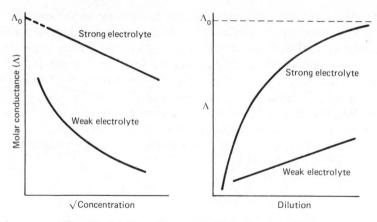

Fig. 5.5 Molar conductance of electrolyte solutions

where $\lambda_{0_M}{}^+$ and $\lambda_{0_A}{}^-$ are termed *limiting ion conductances* of the cation and anion respectively. From collections of limiting ion conductances values of Λ_0 for most weak electrolytes may be calculated.

There are a great many applications of conductance measurements in chemistry. These include the following.

(a) The determination of the solubility of sparingly soluble salts.
(b) The determination of the basicity of an acid.
(c) The investigation of the nature of complex ions in solution.
(d) As a means of following the rates of some ionic reactions.
(e) The determination of the extent of salt hydrolysis in solution and hence the calculation of the hydrolysis constant.
(f) The determination of the degree of dissociation and hence the dissociation constant of weak electrolytes in solution. The degree of dissociation, α, is approximately given by Λ/Λ_0.

A very important application of electrolytic conductance is the *Coulter counter*. This is an electronic particle counter which may be used to count numbers of erythrocytes, leukocytes and platelets. Any physiological investigation which involves the counting of cells may use this or related instruments. Not only can cells be counted but also the particle concentration in any suspension can be determined.

Figure 5.6 shows a schematic representation of a Coulter counter. The suspension of the material in a supporting electrolyte is drawn through a fine aperture, on either side of which is an electrode. The particle concentration of the suspension is previously adjusted so that the particles pass through the aperture more or less singly.

As a particle passes through the aperture it effectively displaces electrolyte

159

within the aperture and causes a transient decrease in the electrical conductivity between the electrodes. This produces a voltage impulse which is proportional to the volume of electrolyte displaced or the size of the particle. The voltage impulses are amplified and fed to a size-discriminating circuit, which accepts only signals within a predetermined size range. These signals are counted and digitally recorded and also displayed on an oscilloscope. Thus only particles within a certain size range are counted. A complete spectrum of particle sizes in a sample may be obtained by successive counts on the same sample by using apertures of different sizes and an appropriate setting of the threshold circuit.

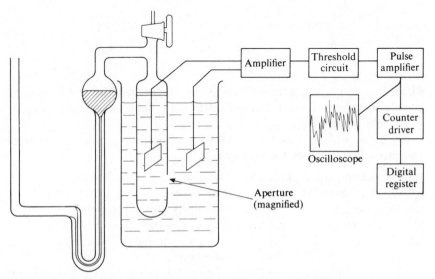

Fig. 5.6 Schematic representation of a Coulter counter

In addition to counting of cells, the Coulter counter may be used to count particles in emulsions, pigments, powders and fibres. These may include abrasives, ceramic materials, air pollutants, paints and inks.

Certain models of Coulter counter simultaneously measure the white cells and the red cells. The equipment can be fitted with a small computing device which calculates the mean cell volume. From the red cell count and the mean cell volume, the computer calculates the haematocrit without the need for centrifugation. Also included in the instrument is a haemoglobinometer. All of this information may be obtained from a 1-ml sample of whole blood in a very short time and printed onto a data card.

Blood platelets may be successfully counted with a Coulter counter or similar instrument. The platelet count is of great importance in treatment of *thrombocytopaenia* (platelet depletion), and in connection with platelet

160

adhesiveness associated with thromboembolism and during anti-coagulant therapy.

Conductimetric titrations

As we have seen, the electrical conductance of an electrolyte solution varies with the concentration of dissolved electrolyte. This fact may be utilized in quantitative analysis, either by using the conductance as a direct measure of the quantity of electrolyte present, or by using the conductimetric method as a means of detecting the end-point in a normal titration. The latter technique is referred to as a *conductimetric titration*.

Conductimetric titrations are especially useful in analyses of samples where it would be impossible to use the normal indicator reagents to detect the end-point. This would be the case if the sample were contaminated with some highly coloured material which would mask the colour change of the indicator. The conductance is measured after incremental volumes of titrant are added, and the readings continued until well after the end-point. The conductance readings are then plotted against the cumulative volume of titrant and the end-point in the titration obtained from the graph. A great many titrations may be carried out in this way. Figures 5.7(a), (b), (c) illustrate the types of graph obtained for some familiar titrations.

After the end-point there is nearly always a dramatic change in the conductance. In the case of acid–base titrations, this is due to the high mobility of hydrogen ions and hydroxyl ions, which gives them high ionic conductances. At the end-point in an acid–base titration the concentrations of these two ions

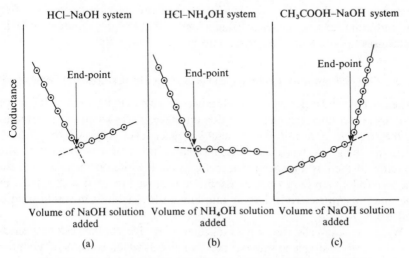

Fig. 5.7   Conductance changes during some simple acid–base tritrations

161

are at a minimum. After the end-point, when more titrant is added, the excess hydrogen ion or hydroxyl ion, whichever is being added, causes the conductance to change markedly.

In the titration of HCl with NaOH solution the reaction may be written as

$$H^+ + Cl^- \xrightarrow{\text{NaOH}} Na^+ + Cl^- + H_2O$$

Thus the highly mobile H^+ ion is being replaced by the less mobile and hence less conducting Na^+ ion, and the conductance of the solution falls [Fig. 5.7(a)]. After the end-point, excess NaOH is being added and since the hydroxyl ion is highly conducting the conductance of the solution rises. The end-point of the titration thus corresponds to a minimum in the graph.

Similar behaviour may be observed in the HCl–NH$_4$OH titration. The reaction may be written as

$$H^+ + Cl^- \xrightarrow{\text{NH}_4\text{OH}} NH_4^+ + Cl^- + H_2O$$

In this reaction, the highly conducting H^+ ion is being replaced by the less conducting NH_4^+ ion, and the conductance of the solution falls [Fig. 5.7(b)]. After the end-point, the additional ammonium hydroxide added does not change the conductance of the solution very much, since it is a weak electrolyte and does not provide many ions in solution.

The titration of acetic acid (a weak electrolyte) with NaOH may be represented by

$$CH_3COOH \xrightarrow{\text{NaOH}} Na^+ + CH_3COO^- + H_2O$$

Thus, the titration is accompanied by the production of sodium ions and acetate ions, and therefore the conductance of the solution increases. After the end-point, excess NaOH is being added and the highly conducting OH^- ion causes the conductance to rise more sharply [Fig. 5.7(c)].

5.4.4 Electrode potential, electrodes, and potentiometric measurements including pH

Whenever a metal is placed into a solution of its own ions, a potential difference (voltage) is set up at the metal–solution interface. This potential is referred to as the *electrode potential*. If the metal has a tendency to pass into solution, then the metal electrode assumes a negative polarity with respect to the solution. If there is a tendency for metal to be deposited from solution onto the electrode, then the electrode assumes a positive potential with respect to the solution. An electrode dipping into ions with which it is in equilibrium is called a *half-cell*.

When two half-cells are coupled together, they give a voltaic cell or *electrochemical cell*. A simple example is the *Daniell* cell which consists of a copper electrode dipping into a solution of copper sulphate, and a zinc electrode dipping into zinc sulphate. The two half-cells are separated from each other by a porous-pot membrane, which prevents physical mixing of the two electrolyte solutions. It is common to represent such a cell as:

$$\text{Zn} \, | \, \text{Zn}^{2+} \text{ solution} \, | \, \text{Cu}^{2+} \text{ solution} \, | \, \text{Cu}$$
$$\text{(a)} \qquad\qquad \text{(b)} \qquad\qquad \text{(c)}$$

where the vertical lines (a), (b), and (c) represent phase boundaries. At the junction of the two electrolyte solutions at the porous-pot membrane (b) there is often a small potential which arises from differences in activities and hence chemical potentials of electrolyte each side of the membrane. This potential is called the *liquid-junction potential*, and is always present even though it may only be very small. If the two half-cells are joined together in the external circuit by an electrical conductor, the cell has an electromotive force (emf) which is the difference in the potentials at (a), (b), and (c).

When the cell is producing an emf in this way, there are chemical reactions taking place within the cell, and the conversion of chemical energy into electrical energy is taking place. At the zinc electrode, the reaction is that of *oxidation*, and involves the removal of electrons from the metal to give zinc ions:

$$\text{Zn} \rightarrow \text{Zn}^{2+} + 2e^- \quad \text{Electrode potential} = E_{\text{ox}}$$

At the copper electrode, *reduction* takes place (addition of electrons) and copper is deposited:

$$2e^- + \text{Cu}^{2+} \rightarrow \text{Cu} \quad \text{Electrode potential} = E_{\text{red}}$$

Thus the overall cell reaction is

$$\text{Zn} + \text{Cu}^{2+} \rightarrow \text{Zn}^{2+} + \text{Cu}$$

For a given electrode $E_{\text{ox}} = -E_{\text{red}}$. If the electrode reaction is spontaneous in the direction written then the value of the electrode potential is positive. In the Daniell cell, oxidation of zinc to zinc ions is spontaneous and thus E_{ox} is positive and E_{red} is negative. On the other hand, the reduction of copper ions to copper is the spontaneous reaction also, and hence E_{red} for copper is positive and E_{ox} is negative. In the absence of a liquid junction potential, the emf of the cell is given by

$$E \quad = \quad E_{\text{red}} \quad + \quad E_{\text{ox}} \qquad\qquad (5.33)$$
$$\text{(emf of the} \quad \text{(right-hand} \quad \text{(left-hand}$$
$$\text{cell)} \qquad \text{electrode)} \qquad \text{electrode)}$$

Standard electrode potentials

It is not possible to measure directly single electrode potentials, only the emf of a cell containing two electrodes. In order to ascribe single electrode potentials, it is necessary to give a zero value of potential to one electrode and then measure all other electrode potentials relative to this one electrode by measuring the emf of a suitable cell containing this electrode. The electrode chosen for this purpose is the *hydrogen electrode*, which is assumed to have zero electrode potential when hydrogen gas at 1 atm pressure ($101\cdot3$ kN m^{-2}) is bubbled over a platinized platinum electrode dipping in a solution of hydrogen ions at unit activity at 25°C.

The recommended convention for quoting standard electrode potentials is that defined by the International Union of Pure and Applied Chemistry (IUPAC) and is sometimes referred to as the European convention. Electrode potentials are always quoted as *reduction potentials*. Thus the electrode potential of zinc is negative and that of copper is positive.

Table 5.3(a) contains a selection of half-cell reactions and the corresponding standard electrode potentials.

Table 5.3 (a)   Standard electrode potentials

$E^{\ominus}$ (V)	Half-cell reaction	$E^{\ominus}$ (V)	Half-cell reaction
$1\cdot77$	$H_2O_2 + 2H^+ + 2e^- = 2H_2O$	$0\cdot00$	$2H^+ + 2e^- = H_2$
$1\cdot70$	$MnO_4^- + 4H^+ + 3e^- = MnO_2 + 2H_2O$	$-0\cdot13$	$Pb^{2+} + 2e^- = Pb$
$1\cdot51$	$MnO_4^- + 8H^+ + 5e^- = Mn^{2+} + 4H_2O$	$-0\cdot44$	$Fe^{2+} + 2e^- = Fe$
$1\cdot33$	$Cr_2O_7^{2-} + 14H^+ + 6e^- = 2Cr^{3+} + 7H_2O$	$-0\cdot76$	$Zn^{2+} + 2e^- = Zn$
$1\cdot23$	$O_2 + 4H^+ + 4e^- = 2H_2O$	$-1\cdot66$	$Al^{3+} + 3e^- = Al$
$0\cdot80$	$Ag^+ + e^- = Ag$	$-2\cdot37$	$Mg^{2+} + 2e^- = Mg$
$0\cdot77$	$Fe^{3+} + e^- = Fe^{2+}$	$-2\cdot71$	$Na^+ + e^- = Na$
$0\cdot68$	$O_2 + 2H^+ + 2e^- = H_2O_2$		
$0\cdot60$	$MnO_4^- + 2H_2O + 2e^- = MnO_2 + 4OH^-$		
$0\cdot38$	$Cu^{2+} + 2e^- = Cu$		
$0\cdot22$	$AgCl + e^- = Ag + Cl^-$		
$0\cdot15$	$Cu^{2+} + e^- = Cu^+$		

Oxidation–reduction reactions which involve hydrogen ions or hydroxyl ions have electrode potentials which vary with pH. For such reactions, it is customary to quote the standard electrode potential at pH 7 rather than at unit activity of hydrogen ion, and the values are designated as $E_7^{\ominus\prime}$ (often called *formal potentials*). These values at pH 7 are of much more significance in biochemical systems where conditions corresponding to unit activity of hydrogen ions are rarely encountered. Some values of standard electrode potentials at pH 7 are given in Table 5.3(b).

Table 5.3 (b) Standard electrode potentials at pH 7 ($E_7^{\ominus\prime}$) of some biochemical reactions

Reaction	$E_7^{\ominus\prime}$ (V)
$O_2 + 4H^+ + 4e^- = 2H_2O$	0·82
$NO_3^- + 2H^+ + 2e^- = NO_2^- + H_2O$	0·42
$O_2 + 2H^+ + 2e^- = H_2O_2$	0·30
Cytochrome a; ferric/ferrous	0·29
Cytochrome c_1; ferric/ferrous	0·22
Cytochrome b; ferric/ferrous	0·04
Fumaric acid + $2H^+$ + $2e^-$ = succinic acid	0·03
Pyruvate/lactate	−0·19
Acetoacetate/β-hydroxybutyrate	−0·27
$NAD^+/NADH$	−0·32
Uric acid/xanthine	−0·36
$2H^+ + 2e^- = H_2$	−0·42
Acetate + CO_2/pyruvate	−0·70

The importance of standard electrode potentials lies in the fact that they are simply related to the standard free-energy change ($\Delta G^{\ominus}$) for the reaction by the equation

$$\Delta G^{\ominus} = -nFE^{\ominus}$$

or

$$\Delta G_7^{\ominus\prime} = -nFE_7^{\ominus\prime} \qquad (5.34)$$

where n is the number of electrons involved in the reaction, and F is the *Faraday* (96 487 coulomb mole^{-1}). The values of standard electrode potential are thus some measure of the spontaneity or driving force of a reaction *under the standard conditions*. They are also of importance because of the relationship of $\Delta G^{\ominus}$ with the equilibrium constant K_c in the Van't Hoff isotherm (section 3.5).

The equation for the emf of a cell

The emf of a cell depends upon the nature of the reaction in the cell, the activities of the reactants and products and the temperature. If the cell reaction is of the form

$$a\text{A} + b\text{B} = c\text{C} + d\text{D},$$

the cell emf is given by the expression

$$E = E^{\ominus} + \frac{RT}{nF} \ln\left(\frac{a_A^a \, a_B^b}{a_C^c \, a_D^d}\right) \qquad (5.35)$$

165

$E^\ominus$ in this case is the *standard emf of the cell* when all the reactants and products are at *unit activity*. This is a very important equation in electrochemistry and is known as the *Nernst* equation.

The electrode potential of individual electrodes may be represented by an equation analogous to the Nernst equation,

$$E = E^\ominus + \frac{RT}{nF} \ln \left(\frac{[\text{oxidized reagent}]}{[\text{reduced reagent}]} \right) \tag{5.36}$$

where $E^\ominus$ is the standard electrode potential. If the electrode reaction is of the form

$$M^{n+} + ne^- = M$$

then eq. (5.36) becomes

$$E = E^\ominus + \frac{RT}{nF} \ln \left(\frac{a_{M^{n+}}}{a_M} \right) \tag{5.37}$$

The activity of the metal electrode a_M may be regarded as unity, and thus the electrode potential is related to the activity of metal ions in solution:

$$E = E^\ominus + \frac{RT}{nF} \ln a_{M^{n+}} \tag{5.38}$$

In dilute solutions, the ionic activity approaches their concentrations.

Types of electrodes

(a) Metal–metal ion electrodes This type of electrode has been discussed above; the metal of the electrode takes part in the half-cell reaction.

(b) Metal–insoluble salt electrodes These electrodes consist of a metal in contact with a layer of a sparingly soluble salt of the metal which is in turn in contact with a solution containing anions which are common to the salt. The *calomel electrode* is of this type and may be represented as

$$Hg|Hg_2Cl_2 \text{ (solid), } Cl^-$$

The calomel electrode is a very useful standard electrode and is often used as an alternative to the standard hydrogen electrode. The electrode reaction is

$$Hg_2Cl_2 + 2e^- = 2Hg + 2Cl^-$$

It is common practice to use saturated potassium chloride in the electrode when it is being used as a standard electrode. The electrode then has a potential of $0.2444 - 0.0025 \, (t - 25)$ V where t is the temperature in °C.

Silver–silver halide electrodes also belong to this class of electrode, for example the silver–silver chloride electrode, $Ag|AgCl,Cl^-$, the electrode reaction of which is

$$AgCl + e^- = Ag + Cl^-$$

Like the calomel electrode, the silver–silver chloride electrode can be used as a standard electrode, and is often used as such in conjunction with glass electrodes in the measurement of pH. The electrode may also be used in biological systems as a microelectrode in the measurement of injury potential of muscle and also membrane potential. It is also used to measure electrical activity in the brain (electro-encephalography).

(c) Gas electrodes These electrodes consist of a solution which is saturated with the gas concerned as it is bubbled over the surface of an inert metal electrode inserted in the solution. The most common example is the *hydrogen electrode*, in which hydrogen is bubbled over the surface of a platinized platinum electrode, which is inserted in a solution containing hydrogen ions. The platinized surface catalyses the reaction

$$H_2 + 2e^- = 2H^+$$

The electrode is represented as $Pt, H_2/H^+$.

The *oxygen electrode* is another example of this type, and has been used in the analysis by potentiometric titration of alkaloids such as quinine, cocaine, cinchonidine and strychnine. It is also used to measure oxygen concentrations in solutions [section 5.4.6(b)].

(d) The glass electrode and measurement of pH Of all the potentiometric measurements made in chemical laboratories, by far the most common is the measurement of hydrogen-ion activity using a *glass electrode* by means of a commercial pH meter. The glass electrode consists of a silver–silver chloride electrode immersed in 0·1 M HCl inside a glass bulb. The glass bulb is placed in the solution being measured. The bulb is extremely thin, and is made from specially conducting glass which develops a potential due to differences in hydrogen ion activity on the inside and the outside surfaces. As the hydrogen ion concentration changes in the external solution, so the accompanying change in potential on the outside surface of the bulb is transmitted to the inside surface, which in turn is transmitted to the internal silver–silver chloride electrode.

In order to measure pH, the glass electrode is coupled with a standard electrode, such as a calomel electrode or another silver–silver chloride electrode, to form a cell such as the one illustrated.

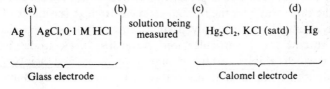

167

At the junctions (a), (b), (c) and (d), there exist potentials which contribute to the measured value of the cell emf, E. This may be expressed in the equation

$$E = E_g + 0\cdot0591 \text{ pH} \tag{5.39}$$

where E_g includes the potentials of the standard electrodes in the cell and also includes contributions to what are called *asymmetry potentials*, which arise from strains within the glass of the glass bulb. For a particular electrode, E_g is a constant, but it is not perfectly reproducible from one electrode to another. Thus, in order to measure pH with a given glass electrode, the cell being used has to be initially calibrated with a solution of known pH. Thus, pH is a *measured* function in physical chemistry and *not* a calculated function as originally defined by *Sørensen*, i.e., pH does *not* equal $-\log_{10}[\text{H}^+]$, although in some solutions it may be fairly close to this.

The British scale of pH is defined in British Standard Specification BSS 1647 (1950), for which a $0\cdot05$ M solution of potassium hydrogen phthalate at $25°\text{C}$ is defined as having a pH of $4\cdot00$. It is perhaps worth noting that the American scale of pH as specified by the National Bureau of Standards is marginally different from the British standard.

Glass electrodes can be used to measure the pH of a great variety of systems. In addition to ordinary chemical solutions, the pH of biological systems, suspensions, and semi-solids such as butter, cheese, and soil may be measured. Glass electrodes can be obtained for the measurement of the pH of surfaces such as damp paper, skin, and leather, and also for the measurement of pH in the stomach. Microelectrodes are also available for the measurement of blood plasma pH so that only small sample volumes of the order of $0\cdot02$ ml are needed. Using glass electrodes of a few microns in diameter, it is possible to measure intracellular pH, for example skeletal muscle pH in crabs, frogs, and rats.

The electrodes that make up the cell are connected to a pH meter, which is basically an electronic potentiometer. Due to the high electrical resistance of glass, the current from the cell is very small, even though its voltage may be appreciable. The galvanometer of the pH meter makes use of the cell current to indicate the measurement and therefore the cell current has to be amplified. Commercial pH meters therefore contain direct-current amplification circuits for this purpose.

(e) Specific ion electrodes A recent development in chemical potentio-metry has been the attempt to produce electrodes which are specific for given ions in the same way that the normal glass electrode is specific for hydrogen ion. The attempt has been only partially successful, since no electrode is entirely specific for a particular ion. Nevertheless, electrodes have been developed which exhibit a certain amount of specificity, and their performance will no doubt be improved considerably in the near future. Many of these

electrodes are available commercially, and provided that the limits of specificity are not exceeded, then they can be used to perform useful analyses, often using a conventional pH meter.

The various specific ion electrodes may be classified as follows:

(*i*) *Solid-state electrodes* In this type, the membrane of the electrode usually consists of a single crystal or a compressed disc of composite material which is sealed into the bottom of a tube. Inside the tube are the internal reference electrode and the internal reference solution analogous to the glass electrode system. Electrodes can be made which are specific to the following ions: F^-, Cl^-, Br^-, I^-, S^{2-}, Ag^+, Cu^{2+}, Pb^{2+}, Cd^{2+}, CN^-.

(*ii*) *Heterogeneous membrane electrodes* Here, the active material which develops the potential is dispersed in an inert matrix which can be silicone rubber, polyvinyl chloride, polystyrene or polyethylene. Examples of this type of electrode are those for the measurement of Cl^-, Br^-, I^-, S^{2-}, Ag^+.

(*iii*) *Liquid ion-exchange membrane electrodes* In these electrodes, the ion to be measured is attached to a large organic molecule which is sparingly soluble in water, and acts as an ion-exchange system. It is usual to separate the liquid ion-exchange material from the solution to be measured by a thin sheet of 'cellophane' or cellulose acetate. The potential is then generated at this membrane surface.

Examples of this type of electrode include those for the measurement of Cl^-, ClO_4^-, NO_3^-, Ca^{2+}, Ca^{2+}/Mg^{2+}, Cu^{2+}, Pb^{2+}, BF_4^-. The calcium ion electrode based on this principle is of some importance and has been used for the measurement of calcium ion in hard water, sea water, serum, plasma and cerebro-spinal fluids. It is not of great use in living systems because of its size, but it is of interest as a possible means of distinguishing between bound calcium and ionic calcium in biological fluids.

(*iv*) *Cation sensitive glass electrodes* These electrodes are similar to the normal glass electrode for pH measurement, but the glass is of special composition. They are limited to the univalent cations Na^+, K^+, Ag^+, Li^+, NH_4^+. They will selectively detect the presence of one of these cations provided that hydrogen ion and other interfering cations are present only in small amounts. Their chemical uses include the detection of salinity in river waters, the detection of impurities in pharmaceuticals, and the control of water treatment. Their biological and clinical uses include the study of cation balance in soil, and measurements of electrolyte balance in serum, urine, and kidney extracts.

5.4.5 Redox electrodes and redox reactions

Redox electrodes consist of an inert metal (usually bright platinum) placed in a solution containing a dissolved substance which is present in its *oxidized form and its reduced form in equilibrium with each other*. This equilibrium may

169

be displaced either way by the supply or withdrawal of electrons at the surface of the inert metal electrode.

A simple example of this class of electrode is the ferric–ferrous redox electrode, $(Pt)|Fe^{3+}, Fe^{2+}$. The electrode potential is given by the Nernst equation,

$$E = E^{\ominus} + \frac{RT}{F} \ln \left(\frac{a_{Fe^{3+}}}{a_{Fe^{2+}}} \right) \tag{5.40}$$

or in dilute solutions

$$E = E^{\ominus} + \frac{RT}{F} \ln \left(\frac{[Fe^{3+}]}{[Fe^{2+}]} \right) \tag{5.41}$$

where the activity terms may be replaced by the concentration terms represented by square brackets.

The values of reduction potential for various systems permit a quantitative treatment of redox reactions to be made. In general, the oxidized form of a redox couple oxidizes the reduced form of another couple if the reduction potential of the first couple is more positive.

Since the standard free-energy change of a reaction occurring in a cell is related to the standard potential of the cell, it is often possible to calculate values of $\Delta G^{\ominus}$ from tables of standard reduction potentials, and hence calculate the position of equilibrium in the cell reaction. This also gives some indication of the spontaneity of the reaction under standard conditions. As mentioned in section 3.5, this is only semiquantitative, as the conditions in biochemical reactions rarely correspond to those of the standard conditions of unit activity of reactants and products. A simple example is the biochemical redox reaction of the conversion of β-hydroxybutyrate ion to acetoacetate ion (with oxygen as the eventual oxidant). At pH 7 the reaction may be treated as

$$CH_3\overset{\overset{O}{\|}}{C}CH_2CO_2^- + 2H^+ + 2e^- = CH_3CH(OH)CH_2CO_2^-, \quad E_7^{\ominus\prime} = -0.27 \text{ V,}$$

and

$$\tfrac{1}{2}O_2 + 2H^+ + 2e^- = H_2O, \quad E_7^{\ominus\prime} = 0.815 \text{ V}$$

so that for the oxidation reaction

$$CH_3CH(OH)CH_2CO_2^- + \tfrac{1}{2}O_2 = CH_3\overset{\overset{O}{\|}}{C}CH_2CO_2^- + H_2O$$

the cell potential would be $0.815 - (-0.27)$ V $= 1.085$ V. Thus the value of $\Delta G_7^{\ominus}$ ($= -nFE_7^{\ominus\prime}$) is $-2 \times 23\,000 \times 1.085$ cal mole^{-1} or -49.94 kcal mole^{-1} (-208.9 kJ mole^{-1}), indicating how favourable the oxidation process is.

Some chemical systems can undergo reduction or oxidation in a series of steps. This means that the product of the first step becomes a reactant in the second step and hence the reactions appear as *coupled reactions*. Many coupled reactions occur in the metabolic processes of living organisms. The primary source of energy in living organisms is the oxidation of foodstuffs by molecular oxygen to give ultimately carbon dioxide and water. This is always achieved by means of stepwise oxidation reactions which are coupled together. The reason for this is that the complete oxidation of 1 gram mole of glucose would release 2871 kJ (686 kcal) of energy. No living organism could survive the liberation of so much energy in one step. It is by means of a long sequence of coupled reactions that the organism can harness this amount of energy, by allowing it to be released in small quantities at each step in the particular metabolic process.

An example of such a process is the *respiratory chain* of the mitochondrion The overall reaction is the oxidation of nicotinamide adenine dinucleotide (NADH) which, if it occurred in one step with molecular oxygen, would release $219 \cdot 5$ kJ mole^{-1} ($52 \cdot 4$ kcal mole^{-1}) of energy, which would result in the

Table 5.4   The respiratory chain

Reaction	$E_7^{\ominus'}$ (V)	$\Delta G_7^{\ominus'}$, 25°C (kJ mole^{-1})	(kcal mole^{-1})
(1) NADH + H$^+$ + FAD = NAD$^+$ + FADH$_2$ $-0 \cdot 32$ V $\qquad\qquad\qquad\quad$ $-0 \cdot 05$ V	$0 \cdot 27$	$-51 \cdot 8$	$-12 \cdot 4$
(2) FADH$_2$ + oxidized ubiquinone = FAD + reduced ubiquinone $-0 \cdot 05$ V $\qquad\qquad\qquad\qquad\qquad$ $0 \cdot 10$ V	$0 \cdot 15$	$-28 \cdot 8$	$-6 \cdot 9$
(3) Reduced ubiquinone + 2Cyt b_{ox} = oxidized ubiquinone + 2Cyt b_{red} + 2H$^+$ $0 \cdot 10$ V $\qquad\qquad\qquad\qquad\qquad\qquad$ $0 \cdot 04$ V	$-0 \cdot 06$	$+11 \cdot 7$	$+2 \cdot 8$
(4) 2Cyt b_{red} + 2Cyt $c_{1, ox}$ = 2Cyt b_{ox} + 2Cyt $c_{1, red}$ $0 \cdot 04$ V $\qquad\qquad\qquad\qquad$ $0 \cdot 22$ V	$0 \cdot 18$	$-34 \cdot 7$	$-8 \cdot 3$
(5) 2Cyt $c_{1, red}$ + 2Cyt a_{ox} = 2Cyt $c_{1, ox}$ + 2Cyt a_{red} $0 \cdot 22$ V $\qquad\qquad\qquad\qquad$ $0 \cdot 29$ V	$0 \cdot 07$	$-13 \cdot 4$	$-3 \cdot 2$
(6) 2Cyt a_{red} + $\frac{1}{2}$O$_2$ + 2H$^+$ = 2Cyt a_{ox} + H$_2$O $0 \cdot 29$ V $\qquad\qquad\qquad\qquad$ $0 \cdot 82$ V	$0 \cdot 53$	$-102 \cdot 2$	$-24 \cdot 4$
Overall reaction is: $\frac{1}{2}$O$_2$ + NADH + H$^+$ = NAD$^+$ + H$_2$O	$1 \cdot 14$	$-219 \cdot 2$	$-52 \cdot 4$

Cyt a = cytochrome a; Cyt b = cytochrome b; Cyt c_1 = cytochrome c_1. FAD represents the FAD moiety in flavoprotein. Processes (1), (4) and (6) release sufficient free energy for the synthesis of ATP from ADP.

destruction of the living organism. By means of the series of reactions in the respiratory chain, this large amount of energy is released in smaller packets (see section 9.2.7). Table 5.4 gives the reactions involved with the cell potentials at pH 7 for each step, and the corresponding changes in standard free energy. The half-cell potentials are presented beneath the reduced form of the particular compound.

5.4.6 Electroanalytical techniques

(a) Potentiometric titration In this technique, the changes in concentration of the reactant during the course of a titration are followed by measuring the changes in potential of a suitable electrode. Thus acid–base titrations may be followed potentiometrically by means of a glass electrode. If incremental volumes of titrant are added and the pH of the solution measured after each addition, one obtains the characteristic titration curves shown in Fig. 5.8.

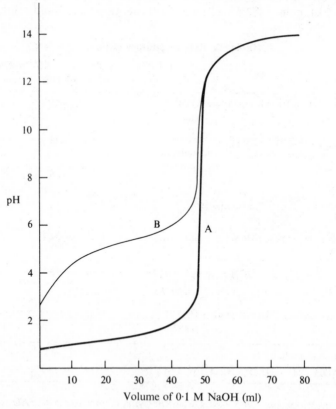

Fig. 5.8   pH titration curves of 50 ml each of 0·1 M HCl (curve A) and acetic acid (curve B) with 0·1 M NaOH

172

Many other potentiometric titrations are possible. For example, the titration of silver nitrate with sodium chloride may be followed potentiometrically using a silver electrode or silver–silver chloride electrode and using a calomel electrode as a reference electrode. Similarly, redox titrations in chemical and biological systems may be followed potentiometrically using suitable electrodes.

(b) Polarography If a constant potential is applied to two inert polarizable electrodes dipping into a solution of an electrolyte, then, if electrolysis occurs, the current decreases logarithmically with time. If, however, one of the electrodes is a micro-electrode in which the electrode surface is continually renewed, then the measured current during electrolysis will depend *not* on the

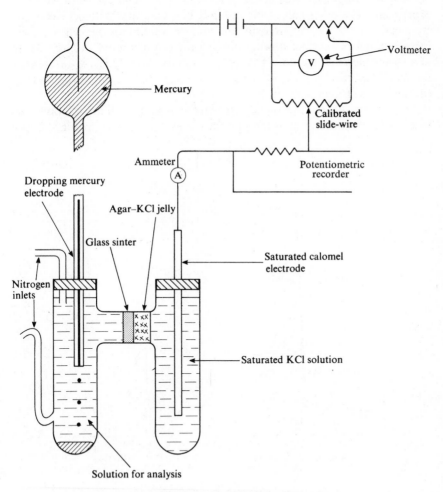

Fig. 5.9 A simple polarograph

173

applied voltage to the cell but on the *rate of diffusion* of reacting substance to the electrode, and hence on its concentration. The current under these circumstances can then be used as a direct measure of electrolyte which is undergoing electrolysis. The most commonly used micro-electrode is the dropping-mercury electrode (d.m.e.). The study of the current–voltage relationships with such an arrangement is called *polarography*. The complete current–voltage curve is referred to as a *polarogram*.

A simple arrangement for the study of polarography is shown in Fig. 5.9. Small droplets of mercury (which act as the cathode) issue from a capillary tube (about 0·08 mm internal diameter) and fall through the solution being analysed. Prior to the experiment, nitrogen is blown through the solution to be analysed to remove dissolved oxygen, which would interfere with the experiment. The other half of the cell may be a saturated calomel electrode. By means of the electrical circuit, the voltage applied to the cell is slowly increased and the current flowing through the cell measured. A large excess of a strong electrolyte is added to the solution to be analysed, to ensure that the very small current is due to diffusion of ions to the mercury droplets only (the diffusion current is about 10^{-4} to 10^{-8} A).

At a certain value of the applied voltage the metal ions in the solution start to be reduced, and the diffusion current increases as shown in Fig. 5.10(a).

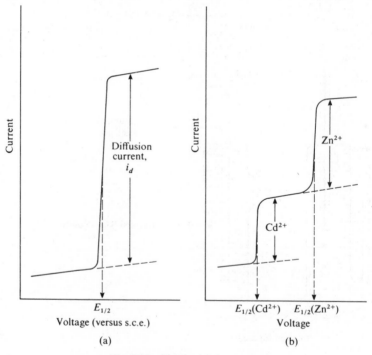

Fig. 5.10 Idealized polarograms

174

The optimum range of concentration of the metal ion being analysed is in the region 10^{-3} to 10^{-5} M. The steps in polarograms as illustrated in Fig. 5.10(b) are often called *polarographic waves*. The value of the applied potential at the steepest point of the polarographic wave is called the *half-wave potential* and its value is characteristic of the reducible substance. Each value of the diffusion current, i_d, for each reducible substance present, is proportional to its concentration in the solution. Thus calibration graphs may be drawn from polarograms of solutions of *known* composition using the values of the diffusion current. Then, using the diffusion current obtained from the polarogram of the solution being analysed, the concentration of reducible substance may be interpolated from the calibration graph previously prepared. The method is not restricted to inorganic cations, but is applicable also to organic compounds, for example carbonyl compounds.

A great many developments have been made in the instrumentation for polarography, all of which have extended the range of application of the technique to more and more dilute solutions. Notable among these is *cathode-ray polarography*. In this method, the whole polarogram is produced in the lifetime of a single drop of mercury from the d.m.e. The voltage sweep is rapidly applied when the formation of the drop is almost complete, and the current–voltage relationship is displayed on the screen of a cathode-ray tube. Even higher sensitivity can be achieved by the method of *differential* cathode-ray polarography, where two cells are used in parallel. One of these cells contains the material to be analysed plus the supporting electrolyte, while the other cell contains only the supporting electrolyte. In this way, effects due to the presence of slight amounts of impurities are eliminated and the limit of measurement of reducible substance is extended to 10^{-7} to 10^{-8} M. Polarography is therefore ideally suited to the analysis of minute quantities of inorganic and organic substances. For inorganic compounds, using cathode-ray polarography, the technique is comparable in sensitivity and in its limit of detection with atomic absorption spectroscopy (chapter 6).

There are a great many analytical applications of polarography. These include the analysis of food and beverages, drugs and antibiotics, and animal and poultry feeds. Lead, manganese, aluminium, copper and cadmium have all been determined in blood and urine. Also, in the physiological field, amino acids containing thiol and disulphide linkages have been determined. The measurement of nitro-imidazoles in tissues has been carried out and also the amounts of coproporphyrin and related compounds in urine have been measured using polarography.

Polarography is not restricted to the use of a d.m.e. The oxygen electrode may be used as a polarographic-type electrode and is extensively used in this way in biological applications. It is especially useful for following the rate of uptake of oxygen by cells and tissue homogenates and also enzyme-catalysed redox reactions. As the reaction proceeds, the dissolved oxygen concentration

175

is changing and its concentration is monitored by measurement of the diffusion current produced by its reduction at the cathode.

An electrode commonly used for such measurements is the Clark oxygen electrode. This usually takes the form of a cell made up from a standard reference electrode such as a silver–silver chloride electrode or calomel electrode and an inert electrode, such as platinum or gold electrode, at which the dissolved oxygen is reduced (i.e., the cathode). If a slowly increasing voltage is applied to the cell, the current increases also until eventually a plateau of current is reached. Thus, above a certain voltage, the current remains steady over a voltage range of about 100 mV. The actual value of the current within this range is proportional to the rate of reduction of oxygen at the cathode, which is in turn proportional to the concentration of dissolved oxygen in the solution.

5.5 MEMBRANE PHENOMENA

5.5.1 Osmosis and osmotic pressure

If a solution is separated from a sample of pure solvent by a membrane which allows passage of solvent through it but not dissolved solute, then the solvent tends to diffuse through the membrane into the solution. A membrane which allows such a process to occur is termed a *semi-permeable membrane*, and the process is referred to as *osmosis*. To prevent the natural process of osmosis from taking place, it would be necessary to apply a pressure to the solution in order to oppose the diffusion of solvent through the membrane. The pressure required to do this is called the *osmotic pressure* of the solution. It corresponds to the pressure that must be exerted on the solution so that the chemical potential of the solvent has the same value on both sides of the semi-permeable membrane. Provided that the membrane is truly semi-permeable, then the osmotic pressure of a given solution is independent of the nature of the membrane.

If the membrane is permeable to some solutes as well as solvent molecules, then it is no longer truly semi-permeable and is referred to as a *leaky membrane* (or Donnan membrane). The osmotic pressure observed with a leaky membrane differs from that observed with a semi-permeable membrane and the ratio of the two values of osmotic pressure is called the *reflection coefficient*, σ, of the leaky membrane. The value of the reflection coefficient for a leaky membrane lies in the range zero to unity.

When two solutions have the same value of osmotic pressure they are said to be *isosmotic*. If one solution has a higher osmotic pressure than a second solution, it is said to be *hyperosmotic* to the second solution. If it has a lower osmotic pressure than the second solution, then it is said to be *hypo-osmotic* to the second solution.

If two solutions are separated by a membrane and no *net* flow of material occurs across the membrane, then the solutions are termed *isotonic*. Two solutions may be isotonic without being isosmotic. If red blood cells are placed in a hypotonic solution they swell and may burst (*haemolyse*). If, on the other hand, they are placed in a hypertonic solution, the cells shrink and assume an irregular shape due to the passage of solution out of the cell. A solution of 0·16 M sodium chloride (approximately 0·95 per cent) or a 0·3 M non-electrolyte solution is isotonic with red blood cells, and they neither shrink or swell. However, if the contents of the red cells were extracted and their osmotic pressure measured, it would be found to be different from the 0·16 M sodium chloride solution with which it was isotonic. The reason for this is that the red cell membrane is not a semi-permeable membrane.

In general it is found that

(a) the osmotic pressure of a solution at a given temperature is proportional to the concentration of dissolved solute, and
(b) the osmotic pressure of a solution of a given concentration is proportional to the absolute temperature.

Van't Hoff showed that for dilute solutions of non-electrolytes the osmotic pressure, Π, is given by

$$\Pi = kcT \qquad (5.42)$$

where k is a constant, c is the molar concentration of solute and T is the absolute temperature. This equation can also be written in the form

$$\Pi V = knT \qquad (5.43)$$

where n is the number of moles of solute in V litres of solution. The constant k can be identified with the gas constant R and hence

$$\Pi V = nRT \qquad (5.44)$$

which is analogous to the equation $PV = nRT$ for gases. Thus the osmotic pressure of a dilute solution should be the same as the pressure the solute would exert if it were a gas occupying the same volume V as the solution. One gram mole of non-electrolyte dissolved in 22·4 litres of solution would ideally have an osmotic pressure of 1 atm at 0°C.

Equation (5.44) is strictly only applicable to dilute solutions of non-electrolytes. For an electrolyte yielding i ions in solution, the equation should be

$$\Pi V = inRT \qquad (5.45)$$

For concentrated solutions, deviations from ideality occur and the osmotic pressure is more correctly given by

$$\Pi \bar{V}_s = -RT \ln a_s \qquad (5.46)$$

177

where $\bar{V}_s$ is the partial molar volume of the solute and a_s is its activity. The *osmolarity* of a solution is a function which may be used to measure the activity of the solvent and solute in a solution. It has been suggested that osmolarity may be used to measure the osmotic pressure of a solution. One osmol is the osmotic pressure of an ideal one molar solution of a non-electrolyte at $0°C$, in other words, equivalent to 22.4 atm. In actual practice it is far easier to measure osmolarity by an alternative technique to osmotic pressure. The one most commonly used is the *cryoscopic method* (section 5.4.2).

5.5.2 Donnan membrane phenomena

If the membrane separating two solutions is not truly semi-permeable, but is permeable to some solutes but not others then it is referred to as a *Donnan membrane*. Such a membrane gives rise to an unequal distribution of diffusible solutes on either side of it. The phenomenon may be illustrated in terms of an aqueous solution of sodium chloride and the sodium salt $Na^+ R^-$, where R^- is a large organic anion. The two solutions are separated by a membrane which is permeable to sodium ions, chloride ions and water, but not the anion R^-. If the initial concentrations are represented by

$$\begin{array}{cc|cc} Na^+ & R^- & Na^+ & Cl^- \\ c_2 & c_2 & c_1 & c_1 \end{array}$$

the final equilibrium condition depends upon several factors:

(a) Electroneutrality must be maintained, which means that equal quantities of sodium and chloride ions must diffuse through the membrane. If the volumes of both solutions are equal and x moles of sodium chloride diffuse from right to left, then the equilibrium situation may be represented by

$$\begin{array}{ccc|cc} Na^+ & R^- & Cl^- & Na^+ & Cl^- \\ (c_2 + x) & c_2 & x & (c_1 - x) & (c_1 - x) \end{array}$$

(b) The chemical potentials of sodium chloride must be the same at equilibrium on either side of the membrane. Since chemical potential is related to activity, the relation

$$\mu_{NaCl(1)} = \mu_{NaCl(2)}$$

gives

$$a_{Na^+(1)} \, a_{Cl^-(1)} = a_{Na^+(2)} \, a_{Cl^-(2)} \tag{5.47}$$

If the solutions may be regarded as approaching ideality, so that the activities may be replaced by concentrations, then

$$(c_2 + x)x = (c_1 - x)^2$$

which gives on rearrangement

$$\frac{x}{c_1} = \frac{c_1}{c_2 + 2c_1} \tag{5.48}$$

The ratio x/c_1 represents the amount of sodium chloride originally present on the right-hand side of the membrane, which has diffused through the membrane to the left-hand side. Table 5.5 illustrates some results based on

Table 5.5 Diffusion through an ideal Donnan membrane

Initial NaR molarity (c_2)	Initial NaCl molarity (c_1)	Initial ratio c_2/c_1	Percentage NaCl diffused $100\,(x_1/c_1)$
0·01	1·0	0·01	49·7
0·1	1·0	0·1	47·0
1·0	1·0	1·0	33·0
1·0	0·1	10·0	8·3
1·0	0·01	100·0	1·0

eq. (5.48). It can be seen from this simple calculation that the proportion of sodium chloride which diffuses through the membrane varies markedly with the initial ratio c_2/c_1.

(c) At equilibrium, the chemical potential of the solvent must also be equal on either side of the membrane. The total salt concentrations either side of the membrane are different at equilibrium, and thus the only way the solvent chemical potentials can be equalized is by a pressure difference either side of the membrane. This manifests itself as an osmotic pressure.

(d) When the solutions either side of the membrane are at equilibrium with respect to each other, the Gibbs free-energy change is zero, i.e., $\Delta G = 0$. When this is the case, the ionic chemical potentials (partial molar free energies) of the ions must be equal on both sides of the membrane. Thus,

$$\mu_{Na^+(1)} = \mu_{Na^+(2)}$$

and

$$\mu_{Cl^-(1)} = \mu_{Cl^-(2)}$$

179

The value of chemical potential of a given ion, i, in the presence of an electric potential is given by

$$\mu_i = \mu_i^{\ominus} + RT\ln a_i + nFE$$

where n is the valency of the ion, F is the Faraday and E is the electric potential. Thus with the above equations, one can easily obtain

$$RT\ln a_{Na^+(1)} + nFE_1 = RT\ln a_{Na^+(2)} + nFE_2$$

and

$$RT\ln a_{Cl^-(1)} + nFE_1 = RT\ln a_{Cl^-(2)} + nFE_2.$$

Since for sodium ion $n = +1$ and for chloride ion $n = -1$, the above equations yield

$$\Delta E = E_2 - E_1 = \frac{RT}{F}\ln\left(\frac{a_{Na^+(2)}}{a_{Na^+(1)}}\right)$$

and (5.49)

$$\Delta E = E_2 - E_1 = -\frac{RT}{F}\ln\left(\frac{a_{Cl^-(2)}}{a_{Cl^-(1)}}\right)$$

The potential difference (ΔE) across the membrane is termed the *Donnan membrane potential*. This potential is often used as a part explanation of cell-membrane potentials (section 5.5.3). If

$$a_{Na^+(2)} > a_{Na^+(1)} \quad \text{and} \quad a_{Cl^-(2)} < a_{Cl^-(1)}$$

then ΔE is positive, and in fact the side of the membrane which is away from the anion R^- is positive relative to the side which acts as a barrier to R^-.

The measurement of the Donnan membrane potential can be made using two identical reference electrodes in a cell arrangement such as

$$\text{Ag} \mid \text{AgCl, KCl} \mid \text{solution (2)} \mid\mid \text{solution (1)} \mid \text{KCl, AgCl} \mid \text{Ag}$$

Membrane

The emf of this cell is the sum of the membrane potential and the two liquid–junction potentials, but the latter are usually neglected. Membranes which can be made from synthetic ion-exchange polyelectrolytes have the properties of Donnan membranes, and have some characteristics which resemble those of cell membranes, and have been extensively studied because of this.

The transport of materials which may occur across membranes is often used for the purification of solutions of proteins, nucleic acids, and other large biological molecules from inorganic ions and small organic molecules. The impurity substances pass through the membrane, leaving behind the large molecules. The process is termed *dialysis*, and forms the basis of renal dialysis by artificial kidney machines.

Osmosis and Donnan membrane phenomena play an important role in living organisms. The distribution of water and some solutes in plant and animal tissues is often dependent on the phenomena. All plant and animal tissues are made up of cells. In animals, the cells may be regarded as protoplasm, which is surrounded by a membrane known as the *plasma membrane*. Animal cells have the ability to regulate the changes in concentrations of solutes inside the cell within certain limits, irrespective of the changes in concentrations of solutes in the extracellular liquid. This property is at least in part dependent on the plasma membrane.

The structure and organization of cell membranes is receiving a great deal of attention at present. There are two popular models which are used to represent the structure of biological membranes, both of which are based upon layers of protein and phospholipid. In the first of these (the *Danielli* model) the membrane is envisaged as being made up of a double or multiple bimolecular leaflet of protein and phospholipid as shown in Fig. 5.11(a). An alternative to this model is where the phospholipid is present as a series of globular micelles (section 5.7.2) embedded in a protein layer. It has even been suggested that a dynamic equilibrium may be present between the layer type of structure [Fig. 5.11(a)] and the globular type of structure [Fig. 5.11(b)].

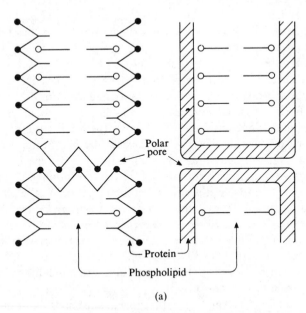

(a)

Fig. 5.11 (a) Bimolecular-layer model of membranes

181

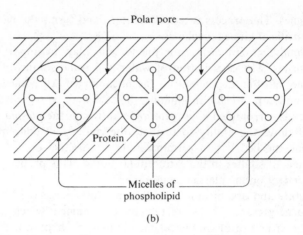

Fig. 5.11 (b)   Globular–micellar model of membrane structure

The materials for all the chemical processes of the cell have to come from the outside of the cell through the plasma membrane and into the interior of the cell. The process of osmosis through the membrane is therefore of vital importance to the existence of the cell. Normally the plasma membrane is permeable to water, ions and small non-electrolytes, but is usually impermeable to the large protein molecules in the inside of the cell. In general, the passage of material through cell membranes may be achieved by either a *passive* mechanism or by an *active-transport* mechanism. The passive mechanism (diffusion and osmosis) involves the material transport from more concentrated solution to more dilute solution. The membrane permeability for a given substance is often related to its partition coefficient between water and lipid-type solvents. Water and small inorganic ions can pass through the membrane fairly easily. Glucose and amino acids can pass through the cell membrane, but it is not certain whether or not the process is energy assisted. Large biological molecules such as polysaccharides and proteins may sometimes pass through cell membranes, but there is likely to be a special mechanism involved rather than simple diffusion under a concentration gradient.

The movement of material across a cell membrane can take place *against* a concentration gradient, and this is referred to as *active transport*. Such mechanisms are often described as *pumping mechanisms*. For such processes to occur, energy from the metabolic activity of the cell must be utilized and it is thought that the ATP to ADP conversion provides this. One possible mechanism might be based on the location in the cell membrane of enzymes which are specific for this conversion.

One suggestion concerning active transport against concentration gradients is that the process is facilitated by carriers present inside the cell membrane.

182

These carriers are thought to form a complex with the given ion or molecule and increase its lipid solubility. In the cellular membranes of muscles, nerves and erythrocytes, the transport of sodium and potassium ions is thought to occur via an exchange pumping mechanism which involves a carrier molecule. As one potassium ion enters the cell, it is exchanged for a sodium ion leaving. The carrier is thought to be phosphatidic acid, which on arrival at the inner side of the membrane with a potassium ion is then converted to a sodium ion carrier. This complex then travels back through the membrane towards the outside of the cell, using energy derived from ATP, and on arrival at the outer boundary is converted back to a potassium carrier again.

5.5.3 Membrane potential and nerve-impulse transmission

Because of the Donnan membrane equilibrium the membrane of the cell possesses an electrical potential. This normally amounts to 10 to 100 mV across a membrane of approximately 75 Å (7500 pm) thickness, or a potential gradient of 1300 to 13 000 V/mm, which is very high. All living cells maintain this potential difference across the membrane, and it is referred to as the *resting potential*. The outside of the cell is normally positive relative to the inside of the cell membrane. In the case of nerve cells and muscle cells, the resting potential is large, and is of the order of 70 to 80 mV.

A nerve cell consists of a main cell body with a nerve fibre. The nerve fibre consists of an inner core called the *axon*, which is surrounded by an outer insulating sheath called the *myelin sheath*. It is the nerve axon which is important in the transmission of electrical impulses.

When the membrane of the axon is stimulated, it loses its capability of keeping out sodium ions from the cell. Thus, sodium ions rush into the cell, and when this flow is at a maximum, the potassium ions in the cell commence rapid diffusion out of the cell. Eventually, the out-flow of potassium ceases and the active transport mechanisms start to restore the original concentrations of sodium and potassium ions within the cell.

As a result of the rapid ionic movement across the axon membrane, remarkable changes in the resting potential are produced at the membrane surface. If the stimulation of the axon is of sufficient intensity, the resting potential rapidly approaches zero and is transiently reversed in sign. This phenomenon is referred to as an *action potential* (also known as a *spike potential*). This is propagated along the nerve fibre and constitutes what is known as a nerve impulse. The action potential is shown schematically in Fig. 5.12.

The function of a nervous system depends upon some mechanism of transmission of the action potential from one nerve cell to a succeeding nerve cell or from a nerve cell to a muscle fibre. At the junction of the nerve system and the muscle, a chemical is liberated on the arrival of the nerve impulse. In the case of vertebrate skeletal muscle, this chemical is acetyl-choline. This substance causes depolarization of the muscle membrane (i.e., a change in resting potential) and the development of an action potential on the muscle fibres.

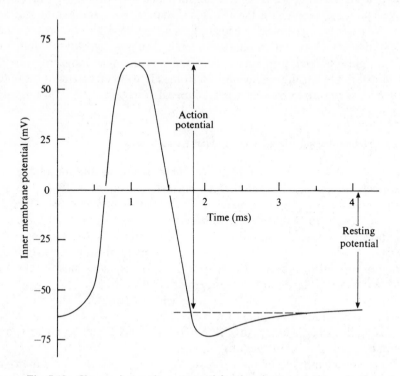

Fig. 5.12   Changes in membrane potential giving rise to an action potential

This last action finally results in the contraction of the muscle. The energy for the muscular contraction is provided by the conversion of ATP to ADP, and this process is accompanied by a dramatic change in the molecular shape of the muscle protein. The effect of the acetyl-choline on the muscle-cell membrane is removed after the muscular contraction by the enzyme *acetyl-cholinesterase*, which is concentrated near the junctions of nerve cells and muscle fibre. In the case of vertebrate smooth muscle, the chemical which causes depolarization of the muscle membrane may be either acetyl-choline or noradrenaline, according to the type of nerve fibre concerned, i.e., whether it is part of the parasympathetic or sympathetic divisions of the visceral nervous system.

The transmission of a nerve impulse between nerve cells, as opposed to that between a nerve cell and a muscle fibre, is achieved in a similar way, by release

184

of a chemical compound which has a depolarizing effect on the membranes of a succeeding nerve cell. This causes the development of an action potential on the membrane of the succeeding nerve cell, which ultimately affects the next cell, and so on.

Every time the cardiac muscle causes the heart to beat, electrical changes occur within it. These electrical potentials then spread to the surface of the body and may be recorded by having electrodes (usually metal) placed at a pair of points on the body (often on both arms and on the left foot, or on the back and on the chest). The record of these potential differences between these electrodes over a period of time is termed an *electrocardiograph* (ecg), and it is widely used as a clinical diagnosis of heart complaints. Since the heart is not the only source of potentials at the body surface, the potentials from other muscular contractions must be minimized, and this is usually achieved with the patient lying down.

5.6 ACID AND BASE PROPERTIES

5.6.1 Acid and base strength

There are two important theories of acid–base behaviour. One of these is known as the *Brønsted–Lowry* theory and regards an acid as a substance which may donate protons and a base as a substance which can accept protons (hydrogen ions). The alternative theory is the *Lewis* theory which regards acids as compounds which can accept a pair of electrons and a base as a compound which can donate a pair of electrons (often a lone pair). Thus compounds such as BF_3 and transition metal ions with vacant d orbitals may be regarded as Lewis acids.

The Brønsted–Lowry theory, while being less comprehensive than the Lewis theory, is far easier to place on a quantitative basis. A monobasic acid HA may be regarded as undergoing dissociation in aqueous solution according to

$$HA + H_2O \rightleftharpoons H_3O^+ + A^-$$

The H_3O^+ ion is termed the *hydroxonium* ion or *hydronium* ion, although it is common practice in solution chemistry to simply refer to it as *hydrogen* ion. The equilibrium constant for this reaction is called the *acid dissociation constant*, K_a,

$$K_a = \frac{a_{H_3O^+} \, a_{A^-}}{a_{HA}} = \frac{[H_3O^+][A^-]}{[HA]} \frac{f_{H_3O^+} \, f_{A^-}}{f_{HA}} \qquad (5.50)$$

where the a terms are activities and the f terms are activity coefficients. In dilute solutions, where the behaviour approaches ideality, the dissociation

185

constant approximates to $[H_3O^+][A^-]/[HA]$, where the square brackets represent concentrations (usually molarities).

A further source of hydrogen ions in an aqueous solution is from the self-dissociation of water,

$$2H_2O \rightleftharpoons H_3O^+ + OH^-$$

The product of the ionic concentrations in this reaction is often called the ionic product for water, K_w, and is given by

$$K_w = [H_3O^+][OH^-]$$

At 25°C the value of K_w is $1\cdot08 \times 10^{-14}$, which is usually approximated to 1×10^{-14}.

High values of K_a are obtained for strong acids, and the acids HCl, HNO$_3$, H$_2$SO$_4$ all have values greater than unity. Weak acids have values of K_a considerably less than unity, and it is possible to interpret the values in terms of molecular structure.

Weak bases, such as aniline, dissociate in water in the following manner,

$$PhNH_2 + H_2O \rightleftharpoons PhNH_3^+ + OH^-$$

The basic dissociation constant K_b is given by (neglecting activity coefficients)

$$K_b = \frac{[PhNH_3^+][OH^-]}{[PhNH_2]} \tag{5.51}$$

It is often convenient to quote the values of K_a and K_b in logarithmic form. This is achieved by using the following terminology: $pK_a = -\log_{10} K_a$ and $pK_b = -\log_{10} K_b$. Some typical values of pK_a and pK_b are given and discussed in section 4.2.

If a base B is placed in an acidic solution, it is protonated to an extent depending on its pK_b and the hydrogen ion activity in the solution, according to the equation

$$B + H^+ \rightleftharpoons BH^+$$

The protonated base BH^+ is also called the *conjugate acid* of the base B. The dissociation constant of the conjugate acid is given by

$$K_{BH^+} = \frac{[B][H^+]}{[BH^+]} \frac{f_B f_{H^+}}{f_{BH^+}} \tag{5.52}$$

On taking logarithms and rearranging the terms, eq. (5.52) becomes

$$-\log_{10}[H^+]f_{H^+} = pK_{BH^+} - \log_{10}\left(\frac{[BH^+]}{[B]} \frac{f_{BH^+}}{f_B}\right) \tag{5.53}$$

In dilute solutions of the base f_{BH^+}/f_B tends to unity, and thus eq. (5.66) becomes

$$pH = pK_{BH^+} - \log_{10}\left(\frac{[BH^+]}{[B]}\right) \qquad (5.54)$$

It can be easily shown that $K_b \times K_{BH^+} = K_w$.

Most drugs are either weakly basic or weakly acidic compounds. One of the factors affecting the performance of a drug is its ability to reach the site where it is required. If the drug is to be absorbed in the gastrointestinal tract, then the site of absorption will depend upon its pK_a. The more dissociated is a given drug into ions at a given pH, the more it is water soluble. If the drug is almost undissociated at a given pH then it is usually water insoluble, and most of it is lipid soluble.

Drugs which are weakly acidic are more readily absorbed in the stomach since, in the acid environment, they are largely undissociated. Hence the more *lipophilic* (lipid soluble) is the acid drug, the faster is its absorption in the stomach.

Drugs which are weakly basic are more readily absorbed in the intestine since, due to the intestine alkalinity, they are then only slightly dissociated. Hence the more lipophilic is the basic drug, the faster is its absorption in the intestine.

The lowest pK_a of an acid drug which is compatible with rapid absorption in the stomach is a pK_a of about 3. The highest pK_a of a basic drug which still permits rapid absorption in the intestine is a value of about 7·8.

5.6.2 Polyprotic acids, polyamines and amino acids

Compounds which possess more than one acidic hydrogen atom are called polyprotic acids. Such acids undergo dissociation into ions by a succession of equilibria, each stage having a particular value of dissociation constant. Thus oxalic acid, HOOCCOOH, dissociates into ions in two stages. The dissociation constant for the loss of the first proton is $5·6 \times 10^{-2}$, and the dissociation constant for the loss of the second proton is $5·3 \times 10^{-5}$.

When polyprotic acids are titrated with a strong base such as sodium hydroxide, the titration proceeds in a stepwise manner as successive hydrogen ions are neutralized. Thus the pH potentiometric titration curve for such acids exhibits points of inflexion at each stage of the neutralization process. This is shown for the first and second stages in the neutralization of phosphoric acid in Fig. 5.13(a).

Polyamines are compounds which contain two or more amine groups, and because of this, function as polybases. The titration curves for polyamines are very similar to those for polyprotic acids, and contain several points of inflexion corresponding to the various stages of neutralization. In a chemical

187

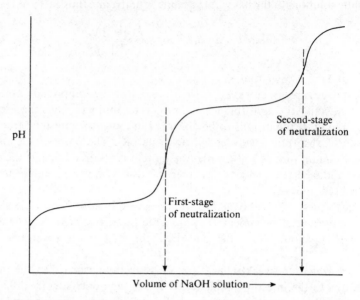

Fig. 5.13 (a)   pH titration curve for a polyprotic acid (phosphoric acid)

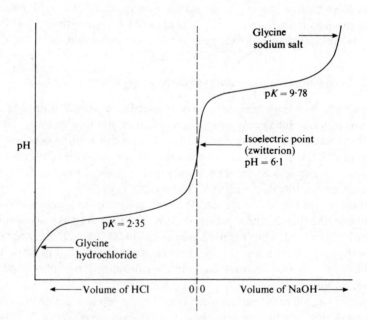

Fig. 5.13 (b)   pH titration curve for glycine

system where transition-metal ions are also present, there would be competition between the metal ions and the hydrogen ions for the polyamine as a chelating agent and a Brønsted base respectively.

Amino acids contain both basic and acidic groups. The simplest amino acid, glycine, CH_2NH_2COOH, contains one amino group and one carboxylic acid group, and hence can act as an acid as well as a base (see also section 7.1).

As the pH of a solution of an amino acid is varied, the acid may change from a cationic species to a zwitterion, and then eventually to an anionic species in solution. The pH at which the amino acid exists as an electrically neutral zwitterion is called the *isoelectric point*—pH. This value is different for different amino acids, and this is of great importance in the separation of mixtures of amino acids using ion-exchange resins as in the *amino acid auto-analyser*, and also in electrophoretic separation. Figure 5.13(b) illustrates the pH titration curve for a solution of glycine.

The dissociation equilibria of glycine may be summarized as follows.

$$
\underset{\text{Cation}}{\overset{NH_3^+}{\underset{COOH}{|\atop CH_2}}} \quad \overset{pK = 2\cdot4}{\rightleftharpoons} \quad \underset{\text{Zwitterion}}{\overset{NH_3^+}{\underset{COO^-}{|\atop CH_2}}} \quad \overset{pK = 9\cdot8}{\rightleftharpoons} \quad \underset{\text{Anion}}{\overset{NH_2}{\underset{COO^-}{|\atop CH_2}}}
$$

$$\xleftarrow{\text{Acid}} \quad pH = 6\cdot1 \quad \xrightarrow{\text{Alkali}}$$

Many of the naturally occurring amino acids have characteristic side chains which influence their acid–base properties. Thus valine, $(CH_3)_2CHCHNH_2$-COOH; glutamic acid, $COOH(CH_2)_2CHNH_2COOH$; and lysine, $NH_2(CH_2)_4CHNH_2COOH$, are respectively neutral, acidic, and basic in character. These characteristic side chains make the pH titration curves of these substances slightly more complicated than that for glycine. The dissociation equilibria for glutamic acid and lysine may be represented as shown on page 190. Note that the isoelectric pH value is the average of the pK values either side of the zwitterion form of the amino acid.

Proteins consist of molecules formed by the condensation of the α-amino group of one amino acid and the α-carboxyl group of the adjacent amino acid. This means that in principle it is only the terminal amino group at one end of the protein and the terminal carboxyl group at the other end of the protein molecule that are capable of ionization to give α-NH_3^+ and α-COO^- groups. However, proteins contain large numbers of ionizable groups along their chain length, and these must be due to the side chains of component amino acids which have acidic or basic properties as discussed above. It is these ionizable groups along the folded chains of a protein which are usually found on the outside of the protein structure (e.g., the ionizable side chains of amino acids such as glutamic acid, lysine, histidine, and others). The amino-acid

189

$$
\begin{array}{c}
\text{COOH} \\
| \\
(\text{CH}_2)_2 \\
| \\
\text{CHNH}_3^+ \\
| \\
\text{COOH}
\end{array}
\;\xrightleftharpoons{\;pK=2{\cdot}1\;}\;
\begin{array}{c}
\text{COOH} \\
| \\
(\text{CH}_2)_2 \\
| \\
\text{CHNH}_3^+ \\
| \\
\text{COO}^-
\end{array}
\;\xrightleftharpoons{\;pK=4{\cdot}1\;}\;
\begin{array}{c}
\text{COO}^- \\
| \\
(\text{CH}_2)_2 \\
| \\
\text{CHNH}_3^+ \\
| \\
\text{COO}^-
\end{array}
\;\xrightleftharpoons{\;pK=9{\cdot}5\;}\;
\begin{array}{c}
\text{COO}^- \\
| \\
(\text{CH}_2)_2 \\
| \\
\text{CHNH}_2 \\
| \\
\text{COO}^-
\end{array}
$$

Glutamic acid zwitterion

$$\text{pH} = 3{\cdot}1 = \frac{2{\cdot}1 + 4{\cdot}1}{2}$$

$$
\begin{array}{c}
\text{NH}_3^+ \\
| \\
(\text{CH}_2)_4 \\
| \\
\text{CHNH}_3^+ \\
| \\
\text{COOH}
\end{array}
\;\xrightleftharpoons{\;pK=2{\cdot}2\;}\;
\begin{array}{c}
\text{NH}_3^+ \\
| \\
(\text{CH}_2)_4 \\
| \\
\text{CHNH}_3^+ \\
| \\
\text{COO}^-
\end{array}
\;\xrightleftharpoons{\;pK=9{\cdot}2\;}\;
\begin{array}{c}
\text{NH}_3^+ \\
| \\
(\text{CH}_2)_4 \\
| \\
\text{CHNH}_2 \\
| \\
\text{COO}^-
\end{array}
\;\xrightleftharpoons{\;pK=10{\cdot}8\;}\;
\begin{array}{c}
\text{NH}_2 \\
| \\
(\text{CH}_2)_4 \\
| \\
\text{CHNH}_2 \\
| \\
\text{COO}^-
\end{array}
$$

Lysine zwitterion

$$\text{pH} = 10{\cdot}0 = \frac{9{\cdot}2 + 10{\cdot}8}{2}$$

residues in the protein which possess non-ionizable side chains (e.g., valine and tryptophan) are often confined to the centre of the protein structure and are involved in hydrophobic interactions with one another. Both the interaction of the ionizable groups with themselves and the hydrophobic interactions influence the overall shape of the protein in solution. If the pH of the solution is changed, however, changes in the ionic interactions occur as a result of acid–base behaviour of the side chains, and this may result in a change in shape of the protein. This may in turn influence the biological activity of the protein. In the case of an enzyme, studies on the way in which pH affects the catalytic activity may give information concerning the ionizable groups at the active site of the enzyme.

At a certain value of pH, a protein possesses no nett charge, and this is at its isoelectric point. It is at this value of pH that the protein is immobile in electrophoresis (section 5.7.3), and is least soluble and most easily precipitated from solution. The differences in isoelectric points of proteins enable their separation to be carried out from mixtures using electrophoresis or ion-exchange chromatography. If the pH of the solution is higher than that of the isoelectric point of a protein then the protein possesses an overall negative charge, whereas at a pH lower than the isoelectric point, it possesses a positive charge.

The permeability of cell membranes to low-molecular-weight metabolites is dependent on whether the compounds are ionized or un-ionized. The membranes are less permeable to ionized metabolites, and hence the intra-cellular concentrations of such compounds are more easily maintained when they are ionized, and this will depend upon pH.

5.6.3 Salt hydrolysis and buffers

It is only solutions of salts of strong acids and strong bases that are neutral. Solutions of other salts in water are not neutral, and this is due to *salt hydrolysis*. An example of this is potassium acetate (K^+Ac^-) which is a salt of a strong base and a weak acid. When this salt is dissolved in water, the anion takes part in a reaction with the solvent,

$$Ac^- + H_2O \rightleftharpoons HAc + OH^-$$

Thus, undissociated acetic acid and hydroxyl ion are the products of this hydrolysis reaction. The presence of the hydroxyl ion imparts slight alkalinity to solutions of potassium acetate. Similar examples are solutions of Na_2CO_3, NaS, and KCN, where the anion is partially hydrolysed by the solvent water. The equilibrium constant for the hydrolysis reaction, K_h, is related to the dissociation constant of the weak acid from which the salt was derived by the equation

$$K_h = K_w/K_a$$

If a salt is formed from a strong acid and a weak base, then aqueous solutions of the salt are slightly acidic, due to hydrolysis of the cation. For example, a solution of ammonium chloride is slightly acidic, due to the reaction

$$NH_4^+ + H_2O \rightleftharpoons NH_4OH + H^+$$

Similar examples are NH_4HSO_4, $FeCl_3$, and $CuSO_4$. The hydrolysis constant in this case is related to the dissociation constant of the weak base from which the salt was derived by the equation

$$K_h = K_w/K_b$$

Solutions which contain a mixture of a weak acid and its salt with a strong base have the capability of resisting changes in pH when either acid or alkali is added to the solution. These solutions are called *buffer solutions*. A simple example is an aqueous solution containing acetic acid and sodium acetate. The addition of hydrogen ions would result in the formation of more undissociated acetic acid and hence the pH of the solution would change only slightly. On the other hand, the addition of hydroxyl ions to the solution would result in formation of further sodium acetate by reaction with the acetic acid.

An aqueous solution of a salt of a weak acid and a strong base (sodium acetate) acts as a buffer solution on its own in the absence of acetic acid, but it does so only towards addition of acid, and not alkali. Similarly, an aqueous solution of a strong acid and weak base (ammonium chloride) acts as a buffer solution, but only towards the addition of alkali.

The pH of a buffer solution containing a mixture of a weak acid and one of its salts with a strong base is approximately represented by the *Henderson–Hasselbalch* equation

$$pH = pK_a + \log_{10}\left(\frac{[salt]}{[free\ acid]}\right) \qquad (5.55)$$

where pK_a is the pK of the weak acid and the square brackets represent concentrations. When applied to mixtures of a weak base and one of its salts formed with a strong acid, the Henderson–Hasselbalch equation may be written

$$pH = pK_a + \log_{10}\left(\frac{[base]}{[salt]}\right)$$

Using these equations, it is possible to calculate the pH of buffers made up from solutions of salts of weak acids or weak bases. The value of pH obtained may only be approximate, since the Henderson–Hasselbalch equation is a limiting equation and it assumes that the activities of the solutes in solution may be replaced by their values of concentration, and also assumes that $pH = -\log_{10}[H^+]$. For example, the pH of a solution containing 0·125 gram mole per litre of sodium acetate and 0·25 gram mole per litre of acetic acid may have its pH calculated as follows. The pK_a of acetic acid is 4·74, thus

$$pH = 4·74 + \log_{10}\left(\frac{0·125}{0·25}\right)$$

$$= 4·74 + \log_{10}(0·5)$$

$$= 4·74 + \bar{1}·699$$

$$= 4·74 - 0·301 = 4·44.$$

Buffer systems are of great importance in the control of the pH of body fluids and tissues. In the blood, the buffering systems are protein/protein anion, $HPO_4^{2-}/H_2PO_4^-$, and HCO_3^-/H_2CO_3. Of these, the bicarbonate–carbonic acid is the most important. In blood plasma, the concentrations of bicarbonate ion and carbonic acid are approximately 0·025 M and 0·00125 M respectively. Since the pK_a of carbonic acid is 6·1 the pH of plasma will be given by

$$pH = 6·1 + \log_{10}\left(\frac{0·025}{0·00125}\right) = 7·4.$$

The bicarbonate–carbonic acid buffer is the main buffering system in tissue fluids such as spinal fluid and lymph. It is an efficient buffering system against the acids produced in tissue-cell metabolism, e.g., phosphoric acid, lactic acid, acetoacetic acid, and β-hydroxybutyric acid. These acids are converted to their anions and the bicarbonate is converted to carbonic acid. The carbonic acid decomposes into carbon dioxide by an enzyme-catalysed process, and the carbon dioxide is exhaled via the lungs. This latter reaction makes the bicarbonate–carbonic acid system an even more effective buffer.

Proteins can sometimes act as buffers. For example, the interior of erythrocytes are buffered not only by the bicarbonate–carbonic acid buffer but also by the protein haemoglobin. At the blood pH of 7·4, the haemoglobin exists partly as ionized and partly as un-ionized compound. Similarly, the oxy-haemoglobin exists partly as an ionized compound. The equilibria involved along with the appropriate forms of the Henderson–Hasselbalch equation are as follows:

$$H \cdot Hb \quad \overset{pK_a = 8 \cdot 18}{\rightleftharpoons} \quad H^+ + Hb^-$$

$$7 \cdot 4 = 8 \cdot 18 + \log_{10} \left(\frac{[Hb^-]}{[H \cdot Hb]} \right)$$

and for oxyhaemoglobin

$$H \cdot HbO_2 \quad \overset{pK_a = 6 \cdot 62}{\rightleftharpoons} \quad H^+ + HbO_2^-$$

$$7 \cdot 4 = 6 \cdot 62 + \log_{10} \left(\frac{[HbO_2^-]}{[H \cdot HbO_2]} \right)$$

Using the above equations, it is possible to calculate that at the normal pH of blood, 85 per cent of the haemoglobin is in its un-ionized form ($H \cdot Hb$), but only 14 per cent of the oxyhaemoglobin is in its un-ionized form ($H \cdot HbO_2$). When oxyhaemoglobin gives up its oxygen, there is an uptake of hydrogen ions which is partly counteracted by the production of hydrogen ions by the CO_2–carbonic acid system. The de-oxygenation of oxyhaemoglobin therefore controls to some extent the amount of CO_2 that can be carried by blood in the forms of carbonic acid and bicarbonate ions.

5.7 SURFACE PHENOMENA

5.7.1 Adsorption isotherms

Whenever a solid is exposed to a gas or to a liquid, it has adhering to its surface molecules from the gas or the liquid phase with which it is in contact. If the molecules are adhering just to the surface of the solid, the phenomenon is referred to as *adsorption*. If penetration occurs into the solid then the process is termed *absorption*. A study of adsorption has shown that there are two main categories, namely:

(a) physical attraction between the adsorbed substance and the surface
   (*Van der Waal's adsorption*),

(b) chemical attraction between the adsorbed material and the surface (*chemisorption*).

In the case of physical adsorption, the heat of adsorption is usually small (about 5 kcal mole^{-1} or 20 kJ mole^{-1}) and the equilibrium between the adsorbed material and the solid is rapidly attained whenever the pressure (or concentration) and temperature are changed. The extent of adsorption is increased by lowering the temperature and raising the pressure or concentration.

In the case of chemisorption, the heat of adsorption may be in the range 80 to 400 kJ mole^{-1} (20 to 100 kcal mole^{-1}) due to the formation of true chemical bonds. The process is often almost irreversible, and desorption is usually very difficult.

The mathematical expression which relates the extent of adsorption on a solid as a function of pressure or concentration of material being adsorbed is called an *adsorption isotherm*. The simplest adsorption equation for physical adsorption is the *Freundlich* isotherm, which is an empirical equation,

$$\frac{x}{m} = kp^{1/n} \qquad \text{or} \qquad \log_{10}\left(\frac{x}{m}\right) = \log_{10}k + \frac{1}{n}\log_{10}p \qquad (5.56)$$

where x is the amount of adsorbed material on m grams of solid at a pressure p, and k and n are constants for a given solid and absorbate at a given temperature. If the equation is obeyed under the conditions of investigation, a graph of $\log_{10}(x/m)$ against $\log_{10}p$ should be linear, with a gradient of $1/n$ and an intercept of $\log_{10}k$. Hence, the constants k and n may be evaluated and used to characterize the system of solid and absorbate. In the case of adsorption of a solute from a solution onto a solid, the equation would be $x/m = kc^{1/n}$, where c is the concentration of solute in the solution which is in equilibrium with the adsorbed solute.

A further adsorption isotherm which has a theoretical basis is the *Langmuir isotherm*, the equation for which is

$$\frac{x}{m} = \frac{k_1 k_2 p}{1 + k_1 p} \qquad (5.57)$$

where k_1 and k_2 are constants characteristic of the system. If the isotherm is obeyed, then a graph of pm/x against p is linear, having a gradient of $1/k_2$ and an intercept of $1/k_1 k_2$ from which k_1 and k_2 may be obtained.

5.7.2 Surface-active agents

The presence of a dissolved solute in a solution usually influences the value of the surface tension at the air–liquid interface. If a solute causes an increase

194

in surface tension, then the concentration of solute at the surface is less than its concentration in the bulk of the liquid. This is termed *negative adsorption* and is typical of solutions of low-molecular-weight electrolytes. If the solute lowers the surface tension, then the solute concentrates at the surface of the liquid, and the surface concentration is greater than that in the body of the liquid. Such solutes are said to be *surface active*.

Surface-active agents invariably possess a molecular structure consisting of a *hydrophobic* (water-hating) tail and a *hydrophilic* (water-loving) head. At the surface of their aqueous solutions, the hydrophobic tails are pushed out of the liquid, which causes the surface water molecules to be forced apart, thereby lowering the surface tension of the liquid. There are three types of surface-active agent (*surfactant*) as follows.

(a) Anionic In these cases the active species is an anion, for example the anions of long-chain fatty acids, such as palmitate or alkyl aryl sulphonate ions.

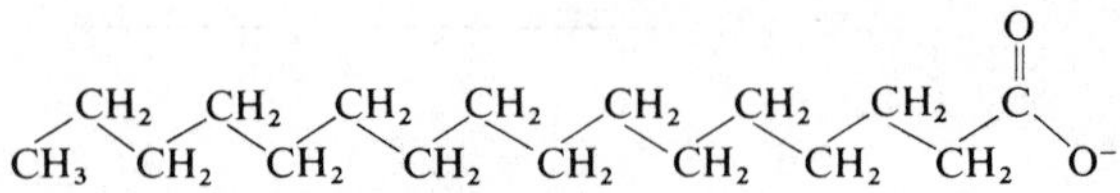

$$CH_3-CH_2-CH_2-CH_2-CH_2-CH_2-CH_2-CH_2-CH_2-CH_2-CH_2-CH_2-CH_2-CH_2-CH_2-\underset{\|}{\overset{O}{C}}-O^-$$

Palmitate ion

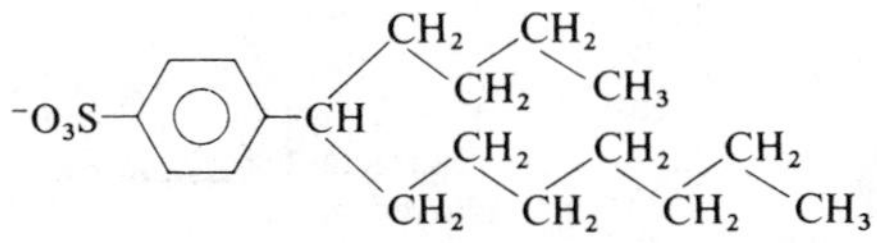

$$^-O_3S-\text{(ring)}-CH \begin{cases} CH_2-CH_2-CH_2-CH_3 \\ CH_2-CH_2-CH_2-CH_2-CH_2-CH_3 \end{cases}$$

Alkyl aryl sulphonate ion

(b) Cationic In these cases the active species is a cation, such as cetyl trimethyl ammonium ion.

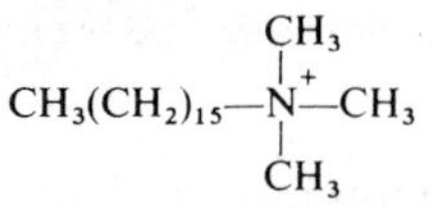

$$CH_3(CH_2)_{15}-\overset{CH_3}{\underset{CH_3}{\overset{|}{N^+}}}-CH_3$$

(c) Nonionic Here, the active species has a polar head, which is hydrophilic without dissociating to form an ion. This type are usually very water soluble, e.g.,

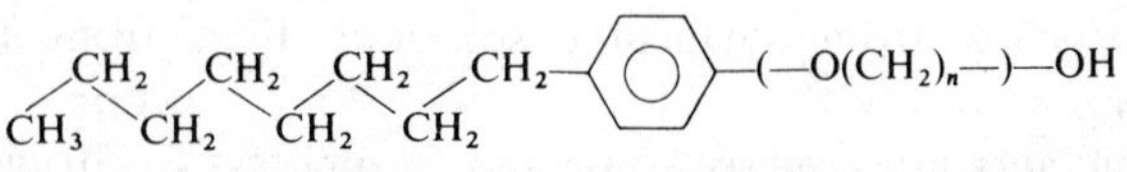

$$CH_3-CH_2-CH_2-CH_2-CH_2-CH_2-CH_2-CH_2-\text{(ring)}-(-O(CH_2)_n-)-OH$$

Above a certain concentration in the solution, surfactants do not cause any further lowering of the surface tension. This is due to the formation of spherical or laminar aggregates of surfactant molecules which are referred to as *micelles*, and which contain about 50 to 100 surfactant molecules. The

195

concentration at which this occurs is termed the *critical micelle concentration* (c.m.c.). Once the c.m.c. has been exceeded, the solutions have the ability to dissolve substances which are normally insoluble in water; a process which is given the name of *solubilization*. The formation of micelles and their action in solubilization are shown in Fig. 5.14.

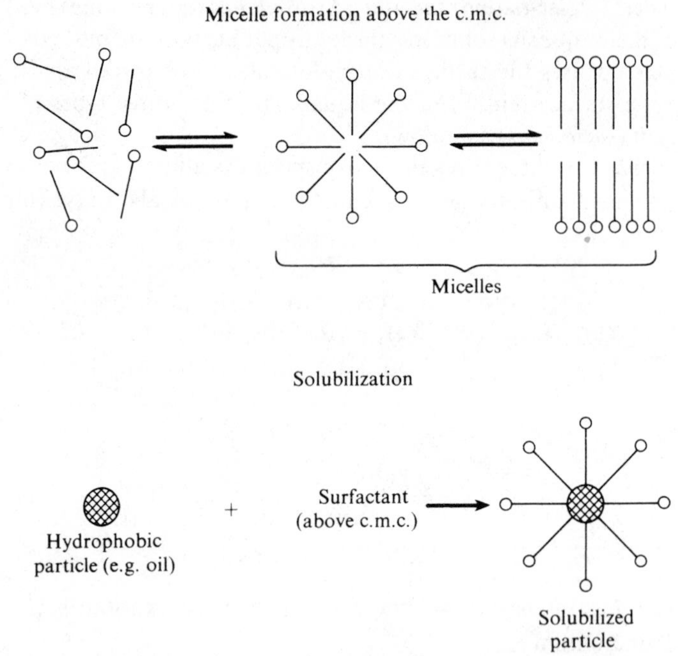

Fig. 5.14 The formation of micelles and the mechanism of solubilization

Surfactants have some importance in pharmacy, in that they can increase the rate of absorption through skin and mucous membrane. It is thought that they improve the wetting properties of skin. With lipophilic drugs the surfactant improves the distribution of the drug by incorporating it inside the surfactant micelles. Vitamins A, D, and E are lipid soluble and are more efficiently absorbed from surfactant solutions than from hydrophobic environments.

When surfactants are used as absorption promoters for drugs, great care must be taken to ensure that the surfactant and the drug are not incompatible. Thus, an anionic surfactant should not be used with a drug which will be absorbed as a cation, and vice versa.

Anionic surfactants are especially effective drug-absorption promoters, since in addition to their influence in degree of wetting and solubilization, they are able to affect cell membranes directly. They can also form complexes with calcium and magnesium ions in the intestinal wall.

Cationic surfactants, in particular the quaternary ammonium salts such as cetyl trimethyl ammonium bromide, have a certain amount of anti-bacterial action in addition to their surface-active properties. Since skin is slightly negatively charged, the cationic surfactant molecules are very readily adsorbed onto the surface of skin, but they will not penetrate it very easily. They will do this only if the surface of the skin is broken.

5.7.3 Electrophoresis

Electrophoresis refers to the migration of charged particles in an electric field. Like the chromatographic methods described in section 6.1, the electro-phoresis technique can be used to separate and identify closely related sub-stances. There are three different types of electrophoresis, which are as follows.

Particle microelectrophoresis

This refers to the migration of solid particles under the influence of an electric field. The individual particles are observed microscopically (section 8.1.1).

Moving-boundary electrophoresis

This method is based upon the study of the migration of the boundary of some material or mixture either dissolved or suspended in a buffer solution of accurately defined pH. This solution or suspension is then carefully layered *below* a buffer solution of the same composition, and the movement of the boundary between the two solutions is observed when an electric field is applied.

Although the method may be used to study the electrophoretic migration rates of proteins and protein interactions in solution, the method is very poor for the complete separation of components in a mixture and their identifica-tion. For this purpose, the several methods of *zone electrophoresis* are used and have achieved some importance in biochemical and medical fields.

Zone electrophoresis

In this method, the mixture to be separated is applied to a supporting porous solid. This stabilizes the solution containing the mixture against diffusion, and allows a complete separation of the mixture into zones of material of differing electrophoretic mobility. The method is extremely useful for the purposes of separation of mixtures but is less useful for the measurement of

197

absolute electrophoretic mobilities, since the values obtained are relative to the supporting medium. Nevertheless, the method is a valuable complementary technique to chromatography for separation and identification of unknown materials in small quantities.

There are two types of equipment available for zone electrophoresis, low-voltage electrophoresis (LVE), which operates at about 300 V and a potential gradient of about 10 V/cm down the supporting medium; and high-voltage electrophoresis (HVE), which operates at about 5000 V and potential gradients of about 100 V/cm of supporting medium. The HVE technique affords much faster separation of components in a mixture, but the supporting medium has to be cooled very efficiently, whereas for LVE the operating conditions are less stringent. A variety of supporting media is available and includes paper, fabric, powders, gels and membranes. These will now be discussed together with some of their applications.

(a) Paper electrophoresis Most of the work has been carried out on Whatman number 1 or 3 MM papers. Most substances can be located at the conclusion of the electrophoresis by reagents used in chromatography. Some of the applications of paper electrophoresis are as follows.

(i) Separation of serum proteins It is possible to use paper electrophoresis in clinical diagnosis by visually assessing the strips after electrophoresis. For normal adults, using a barbitone buffer at pH 8·6, the serum proteins are separated into five fractions, which are (in order of decreasing mobility) albumin, α_1-globulin, α_2-globulin, β-globulin, and γ-globulin. If plasma is used instead of serum, then the fibrinogen appears at a position between the β- and γ-globulins. Since it is in this region that any abnormality becomes apparent, it is preferable to use serum rather than plasma if the method is used in clinical diagnosis. The use of cellulose acetate membrane as a supporting medium has some advantages over the use of paper for this purpose.

(ii) Separation of serum lipoproteins The electrophoretic migration pattern may differ for these substances when certain clinical conditions are present. These include myocardial infarction, nephrosis, hypo-thyroid condition, and certain diabetic conditions.

(iii) Separation of amino acids The behaviour of amino acids is often more predictable in electrophoresis than in paper chromatography, and the method may be used as a method of detection and identification of specific amino acids.

(iv) Separation of nucleotides The technique may be used to separate nucleotides (see section 7.4.1), especially the monophosphate derivatives.

(v) Separation of haemoglobins The method may be used for the separation and identification of the variants of normal haemoglobins in clinical investigations, and also in genetic and anthropological studies.

(b) Cellulose acetate membrane (CAM) electrophoresis An alternative supporting medium to paper is CAM, which is a continuous micro-porous sheet. This structural difference in the supporting medium gives CAM some

advantages over paper. The adsorption on CAM is minimal, and macro-molecular substances separate more quickly than on paper and the separations are better. CAM can be used on its own or also in conjunction with agar for immuno-diffusion studies (see later). It can also be cut in sections after the separation, and the pieces dissolved in common solvents, which makes spectrophotometric estimation possible. It is also very suitable for the separation of radioactively labelled compounds, since it has a low background count, which is of some advantage in the radiological detection of the separated compounds.

The applications of CAM electrophoresis are essentially the same as paper electrophoresis.

(c) Immuno-electrophoresis This is a slight variation on zone electro-phoresis, and enables specific antibody–antigen reactions to be studied. After normal electrophoresis has been carried out on the strip of supporting medium (paper or CAM), the strip is placed in contact with one side of a thin slab of agar jelly. On the other side of the agar is placed a strip of filter which has been impregnated with the anti-serum. The separated fractions diffuse into the agar, as also does the anti-serum. When the anti-serum meets the corresponding antigen a precipitate is formed (usually as a line), and this enables the reaction to be characterized. This method is often called the *transfer method*.

The immuno-diffusion process following the electrophoretic separation may also be carried out using a strip of cellulose acetate instead of the agar jelly. This makes the method very sensitive, since only minute quantities of material are needed. The disadvantage is that for formation of precipitation lines cannot be followed visually, and this has to wait for staining and clearing of the CAM.

(d) Gel electrophoresis In this method, the materials being separated move through a gel under the influence of the electric field. The gels used are agar or starch gels, but polyacrylamide gels have been used more recently.

The material being studied (serum, haemoglobin, or other protein extracts) is introduced into the gel by wetting strips of filter paper with the sample, and then inserting the strip into a cut made in the gel with a razor blade. The gel is then pressed back into position. Electrical contact is made between the buffer-bath and the gel with heavy wick papers soaked in the buffer solution.

As the electrophoresis proceeds, the buffer and the components of the mixture pass through the gel, and the components separate according to their electrophoretic mobilities through the gel. At the conclusion of the experiment, the separated parts in the gel may be sliced out if required.

In recent years, *polyacrylamide gel electrophoresis* (PAGE) has been used to an increasing extent. The gels are made as required by dissolving acrylamide monomer and the cross-linking agent N,N'-methylene-bis-acrylamide in water or buffer solution. The pore size of the gel may be controlled by the amount of cross-linking agent used. The gel may be cast into slabs and used as described above, or cast in the form of rods for *disc electrophoresis* as it is termed.

The technique of PAGE is much quicker and easier than the use of starch gel or agar gel. Photography and densitometry of the separated fractions are also easier, since the acrylamide gel is transparent.

Gel electrophoresis may be used for the separations of serum, haemoglobin, blood, enzymes, and RNA. In the case of ribosomal RNA PAGE disc electrophoresis is very successful, since not only is its migration controlled by its electrophoretic mobility in the gel, but also by molecular size and shape, due to the molecular sieving action of the acrylamide gel.

A variant of gel electrophoresis is the method of *isoelectric focusing*. In this method, the gel is prepared so that it has a pH which varies from one end to the other. Thus the components of the mixture undergo electrophoresis through a controlled pH gradient. In the separation of proteins and amino acids by this technique, the components migrate until they reach a region of the gel where the pH corresponds to their isoelectric point, and then remain in that region. At the end of the experiment the components are therefore fractionated within the gel in order of their isoelectric points. It is possible to produce sharply focused zones within the gel by this method.

(e) **Thin-layer electrophoresis**   Electrophoresis may be carried out on thin-layer plates. Contact with the buffer solution is made by means of filter-paper wicks, and the plate is allowed to be wetted by the buffer by capillary action. The method is quick and allows easy removal of the separated substances. The location of the zones may be made using the spray reagents used for thin-layer chromatography (TLC).

Bibliography

1. L. Saunders, *Principles of Physical Chemistry for Biology and Pharmacy*, Oxford UP, 1971.
2. J. G. Morris, *A Biologists Physical Chemistry*, 2nd Edn, Arnold, 1974.
3. V. R. Williams and H. B. Williams, *Basic Physical Chemistry for the Life Sciences*, 2nd Edn, Freeman, 1973.
4. R. A. Robinson and R. H. Stokes, *Electrolyte Solutions*, Butterworths, 1959.
5. C. W. Davies, *Electrochemistry*, Butterworths, 1967.
6. R. P. Bell, *The Proton in Chemistry*, Chapman and Hall, 1973.
7. A. R. Denaro, *Elementary Electrochemistry*, Butterworths, 1971.
8. D. M. Freifelder, *Physical Biochemistry*, Freeman, 1976.
9. V. A. Bloomfield and R. E. Harrington, *Biophysical Chemistry* (*Scientific American* reprints) Freeman, 1975.
10. J. Koryta, *Ion Selective Electrodes*, Cambridge University Press, 1975.
11. J. Kavanau, *Structure and Function in Biological Membranes*, Holden-Day, 1965.
12. I. Smith and J. G. Feinberg, *Paper and Thin-layer Chromatography and Electrophoresis*, Longmans, 1972.
13. D. J. Shaw, *Electrophoresis*, Academic Press, 1969.
14. D. J. Shaw, *Introduction to Colloid and Surface Chemistry*, Butterworth, 1970.

6. Chromatography and spectroscopy

6.1 CHROMATOGRAPHY

6.1.1 Introduction

The term *chromatography* is used to describe a range of practical techniques for the separation of mixtures into pure molecular species. These techniques are of special interest to the biologist, since such separations have made possible the isolation in a pure form of most of the molecules which play such a vital part in the functioning of living organisms. In fact, the technique of chromatography was developed by a botanist—Tswett—over sixty years ago for the separation of plant pigment mixtures. The technique he developed (adsorption chromatography) is now only one of a range of separation methods available to a modern biochemist. This range of techniques is summarized in Table 6.1.

Table 6.1 Stationary and mobile phases in chromatography

Stationary phase	Mobile phase	Technique
1. Solid	Gas	Adsorption (gas) chromatography
2. Liquid	Gas	Gas–liquid chromatography
3. Solid	Liquid	Adsorption (liquid) chromatography
4. Liquid	Liquid	Partition chromatography
5. Ion-exchange resin (solid)	Liquid	Ion-exchange chromatography
6. Xerogel	Liquid	Gel filtration
7. Xerogel + Ligand	Liquid	Affinity chromatography

All the techniques are based on the principle that the components of a mixture may be separated and concentrated into zones by passage through a two-phase system: one stationary and one mobile. The names given to the phases exactly describe their role: the mobile phase carries the mixture through the static stationary phase.

The physico-chemical principles on which the methods of separation given in Table 6.1 are based vary widely, and each will be dealt with in a separate section. However, from the practical point of view, there are a number of features common to all the methods. For example, the separations are performed in two ways: firstly, using a column in which the stationary phase is held, or secondly, using a layer or sheet containing the stationary phase across which the mobile phase passes. Another common feature is that the separation process is in two stages. Firstly, the *elution* or *development* process, where the actual separation takes place on the column or on the layer; secondly, the *detection* process whereby the separated zones are treated in such a way that they may be clearly distinguished from the mobile phase. The name chromatography arose because the first separations were of highly coloured materials and no detection was necessary. Today, the vast majority of mixtures separated by these techniques are colourless, and the detection of the components of the mixture is an equally important part of the method.

6.1.2 Gas chromatography

There are two distinct techniques in this branch of chromatography. They are *adsorption–gas* or *gas–solid* chromatography and *gas–liquid* chromatography. In the former, the stationary phase is a solid and the mobile gas phase carries the gaseous mixture through the solid. Separation is achieved through the different degrees of adsorption of the components of the mixture on the stationary phase. In gas–liquid chromatography, where the stationary phase is a liquid, separation is achieved through differences in the solubility of the components of the gaseous mixture in the stationary phase. Both techniques require a similar instrumental arrangement. The technique of adsorption–gas chromatography has proved to be useful in the analysis of gaseous mixtures, such as those of hydrocarbons from petroleum sources. Gas–liquid chromatography has proved to be the most versatile of all the chromatographic methods. It has been found possible to separate and analyse a very wide variety of complex mixtures. The only limiting factor is that the components of the mixture must be vaporized to give heat-stable vapours up to a temperature of 300°C. It is for these reasons that the technique is of great use in all branches of chemistry.

The basic layout of a gas chromatograph is shown in Fig. 6.1(a). The mobile phase, known in this case as the carrier gas, has to be chemically inert, and nitrogen, argon, or helium are used. The mixture to be separated is introduced as a liquid to the stream of carrier gas through an injection device, where it vaporizes and passes into a column containing the stationary phase dispersed on the surface of an inert solid. The column is in an oven whose temperature can be precisely regulated. Separation takes place during passage through the column and the components of the mixture emerge in well separated zones. The outlet from the column passes through the detector, which analyses the gas stream and indicates via a pen-recorder the emergence of each component [Fig. 6.1(b)].

There are several methods used for detecting the presence of compounds in the outlet carrier-gas stream. These fall into two basic types: firstly, the differential concentration detectors, which measure the relative concentration of components on the carrier gas, and secondly, the differential mass detector

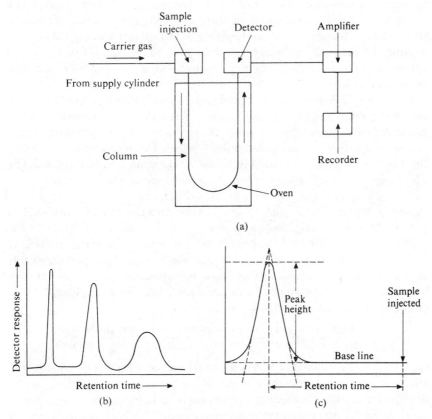

Fig. 6.1   (a) Schematic layout of a gas chromatograph. (b) Schematic recorder-trace from a gas–liquid chromatograph. (c) An idealized gas–liquid chromatography peak showing the significance of retention time

which measures the absolute amount of the components as they pass through the detector. The common *flame ionization* detector is of the first type. It consists of a flame in which the components of the mixture in the carrier gas are combusted as they leave the column. Hydrogen gas is mixed with the carrier-gas stream and air is supplied in a combustion chamber to maintain a small flame. A potential is applied between an electrode placed above the flame and an electrode at the base of the flame. During the combustion of organic compounds, ions are produced, and some of these are attracted to the electrode;

203

this produces a small current which, after amplification, gives a signal to the recorder. This method of detection is extremely sensitive, and the detection limit for a typical organic compound is about 10^{-12} g s^{-1}.

The other common detector found in commercial gas chromatographs is the *thermal conductivity* or *Katharometer* detector. This method is less sensitive, having a detection limit of about 10^{-8} g s^{-1}. The change in thermal conductivity of the carrier gas as a component emerges is measured by means of the change in resistance of platinum wire. All components in a mixture are detected whether organic or inorganic. This method has proved to be the most satisfactory in an apparatus for the separation of larger quantities, i.e., *preparative* rather than analytical work.

Since the mobile phase in gas–liquid chromatography is both physically and chemically inert, the factors that can be altered to achieve separation for a particular mixture are firstly the temperature at which the analysis is performed and secondly the nature of the stationary phase. The general rule in selecting the liquid phase is that it should be *similar* to the components of the mixture. Thus, the separation of hydrocarbons is best achieved on a non-polar stationary phase such as squalene. On the other hand the separation of esters such as those of fatty acids takes place most efficiently on a more polar liquid such as polyethylene glycol adipate—*a polyester*.

The stationary phase is dispersed in a volatile solvent, and the solution used to coat the surface of the solid used to pack the column. Each particle of this system acts as a *partitioning unit*, and thus in the passage of a mixture through the column, many thousands of individual partitions occur. Each partition is governed by the distribution law: i.e., the ratio

$$\frac{\text{Concentration of one component in the gas phase}}{\text{Concentration of the same component in the liquid phase}}$$

is a constant, the value of which depends on the nature of the species and the temperature. Thus, although there may be only a very small difference in the distribution constant between the components of a mixture, complete separation is achieved because so many partitions occur.

Gas–liquid chromatography separation is not only carried out isothermally (i.e., at a fixed temperature), but also with temperature variation during the analysis. This latter technique is known as *temperature-programmed gas–liquid chromatography*. It is of particular importance in the separation of mixtures of a large number of components, where there is a wide range of volatility. For example, a mixture of amino acids from a typical protein hydrolysate may be separated as the corresponding N-trifluoroacetyl amide methyl esters (Fig. 6.2).

The most important aspect of gas chromatography is the fact that, under a given set of operating conditions, a particular compound is always eluted at a definite time, the *retention time* (t_R). If the flow of carrier gas is constant, then the retention time corresponds to a definite volume of gas passed, the *retention volume* (V_R). The retention time is usually worked out from the recorder trace [Fig. 6.1(c)]. The identification of a component is made by comparing the retention time of a peak in a mixture with that obtained from the pure compound under identical conditions.

It is possible to obtain a quantitative estimate of the amount of each component from the recorder trace. If the peaks are symmetrical, it may be assumed that there is a linear relationship between peak area and concentration.

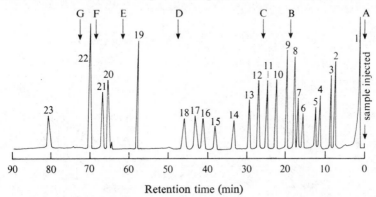

Fig, 6.2 Separation of TFA-amino acid methyl esters by gas–liquid chromatography (by permission of A. Dabre and A. Islam, 1968, and editor of the *Biochemical Journal*). A at 100°C with 1 C/min rise; B 3°C/min rise; C held at 140°C; D 5°C/min; E held at 210°C; F 5°C/min rise; G held at 230°C. Peaks: (1) solvent; (2) α-aminoisobutyric acid; (3) alanine; (4) valine; (5) glycine; (6) isoleucine; (7) threonine; (8) leucine; (9) norleucine; (10) serine; (11) proline; (12) aspartic acid; (13) cysteine; (14) homoserine; (15) hydroxyproline;(16) methionine;(17) glutamic acid;(18) phenylalanine;(19) tyrosine;(20) lysine;(21) tryptophan; (22) arginine; (23) cystine.

Gas–liquid chromatography represents the most versatile method for the separation and analysis of complex mixtures. Its application in biological chemistry is enormous. Not only may naturally volatile compounds like lipids be analysed with great sensitivity and precision, but also compounds such as amino acids, carbohydrates and nucleic acid components. These latter compounds are polar, and volatile derivatives have first to be prepared before gas–liquid chromatography analysis can be carried out.

6.1.3 Liquid–adsorption and liquid–liquid partition chromatography

Historically, these two techniques were the first to be developed. They are still used extensively, but they cannot equal gas–liquid chromatography in precision and sensitivity. On the other hand, they are invaluable in the analysis of non-volatile compounds and those which are thermally unstable. Furthermore, the equipment required in these methods is relatively simple and inexpensive. The separations are carried out either in columns or on paper or thin layers. Typical apparatus for the development process is shown in Fig. 6.3.

205

In general, paper and thin-layer chromatography are used for analytical purposes or for very small-scale preparative work, while column chromatography is used for most preparative scale work. In a column technique, the components of a mixture are eventually displaced from the column in well-separated zones, and each zone collected as a series of fractions. In a paper or thin-layer technique, development is continued until the mixture components are well separated, but remain on the chromatogram. After detection, the components appear as a series of spots. The position of the spots is recorded in terms of an R_F value. This is defined as the ratio

$$\frac{\text{Distance moved by the compound}}{\text{Distance moved by the solvent}} = R_F \text{ value of the compound}$$

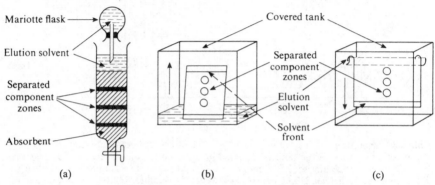

Fig. 6.3 (a) Arrangement for column chromatography. (b) Upward development of a thin-layer chromatogram. (c) Downward development of a paper chromatogram

R_F values are of great assistance in the identification of compounds in mixtures, since the value is a constant under the particular conditions of the separation. The principles involved in liquid–adsorption and liquid–partition chromatography are very different, and are best considered separately.

(a) Liquid–adsorption chromatography The separation of a mixture in this method depends on the different degrees of adsorption of the components on the material (the *adsorbent*) which makes up the *column* or the *layer*. Many materials with different adsorbing power have been used for this purpose, ranging from very strongly adsorbing charcoal and alumina, through less adsorbing silica, to very weakly adsorbing starch. In thin-layer chromatography three main layer materials are used: alumina, kieselgel (*activated* silica-gel) and kieselguhr (*inactive* silica-gel).

In general, the adsorption affinity of compounds (including the elution solvent) increases, the more polar or polarizable the molecule. A set of empirical rules is available, from which the degree of adsorption of a compound may be estimated. Alkanes are hardly adsorbed at all. The double bond in alkenes raises the adsorption affinity and the extent increases with the number of double

206

bonds, particularly if they are conjugated. The introduction of functional groups raises the adsorption affinity. In order of increasing affinity the order of some common functional groups is —O—R, —NO$_2$, —CO—R, —O—CO—R, —NH$_2$, —OH, —CO·NH$_2$, —COOH. In compounds with more than one functional group, the adsorption affinity of the groups is usually additive, particularly if they are well separated in the molecular structure.

The rate of migration of a compound through the adsorbent depends also on the nature of the eluting solvent. The more polar or polarizable the solvent, the greater is its elutive power. Thus, hydrocarbons have weak elutive power and alcohols strong elutive power, while solvents like chloroform, acetone and ether have intermediate power. It is found that mixtures of two or three solvents of different polarity often give better separation than chemically homogeneous solvents. In practice, it is found more convenient to change the composition of the solvent to effect a separation, rather than to use different absorbents.

Liquid–adsorption chromatography is a valuable method for the analysis and separation of mixtures of non-volatile compounds, particularly those which have sufficient functional groups to give polarizable molecules. Extremely polar molecules are separated by liquid–liquid partition chromatography.

(b) Liquid–liquid partition chromatography The principle on which this method operates is identical to that of gas–liquid chromatography. A liquid stationary phase is present in the column or on the paper or thin layer. The mixture, in the mobile liquid phase, passes through the system and partition occurs between the mobile and stationary phases. This method was developed for the separation of very polar organic compounds such as proteins, carbohydrates and amino acids. These polar materials have considerable solubility in water, and this is used as the stationary phase. The support material for a column or a thin layer is powdered cellulose, and the cellulose fibres of paper hold the aqueous stationary phase in paper chromatography. The mobile phase in these separations poses some problems, since it must be immiscible with the stationary phase and yet be sufficiently polar for the compounds to have appreciable solubility. Mixtures of two or more are used for the mobile phase, and the composition is usually arrived at by trial and error.

Liquid partition chromatography as a column technique for the preparative scale separation of polar materials like proteins has been largely superseded by other methods. Two of these—ion-exchange chromatography and gel-filtration—are described in the next two sections. A third—counter-current distribution—is conveniently mentioned here, since the principle on which it is based is identical to that of liquid partition chromatography. In counter-current distribution, a mixture is partitioned between two immiscible liquid phases which move relative to one another. The usual form of the apparatus required comprises a series of extraction tubes, through which the less dense (upper) of the two phases moves. Each extraction is performed by shaking the tubes and, after a period to allow the phases to separate, transfer of the upper phase is effected. The components of the mixture progress through the tubes as a result of the movement of the phases, but at different rates. These rates depend on the distribution coefficients of the components in the two phases; when these coefficients are different, separation is achieved.

Liquid partition chromatography as a paper or thin-layer technique is still widely used. As well as being the usual method for the analysis of polar compounds, it may be adapted for the separation of non-polar compounds. This adaptation is known as *reversed-phase partition chromatography*. The natural aqueous stationary phase found in paper and thin-layer materials is displaced by immersion in a non-polar solvent such as liquid paraffin. The system is then eluted with an immiscible polar solvent system. The separation and analysis of lipids, for example, fatty acid esters, has been accomplished by such a technique.

6.1.4 Ion-exchange chromatography

This method of chromatography is used exclusively for the separation of mixtures of ionic species. Since these occur mainly in inorganic systems, this method has found wide application in this part of chemistry. There are, however, a number organic compounds which exist in the form of ions, and in the separation of this type of compound ion-exchange chromatography has proved invaluable. It is this aspect of the method that will be considered here.

Ion-exchange separation may be carried out by both column, paper and thin-layer methods. The column technique has been most fully developed since the ion-exchange resins used have great mechanical and chemical stability. There are two types of ion-exchange resin. *Cation-exchange resins* are used for the separation of mixtures of cations and *anion-exchange resins* are used for the separation of mixtures of anions. One example and application of each will be described.

(a) Ion-exchange separation of amino acids   The resin used for this purpose is a sulphonated polystyrene polymer (Fig. 6.4). This is made by the polymerization of styrene in the presence of a small amount of divinyl benzene, which gives a specific amount of cross linking. The cross linking renders the polymer insoluble, and the amount of cross linking is controlled so that the system swells in water and is accessible to water molecules and ionic species. The sulphonic acid groups are introduced after polymerization, and provide a stationary anionic system which binds mobile cations.

When an amino-acid mixture in a solution of pH 3–5 is passed through this system, the amino acids present as cationic species become separated due to differences in the extent of the interaction between the negative charge on the resin and the positive charge on the amino acids. This is because the effectiveness of these positive charges changes with the nature of the amino-acid side chain (see Table 7.1). Even the slight difference in the branching of the alkyl

208

side chain of leucine and isoleucine makes a sufficient difference in the ionic interactions to effect complete separation (see Fig. 6.5).

The separation of amino-acid mixtures in this way has become the standard laboratory method of analysing protein hydrolysates and is the basis of the commercial *amino-acid analysers*. The amino acids are detected, as they emerge from the column, by the colorimetric reaction with ninhydrin. The coloration may be used to give a quantitative estimate of the relative amount of a particular amino acid present.

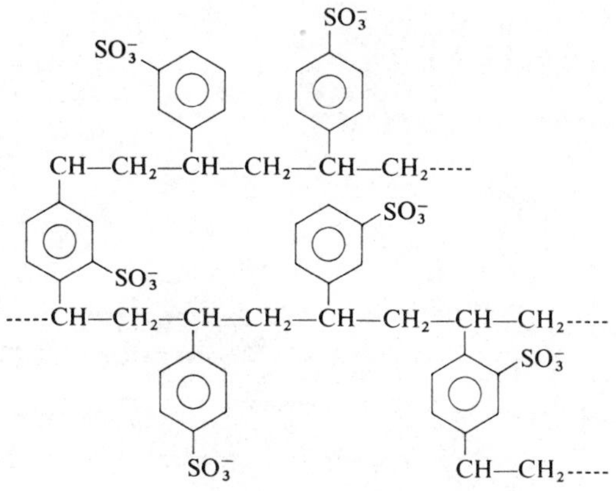

Diagrammatic representation of a sulphonated polystyrene resin

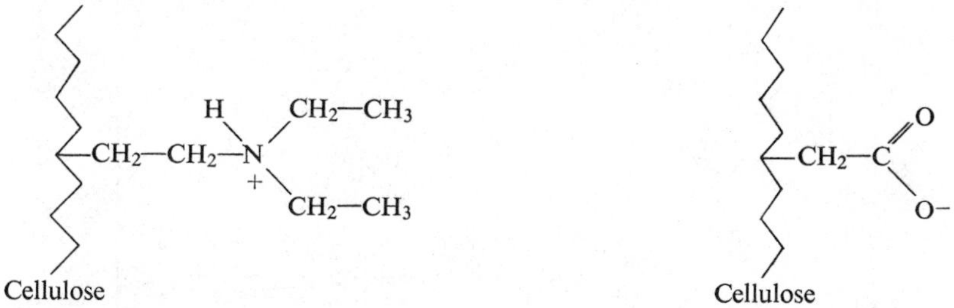

DEAE-cellulose
(Diethylaminoethyl-cellulose)

CM-cellulose
(Carboxymethyl-cellulose)

Fig. 6.4 Common ion-exchange materials used in biochemical separations

(b) Ion-exchange separation of nucleic acid components The structural units of nucleic acids are nucleotides. These are phosphate esters of nucleosides (for structures, see section 7.4.1). As such, they bear an anionic charge in aqueous solution, and are amenable to separation and analysis on an anion-exchange column. The most common anion-exchange materials are chemically modified celluloses; for example, the very weakly basic 'ecteola-cellulose' and

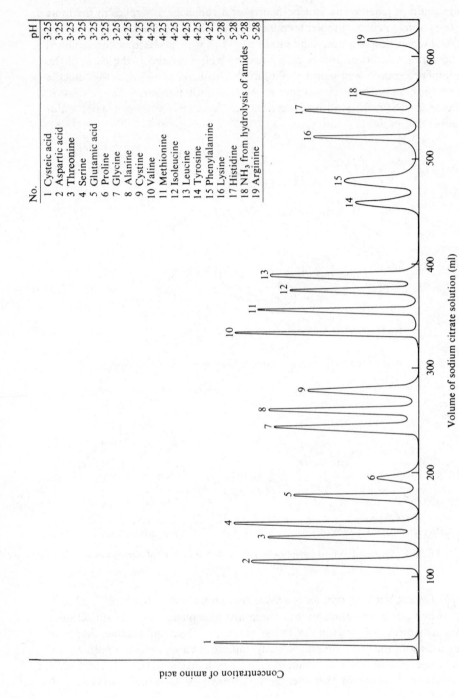

No.		pH
1	Cysteic acid	3·25
2	Aspartic acid	3·25
3	Threonine	3·25
4	Serine	3·25
5	Glutamic acid	3·25
6	Proline	3·25
7	Glycine	3·25
8	Alanine	4·25
9	Cystine	4·25
10	Valine	4·25
11	Methionine	4·25
12	Isoleucine	4·25
13	Leucine	4·25
14	Tyrosine	4·25
15	Phenylalanine	4·25
16	Lysine	5·28
17	Histidine	5·28
18	NH₃ from hydrolysis of amides	5·28
19	Arginine	5·28

Volume of sodium citrate solution (ml)

Concentration of amino acid

Fig. 6.5 Column fractionation of an amino-acid mixture on an ion-exchange resin

210

the more strongly basic diethylaminoethyl cellulose (DEAE-cellulose) [Fig. 6.4].

Nucleoside mono-, di- and triphosphates are easily separated from one another, since they bear very different anionic charges. Separations within each of these ester groups are more difficult and depend on the partial reduction of the negative charge on the phosphate moiety by a positive charge on the heterocyclic base. Since the extent of the positive charge on the heterocyclic base is different in each nucleotide, the way in which they interact with the ion-exchange material is different.

Paper and thin-layer ion-exchange techniques are available for analytical purposes. Sheets of chemically treated cellulose or cellulose impregnated with ion-exchange resin are used. Finely powdered modified cellulose ion-exchange materials are used in the thin-layer technique.

(c) *Ionophoresis* In structural studies on ribonucleic acids (RNA), a complex mixture of oligoribonucleotides is produced by partial enzymic hydrolysis. The separation of these mixtures was first carried out by ion-exchange chromatography on DEAE-cellulose. A more rapid method of greater resolution and sensitivity was devised by Sanger and his co-workers and is termed *ionophoresis*. In this method, high-voltage electrophoresis is carried out on ion-exchange paper. A two-dimensional technique is performed in which the oligonucleotide mixture is subjected to electrophoresis on cellulose acetate and then the partially separated mixture is transferred to a DEAE-cellulose paper and a further electrophoretic separation performed [Fig. 6.6(a)]. Separation occurs through a combination of differences in electrophoretic mobility and ion-exchange binding of the negatively charged oligonucleotides. In the electrophoretic migration, the more anionic components move faster and their progress is slowed on the DEAE-cellulose by binding to the positive charges on the paper. In order to increase the sensitivity of the method, the oligonucleotides in the mixture are labelled with ^{32}P atoms at their 5′-hydroxyl termini (section 8.1.2). This is carried out by treatment with ^{32}P-ATP and a polynucleotide phosphokinase. After the separation is complete, the positions of the radioactive spots are detected by *autoradiography*. In this procedure, the DEAE-cellulose paper is placed on a photographic sheet and, after a suitable exposure time, the sheet is developed to reveal a series of dark spots [Fig. 6.6(b)]. Ionophoresis with radioactive nucleotides is a method of precision and sensitivity; as little as 1 mg of the RNA is needed in the initial enzymic hydrolysis.

6.1.5 Gel filtration

Gel filtration is the name used to describe molecular sieve action on xerogels. The phenomenon of molecular sieve action, whereby a mixture of molecules becomes separated on the basis of size, has been known for many years. It has

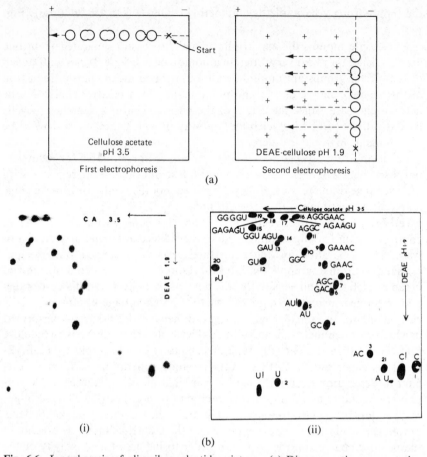

Fig. 6.6 Ionophoresis of oligoribonucleotide mixtures. (a) Diagrammatic representation of two-dimensional ionophoresis of oligoribonucleotide mixtures. (b) A two-dimensional fractionation of a pancreatic ribonuclease hydrolysate of 5S ribosomal-RNA. (i) A radio-autograph showing most of the oligonucleotide products. (ii) The position of all the major oligoribonucleotides and their sequences (see section 8.1.2); B is a spot of blue dye used as a marker in these separations. (By permission of G. C. Brownlee. From *Determination of Sequences in RNA*, North-Holland Publishing Co., 1972).

been frequently observed in ion-exchange resins and materials of similar action. Starch was the first of the xerogels to be used in this technique, and in the last ten years great advances have been made with the aid of synthetic xerogels. A xerogel may be simply defined as a polymeric material which swells greatly in a solvent to produce a gel system. Most of the common xerogels are hydrophilic and swell in aqueous solutions. A swollen xerogel contains regions which differ in their degree of accessibility for solutes. The accessibility depends on the steric relationships between the solute molecules and the gel network. In order to explain molecular sieve action in these systems in a simple qualitative manner, consider the case of a mixture of small, medium and large molecules being eluted through a xerogel. It will be seen from Fig. 6.7 that, at each level

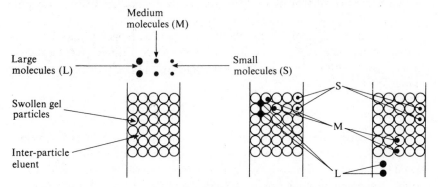

Fig. 6.7 Diagrammatic representation of the gel-filtration process

in the passage through the system, the small molecules penetrate almost completely into the gel system, the medium-sized molecules penetrate partially, and the large molecules do not penetrate at all. Thus, the small molecules are retained longest on the column, the medium-sized molecules for less time and the large molecules pass straight through in the eluent surrounding the gel system.

Great impetus was given to the development of this separation technique with the introduction of synthetically cross-linked dextran polymers in 1959. The advantage of these materials compared with a natural xerogel such as starch is that the degree of cross linking can be precisely controlled, and thus gives a gel system with definite and reproducible characteristics with regard to the extent of penetration of molecules. These synthetic xerogels have been marketed under the trade name *Sephadex* (Table 6.2), and in recent years their use in biochemistry has been very extensive.

Table 6.2   Sephadex gel-filtration media

	W_r	Exclusion limit (approximate)
Sephadex G-10	$1 \cdot 0 \pm 0 \cdot 1$	700
Sephadex G-15	$1 \cdot 5 \pm 0 \cdot 2$	1 500
Sephadex G-25	$2 \cdot 5 \pm 0 \cdot 2$	5 000
Sephadex G-50	$5 \cdot 0 \pm 0 \cdot 3$	10 000
Sephadex G-75	$7 \cdot 5 \pm 0 \cdot 5$	50 000
Sephadex G-100	$10 \cdot 0 \pm 1 \cdot 0$	100 000
Sephadex G-150	$15 \cdot 0 \pm 1 \cdot 5$	150 000
Sephadex G-200	$20 \cdot 0 \pm 2 \cdot 0$	200 000

The practical techniques required in gel filtration are similar to those of liquid partition chromatography, since the separations are carried out either in a column or on a thin layer. Apart from the use as a method of separation, gel filtration has a further use not found in any of the other chromatographic techniques, that is as a method of molecular-weight determination.

It is possible to distinguish a number of regions in a xerogel system. The total volume of the system (V_t) is the sum of the volume of liquid outside the gel grains (V_o), the volume of liquid inside the gel grains (V_i) and the volume of the gel matrix (V_g),

$$V_t = V_o + V_i + V_g \qquad (6.1)$$

V_o may be easily measured by applying to the system a molecular species completely excluded from the gel system. The degree of swelling is closely related to the degree of cross linking, and decreases as the latter increases. This feature is conveniently measured by the solvent (water) regain (W_r in Table 6.2), which is the amount of solvent taken up by one gram of dry xerogel. V_i is the weight of dry xerogel (a) times the solvent regain (W_r).

It is possible to define a parameter in gel filtration analogous to the partition constant in liquid–liquid or gas–liquid chromatography; in this case it is called the *distribution coefficient*, K_d. This parameter relates to the fraction of inner volume that is accessible to a particular molecular species. If V_e is the elution volume (Fig. 6.8) in which a particular molecular species is eluted, then

$$V_e = V_o + K_d V_i \qquad (6.2)$$

Thus,

$$K_d = \frac{V_e - V_o}{V_i} = \frac{V_e - V_o}{aW_r} \qquad (6.3)$$

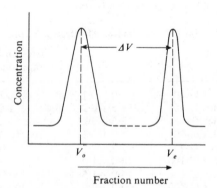

Fig. 6.8   Elution diagram for gel filtration

214

For a molecular species completely excluded, V_e equals V_o and K_d is zero. When the gel system is completely penetrated, for example, by a small ion, then K_d equals 1. The molecular weight of a particular species may be determined by comparing its ΔV value with those of compounds of known molecular weight eluted under the same conditions. More precise values of molecular weight may be obtained by calibrating a xerogel column with a series of compounds and obtaining a graph of $K_d^{1/3}$ versus $MW^{1/2}$. Such graphs are usually linear, and the molecular weight of an unknown is then determined from its K_d-value. Apart from molecular-weight determination, the main use of gel filtration has been in the isolation and purification of mixtures of biopolymers. This ranges from simple desalting to fractionation of complex mixtures of proteins. A highly cross-linked xerogel (e.g., G-25) would be used for the former process, and one of the less cross-linked xerogels for the latter process. Xerogels with exclusion limits higher than that of G-200 are available for the fractionation of nucleic acids and viruses.

All the xerogels and their uses mentioned so far have been for the separation of hydrophilic molecules, and the xerogels swell significantly only in water. The technique of gel filtration has recently been extended by the introduction of xerogels which swell in polar organic solvents. *Sephadex LH* is such a material, swelling in alcohols and chloroform to give a gel system approximating to G-25. Using such a system, the separation of lipids is possible.

6.1.6 Affinity chromatography

While gel filtration and other methods described in the previous sections have achieved widespread usage in the separation of sensitive, biologically active molecules such as proteins, they all suffer from the disadvantage that repeated fractionation is necessary to achieve a high degree of purity. In many cases, the required protein may be present at levels of less than one per cent in a complex mixture which contains other species of protein of similar size and structure. In the repeated separations necessary to achieve a high degree of purity of the required protein, some denaturation as well as loss of material may arise. Affinity chromatography affords a method in which the required protein may be recovered in good yield in a single operation under conditions well suited to maintaining its natural conformation and biological activity.

A feature of most *functional* proteins, such as enzymes, is that they interact in a highly specific manner with other molecules (*ligands*). Affinity chromatography makes use of these specific interactions between protein and ligand. A column is prepared in which a ligand of the required protein is covalently bonded to an insoluble matrix. When a solution containing this protein is passed through the column, it becomes bound to the column while all other species pass through. Even slightly modified or denatured molecules of the

215

protein do not bind to the ligand groups and are thus removed. When the column has been washed free of all contaminants, the required protein is eluted in a very pure form by either changing the pH or ionic strength of the eluent or by the addition of free ligand to the eluent.

At first sight this technique would appear to be superior to the other chromatographic methods for the isolation and purification of materials such as enzymes. Since its introduction in 1968, the technique of affinity chromatography has been extensively developed; the main limitation found so far is that of trying to simulate the natural affinity between protein and ligand on

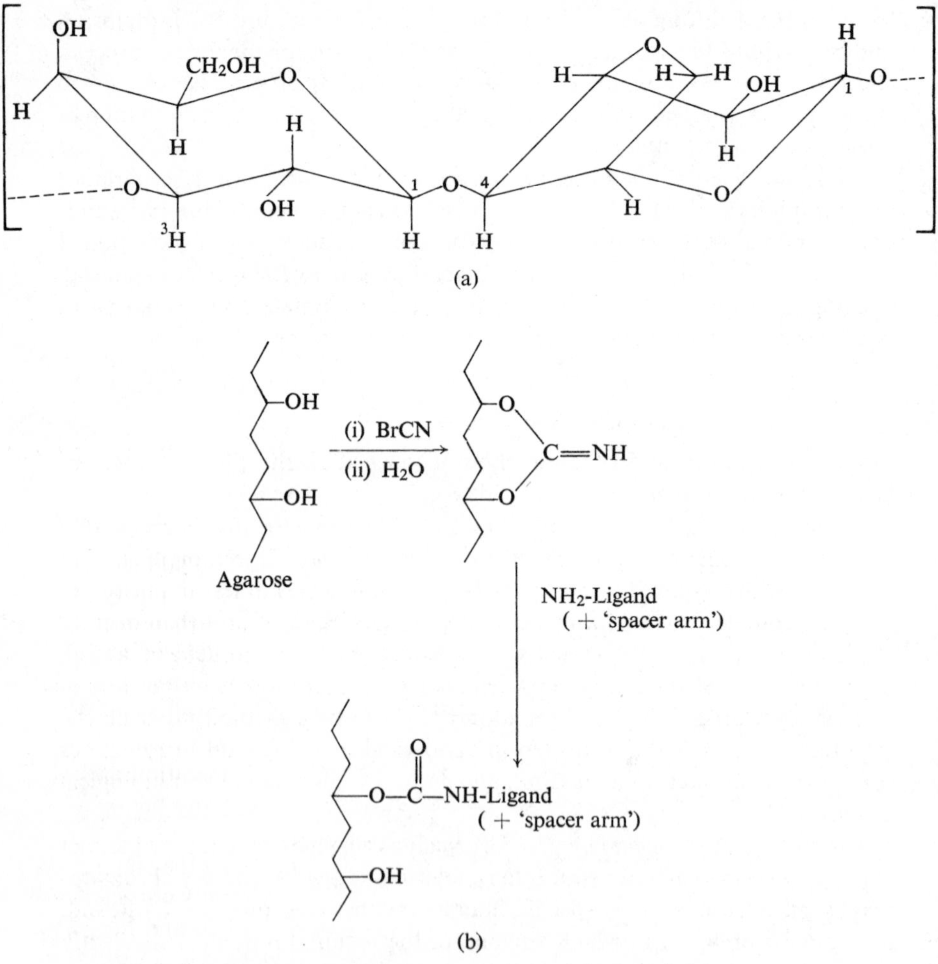

(a)

(b)

Fig. 6.9 Agarose and ligand bonding in affinity chromatography. (a) The repeating disaccharide unit of agarose (D-galactosyl-$\beta(1 \rightarrow 4)$-3,6-anhydro-L-galactose). (b) The use of cyanogen bromide for bonding the ligand to agarose for affinity chromatography

the heterogeneous system of insoluble ligand and water-soluble protein. The support or matrix to which the ligand is bound must conform to stringent criteria; for example, it must consist of spherical gel particles with good flow properties (cf. gel filtration), a porous chemically inert macromolecular network must be present through which unbound protein molecules may freely pass and suitable functional groups must be present on the matrix to which the ligand can be bonded. Of the numerous support materials tried, the most successful are those based on *agarose* gels. Agarose is a linear polysaccharide consisting of alternating residues of D-galactose and 3,6-anhydro-L-galactose [Fig. 6.9(a)]. The gel is available in a beaded form with good flow properties and swells in water to form a loose network readily penetrated by large molecules ($MW > 10^6$). Ligands may be bonded to the hydroxyl groups, usually with aid of cyanogen bromide [Fig. 6.9(b)]. In bonding the ligand to the matrix, it is important to allow a large enough distance between the two, since *direct* attachment usually produces a column that has little affinity for the particular protein. The importance of the length of the *spacer arm* holding the ligand is illustrated in Fig. 6.10. In some cases, suitably constructed *spacer arms* exert as great an infinity as the ligand; Fig. 6.10(a) shows a *spacer arm* binding, by hydrophobic interaction, to a region of protein adjacent to the ligand affinity site.

The choice of ligand for a particular separation will, of course, depend on the protein being isolated. To illustrate the method, a few examples involving *coenzyme* ligands will be described. In enzymic oxidation reactions requiring the coenzymes NAD^+ and $NADP^+$ (structures, see section 7.4.2), it is known that *in vivo* the enzymes bind coenzyme to form a binary complex which later binds substrate. Thus a column containing NAD^+ bound to ϵ-amino-hexanoyl-Sepharose is effective in retaining lactate and glyceraldehyde-3-phosphate dehydrogenases. The enzymes can be displaced by eluting the column with eluent containing free NAD^+. A similar affinity has been observed between 6-aminohexyl-AMP-Sepharose and these dehydrogenases. In the same way, pyridoxamine phosphate joined by a spacer arm to Sepharose can be used to separate a transaminase (section 9.4.2) from contaminating proteins while direct attachment of the ligand to the matrix was not effective [Fig. 6.10(b)].

6.2 SPECTROSCOPIC METHODS

6.2.1 The electromagnetic spectrum, molecular quantization and energy transitions

Electromagnetic radiation is a form of radiant energy which possesses wave properties. It is usually characterized by its wavelength (λ) which is the linear distance between successive peaks in the wave amplitude. The common units of wavelength are the micron (μm) (1 μm $= 10^{-6}$ m), the millimicron (1 m$\mu =$ 10^{-9} m $= 1$ nanometre, nm), and the angstrom (1 Å $= 10^{-8}$ cm $= 0\cdot1$ nm $= 100$ picometre, pm). The range of wavelengths of most interest in chemistry is from

217

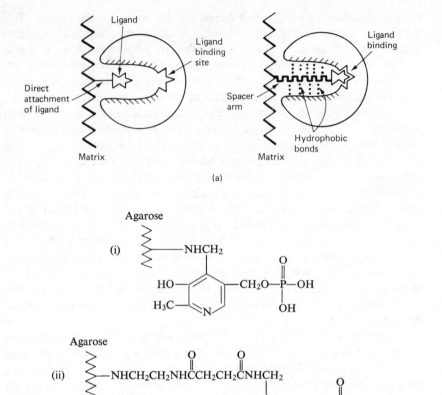

(a)

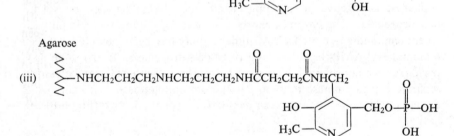

(b)

Fig. 6.10 Ligand–protein interaction in affinity chromatography. (a) A diagrammatic representation of the interaction between matrix-bound ligand and protein showing the necessity of a 'spacer arm' joining the ligand to the matrix. (b) Affinity matrices using pyridoxamine phosphate as ligand with 'spacer arms' of increasing length. (i) Pyridoxamine phosphate directly joined to CNBr-activated agarose. (ii) Pyridoxamine phosphate joined to succinylated aminoethyl-agarose. (iii) Pyridoxamine phosphate joined to succinylated 3,3'-diamino-dipropylamine-agarose. (By permission of J. V. Miller, P. Cuatre-Casas and E. B. Thompson, 1972, and the editor of *Biochim. Biophys. Acta*)

218

about 100 μm to about 100 pm, although electron spin resonance and nuclear magnetic resonance involve microwaves (centimetre wavelengths) and radio waves (metre wavelengths) respectively.

The study of the interaction of light with matter is known as *spectroscopy*. The graph of the amount of light absorbed by a substance as a function of wavelength is known as an *absorption spectrum*. The absorption spectrum of a substance is nearly always characteristic of the substance in some region of wavelength.

The wavelength (λ) and velocity (v) of light are related to its frequency (ν) by the equation

$$v = \nu\lambda \qquad (6.4)$$

The number of wavelengths per centimetre (the reciprocal of wavelength *in vacuo*) is called *wavenumber* ($\bar{\nu}$, quoted as cm^{-1} or mm^{-1}) and is used to specify certain electromagnetic radiation.

In addition to possessing wave properties, electromagnetic radiation also shows some particulate properties (see chapter 1). These particles are called *photons*. When radiation interacts with matter, it is the energy content of the photons which is important. For any particular radiation of frequency ν, the quantum energy content of each of its photons is $h\nu$, where h is Planck's constant.

All the forms of molecular energy (translational, rotational, vibrational, and electronic) are quantized. With the exception of translational energy, the absorption of quanta of suitable energy by molecules may cause transitions between molecular energy levels. Far-infrared and microwave radiation produces rotational energy transitions within the molecules. Infrared radiation produces excitation of molecular vibrations in addition to rotational energy changes. Visible and ultraviolet radiation may cause electronic transitions between molecular orbitals, superimposed on which are vibrational and rotational energy changes. X-radiation and γ-radiation may possess sufficient energy to break chemical bonds and hence cause chemical decomposition.

Thus the absorption of radiation by matter is concerned with the interaction of photons with molecules such that the energy of the photons $h\nu$ corresponds to differences in energy between the molecular energy levels. Since the energy levels of molecules are often unique for a particular substance its absorption spectrum is characteristic.

The differences in energy between electronic energy levels in molecules are in the region of 35000 cm^{-1}, corresponding to 420 kJ mole^{-1} (100 kcal mole^{-1}), while the differences between vibrational energy levels are approximately 1750 cm^{-1}, which corresponds to 21 kJ mole^{-1} (5 kcal mole^{-1}), and those between rotational energy levels are approximately $3\cdot3$ cm^{-1} ($0\cdot04$ kJ mole^{-1}; $0\cdot01$ kcal mole^{-1}).

6.2.2 The Beer–Lambert law and quantitative measurement

When a parallel monochromatic beam of light passes through a solution containing an absorbing species, the intensity of the beam is reduced. If the incident beam has an intensity I_0 and the emergent beam an intensity I, then these are related by the *Beer–Lambert law*,

$$I = I_0 10^{-\varepsilon c l} \tag{6.5}$$

where c is the concentration of solute expressed either as mole litre^{-1} or mole m^{-3}, l is the optical path length of the absorbing solution and ε is a constant for the solute called the *molar extinction coefficient* or the *molar absorptivity*, which varies with the wavelength of the light. The ratio I/I_0 is called the *transmission T* and hence

$$\log_{10} T = \log_{10}(I/I_0) = -\varepsilon c l \tag{6.6}$$

The term $-\log_{10} T$ is termed *optical density* or *absorbance A*, so that

$$A = \varepsilon c l \tag{6.7}$$

Therefore the absorbance of a substance should vary in a linear manner with concentration of absorbing solute. Figure 6.11 illustrates the variation of absorbance A and percentage transmission as a function of concentration at a given wavelength and optical path length.

Equations (6.6) and (6.7), along with graphs such as Fig. 6.11, form the basis of spectrophotometric analysis. If ε is known at a given wavelength for a certain substance, then the measurement at that wavelength of A or T allows the concentration to be calculated, provided that the Beer–Lambert law is obeyed. Alternatively, a calibration graph such as Fig. 6.11 could be previously prepared, using solutions of known concentration, and then the graph used to interpolate values of concentration from measured values of absorbance or transmission. This method could be used even if Beer's law were not obeyed for the particular system.

Over certain ranges of wavelength, the absorbance rises to a maximum and the transmission falls to a minimum. This is referred to as an *absorption peak*. It is usual to use the values of absorbance at the absorption peak in quantitative analysis, so that the measurements have the greatest sensitivity with respect to solute concentration. An equally important reason for measuring absorbance at the absorption peak is that the value obtained is least sensitive to errors in wavelength setting of the spectrophotometer.

The basic requirements of a spectrophotometer are as follows.

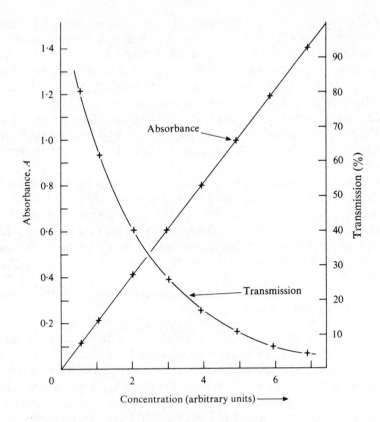

Fig. 6.11 Variation of absorbance and transmission with concentration according to the Beer–Lambert law

(a) A light source which provides as broad a spectrum of wavelengths as possible. For measurements in the visible region a tungsten filament lamp is commonly used. In the near-ultraviolet region a hydrogen lamp, deuterium lamp or xenon lamp may be used. In the infrared region the light sources used are either the *Nernst glower*, which is a hollow rod of yttrium and zirconium oxides heated to about 1450°C, or the *Globar*, which is a rod of silicon carbide heated to about 1200°C.

(b) A monochromator which serves to diffract the beam of light from the source into a narrow band of wavelengths. Selected wavelengths are then presented successively to the sample being investigated by means of a monochromator slit. The simplest monochromators are optical filters which usually transmit a bandwidth of about 50 nm (50 mμ). The most satisfactory monochromators, however, involve prisms or diffraction gratings (or both). For some wavelength ranges, these can resolve a polychromatic (many wavelengths) beam of light into a band as narrow as 0·1 nm, although for other regions the band may be as wide as 20 nm. In the ultraviolet region, quartz prisms are used, since glass absorbs wavelengths below about 340 nm. In the region 350–1000 nm, glass prisms give excellent dispersion of light. In the infrared region, the most common prism materials are polished samples of sodium chloride, calcium flouride, or potassium bromide.

(c) An absorption cell in which the sample being investigated is placed. The cell is usually constructed with materials used for the prism, namely quartz, glass and ionic halides for the ultraviolet, visible and infrared regions respectively.

(d) A detector to sense the absorption of light energy by the sample. The detector is usually made to compare the light transmitted by a cell containing solvent with that transmitted by the solution containing the sample. In the visible and ultraviolet regions, photoelectric detectors such as photocells or photomultipliers are used. In the infrared region, thermal detectors are used, i.e., thermocouples in the bolometer detector or gas thermometry in the Golay detector.

(e) A meter or recorder calibrated in terms of absorbance or transmission is used to obtain the absorption spectrum.

It is possible in all forms of spectrophometry for deviations from Beer's law to occur. Figure 6.12 shows the most common form of deviation from the Beer's law plot. A common reason for this is spectral impurity from the monochromator. Beer's law is strictly valid only for monochromatic radiation, and few monochromators provide this. The effect is more apparent when the absorption band for the sample is narrow and the instrument bandwidth is fairly wide, which is often the case in infrared spectroscopy.

The type of deviation shown in Fig. 6.12 can also occur at high concentrations of the absorbing species. The molecules are so close together as to influence the molecular energy levels, and hence affect the electronic transition or vibrational transition taking place.

6.2.3 Spectroscopic measurements in the ultraviolet, visible and infrared regions

(a) Ultraviolet and visible spectroscopy The action of visible and ultraviolet light on a chemical compound is to excite electrons within the molecules. This involves the promotion of an electron from a bonding molecular orbital to an antibonding orbital of higher energy. This is illustrated in Fig. 6.13. It can be seen that the energy needed for promotion of an electron is greatest for $\sigma \rightarrow \sigma^*$ transitions and least for $n \rightarrow \pi^*$ transitions. Thus, the former occur in the far ultraviolet and the latter in the visible region or the near ultraviolet (Table 6.3).

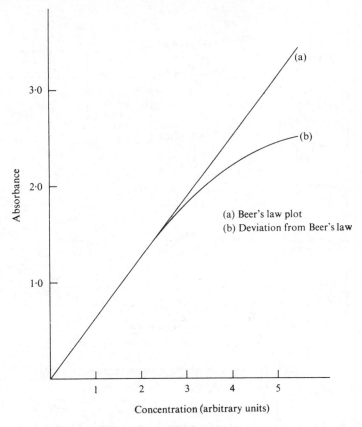

Fig. 6.12 Deviation from Beer's law

Electronic transitions within a molecule can often be associated with a given group in the molecule. This group is termed the *chromophore*. By studying the effects of substituents in a molecule upon the electronic absorption spectrum the technique may be used in a diagnostic manner for the identification of unknown compounds. When a substituent within a molecule causes a displacement of the absorption peak to a *higher* wavelength the effect is termed a *bathochromic* shift. If the absorption band is moved to a lower wavelength the effect is termed a *hypsochromic shift*. Bathochromic shifts are often accompanied by an increase in the intensity of absorption. Hypochromic shifts may occur when a positive charge is introduced within a molecule (such as protonation of a base) or when the solvent is changed from a non-polar to a polar character.

A number of absorption maxima for some common organic compounds is shown in Fig. 6.14. It is possible by means of empirical rules (Woodwards rules) to correlate shifts in these maxima with structural features in related

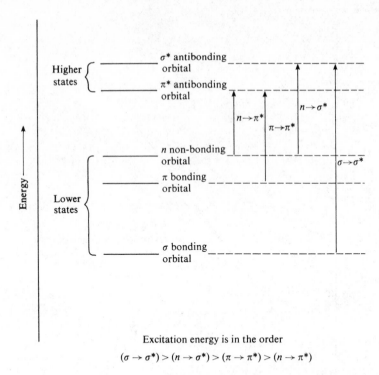

Excitation energy is in the order

$$(\sigma \to \sigma^*) > (n \to \sigma^*) > (\pi \to \pi^*) > (n \to \pi^*)$$

Fig. 6.13 Electronic transitions between molecular orbitals

Table 6.3 Examples of electronic transitions in organic chromophores

Compound	Transition	λ_{max} (nm)
H_3C—CH_3	$\sigma \to \sigma^*$ of C—C bond molecular orbitals	135
H_2C=CH_2	$\pi \to \pi^*$ of C=C π bond	165
CH_3—OH	$n \to \sigma^*$ promotion of electron from lone pair on O atom to σ^* orbital of C—O bond	183
$\begin{array}{c} CH_3 \\ \diagdown \\ C{=}O \\ \diagup \\ CH_3 \end{array}$	$\pi \to \pi^*$ within the C=O π bond	188
	$n \to \pi^*$ promotion of electron from lone pair on O atom to π^* of C=O	279
CH_2=CH—CH=CH_2	$\pi \to \pi^*$ of delocalized orbital due to conjugation	217
1:3:5-hexatriene	$\pi \to \pi^*$ of delocalized orbital due to conjugation of three double bonds	258
β-carotene	$\pi \to \pi^*$ of delocalized orbital due to conjugation of eleven double bonds	451

224

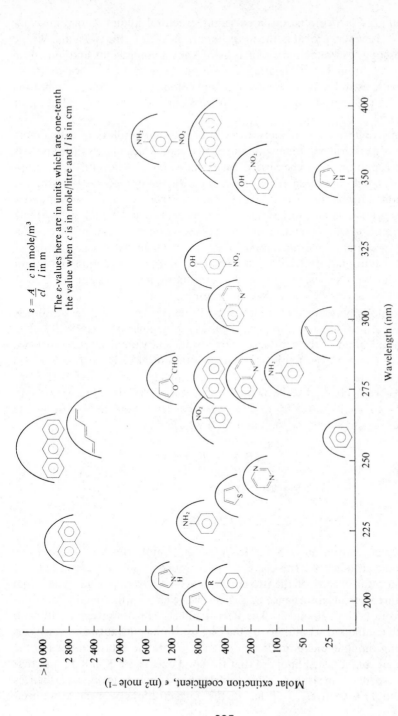

Fig. 6.14 Approximate ultraviolet absorption peaks for some organic compounds [reproduced by kind permission of Dr. J. C. Tebby (North Staffordshire Polytechnic)]

$$\varepsilon = \frac{A}{cl} \quad \begin{array}{l} c \text{ in mole/m}^3 \\ l \text{ in m} \end{array}$$

The ε-values here are in units which are one-tenth the value when c is in mole/litre and l is in cm

Wavelength (nm)

Molar extinction coefficient, ε (m^2 mole^{-1})

225

compounds. Such correlations are used in structural studies on organic compounds. However, probably the most important use of ultraviolet and visible spectroscopy is in quantitative analysis of known compounds and ions. Prepared calibration graphs relating concentration with absorbance or transmission are used. In many cases the inherent colour of a substance may be used directly in the analysis; in other cases the colour is developed by addition of a reagent.

Complexing reagents are known which form coloured solutions with almost every inorganic ion and many organic compounds which allows their analysis by spectrophotometry to be carried out. Simple examples include the development of a red coloration from ferric ion with thiocyanate or thioglycollic acid and the formation of an intense blue colour from cobalt ion with ammonium thiocyanate in acetone. Similarly, amino acids may be analysed by their colour reaction with ninhydrin and there are several reactions which are useful for the spectrophotometric analysis of proteins. There are a large number of clinical spectrophotometric analyses which involve the production of a colour by reaction with specific reagents and it is the most important single method of quantitative analysis in pathology laboratories.

If the molar absorptivity (extinction coefficient) is known for the substance, either on its own or as a complex, then it is sometimes possible to calculate the concentration of the substance from a single measurement of absorbance or transmission. For example, a certain solution of NADH (section 7.4.2) in a 1 cm path-length cell was found to have an optical transmission of 15·8 per cent at 340 nm. Given that the molar absorptivity of NADH at this wavelength is $6·22 \times 10^3$ mol^{-1} litre cm^{-1}, what is the concentration of NADH in the solution? From equations (6.6) and (6.7) we see that

$$-\log_{10} T = A = \varepsilon c l$$

and thus

$$-\log_{10}(0·158) = A = 6·22 \times 10^3 \, cl$$

i.e.,

$$c = 0·801/6·22 \times 10^3 = 1·29 \times 10^{-4} \text{ mol litre}^{-1}$$

Thus the concentration of NADH is $1·29 \times 10^{-4}$ mol litre^{-1}.

In some chemical systems there are two absorbing substances present and the absorption spectra of the two components may overlap. This means that a measurement of absorbance at a given wavelength will contain contributions from both components. The Beer–Lambert law, however, is still valid for each compound separately. By making measurements at two wavelengths and using simultaneous equations, we can calculate the concentrations of the individual components. Suppose that the components are X and Y, and that the absorbance is measured at two wavelengths λ_1 and λ_2 giving absorbances of A_1 and A_2 respectively. To calculate the concentrations of X and Y, we need

226

to know the molar absorptivities at λ_1 and λ_2, i.e., $\epsilon_{X(1)}$, $\epsilon_{Y(2)}$, $\epsilon_{Y(1)}$, and $\epsilon_{X(2)}$. At λ_1

$$A_1 = \epsilon_{X(1)} c_X l + \epsilon_{Y(1)} c_Y l$$

and at λ_2

$$A_2 = \epsilon_{X(2)} c_X l + \epsilon_{Y(2)} c_Y l$$

Solution of these two simultaneous equations gives the concentrations of X and Y. For example, the absorbances of a solution containing NAD$^+$ and NADH were 0·21 at 340 nm and 0·85 at 260 nm when measured in a 1 cm path-length cell. The molar absorptivity of both NAD$^+$ and NADH at 260 nm is $1·8 \times 10^4$ mol^{-1} litre cm^{-1}. The molar absorptivity of NADH at 340 nm is $6·22 \times 10^3$ mol^{-1} litre cm^{-1}, while that for NAD$^+$ is 15 mol^{-1} litre cm^{-1}. Thus, at 260 nm

$$0·85 = 1·8 \times 10^4 c_x + 1·8 \times 10^4 c_y$$

and at 340 nm

$$0·21 = 6·22 \times 10^3 c_x + 15 c_y$$

where c_x and c_y represent the concentrations of NADH and NAD$^+$ respectively. Solution of these two simultaneous equations gives $c_x = 3·37 \times 10^{-5}$ mol litre^{-1} and $c_y = 1·35 \times 10^{-5}$ mol litre^{-1}.

Although one can, in principle, apply this method to mixtures of many components, in actual practice it is not really advisable to use the method for more than three components.

(b) Infrared spectroscopy The infrared absorption spectrum of a compound is one of its most characteristic properties. Infrared radiation used in chemical spectroscopy has wavelengths in the range 2·5 to 16 μm (about 4000 to 625 cm^{-1}). The absorption of infrared energy by a compound causes excitation of molecules between vibrational energy levels. Usually, this is from the lowest vibrational energy level to the first excited level, giving rise to absorption bands referred to as *fundamental* bands.

Although the infrared spectrum is characteristic of the molecule as a whole, the spectra of all molecules contain certain common characteristics. These can be summarized as follows.

(i) In the region 3600–1500 cm^{-1}. Absorption due to bonds of the type X—H (e.g., N—H, O—H, C—H).
(ii) In the region below 1600 cm^{-1}. Absorption due to vibration of bonds of the type C—C, C—N, C—O, C—halogen.

(iii) In the region 1300–650 cm⁻¹. The absorption bands in this region are usually quite characteristic and unique for a given molecule. This region is frequently called the *fingerprint* region.

A polyatomic molecule of N atoms has in principle $3N - 6$ possible fundamental vibrations ($3N - 5$ for linear molecules). Thus benzene, with twelve atoms, has thirty fundamental vibrations. Not all of these, however, can be excited by infrared radiation, only those vibrations which are accompanied by a transient change in dipole moment. Thus, the infrared spectrum of benzene contains less than thirty absorption peaks.

The types of vibrations within molecules can be classified as follows.

(i)   Stretching.
(ii) Bending.
(iii) Vibrations of whole groups; these are subdivided into wagging, rocking, twisting, scissoring and breathing modes. Unsymmetrical breathing modes are referred to as skeletal vibrations.

Usually an absorption band for a particular group appears many times within a narrow range of frequency. When this occurs, it is said to have *characteristic group frequency*. The spectral positions of characteristic group frequencies vary only slightly with molecular structure, and hence they are of great use in identification of unknown compounds. Figure 6.15 illustrates the

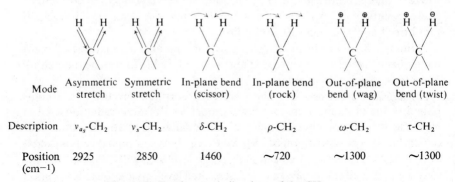

Mode	Asymmetric stretch	Symmetric stretch	In-plane bend (scissor)	In-plane bend (rock)	Out-of-plane bend (wag)	Out-of-plane bend (twist)
Description	v_{as}-CH_2	v_s-CH_2	δ-CH_2	ρ-CH_2	ω-CH_2	τ-CH_2
Position (cm⁻¹)	2925	2850	1460	~720	~1300	~1300

Fig. 6.15 Fundamental vibrations of the CH_2 group

fundamental vibrations of the CH_2 group, along with the method of description and spectral position in terms of wavenumber. Since many organic compounds contain CH_2 and CH_3 groups these absorption bands appear in the infrared spectra of most compounds. Other groups which have corresponding fundamental vibrations are —NH_2, —NO_2, and —CO_2^-, but the absorption bands appear at different spectral positions.

The relationship between molecular structure and infrared absorption bands is usually presented in the form of *correlation charts*. By means of such charts, the identification of structural features and functional groups in an unknown compound may be deduced from its infrared spectrum. In Fig. 6.16, a *hypothetical* infrared spectrum is shown containing some of the more common functional-group absorption frequencies. Infrared spectroscopy is used primarily for structural investigations in organic chemistry, although in recent years its importance has been somewhat overshadowed by other methods, notably NMR spectroscopy.

6.2.4 Flame photometry and atomic absorption spectrophotometry

In flame photometry, the intensity of light emitted by substances which have been excited by the heat of a flame is measured. The light intensity is related to the concentration of the substance in the sample placed in the flame. The technique is particularly useful for the analysis of elements which are easily excited by a flame, namely the metals sodium, potassium, lithium and calcium. The sample is dissolved in water prior to the analysis.

A flame photometer consists of the following components.

(a) An atomizer which sprays the solution into the flame.

(b) A burner whose flame temperature can be controlled by gas and air pressure controls. The gas used is usually town gas or propane although acetylene–oxygen and hydrogen–oxygen are sometimes used for measurements on heavy metals.

(c) A wavelength selector which, in simple instruments, is an optical filter. Filters are quite satisfactory if the measurements are restricted to analyses of sodium, potassium and calcium. If a grating monochromator is used, then the measurements can be extended to include analyses of barium, copper, manganese and strontium, see Table 6.4.

(d) A detector and output which measures the light intensity. The light emitted by the substance falls upon a photoelectric detector. In simple instruments this may be a photocell connected to a galvanometer whose deflections

Table 6.4 Detection limits in flame photometry (Unican SP900)

Element	Al	Ba	Ca	Cr	Co	Cu	Fe	Pb
Wavelength (nm)	484·2	493·4	422·7	425·4	352·7	324·8	372·0	405·8
Sensitivity (ppm)	32	0·2	0·003	0·3	0·5	0·1	0·4	12

Element	Li	Mg	Mn	K	Ag	Na	Sr	Ni
Wavelength (nm)	670·8	285·2	403·3	766·5	328·1	589·0	460·7	352·5
Sensitivity (ppm)	0·0001	0·09	0·02	0·001	0·1	0·0001	0·002	0·3

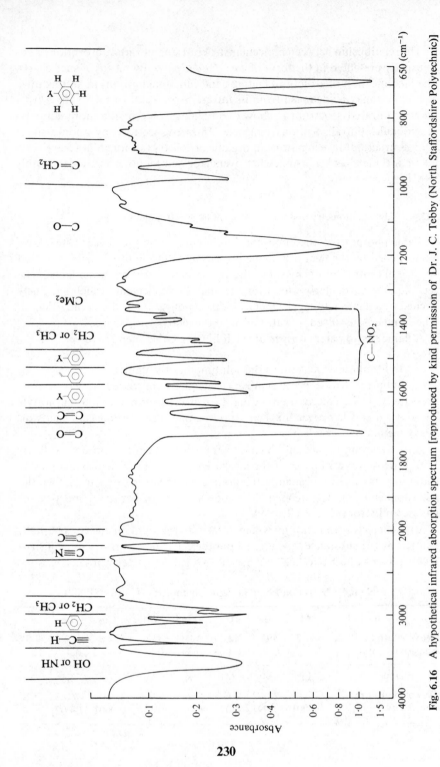

Fig. 6.16 A hypothetical infrared absorption spectrum [reproduced by kind permission of Dr. J. C. Tebby (North Staffordshire Polytechnic)]

are related to concentration. More sophisticated instruments use photomultiplier detectors, which are more sensitive than photocells. In addition, such instruments may employ electronic circuits, which present the result as an integrated value over a period of time, thereby giving greater reliability. The output from the instrument may be given as a digital read-out or print-out. The latter is commonly used in automated instruments in clinical measurements. Automated instruments often employ an internal standard (lithium) against which the element being measured is compared.

The detection limit of an element by flame photometry depends on its ease of excitation in the flame. The most favourable element is sodium, in that a simple instrument would have a detection limit for the metal of about 0·01 parts per million (ppm). An instrument with a grating monochromator and electronic integration of the signal would have a detection limit for sodium of ten to a hundred times lower than this (0·001 to 0·0001 ppm). The ease of analysis by flame photometry is in the order sodium, lithium, potassium, calcium, strontium, manganese, copper, and barium.

Sodium, potassium, and calcium analyses are of great importance in clinical laboratories in connection with electrolyte balance, and it is common practice to carry out such determinations directly on serum. Care is needed in processing of the blood into serum prior to flame photometry, since potassium ions can be rapidly exchanged between the red cells and the serum being formed. The normal concentrations in 100 ml of serum of sodium, potassium and calcium are in the ranges 310–355 mg, 14–20 mg and 8·4–11·6 mg, respectively.

One of the factors which limit the sensitivity of flame photometry is the proportion of the sample which is excited by the flame to emit light. This proportion rarely exceeds 1 per cent, so that approximately 99 per cent of the sample in the flame does not emit light. In *atomic absorption spectrophotometry*, this high proportion of the sample in the flame is irradiated with resonance radiation from a lamp which generates the atomic spectrum of the particular element (hollow-cathode lamps). In this way, the sample is stimulated to absorb light, and so be excited to higher electronic states. The amount of light absorbed is related to the concentration of the particular element in the sample. The fact that most of the element in the flame is available for detection in the atomic-absorption experiment makes the technique several orders of magnitude more sensitive than flame photometry.

Since the resonance spectra for elements are of very narrow line width (10 pm, 0·1 Å), atomic absorption spectrophotometry has excellent selectivity in terms of absence of spectral interference from other elements. It is possible to analyse over sixty elements by this technique.

Atomic absorption may be used in a wide variety of analytical determinations, including the following examples.

(a) Water and effluents Samples taken from waterways may be checked for sodium, potassium, calcium, iron, manganese, copper, nickel, chromium, zinc, cadmium, lead, lithium, and silver.

(b) Food chemistry Direct measurements may be carried out on beer, wine and beverages for the trace-element content. Foodstuffs may also be analysed for trace elements and also contamination by pesticides.

(c) Clinical chemistry Analysis of clinical samples for magnesium is of some importance. In addition, analysis is possible for calcium, lead, iron, cadmium, copper and zinc.

6.2.5 Fluorescence, fluorimetry, and spectrofluorimetry

Fluorescence is the emission of light by a molecule which has been excited by radiation in the visible or ultraviolet region. The fluorescent light is of longer wavelength than the light absorbed by the sample and is emitted by the sample *almost instantaneously* after the initial absorption (less than 10^{-8} s). Phosphorescence is a similar effect in that the emitted light is of longer wavelength than the absorbed radiation, but it is *delayed emission* occurring later than 10^{-4} s after the absorption. Both types of phenomena are forms of *luminescence*.

The intensity of the fluorescent light is proportional to the concentration of the sample and may be used as a quantitative method of analysis (*fluorimetry*). The sensitivity of fluorimetric analysis is usually several thousand times greater than normal absorption spectrophotometry. The method is extremely selective, since fluorescence spectra are very specific. On the rare occasions when fluorescence spectra for two substances overlap, a change in pH of the solution can often eliminate the interference.

The simplest fluorimetric measurement is one in which a sample is irradiated with light from an ultraviolet lamp, and the sample examined for fluorescent light. In clinical samples, this method would detect the presence of porphyrins. The most complete information, however, is obtained with a spectrofluorimeter, a schematic arrangement for which is given in Fig. 6.17.

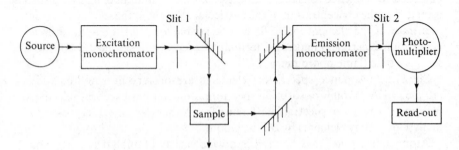

Fig. 6.17 Schematic diagram of a spectrofluorimeter

Light from the source (a mercury lamp or xenon lamp) enters the mono-chromator, and a selected portion passes through the slit 1 and into the sample cell. The fluorescence from the sample is emitted in all directions, but it is usually examined at right angles to the incident beam. The fluorescent beam is selected by wavelength, using the emission monochromator and slit 2, and passes into the photomultiplier. The photomultiplier output is amplified and used to give a reading on a meter or a recorder. The wavelength is found which from the excitation monochromator will generate the fluorescent spectrum of the sample via the emission monochromator. This is illustrated in Fig. 6.18 for anthracene in ethanol, using an excitation wavelength of 250 nm.

Alternatively, if the source is a xenon lamp (which provides a continuous range of wavelengths), then not only may the fluorescent spectrum be obtained, but also the *excitation spectrum*. This is achieved by setting the wavelength of

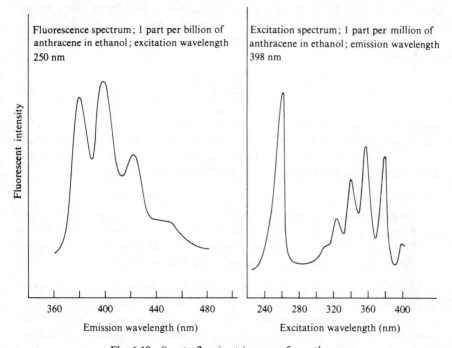

Fig. 6.18 Spectrofluorimetric curves for anthracene

the emission monochromator to correspond to a peak in the fluorescent spec-trum, e.g., 398 nm for anthracene in ethanol. The wavelengths from the excita-tion monochromator are then successively changed, and the photomultiplier output recorded. This produces the excitation spectrum of the sample, which resembles the absorption spectrum obtained with a spectrophotometer. This is an important feature of the technique, since it enables a fluorescent material

233

in the presence of non-fluorescent substances to be identified by means of its excitation spectrum. This spectrum would be similar to its absorption spectrum which would be impossible to obtain in the mixture, due to overlapping of absorption peaks.

Many of the compounds found in living organisms may be analysed by spectrofluorimetry. For example, compounds containing heterocyclic bases such as certain vitamins and their related coenzymes, nucleosides, nucleotides and nucleic acids. Some striking measurements using fluorimetry have involved single enzyme molecules, individual bacteria and isolated ribosomes.

6.2.6 Nephelometry and turbidimetry

These two techniques are used to measure the concentration of suspended material in a liquid, solution, gel or solid matrix. In turbidimetric measurements an incident beam of light of intensity I_0 passes into the sample and the intensity of the transmitted beam I is measured. Thus many types of spectrophotometer may be used to measure turbidity. The turbidity (S) of the sample is given by

$$S = \log_{10}\left(\frac{I_0}{I}\right) = \left(\frac{kbr^3}{r^4 + \alpha\lambda^4}\right)c, \tag{6.8}$$

where r is the average radius of the particles in the suspension, λ is the wavelength of the light used, c is the concentration of particles in the suspension, and k, α, and b are constants. The difference between I_0 and I is due to the light scattered by the suspension. Several points emerge from eq. (6.8):

(a) the turbidity, S, is directly proportional to concentration, c,
(b) turbidity depends strongly on particle radius,
(c) turbidity depends strongly on wavelength. It is common practice to use blue light, since the smaller the value of λ, the higher the turbidity appears, due to greater scattering of blue light than light of longer wavelength.

An interesting application of turbidimetry has been in studies on platelet abnormalities in blood from patients suffering from thromboembolic diseases. An important stage in the extrinsic and intrinsic clotting mechanisms of blood (i.e., spontaneous clotting or thrombosis, and the normal defence mechanism of haemostasis) is aggregation of platelets. The aggregation is accompanied by release of substances which are involved in the clotting reactions. One method of studying the sensitivity of platelets towards aggregation is to measure the amount of ADP or other aggregating agents needed to produce the aggregation of platelets *in vitro* in plasma samples. The onset of aggregation may be measured by a decrease in turbidity or optical density.

Nephelometry is concerned with the measurement of the amount of light scattered by the suspension, i.e., the measurement of $I_0 - I$ or some fraction of

234

it. Figure 6.19 illustrates a simple nephelometer, in which the amount of scattered light is measured by a photocell and the current produced is measured by a galvanometer. The instrument is usually calibrated using a standard etched glass rod which scatters light by a constant amount. Nephelometers are very useful in the study of growth rates of microorganisms. As the growth proceeds it is accompanied by a change in turbidity, and hence a change in light-scattering power.

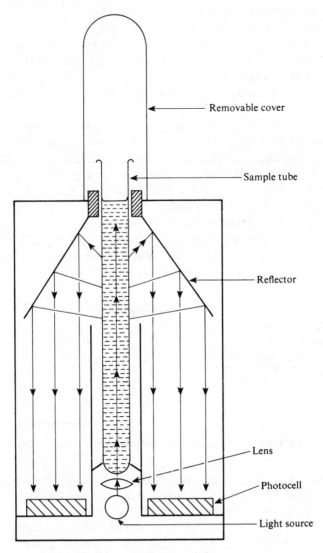

Removable cover

Sample tube

Reflector

Lens

Photocell

Light source

Fig. 6.19 A simple nephelometer

235

Nephelometry and turbidimetry are used to measure concentrations of smokes and aerosols in vapours, and also the particulate concentration in colloids and emulsions. Measurements of scattered light at various angles can give information concerning particle size and shape. The structural changes of proteins in solution when various reagents are added may be studied by nephelometric methods.

6.2.7 Magnetic resonance methods

(a) Electron spin resonance (ESR)   Electron spin resonance spectroscopy is concerned with those molecules in which there are unpaired electrons. Examples include (i) *free radicals*, for example $CH_3^{\bullet}$, $C_2H_5^{\bullet}$, $C_6H_5^{\bullet}$, $(C_6H_5)_3C^{\bullet}$; (ii) *odd electron molecules*, such as the paramagnetic molecules NO, NO_2, and O_2, (iii) *paramagnetic ions and complexes*, such as those of the transition metals.

In a collection of molecules (or ions) containing *one* unpaired electron per molecule (such as a free radical) there will be some molecules in which the unpaired electron has a spin quantum number, s, of $+\frac{1}{2}$, and in others it will be $-\frac{1}{2}$. Associated with each value of s is a permanent magnetic moment, and the substance has paramagnetic properties. Both types of molecule have equal energies under normal circumstances. However, in the presence of a d.c. magnetic field the magnetic moments tend to align themselves either with the direction of the applied field or against it, depending on the spin of the unpaired electron. Thus, instead of one energy value for the molecules, there are two energy levels in the presence of a magnetic field. This is illustrated in Fig. 6.20.

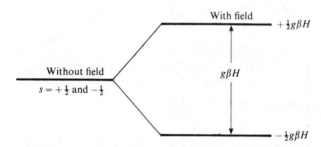

Fig. 6.20   The splitting of an energy level in a magnetic field

The term g is called the spectroscopic splitting factor (close to a value of 2 for free radicals), β is the *Bohr magneton* which equals $eh/4\pi mv$ where e is electronic charge, m is electronic mass, v is the velocity of light, h is Planck's constant, and H is the magnetic field strength applied to the sample. Thus, by means of energy equal to $g\beta h$ (Fig. 6.20), it is possible to excite molecules in the lower energy state to the higher energy state. This may be achieved by irradiation of the sample with electromagnetic radiation of energy $g\beta H$ when the sample is placed in a magnetic field of strength H.

Thus the resonance condition is

$$hv = g\beta H \qquad (6.9)$$

where v is the frequency of the electromagnetic radiation. For a magnetic field strength corresponding to a magnetic flux density of 3000 gauss (0·3 tesla in SI units) v is approximately 8500 megacycles per second (8500 megahertz, MHz). This corresponds to a wavelength of 35 mm for the radiation which is the microwave region of the spectrum. In a magnetic field of flux density 10 000 gauss (1 tesla) the value of v is approximately 28 000 MHz, which is an approximate wavelength of 10·7 mm. [The strength of a magnetic field used to be measured in terms of *oersteds* and this would have the same numerical value as the magnetic flux density expressed in gauss. The SI unit of magnetic field strength is *amperes per metre*^{2} (A m^{-2} or A/m^2), and this is related to the oersted by 1 oersted $= 1000/4\pi$ amperes per metre^2.]

The requirements of an ESR spectrometer are as follows.

(i) A source of radiation of about 35 mm wavelength which is usually provided by an electronic valve called a *klystron valve*.

(ii) An absorption cell which contains the sample. This is placed in a resonant cavity in a microwave tube where the microwave power will be concentrated.

(iii) Surrounding the sample is a homogeneous, stable magnetic field of flux density of about 3000 gauss (0·3 tesla). In addition, some arrangement is needed to be able to vary the flux by about ±100 gauss.

(iv) A detector is incorporated to determine when the specimen absorbs microwave radiation at the resonance condition. The detector is a crystal or a bolometer which is connected to some type of display system such as an oscilloscope or pen-recorder.

The usual method of measurement is to keep the frequency, v, constant and vary the magnetic field strength until the resonance condition is reached. There are two ways of presenting the spectrum so obtained. These are shown for a simple absorption process in Fig. 6.21.

It is common to use the derivative absorption curve which is the mathematical derivative of the absorption curve. In actual practice ESR spectra contain many peaks and fine structure. This arises from a phenomenon known as *hyperfine interaction*, which is due to the interaction of the unpaired electron with *magnetic nuclei within the molecule* in addition to its interaction with the applied magnetic field. The most common magnetic nucleus is that of hydrogen, which is present in all organic molecules. The hyperfine interaction of one or more unpaired electrons within a molecule with the magnetic nuclei of the molecule produces complex ESR spectra which are characteristic of the molecule.

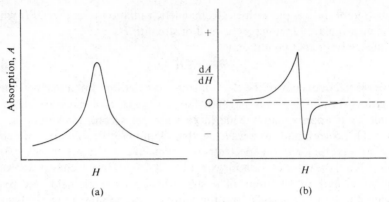

Fig. 6.21 (a) The absorption curve and (b) derivative curve for a simple ESR spectrum

Many studies of free radicals have been carried out using ESR. The production of free radicals in materials by radiation or during chemical and biochemical reactions may be studied by the technique. Most of the applications of ESR in biology and medicine have involved the identification of free radicals produced during metabolic processes. For example, there is a high free-radical content in the skin pigment melanin produced by ultraviolet radiation; similarly, the free-radical content of green leaves is proportional to the amount of illumination they receive.

As a result of ESR studies it is postulated that free radicals are necessary intermediates in biological redox processes. Many studies have been made on the enzyme xanthine oxidase. This enzyme possesses three paramagnetic centres due to molybdenum, iron and FAD. The oxidized state has no ESR signal, but when it reacts with a reducing substrate, the three paramagnetic centres each give an ESR signal.

A recent development in ESR spectrometry of some importance in biology is the technique of *spin-labelling*. This technique uses the fact that molecules containing the nitric oxide (NO) radical produce non-isotropic ESR signals. This means that the signal varies with the orientation and environment of the molecule. The compounds I, II and III have been used as spin-labels, the one called *tempo* (I) has been used most extensively.

The spin-labelling technique has been used in the study of membrane structure. *Tempo* (I) was incorporated into an excitable membrane, and from its

238

ESR signal, the structure of the phospholipid in the membrane was studied. The results have been supplemented by ESR studies, where the stearate derivative of *tempo* was incorporated into the lipid layers of membranes. Both sets of investigation tend to give support to the bilayer theory of membrane structure (section 5.5.2). Similar studies with the stearate derivative of *tempo* incorporated into erythrocyte membranes suggest some differences from excitable membranes, in that there is some axial rotation of the cholesterol molecules in the lipid layers of erythrocyte membranes.

(b) Nuclear magnetic resonance (NMR) An atomic nucleus which possesses different numbers of protons and neutrons has associated with it a magnetic moment which may be characterized by the *nuclear spin quantum number, I*. In the presence of a powerful magnetic field, the possible energy states are $2I + 1$. Thus, the hydrogen nucleus with a value of I of $+\frac{1}{2}$ produces two energy states in a magnetic field. By the absorption of energy from electromagnetic radiation, it is possible for transitions to take place between these two energy states. This is referred to as *nuclear magnetic resonance*.

The resonance condition is given by the equation,

$$v = \mu H / hI \tag{6.10}$$

where v is the frequency of the electromagnetic radiation, H is the magnetic field strength, μ is the nuclear magnetic moment, and h is Planck's constant. Many commercial NMR spectrometers operate at 14 000 gauss (1·4 tesla) and a frequency of 60 MHz. Some instruments are now being produced which operate at 100 MHz and even 220 MHz, making use of more powerful magnetic fields. In all cases, the frequencies used correspond to the radiofrequency region of the electromagnetic spectrum.

The great value of NMR in chemistry is that the magnetic field experienced by a nucleus in a molecule may not be identical to the strength of the applied magnetic field. This is due to the shielding effect of the extranuclear electrons. Thus, different protons within a molecule will experience different electronic shielding, depending on their position, and therefore they will exhibit the nuclear resonance phenomenon at slightly different values of the applied magnetic field. This is known in NMR spectroscopy as the *chemical shift*. As a result of the chemical shift, it is possible to demonstrate that ethyl alcohol has three different types of protons; those in the CH_3 group, those in the CH_2 group, and the proton in the OH group.

The extent of the chemical shift is usually measured relative to the proton magnetic resonance of tetramethylsilane (TMS). It is usually quoted as the *tau value* (τ). This is measured as

$$\tau = 10 - \frac{(\text{frequency difference from TMS}) \times 10^6}{(\text{instrument frequency in Hz})} \tag{6.11}$$

An alternative method of expressing the chemical shift is by the *delta value* (δ) which is simply $10 - \tau$.

The chemical shift is influenced by:

(i) electron density around the various hydrogen nuclei, and hence is dependent on molecular structure,
(ii) the solvent for the measurement,
(iii) the temperature of the measurement to a slight extent. (If hydrogen bonding is present in the sample then temperature affects the τ-value for the proton concerned, since the hydrogen bonding changes in extent),
(iv) the electronegativities of polar groups near a given proton.

Other magnetic nuclei whose NMR spectra have been studied in chemical systems are ^{19}F, ^{31}P, ^{11}B and also ^{13}C and ^{17}O. The chemical shifts of these nuclei occur at higher magnetic fields than for proton resonance, and hence do not complicate the NMR spectra due to protons. Table 6.5 contains values of τ for protons of the CH_3 group when connected to a group R, which illustrates the influence of the group upon the electronic shielding experienced by the protons of the methyl group.

Table 6.5 Some τ-values for CH_3 protons in RCH_3

R	τ-value in CH_3	R	τ-value in CH_3
$CH_3CH{=}CH$	8·30	—I	7·85
—COOR′	8·00	—Ph	7·66
—CN	8·00	—Br	7·30
—COOH	7·93	—Cl	6·95
—CONR$_2'$	7·98	—OH	6·62
—COR′	7·90	—OPh	6·30
—CHO	7·83	—OOCPh	6·10
—NR$_2'$	7·85		

Thus, the τ-values in NMR spectroscopy are analogous to the characteristic group frequencies of infrared spectroscopy. The τ-values allow a compound to be classified into a particular group, even if they do not provide a positive identification. Fortunately, there are other aspects of NMR spectra at high instrument resolution which permit this to be achieved.

At high resolution, the absorption peaks are split into further fine structure. This may be illustrated schematically for diethyl maleate in Fig. 6.22. This fine structure is associated with interactions between the magnetic moments of *different* protons. These interactions occur via the bonding electrons, and are referred to as *electron coupled spin–spin interaction* or as *spin–spin splitting*. The extent of the coupling or splitting is measured by the coupling constant, J, which is the separation between absorption peaks within the fine structure. It is observed only if the chemical shift is greater than the coupling constant. The value of J is independent of the magnetic field strength, whereas the chemical

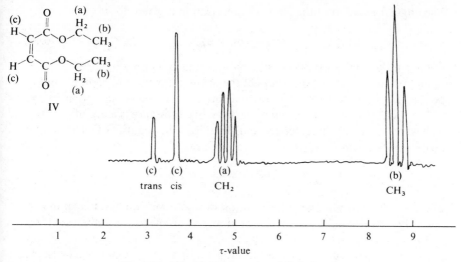

Fig. 6.22 The NMR spectrum of diethyl maleate

shift depends on the field strength. The 100-MHz and 220-MHz instruments ensure that the chemical shift is greater than the J-values, and hence allow the measurement of spin–spin splitting in difficult cases.

Thus the NMR spectrum of a compound is described by

(i) the position of one or more peaks in the spectrum, i.e., the chemical shifts, which are determined by the chemical environment of the protons,

(ii) the number of protons in a similar environment, which determines the intensity of a given peak,

(iii) the number of neighbouring protons, on which depends the degree of spin–spin splitting (provided τ-values are greater than the J-values),

(iv) the geometrical relationships between the interacting protons on which depends the magnitude of the spin–spin splitting.

The greatest use of NMR at the moment is in structural organic chemistry, although there are increasing uses in the biological sciences. Foremost among these will be the use of NMR in studying enzyme conformation in solution.

6.2.8 Optical rotatory power

In chapter 2, it was mentioned that dissymmetric molecules rotate the plane of polarized light, and this gives rise to the phenomenon of optical activity. A beam of plane (or linearly) polarized light can be regarded as being made up of two components: a left and right circularly polarized beam of equal intensity. Optical activity arises because the medium through which the polarized light passes has different refractive indices for the two circularly polarized beams.

241

The angular rotation of the plane of polarization is given by

$$\alpha = \frac{2\pi}{\lambda}(n_L - n_R)\,l \qquad (6.12)$$

where α is the angle of rotation in radians, λ is the wavelength of the light and n_L and n_R are the refractive indices of the medium for left and right circularly polarized light respectively. The angular rotation is measured in a polarimeter.

The rotatory power of a given optically active substance is a useful quantity with which it may be characterized and identified. The quantity which is usually used is *specific rotation* ([α]) which is defined by

$$[\alpha] = \frac{\alpha}{l \times c}$$

where α is the measured angular rotation of a solution containing c grams of optically active material per cm^3 of solution, and l is the path length of solution in decimetres.[1]

This method of calculating the specific rotation assumes that it is a constant independent of concentration; for most practical purposes this is so, but it is still customary to quote the concentration used in the measurement (usually in grams per 100 ml of solvent). Temperature variation can also bring about significant change in specific rotation. In protein molecules, the changes that occur in the rotatory power with change in temperature can be attributed to structural changes in the molecule. Solvent too can play an important part in determining the sign and magnitude of rotation, and thus must always be quoted with the value of specific rotation. It has become traditional for measurements of specific rotation to be made at a fixed wavelength, namely the yellow line (D line) of the sodium arc (589 nm) and the values to be designated as [α]$_D$. *Spectro-polarimeters* are now available, with which measurements of rotatory power can be made at any wavelength between 700 and 180 nm. Measurement of optical rotatory power as a function of wavelength is a technique known as *optical rotatory dispersion* (ORD).

In the region of wavelengths belonging to an electronic absorption band of a molecule, the two forms of circularly polarized light may be absorbed by an optically active substance to different extents. This preferential absorption of one or other of the circularly polarized beams is termed *circular dichroism* (CD), and is a characteristic property of all optically active molecules. Thus, optical rotation and circular dichroism are manifestations of the same phenomenon, optical activity; although the former can be observed at all wavelengths circular dichroism can be observed only within an electronic absorption band. When one of the circularly polarized beams is absorbed preferentially, it is

---

[1] The adoption of the SI units system alters the specific rotation as follows:

$$[\alpha]_D \atop (SI) = \frac{1}{100}\,[\alpha]_D \atop (old) \times \frac{\pi}{180}\ \text{rad m}^2\ \text{kg}^{-1}$$

represented by the *differential dichroic absorption*, $\Delta\varepsilon$, which equals $\varepsilon_L - \varepsilon_R$, where ε_L and ε_R are the molar extinction coefficients for left and right circularly polarized light respectively.

When the optical rotatory dispersion (ORD) is measured in the region of wavelengths corresponding to an absorption band of a molecule, then an unusually shaped ORD curve is obtained, which may involve *a change in the sign of the angular rotation*. This type of behaviour is called a *Cotton effect*, after the name of its discoverer, F. A. Cotton. The various types of Cotton effect together with the corresponding circular dichroism are shown in Fig. 6.23. If the maximum is at the higher-wavelength end it is termed a *positive* Cotton effect, whereas if it is at the shorter-wavelength end it is called a *negative* Cotton effect. It is also possible to observe *multiple* Cotton-effect which can contain several peaks and troughs and also points of inflexion.

The ORD and the CD curves of an optically active compound are very characteristic of its molecular structure and the curves are usually an extremely sensitive way of detecting slight differences in configuration and conformation between closely related stereoisomers. Certain data are taken from the ORD and CD curves in order to characterize an optically active compound. These include the positions of peaks and troughs in the ORD curve and the amplitude and breadth of the Cotton effect. In the case of CD, the values and positions of the maxima in the curve are recorded along with the bandwidth at half peak height (see Fig. 6.23).

ORD and CD measurements have proved particularly useful in characterizing steroids; for example, the two 5α-cholestanones V and VI differ only in the position of the carbonyl group, and yet the two compounds give markedly different ORD and CD curves (Fig. 6.24).

One of the most fruitful applications of the ORD and CD techniques has been in the structural investigation of the three-dimensional structure of polypeptides and proteins. A helical conformation, because it is dissymmetric, endows a molecule in which it occurs with optical rotatory power. Furthermore in the case of polypeptides and proteins, the component amino-acid residues are dissymmetric, producing further rotatory power. When conformational changes take place in these molecules, as for example during *denaturation*, these changes may be followed by ORD and CD measurements.

It is possible to measure the helical content of a protein by means of ORD measurements. With the improved instrumentation of modern spectropolarimeters, measurements may be carried out in the region 240–180 nm and Cotton effects observed. A weak negative Cotton effect (trough at 233 nm) and a strong positive one (peak 198 nm) characterize the helical conformation and afford a good method of estimating the helical content of the polypeptide chain in solution. The ORD curves for a synthetic polypeptide and the protein bovine serum albumin are shown in Fig. 6.25(a). The former is essentially helical in solutions of acidic pH, and a random coil in alkaline pH. The

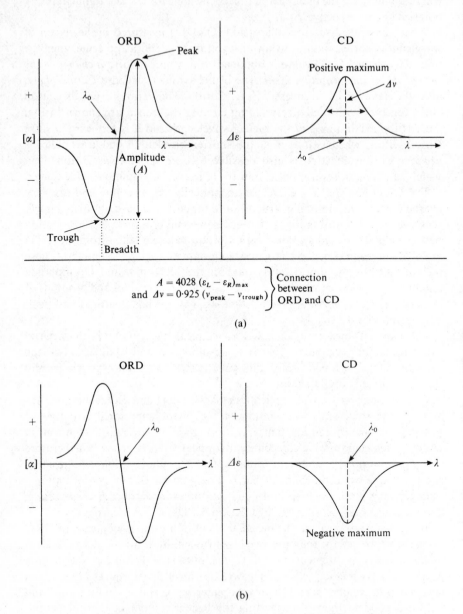

Fig. 6.23 Types of Cotton effect: (a) positive, (b) negative

244

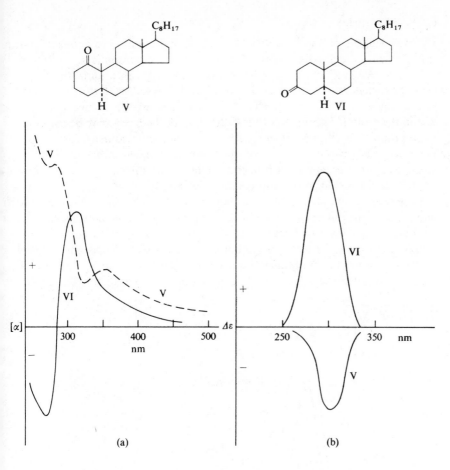

Fig. 6.24 (a) ORD curves and (b) CD curves for two 5α-cholestanones

protein is estimated to contain about 55–60 per cent helical conformation in neutral aqueous solution.

Similar information concerning the helical content of a protein can be obtained from circular dichroism spectra. The pattern obtained for α-helix containing proteins are the two negative CD bands at 209 and 222 nm and a cross-over point at 200 nm (Fig. 6.25b, curve D). In concentrated LiCl solution the loss of helical content of bovine serum albumin is shown by the decreased intensity of the circular dichroism bands (Fig. 6.25b, curve E). It is thought that the slight shift of the dichroic bands to lower wavelengths in concentrated LiCl solutions is associated with the unfolding of the protein molecule.

245

6.2.9 X-ray studies

The wavelengths of the X-rays used in structural studies are about 0·1 nm (1 Å), which is the same order of magnitude as interatomic distances in molecules. When a crystalline specimen is irradiated with a monochromatic beam of X-rays, the electrons of the atoms in the crystal scatter the beam and give a unique diffraction pattern which is related to the atomic positions within the crystal. The angles of the diffraction of the beam may be recorded photographically (Fig. 6.26) or by means of photoelectric detection in conjunction with a potentiometric recorder or even coupled directly to a high-speed electronic computer. From these angles, the dimensions of the unit crystalline cell within the crystal can be calculated.

To obtain a complete structural analysis of a crystalline substance, the intensities of the diffracted beams have to be measured. Calculations are then performed on a hypothetical model structure in an effort to correlate the proposed structure with the X-ray data. By successive calculations a closer correlation is gradually obtained between the model structure and the measured X-ray intensities. Eventually, a structure is deduced for the crystal

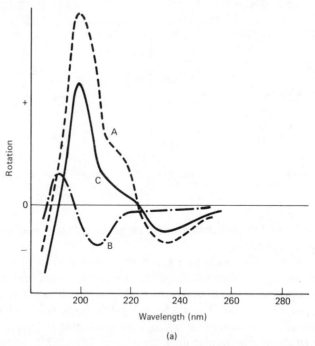

(a)

Fig. 6.25 (a) Cotton effects for poly-α-L-glutamic acid and bovine serum albumin: A, ORD curve of *helical* poly-α-L-glutamic acid; B, ORD curve of *random coil* poly-α-L-glutamic acid; C, ORD curve of bovine serum albumin in water, showing about 55–60 per cent helical content

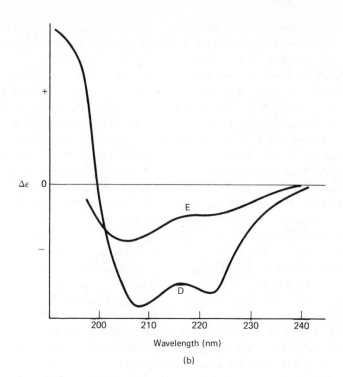

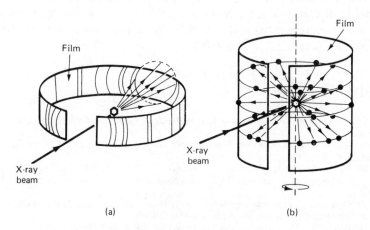

Fig. 6.25 (b) Circular dichroism spectra of bovine serum albumin in 1 M LiCl (D) and 7 M LiCl (E) showing loss of helical content in concentrated LiCl solution

Fig. 6.26 X-ray diffraction; (a) powder crystal photograph, (b) single-crystal rotation photography

247

which may be correct to 0·01 nm (0·1 Å) for small molecules and 0·1 nm to 0·2 nm for complex biological molecules. For measurements of this type, single-crystal specimens are needed.

In general, the larger the number of atoms in a molecule the more scattering centres for the X-ray beam there are likely to be and hence the more complex will be the X-ray diffraction pattern. Thus, the X-ray diffraction patterns of many biological molecules are extremely complex. One of the first of such molecules to have its structure elucidated by X-rays was vitamin B_{12}, (Hodgkin, 1956). More recently, single crystals of several globular proteins have been investigated by the X-ray method, for example lysozyme, ribonuclease, and chymotrypsin (Fig. 8.40). These investigations have met with great success in spite of the great complexities of the X-ray diffraction pattern and extremely lengthy computation involved. For example, Kendrew and his collaborators (1959) have deduced the structure of the myoglobin molecule to a resolution of 0·2 nm (2 Å). These experiments involved the measurement of the intensities of about 10000 diffractions in the X-ray pattern and a great many calculations based upon the intensity measurements.

Similar studies have been carried out on the haemoglobin molecule by Perutz (1960). A novel method of investigation devised by Perutz for use in work with proteins is the *isomorphous replacement method*. In this technique heavy atoms (which are very effective in scattering X-rays due to large numbers of electrons) are introduced into a protein molecule at specific positions without appreciably affecting the structural properties of the protein molecule. The large scattering power of the heavy atom within the protein molecule greatly assists in the interpretation of the X-ray data.

Other major triumphs of the X-ray method have been studies on nucleotide polymers, such as fibrous DNA. The latter measurements led to the double helix model of Watson and Crick (1953) for the DNA molecule. More recently the tertiary structure of yeast tRNA[Phe] has been determined by single-crystal X-ray studies [chapter 8, Fig. 8.48(b)].

Bibliography

1. J. A. Barnard and R. Chayen, *Modern Methods of Chemical Analysis*, McGraw-Hill, 1965.
2. D. H. Williams and I. Fleming, *Spectroscopic Methods in Organic Chemistry*, 2nd Edn, McGraw-Hill, 1973.
3. G. W. Ewing, *Instrumental Methods of Chemical Analysis*, 3rd Edn, McGraw-Hill, 1975.
4. R. L. Pecsok and L. D. Shields, *Modern Methods of Chemical Analysis*, 2nd Edn, Wiley, 1976.
5. K. A. Connors, *A Textbook of Pharmaceutical Analysis*, 2nd Edn, Wiley, 1975.
6. D. R. Browning, *Spectroscopy*, McGraw-Hill, 1969.
7. D. R. Browning, *Chromatography*, McGraw-Hill, 1969; also Harrap, 1973.
8. I. Smith and J. G. Feinberg, *Paper and Thin-layer Chromatography and Electrophoresis*, Longmans, 1972.

9. R. Stock and C. B. Rice, *Chromatographic Methods*, 3rd Edn, Chapman and Hall, 1974.
10. J. C. Touchstone, *Quantitive Thin-Layer Chromatography*, Wiley, 1973.
11. L. Fischer, *An Introduction to Gel-Chromatography*, North-Holland, 1969.
12. G. R. Lowe and P. G. Dean, *Affinity Chromatography*, Wiley-Interscience, 1974.
13. A. B. Littlewood, *Gas Chromatography*, 2nd Edn, Academic Press, 1970.
14. E. Stahl, *Drug Analysis by Chromatography and Microscopy*, Ann Arbor, 1974.
15. R. Porter, *Gas Chromatography in Biology and Medicine*, Churchill, 1969.
16. D. W. Grant, *Gas-Liquid Chromatography*, Van Nostrand–Rheinhold, 1971.
17. C. F. Simpson, *Practical High Performance Liquid Chromatography*, Heyden, 1976.
18. P. R. Brown, *High Pressure Liquid Chromatography, Biochemical and Biomedical Applications*, Academic Press, 1973.
19. M. Pess and J. Bartos, *Colormetric and Fluorimetric Analysis of Organic Compounds and Drugs*, Marcel Dekker, 1974.
20. F. S. Parker, *Applications of Infrared Spectroscopy in Biochemistry, Biology and Medicine*, Hilger, 1971.
21. R. G. J. Miller, *Laboratory Methods in Infrared Spectroscopy*, Heyden, 1965.
22. S. Udenfriend, *Fluorescence Assay in Biology and Medicine*, 2nd Edn, Academic Press, 1970.
23. C. E. White and R. J. Argauer, *Fluorescence Analysis*, Marcell Dekker, 1970.
24. D. J. E. Ingram, *Biological and Biochemical Applications of Electron Spin Resonance*, Hilger, 1969.
25. P. F. Knowles, D. Marsh and H. W. E. Rattle, *Magnetic Resonance of Biomolecules*, Wiley, 1976.
26. R. A. Dwek, *NMR in Biochemistry*, Clarendon Press, 1973.
27. P. Crabbé, *ORD and CD in Chemistry and Biochemistry*, Academic Press, 1972.
28. B Jirgensons, *Optical Activity of Proteins and other Macromolecules*, Chapman and Hall, 1973.
29. C. Nicolau, *Experimental Methods in Biophysical Chemistry*, Wiley, 1973.
30. B. L. Williams and K. Wilson, *A Biologist's Guide to Principles and Techniques of Practical Biochemistry*, Arnold, 1975.

249

7. The structure and properties of some natural organic compounds

7.1 AMINO ACIDS

7.1.1 The structure and properties of α-amino acids

The structural units of proteins are the α-amino acids. The amino acids are joined together by *peptide bonds* in a linear manner (Fig. 7.1) and the constituent amino acids are released when the protein is hydrolysed. The importance of amino acids, however, is not limited to their being components of proteins; for, during amino-acid metabolism, reactions occur in which they serve as precursors for many biologically important compounds. Although well over a hundred α-amino acids have been isolated and identified, only about twenty occur in a typical protein hydrolysate. These *common* amino acids have been grouped together in Table 7.1, on the basis of the nature of the *side chain* (R). These amino acids are usually denoted by a three-letter abbreviation. It will be noticed that proline has a quite different structure to the other amino acids, and is in fact an *imino acid*. However, as it is a usual constituent of proteins it is conveniently considered here. It must be remembered that the less common amino acids may be structurally and biologically very important in particular proteins; for example, hydroxyproline and hydroxylysine in the collagens; or they may be essential for certain metabolic processes, such as ornithine in the urea cycle, but otherwise they are not usually found in proteins.

Owing to the dipolar structure (I) α-amino acids are solids with high melting points. They are soluble or partially soluble in water and relatively insoluble in organic solvents. The physical properties of α-amino acids are more analogous to those of ionic compounds such as ammonium compounds. With

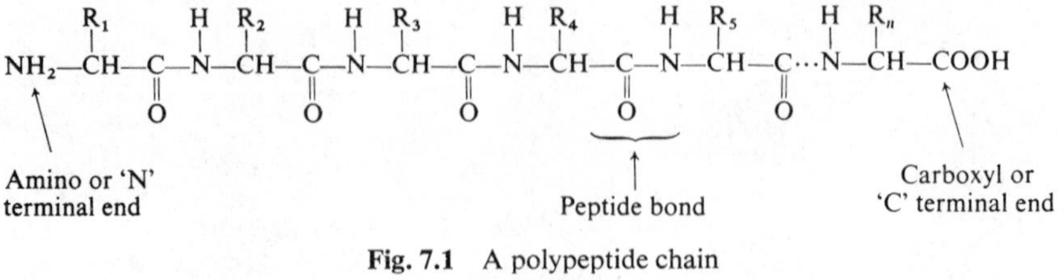

$$NH_2—CH—C—N—CH—C—N—CH—C—N—CH—C—N—CH—C\cdots N—CH—COOH$$

Amino or 'N' terminal end

Peptide bond

Carboxyl or 'C' terminal end

Fig. 7.1 A polypeptide chain

250

the exception of glycine, α-amino acids are dissymmetric. In general only the L-enantiomorph is found as a constituent of proteins. D-Amino acids are relatively rare; D-glutamic acid occurs in the protein of the capsule of anthrax bacillus, and some polypeptide antibiotics contain D-amino acids as part of their structure.

The two functional groups in amino acids may act independently and thus reactions similar to those of simple carboxylic acids and simple primary amines result. In either case, the dipolar structure of the amino acid is destroyed. Salt formation can take place in two ways: in the presence of strong bases (such as NaOH), the carboxylate anion forms a salt with the base cation (II). On the other hand, in acid solution, the amino group is involved in cation formation (III).

$$
\begin{array}{ccc}
& \overset{R}{\underset{|}{}} & \\
Cl^- \ ^+NH_3-CH-C{\displaystyle \mathop{\lessgtr}_{OH}^{O}} & \xleftarrow{\ HCl\ } \quad ^+NH_3-CH-C{\displaystyle \mathop{\lessgtr}_{O^-}^{O}} \quad \xrightarrow{\ NaOH\ } & NH_2-CH-C{\displaystyle \mathop{\lessgtr}_{O^-}^{O}} \ Na^+ \\
\text{III} & \text{I} & \text{II}
\end{array}
$$

Some amino acids have reactive functional groups in their side chains. Further acidic properties arise from the carboxyl groups of aspartic and glutamic acids and from the phenolic group of tyrosine. In a similar way, lysine, arginine, and histidine have a basic reaction arising from their side chain functional groups.

The α-amino group may be acylated. The general type of reaction is:

$$
R'-C{\displaystyle \mathop{\lessgtr}_{X}^{O}} + NH_2\overset{R}{\underset{|}{C}}HCOOH \longrightarrow R'-C{\displaystyle \mathop{\lessgtr}_{NH\overset{R}{\underset{|}{C}}HCOOH}^{O}} + HX
$$

$$\text{IV} \qquad\qquad\qquad\qquad\qquad\qquad\qquad\qquad \text{V}$$

For example, toxic benzoic acid may be expelled from the mammalian body as the benzoyl derivative of glycine–hippuric acid (V; R' = C_6H_5—, R = H). Another important example of this type of reaction is the preparation of N-benzyloxycarbonyl derivatives (V; R' = $C_6H_5CH_2$—O—) using benzyl chloroformate (IV; R' = $C_6H_5CH_2$—O—, X = Cl) which are used extensively as amino (N) protected derivatives in polypeptide synthesis. Like primary amines, the amino group can condense with aldehydes to form Schiff's bases (section 4.5.1) and, under certain conditions, decarboxylation may occur. This reaction takes place in the decarboxylation of amino acids in micro-organisms when the amino acid is present as a Schiff's base of pyridoxal phosphate. Nitrous acid converts the amino group to a hydroxyl group with the evolution of nitrogen. Nitrogen is evolved quantitatively, and this reaction forms the basis of the *Van Slyke* method for estimating the number of primary amino groups in proteins.

The carboxyl group may be esterified (VI) with an alcohol by acid catalysis. Unlike the original amino acids, the esters, particularly methyl and ethyl (VI; R' = CH_3— or CH_3CH_2—) are not very stable. They decompose on heating

Table 7.1 Common amino acids

Name	Abbr.†	Constitutional formula	Isoelectric point (see section 5.6.2)	$[\alpha]_D$ of natural isomer
Neutral alkyl side chains				
Glycine	Gly	$CH_2(NH_3^+)COO^-$	5·97	Inactive
L-Alanine	Ala	$CH_3CH(NH_3^+)COO^-$	6·00	$+2\cdot7°/H_2O$
L-Valine	Val	$(CH_3)_2CHCH(NH_3^+)COO^-$	5·96	$+6\cdot3°/H_2O$
L-Leucine	Leu	$(CH_3)_2CHCH_2CH(NH_3^+)COO^-$	6·02	$-10\cdot4°/H_2O$
L-Isoleucine	Ile	$CH_3CH_2CH(CH_3)CH(NH_3^+)COO^-$	5·98	$+12\cdot2°/H_2O$
Aromatic and heterocyclic side chains				
L-Phenylalanine	Phe	$C_6H_5CH_2CH(NH_3^+)COO^-$	5·48	$-35\cdot5°/H_2O$
L-Tyrosine	Tyr	$p\text{-}OH\cdot C_6H_4CH_2CH(NH_3^+)COO^-$	5·66	$-8\cdot1°/21$ per cent HCl
L-Tryptophan	Trp (Try)	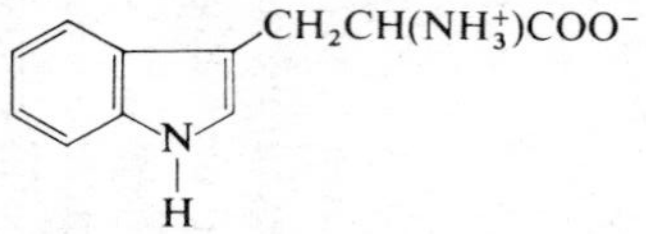 $CH_2CH(NH_3^+)COO^-$ (indole ring)	5·89	$-33\cdot4°/EtOH$
L-Histidine (also a basic amino acid)	His	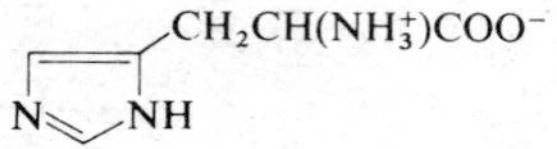 $CH_2CH(NH_3^+)COO^-$ (imidazole ring)	7·59	$-39\cdot7°/H_2O$
L-Proline	Pro	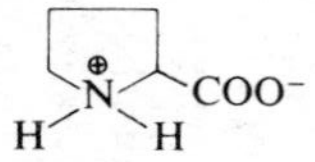 (pyrrolidine ring) COO^-	5·83	$-80\cdot9°/H_2O$

Acidic and amide side chains				
L-Aspartic Acid	Asp	$HOOCCH_2CH(NH_3^+)COO^-$	2·77	$+4\cdot4°/H_2O$
L-Glutamic Acid	Glu	$HOOCCH_2CH_2CH(NH_3^+)COO^-$	3·22	$+11\cdot0°/H_2O$
L-Asparagine	Asn	$NH_2COCH_2CH(NH_3^+)COO^-$	5·41	$-5\cdot4°/H_2O$
L-Glutamine	Gln	$NH_2COCH_2CH_2CH(NH_3^+)COO^-$	5·65	$+8\cdot0°/H_2O$
Basic side chains				
L-Arginine	Arg	$HN{=}C{-}NHCH_2CH_2CH_2CH(NH_3^+)COO^-$ with H_2N	10·76	$+11\cdot4°/\ddagger/H_2O$
L-Lysine	Lys	$NH_2CH_2CH_2CH_2CH_2CH(NH_3^+)COO^-$	9·74	$+19\cdot5°/\ddagger/HCl$
Side chains with alkyl hydroxyl group				
L-Serine	Ser	$HOCH_2CH(NH_3^+)COO^-$	5·68	$+6\cdot9°/H_2O$
L-Threonine	Thr	$HOCH(CH_3)CH(NH_3^+)COO^-$	6·53	$-28\cdot3°/H_2O$
Side chains containing sulphur				
L-Cysteine	Cys	$HSCH_2CH(NH_3^+)COO^-$	5·05	$+5\cdot5°/\ddagger/HCl$
L-Cystine	Cys	$SCH_2CH(NH_3^+)COO^-$	5·06	$-212\cdot0°/1$ per cent HCl
	Cys	$SCH_2CH(NH_3^+)COO^-$		
L-Methionine	Met	$CH_3SCH_2CH_2CH(NH_3^+)COO^-$	5·74	$-6\cdot9°/H_2O$

† Abbreviated designations used for amino acids are those recommended by IUPAC/IUB *Information Bulletin* No. 26.

‡ Value for mono HCl salt.

253

either to give linear polymers—polyamino acids (VII) or by condensation of two amino-acid ester molecules to form a cyclic amide—a diketopiperazine (VIII).

$$\text{VI}\quad NH_2CHC\overset{R}{\underset{O-R'}{\overset{O}{\diagup}}}\quad :NH_2CHC\overset{R}{\underset{O-R'}{\overset{O}{\diagup}}}\quad :NH_2\cdots \longrightarrow NH_2CHC\overset{R}{\underset{NHCHC}{\overset{O}{\diagdown}}}\overset{R}{\underset{NH}{\diagdown}}\cdots$$

VII
Polyamino acid

LiAlH₄   NH₂NH₂

$$\underset{\text{IX}}{NH_2CHCH_2OH}\qquad \underset{\text{X}}{NH_2CHC\overset{R}{\underset{NHNH_2}{\overset{O}{\diagdown}}}}$$

Amino alcohol   Amino acid hydrazide

$$H_2NCHC\overset{R}{\overset{O}{\diagup}}\quad \underset{R'-O}{\overset{O}{\diagdown}}C-CH\overset{NH}{\underset{R}{\diagup}} \longrightarrow \underset{O}{\overset{R}{CH-C}}\overset{O}{\underset{C-CH}{\overset{HN}{}\overset{NH}{}}}\overset{}{\underset{R}{}}$$

VIII
Diketopiperazine

Esterification provides a method of carboxyl protection during peptide synthesis. The normal esterification procedure may be used in the synthesis of ethyl or methyl esters, but the preparation of the frequently used t-butyl $[(CH_3)_3—C—O—]$ and benzyl $(C_6H_5CH_2—O—)$ requires special methods. Selective esterification of the carboxyl groups of amino-acid side chains (aspartic and glutamic acids) is possible.

Reduction of amino acid ethyl or methyl esters with lithium aluminium hydride affords amino alcohols (IX). The reduction of an esterified C-terminal end of a polypeptide chain, and subsequent identification of the amino acid released on hydrolysis is a method used in structure determination on proteins (section 8.4.2).

The carboxyl group can also be converted to an acid chloride, anhydride or hydrazide (X); the latter type of derivative is formed when a polypeptide chain is treated with hydrazine in an alternative method for identifying the C-terminal amino acid.

Owing to the importance of amino acids, numerous colorimetric tests have been devised for their detection and estimation. Ninhydrin (1,2,3-triketo-hydrindene hydrate) is the best general reagent and produces a purple coloration. It is extremely sensitive; 0·1 μg of amino acid can be detected on a thin-layer plate. An alternative reagent is sodium 2,4,6-trinitrobenzene-1-sulphonate. One advantage of this reagent is that the coloration is produced without heating, as compared with that produced by ninhydrin. Coloured copper complexes are formed by amino acids and polypeptides, and this is the basis of the *biuret* method which is used in the assay of proteins. There are also a number of reagents which are more specific. Not only may these be used for individual amino acids, but also on peptides containing them. For example,

254

tyrosine produces a red *azo-dye* when coupled with diazotized α-nitroso-β-naphthol (see Fig. 4.1) or nitrated to give the yellow 3,5-dinitro-4-hydroxyphenylalanine (xanthoproteic acid reaction). The *indole* ring of tryptophan gives a purple colour with Ehrlich's reagent (*p*-dimethylaminobenzaldehyde) and the *imidazole* ring of histidine gives an orange coloration with diazotized sulphanilic acid.

7.1.2 Polypeptide synthesis

The order or *sequence* of amino acids in a polypeptide chain (Fig. 7.1) is of fundamental importance in both protein structure and function. Once the sequence has been elucidated (see section 8.4.2), synthesis of that chain by unambiguous methods is carried out to confirm that structure and also to provide fragments for biological studies. Great advances have been made in polypeptide synthesis in the last twenty years, and much of the progress has been closely aligned to the isolation of polypeptides with hormonal activity (see section 8.4.3). It is now possible, theoretically, to synthesize a polypeptide chain of any length. Molecules such as adrenocorticotrophin with thirty-nine amino acids, the two chains of insulin with a total of fifty-one amino acids and, more recently, ribonuclease with 124 amino acids, have been synthesized.

In order to ensure that specific peptide bond formation takes place, it is necessary to *protect* the non-reacting α-amino and α-carboxyl functions. Furthermore, the functional group of certain amino-acid side chains must also be protected. The preparation of the protected amino acids (XI and XII; Fig. 7.2) also destroys the dipolar structure. Some examples of amino

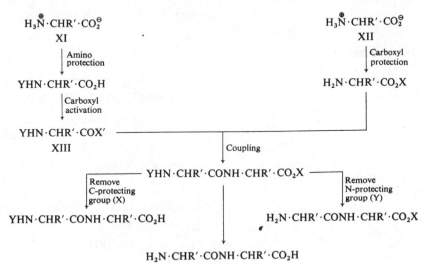

Fig. 7.2 Reaction sequence for the synthesis of a dipeptide

255

(N) and carboxyl (C) protection have already been mentioned in the previous section. Theoretically, the extension of a peptide chain may be accomplished in either of two directions (Fig. 7.2). Selective removal of the amino protecting group, Y, yields a new amino component which may be coupled with another N-protected amino acid. On the other hand, the selective removal of the protecting group, X, yields a new carboxyl component which may be coupled with another C-protected amino acid.

A peptide bond is established between two amino-acid residues in a *coupling reaction* (mechanism, see section 4.7.2). This process requires the activation of the carboxyl group (XIII; Fig. 7.2). During the coupling process there is a danger that the configuration of the asymmetric carbon atom of the carboxyl component may be partially changed (i.e., L→D). This problem is referred to as *racemization* The biological activity may be completely lost if the natural L configuration is not present at each residue. The problem of racemization is largely overcome by adopting a stepwise synthesis procedure starting at the C-terminal end (Fig. 7.3). The most frequently used method of activating a carboxyl group is by means of an *active-ester*, for example *p*-nitrophenyl ester ($X' = —O—C_6H_4\text{-}p\text{-}NO_2$, Fig. 7.3). It is interesting to note that the introduction of this type of carboxyl activation followed the discovery of the similar role played by thiol esters in metabolic reactions. A popular alternative coupling method is by the formation of an activated carboxyl component *in situ*, by, for example, the addition of a condensing agent such as N,N'-dicyclo-hexylcarbodi-imide. The stepwise scheme shown in Fig. 7.3 requires the selective removal of the amino-protecting group, Y. Of the many groups

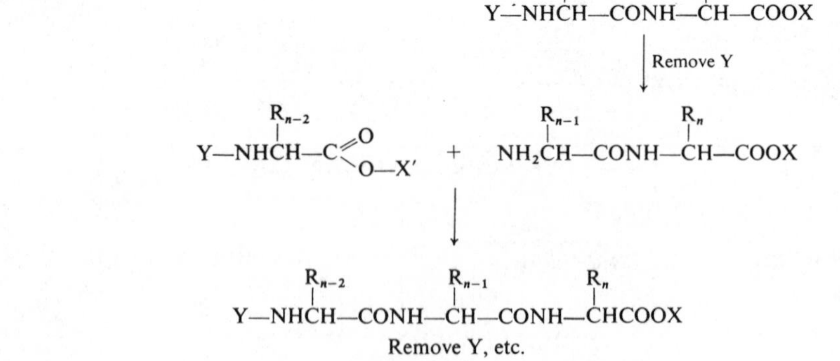

Protecting group Y

$$C_6H_5CH_2—O—\overset{\overset{\text{O}}{\|}}{C}— \text{(abbr. Z)}$$

Protecting group X

$(CH_3)_3C—$ (abbr. OBu^t)

Fig. 7.3 Stepwise synthesis of polypeptide chains

256

available, the most used is the benzyloxycarbonyl group. This may be removed at each stage by catalytic hydrogenation. Protection of the C-terminal end during the entire synthesis is achieved by a *t*-butyl ester which may be removed at the end by mild acid hydrolysis.

In this way, polypeptide chains may be synthesized in good yield, and may, if necessary, be joined to other sections to build up a long chain. A practical problem that arises is that many of the intermediates in a peptide synthesis are difficult to crystallize and purify. An attempt has been made to solve this problem and, at the same time, produce a procedure which can be automated. This is the technique due to Merrifield, in which the C-terminal amino acid is joined to an insoluble resin. The second amino acid is added as the N-protected derivative and a coupling carried out with a condensing agent. After removal of the N-protecting group, a third residue is introduced (Fig. 7.3). In this way, the growing polypeptide chain remains fixed to the resin and is freed from contamination by washing. This technique was used in the total synthesis of the enzyme ribonuclease.

7.2 LIPIDS

7.2.1 Simple lipids

Lipids form a group of organic compounds which are widely distributed in living systems. The term *lipid* cannot be concisely defined, but refers to a large number of compounds which have similar solubility properties. Lipids are soluble in any of a group of non-polar solvents (the so-called *fat solvents*) such as acetone, ether, chloroform, or benzene, and are insoluble in water. The structures of these compounds vary from relatively simple fatty-acid esters to complex lipids like gangliosides, steroids and certain vitamins. In this section, the emphasis is placed on the structure and properties of those lipids which are derivatives of long-chain fatty acids.

The most abundant of the simple lipids are the glycerides, which make up over 98 per cent of the lipid of adipose tissue in mammals. These compounds are esters of fatty acids and a trihydric alcohol—glycerol. The three types of glyceride (II–IV) are shown below. The groups R_1, R_2 and R_3 refer to long-chain fatty-acid residues ranging from C_{12} to C_{24} in length. Naturally occurring glycerides (*fats*) are complex mixtures of triglycerides, and individual tri-

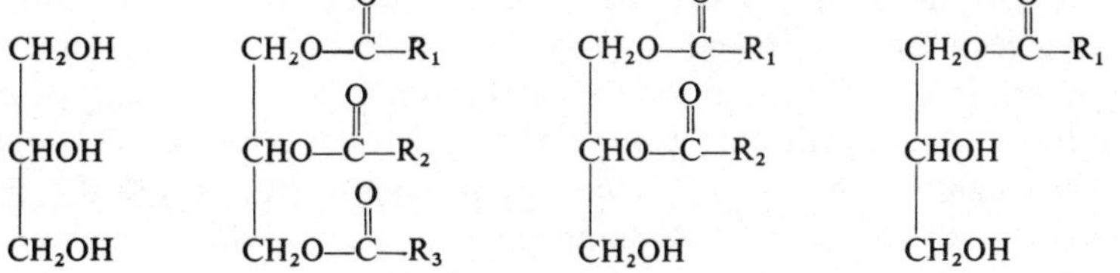

CH_2OH	$CH_2O-\overset{O}{\overset{\|}{C}}-R_1$	$CH_2O-\overset{O}{\overset{\|}{C}}-R_1$	$CH_2O-\overset{O}{\overset{\|}{C}}-R_1$
$CHOH$	$CHO-\overset{O}{\overset{\|}{C}}-R_2$	$CHO-\overset{O}{\overset{\|}{C}}-R_2$	$CHOH$
CH_2OH	$CH_2O-\overset{O}{\overset{\|}{C}}-R_3$	CH_2OH	CH_2OH
I	II	III	IV
Glycerol	Triglyceride	Diglyceride	Monoglyceride

glycerides may themselves contain two or three different fatty acids. The best method of nomenclature in these compounds is to designate the glycerol carbon atoms as 1, 2, 3, although the old system of α, β, α' is still used. In the structural determination, the ester linkages are cleaved by alkaline hydrolysis (section 4.7.2) to yield glycerol and the alkali metal salts of the fatty acids. The free fatty acids are then precipitated by the addition of mineral acid.

Some simple lipids are esters of long-chain acids, and also long-chain alcohols. The alcohols may be open chain, for example, cetyl alcohol $(CH_3(CH_2)_{14}CH_2OH)$ or alicyclic, for example, a sterol. In mammalian tissues, cholesterol esters are the most abundant compounds of this type.

7.2.2 Fatty acids

Most naturally occurring fatty acids have an even number of carbon atoms. This fact can be convincingly explained by the method of biosynthesis (see section 9.3.5). Both saturated and unsaturated fatty acids are found in glycerides, and some of the more common saturated acids are listed in Table 7.2,

Table 7.2 Some saturated fatty acids found in natural fats: $CH_3(CH_2)_nCOOH$

Trivial name	IUPAC name	n	Common source
Butyric	1 Butanoic	2	Milk fat
Caproic	1 Hexanoic	4	Milk fat, palm nut oil
Caprylic	1 Octanoic	6	Palm nut oil
Capric	1 Decanoic	8	Palm nut oil
Lauric	1 Dodecanoic	10	Laurel oil
Myristic	1 Tetradecanoic	12	Nutmeg seed oil
Palmitic	1 Hexadecanoic	14	Major component of most fats
Stearic	1 Octadecanoic	16	Major component of most fats
Arachidic	1 Eicosanoic	18	Peanut oil

together with their names and structures. Among these acids, those with sixteen and eighteen carbon atoms occur most widely. It should be noted that the trivial names are still in common use in this field. The hydrocarbon chain is numbered with the carboxyl carbon atom as number 1.

The most abundant of all unsaturated acids is oleic; it makes up as much as 45 per cent of the fatty-acid content of mammalian body fat. Certain unsaturated fatty acids with more than one double bond are essential for the maintenance of life in Man and animals. Since these fatty acids are apparently not synthesized in sufficient quantities, like vitamins and certain amino acids, they must be present in the diet. Consequently, they have been termed *essential fatty acids*, and sometimes *vitamin F*. Three common members of this group are linoleic, linolenic and arachidonic acids (Fig. 7.4) with two, three and four non-conjugated double bonds respectively. The configuration at all these double bonds, like that in oleic acid (section 2.9), is *cis*.

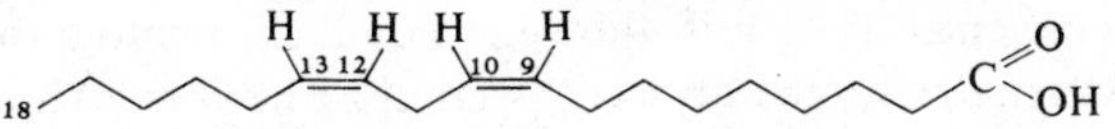

$\Delta^{9,12}$ *cis*-Linoleic acid ($C_{18}H_{32}O_2$)

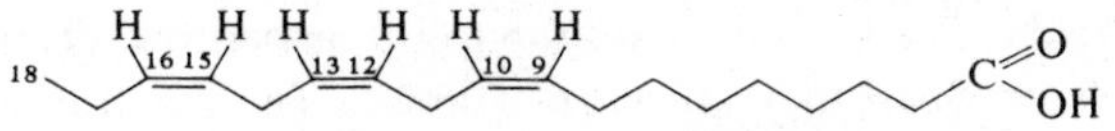

$\Delta^{9,12,15}$ *cis*-Linolenic acid ($C_{18}H_{30}O_2$)

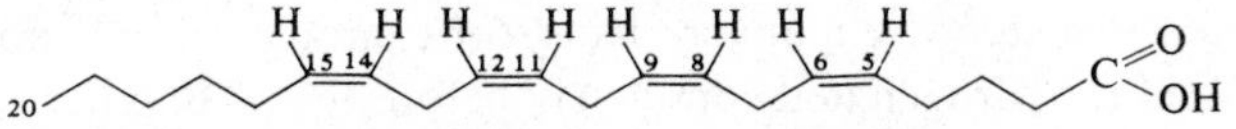

$\Delta^{5,8,11,14}$ *cis*-Arachidonic acid ($C_{20}H_{32}O_2$)

Fig. 7.4 The structures of the essential unsaturated fatty acids. (In writing the structure of long-chain fatty acids it is usual to represent the chain of CH_2 groups by zigzag lines in which each intersection corresponds to a carbon atom; the hydrogen atoms are put in only at the double bonds, to indicate the stereochemistry. In the name, the position of the double bonds is given by a number.)

Properties of fatty acids

(a) Physical properties The saturated fatty acids represent a good example of a homologous series, in which each member differs from the next by one —CH_2— group, but otherwise they are structurally identical. There is a gradation of physical properties, the lower members being liquids and the higher members waxy solids (cf. hydrocarbons). The lower members may be characterized by boiling point or by refractive index; the higher members by melting point or refractive index measured above the melting point.

Examination of the melting point reveals that the values for the even-numbered fatty acids lie on a smooth curve, the values increasing with chain length. The melting points of the odd-numbered acids lie on a similar but different curve. An odd-numbered acid has a melting point lower than the even-numbered homologue preceding it. Thus, the melting points of the homologous series do not rise smoothly with increasing molecular weight, but rise and fall alternately. This alternation of melting point can be observed in other homologous series, and is associated with the molecular arrangement in the solid state. Boiling points do not follow this pattern.

Unsaturated fatty acids have lower melting points than the corresponding saturated acids with the same number of carbon atoms. Melting points fall with increasing unsaturation, and *cis* isomers have lower melting points than the *trans* isomers.

(b) Chemical properties Fatty acids are produced from fat by alkaline hydrolysis. A *saponification number* may be calculated, which represents the number of milligrams of potassium hydroxide required to hydrolyse 1 g of the fat. The number is inversely proportional to the number of carbon atoms in the molecule, and can assist in the identification of fats. The fatty acids in such a hydrolysate are conveniently identified by gas–liquid chromatography as their methyl esters. Alternatively, the glyceryl esters may be converted directly to methyl esters by sodium methoxide, a process called inter-esterification.

Unsaturated fatty acids may be hydrogenated to produce the corresponding saturated fatty acids. The hydrogenation may be carried out on the isolated unsaturated acids or when they are part of lipids. The reaction is best performed by catalytic hydrogenation; the best catalysts are Pt, Pd, Ni or Cu. When there are a number of double bonds present in the molecule, they are hydrogenated in a stepwise manner. Thus, for example, the Δ^{12} double bond in linoleic acid is hydrogenated completely before the Δ^9 bond.

Unsaturated fatty acids are readily oxidized by reagents such as potassium permanganate. The oxidation of these acids by atmospheric oxygen is a process of great commercial and biological interest and is termed *auto-oxidation*. Auto-oxidation takes place by complex free-radical mechanisms and occurs in such diverse processes as the hardening of paints and varnishes or fats becoming rancid.

The addition of iodine across the double bond (see section 4.5.2) in unsaturated fatty acids is used as an analytical method for estimating the *degree of unsaturation*. The *iodine number* is defined as the number of grams of iodine absorbed by 100 g of the fat. Iodine reacts only very slowly, and nowadays it is replaced by more reactive compounds, such as iodine monochloride (Wijs' solution) or iodine monobromide (Hanus' solution).

7.2.3 Complex lipids

These compounds are esters of fatty acids, and may also contain phosphorus and nitrogen in the form of phosphoric-acid residues and nitrogenous bases respectively. The most abundant are the glycerophospholipids or glycerophosphatides, which can make up as much as 70 per cent of the complex lipid content of tissues.

(a) Glycerophosphatides This group of glycerol-containing phospholipids includes phosphatidic acids, phosphatidyl esters, inositol phosphatides, lysophosphatides, and plasmalogens. The phosphatidic acids (V) are diesters of l-glycerophosphoric acid where one of the outer hydroxyl groups of glycerol

V
An L-1-phosphatidic acid

VI
Phosphatidyl choline (a lecithin)

VII
Phosphatidyl ethanolamine

is esterified with phosphoric acid. These are acidic compounds, and are usually found as Ca^{2+} or Mg^{2+} salts. The central carbon of the glycerol moiety is asymmetric. It has been found that only one enantiomorphic form is present and these belong to the L-*series*. Plant phosphatides (from seeds) contain fatty acids of which 20–30 per cent are saturated, while animal phosphatides, on the other hand, usually contain a higher proportion of saturated acids ($\sim$60 per cent).

The phosphatidyl esters are esters of phosphatidic acids and nitrogen-containing alcohols such as choline, ethanolamine and serine or a polyhydroxy alcohol inositol. The lecithins (VI) contain choline and generally two different fatty acids, one of which is unsaturated. They are the most abundant of the naturally occurring glycerophosphatides. The choline–phosphate residue is at C_1 and the configuration at C_2 is L. The molecules exist in the form of zwitter-ions (cf. amino acids). The fatty acids present are mainly C_{18} and C_{22} saturated and C_{22} unsaturated.

Next to the lecithins, the ethanolamine-containing glycerophosphatides (VII) are the most common. These complex lipids are sometimes grouped with those containing serine (VIII) and inositol (IX) residues, and are known as *cephalins*. The three types of compounds occur in brain tissue. Inositol is a hexahydroxycyclohexane, of which there are nine possible stereoisomers. The major form present is one of the seven optically inactive forms, myoinositol (X). This particular isomer was originally isolated from muscle tissue and has been shown to be a growth factor for animals. Although it could be regarded

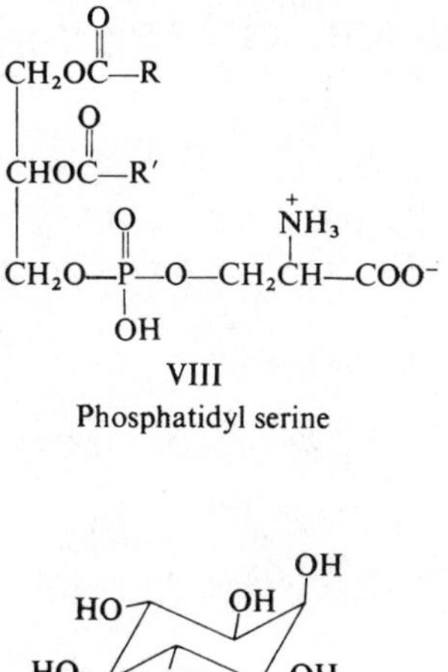

VIII
Phosphatidyl serine

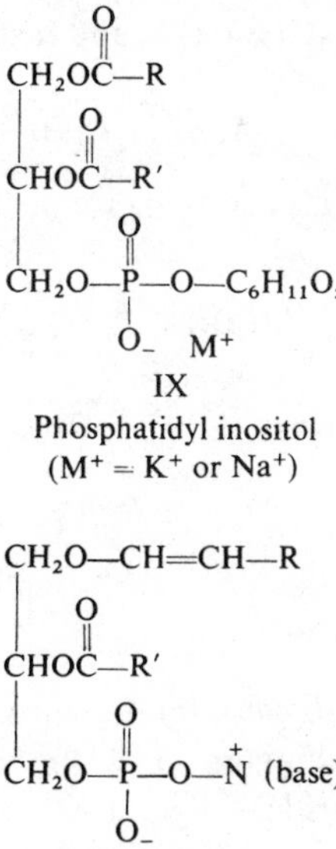

IX
Phosphatidyl inositol
($M^+ = K^+$ or Na^+)

X

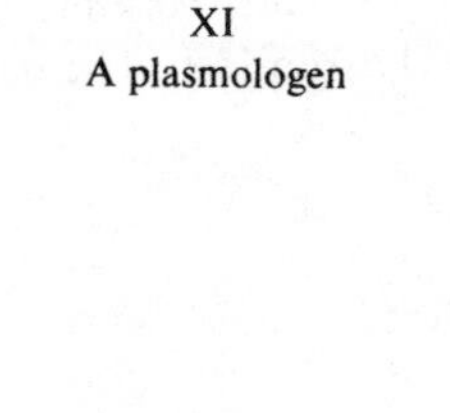

XI
A plasmologen

261

as part of the vitamin B complex (see section 7.4.2), the amount required in the diet is greater than that usually needed for a *vitamin*. This is consistent with the idea that myoinositol is essential as a structural component of tissue rather than as a *catalyst* for biochemical reactions.

Closely related to the phosphatidyl esters are the plasmologens (XI; $\overset{+}{N}$(base) = choline or ethanolamine). On hydrolysis, the vinyl ether residue (—O—CH=CH—) at C_3 of the glycerol moiety produces an aldehyde (RCHO); many of these have been identified as long-chain compounds (C_{14}, C_{16}, C_{18}, and C_{18} unsaturated). This hydrolysis occurs biochemically, and is responsible for the histochemical aldehyde reaction of cytoplasm. Plasmologens are widely distributed in animal tissue, with particularly high concentrations in the myelin of brain, heart nerve, and skeletal muscle.

(b) Sphingolipids This group of complex lipids contains the base sphingosine (XII) or dihydrosphingosine (XIII) in animal tissue. The structurally similar phytosphingosine and dehydrophytosphingosine are found in plant tissue. These bases replace the glycerol residue of other complex lipids. The sphingophosphatides occur in the myelin sheaths of nerves and are called the sphingomyelins. Sphingolipids are especially abundant in the brain, and certain diseases are characterized biochemically by their accumulation. A fatty-acid residue is present in an amide linkage at C_2 and a choline-phosphate or ethanolamine-phosphate moiety is attached to the terminal carbon (C_1). Sphingolipids are separated on the basis of the different fatty-acid residues (XIV; R) which they contain. Acids with twenty-four carbon atoms predominate—for example, lignoceric [$CH_3(CH_2)_{22}$—], α-hydroxylignoceric [$CH_3(CH_2)_{21}CHOH$—] and nervonic [$CH_3(CH_2)_7CH=CH(CH_2)_{12}$—].

XII
Sphingosine

XIII
Dihydrosphingosine

Ceramide

$X = $ —P—O—CH$_2$CH$_2$—$\overset{+}{N}$H$_3$

Sphingoethanolamine
(a sphingomyelin)

XIV

(c) Glycolipids *(i) Cerebrosides* These compounds are structurally related to sphingomyelins, the base–phosphate residue is replaced by a single monosaccharide—sugar (section 7.3.1) residue. The sphingosine–fatty acid moiety (XIV) is called ceramide and a modern name for these compounds is monoglycosyl ceramides. The nature of the fatty acid residue (R; XIV) is used

to distinguish the compounds of this group. Thus, cerasin contains lignoceric acid (*n*–tetracosanoic acid), cerebron (phrenosine) contains α–hydroxyligno-ceric acid and nervone contains nervonic acid ($\varDelta^{15}$ *cis*-tetracosenoic acid). The sugar residue (XIV; X = monosaccharide) in the common monoglycosyl ceramides is D-galactose and they make up the largest single component of the myelin sheath of nerve. D–Glucose is found in cerebrosides from human blood serum. Diglycosyl ceramides or *cytosides* occur where a disaccharide replaces the single monosaccharide; the most common of these contains a lactose residue [Fig. 7.5(a)].

(*ii*) *Globosides, haematosides and gangliosides* Globosides are tetraglycosyl ceramides where an acetylated amino sugar (for example, *N*-acetyl-D-galacto-samine) is present in addition to three monosaccharides. In haematosides, a sialic acid (for example, *N*-acetyl neuraminic acid) is present instead of an acetylated amino sugar. In both types of compound, a short oligosaccharide chain is joined to the ceramide residue. Gangliosides contain monosaccharides, acetylated amino sugar and sialic acid residues in their oligosaccharide chain which is again joined to a ceramide residue [Fig. 7.5(a)]. Gangliosides are characterized on the basis of the number of sialic-acid residues present; they occur not only in the grey matter of the brain but also in many other animal tissues. The biosynthesis and degradation of gangliosides and other glycolipids appears to be essential for normal life Several conditions have been observed in Man, where abnormal degradation occurs. The conditions arise when an enzyme is deficient, due to a genetic defect, that is required for the degradation. Tay-Sachs' and Fabry's diseases occur from abnormal degradation of gang-liosides; in the latter disease, incomplete hydrolysis of the oligosaccharide chain occurs resulting in the accumulation of a triglycosyl ceramide.

Type of glycolipid	*Structural arrangement*
1 Cerebroside (monoglycosyl ceramide)	gal-Cer glc-Cer
2 Cytoside (diglycosyl ceramide)	gal-β (1 → 4)-glc-Cer
3 Haematoside (triglycosyl ceramide)	NANA-β (2 → 3)-gal-β (1 → 4)-glc-Cer
4 Globoside (tetraglycosyl ceramide)	NAcgal-β (1 → 3)-gal-β (1 → 4)-gal-β (1 → 4)-glc-Cer
5 Monoganglioside (contains a single NANA)	NAcgal-β (1 → 3)-gal-β (1 → 4)-gal-β (1 → 4)-glc-Cer 3 ↑ 2β | NANA

Cer = Ceramide (XIV)
gal = D-Galactose
glc = D-Glucose
NAcgal = *N*-Acetyl-D-galactosamine
NANA = *N*-Acetyl neuraminic acid (section 7.3.2).

Fig. 7.5 (a) Structure of glycolipids

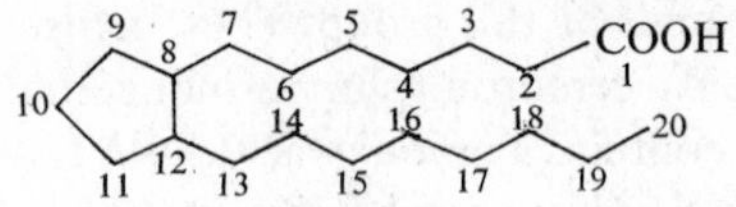

Carbon skeleton of a prostaglandins

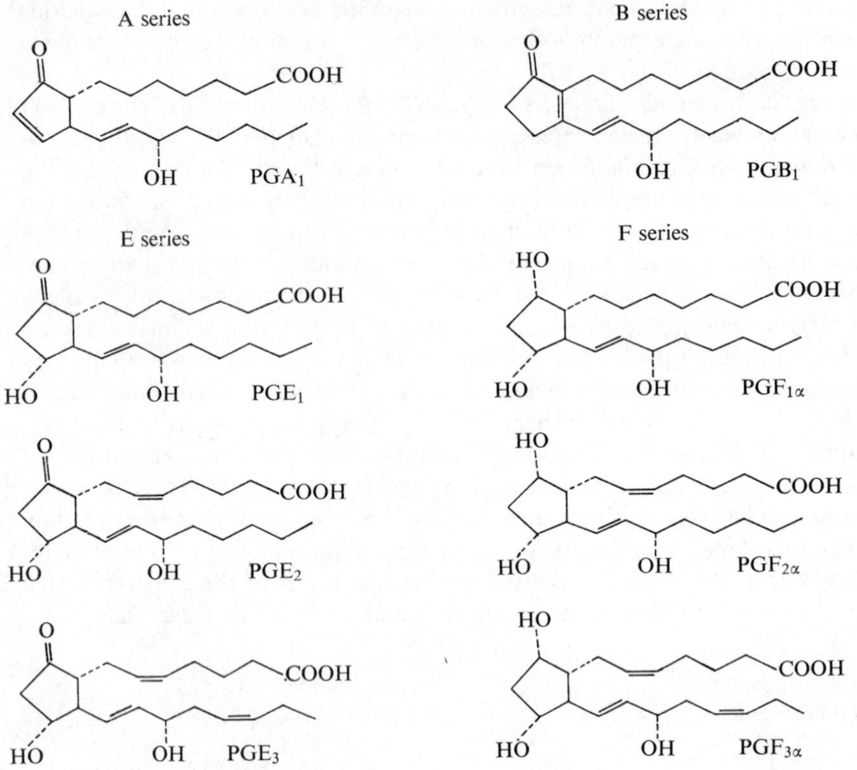

Fig. 7.5 (b) Structure of prostaglandins

(d) *Prostaglandins* These are lipids derived directly from polyunsaturated fatty acids, notably arachidonic acid (Fig. 7.4). They have been extensively studied in recent years owing to their important physiological activity. The general structure of these molecules is shown in Fig. 7.5(b) and they arise by cyclization of the central part of a C_{20} polyunsaturated fatty acid. The outer sections of the hydrocarbon chain are then left as substituents (*side chains*) of a cyclopentane ring. Each prostaglandin is characterized by the presence of hydroxyl and/or keto substituents on the ring; hydroxyl substituents on a side chain and by double bonds in the ring and in the side chains. The major

264

classes of prostaglandin are designated: PGA, PGB, PGE and PGF which is followed by a subscript denoting the number of double bonds *outside* the ring. Specific stereochemistry is present in each prostaglandin: thus, in the A, E and F series, the two hydrocarbon side chains are *trans*, while in the B series they are *cis* [Fig. 7.5(b)]. The stereochemistry of hydroxyl substituents is also characteristic of a particular prostaglandin. (The subscript 'α' refers to the stereochemistry of ring hydroxyl group, for example PGF_{1x}.)

Initially prostaglandins were found in high concentration in tissue from mammalian reproductive organs, but they appear to be present in smaller amounts in many other tissues. Their physiological action appears to be as *modulators* of hormone activity rather than as hormones in their own right. The mechanism of PGE_1 in the hydrolysis of triglycerides in adipose tissue has been studied in detail. This hydrolysis is stimulated by *extra-cellular* hormones such as adrenalin and glucagon, and the presence of PGE_1 inhibits their action at concentrations as low as 10^{-7} M. It seems likely that PGE_1 acts by inhibiting the enzyme adenyl cyclase which catalyses the synthesis of the *intra-cellular* hormone cyclic-AMP (section 9.3.4). Another important aspect of prostaglandin activity is in mammalian reproduction; PGE_2 rapidly induces birth in mammals and PGF_{2x} can act as a contraceptive since it *reduces* the secretion of progesterone, a hormone required for successful implantation of a fertilized ovum in the uterus.

7.3 CARBOHYDRATES

7.3.1 Classification and the structure of monosaccharides

The name *carbohydrates* originated in the observation that many compounds of this class have the empirical composition $C_x(H_2O)_y$, and were at one time referred to as 'hydrates of carbon'. This name has no structural significance and, furthermore, there are a number of carbohydrates whose empirical composition cannot be expressed in this way, for example, deoxyribose ($C_5H_{10}O_4$). A reasonable structural definition is that these compounds are either polyhydroxy-aldehydes, or polyhydroxy-ketones, or a compound which can be hydrolysed to one of these. Carbohydrates are given a name ending -*ose*.

On the basis of structure four groups can be distinguished.

(a) Monosaccharides Structurally, these are the simplest carbohydrates, and they cannot be hydrolysed into more simple compounds of the class. They are polyhydroxy-aldehydes known as *aldoses*, or polyhydroxy-ketones known as *ketoses*. At this stage it is convenient to refer to the presence of an *aldehyde* or *ketone* group; in fact, the carbonyl bond is lost in the formation of the ring structure. Nevertheless, a number of reactions exhibited by simple carbonyl compounds are paralleled by similar reactions in aldoses and ketoses. Monosaccharides are named systematically, according to the number

of carbon atoms they contain. The most abundant are the *hexoses* with six carbon atoms; for example, glucose, galactose and fructose.

(b) Oligosaccharides Molecules of these carbohydrates are made up of a small number of monosaccharide units joined together by *glycosidic bonds*

$$(-\overset{|}{C}-O-\overset{|}{C}-).$$ The most common examples of this class are disaccharides

containing two monosaccharides joined by a single glycosidic bond.

(c) Polysaccharides These are macromolecules containing many of hundreds of monosaccharide units. These are conveniently described with other naturally occurring macromolecules in chapter 8.

(d) Glycosides These contain a non-carbohydrate moiety. Important examples of this type of compound are the *nucleosides* where the carbohydrate residue is a pentose (see section 7.4.1).

Aldoses

The structural investigation of a monosaccharide falls into three stages; these stages will be outlined briefly with reference to the most abundant of all the monosaccharides—(+)-glucose. In the first stage, the constitutional formula is determined. This includes the determination of the number and arrangement of the carbon atoms, the identification and position of the aldehyde or ketone function, and the arrangement of the hydroxyl functions. The evidence for the constitutional formula of (+)-glucose (I) is summarized in Fig. 7.6. The presence of the aldehyde group of an aldose may be deduced by mild oxidation to an *aldonic* acid (e.g. gluconic acid, $C_6H_{12}O_7$)—ketonic oxidation involves loss of carbon.

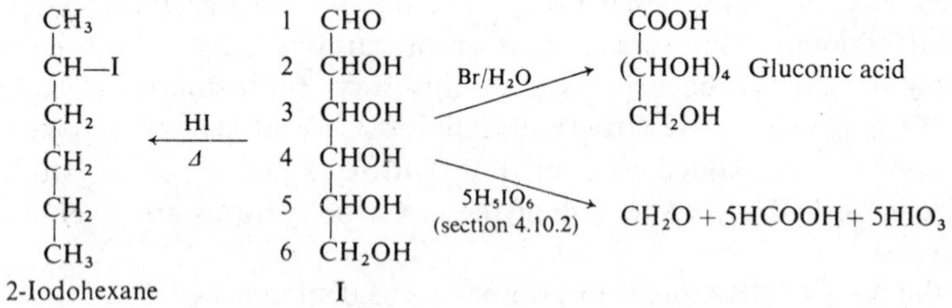

Fig. 7.6 Some reactions of (+)-glucose

Inspection of the constitutional formula (I) reveals that there are four differently substituted asymmetric carbon atoms, and thus there will be 2^4, or 16, stereoisomers. The determination of which of the sixteen is (+)-glucose is the second stage of the structural investigation. Eight of the sixteen stereo-isomers will be related to D(+)-glyceraldehyde, and these are shown in their projection formulae in Fig. 7.7. The configuration at each of the four asym-

266

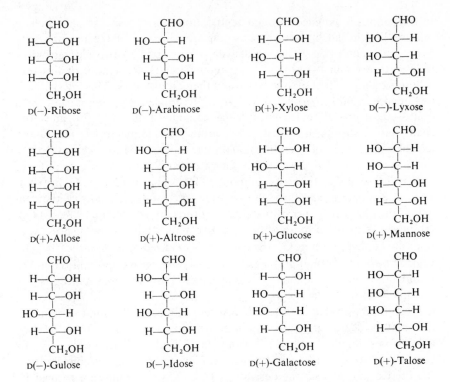

Fig. 7.7 (a) The stereochemistry of the D-aldopentoses and D-aldehexoses (The structures are shown in their planar projection formulae and should be compared with the aldotrioses and tetroses in section 2.8.5.)

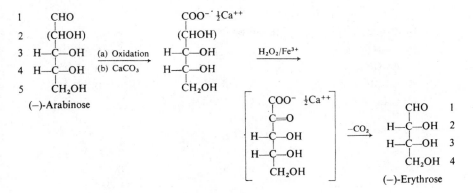

Fig. 7.7 (b) The method of Ruff for degradation of aldoses

267

metric centres is assigned through degradation or synthesis. An aldose chain may be lengthened by one carbon atom, making use of the reaction with hydrogen cyanide. D(+)-Glyceraldehyde is converted to two aldotetroses—D(−)-erythrose and D(−)-threose (see section 2.8.5). Repetition of this procedure would give first aldopentoses and then aldohexoses. Thus by synthesis (+)-glucose could be correlated with D(+)-glyceraldehyde. Alternatively, by a multi-stage degradation, for example the method of Ruff (Fig. 7.7b), an aldose chain may be shortened by one carbon atom. The aldopentose (−)-arabinose may be converted to D(−)-erythrose. Through this degradation, we may deduce that (−)-arabinose has the same configuration at C_3 and C_4 as C_2 and C_3 of (−)-erythrose and is thus a D compound. The configuration at C_2 in D(−)-arabinose is determined through oxidation to the dibasic acid—cf. the configuration of C_2 in (−)-erythrose and (−)-threose (see section 2.8.5). D(−)-Arabinose is oxidized to an optically active acid, while the aldopentose with opposite configuration at C_2—its *epimer*—is oxidized to a *meso*-dicarboxylic acid. The epimer of D(−)-arabinose—D(−)-ribose—is an important, naturally occurring carbohydrate and is found as part of more complex molecules, for example, the ribonucleic acids.

It can be shown that the two aldohexoses (+)-glucose (II) and (+)-mannose (III) may be degraded to or synthesized from D(−)-arabinose. Thus, the two aldohexoses differ in configuration only at C_2 and are thus another pair of epimers. A conveniently practical way of identifying a pair of epimers is by the preparation of osazone derivatives (Fig. 7.8). Osazones are formed by

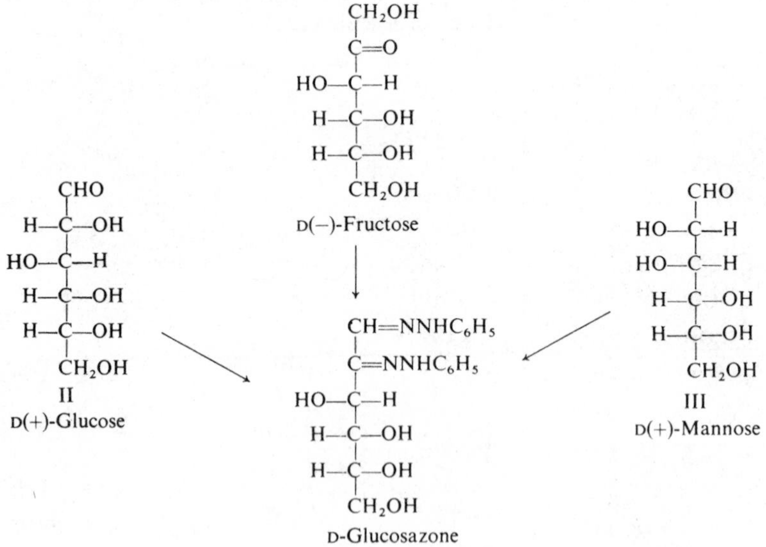

Fig. 7.8 Identification of epimers by the preparation of osazones

reaction with phenylhydrazine, but the reaction is not as simple as that with other carbonyl compounds (section 4.5.1), since two molecules of reagent are added. The asymmetry at C_2 of the aldose is lost, and thus epimers yield identical derivatives.

The final problem is to assign the configuration at C_2, i.e., to determine whether D(+)-glucose has configuration II or III. Several methods are available to do this. For example, the dicarboxylic acid obtained by oxidation of D(+)-glucose is identical with that obtained from L(+)-gulose. For this to be possible, the two aldoses must differ only in the relative positions of the terminal groups, —CHO and —CH_2OH, i.e., rotation of structure II through 180° and interchanging of the terminal groups produces an L-hexose [L(+)-gulose].

There are many properties of aldoses which cannot be explained on the basis of the open-chain structure (II), and require a structure in which no carbonyl group is present. In spectroscopic properties, for example, it would be noticed that there is no carbonyl stretching absorption in the infrared spectrum. A study of the optical rotatory power of monosaccharides provides evidence of further stereoisomers, the existence of which can only be explained by a ring structure. For example, when D(+)-glucose is dissolved in water, the initial angle of rotation changes slowly and eventually reaches a constant value ($[\alpha]_D = +52 \cdot 7°$). This effect, called *mutarotation*, is observed with all monosaccharides, and is due to interconversion among ring stereoisomers called *anomers*. In the case of glucose, the solid state is made up predominantly of the α-anomer, while glucose recrystallized above 100° is the β-anomer. These two anomers may be isolated as the corresponding optically stable methyl ethers which have no reducing properties. The methoxy groups are at C_1 and the anomers arise through asymmetry at this position. Reversible ring closure (hemi-acetal formation, section 4.5.1) occurs from the open-chain (aldehydo-) form to yield an equilibrium system between the anomers (Fig. 7.9). It has been estimated that there is about $0 \cdot 25$ per cent of the open-chain form present in aqueous solution. The proportion of the various isomers in solution varies according to the stereochemistry of the molecules and their environment. A D-ribose solution, for example, contains a high proportion of the open-chain form.

The size of the ring in α- and β-D-glucose was determined by *methylation studies*. The hydroxyl groups are *protected* by means of methoxy groups (IX) and then, after allowing the ring to open, the molecule is cleaved at the hydroxyl group which had been involved in the ring closure. The sequence of reactions is shown in Fig. 7.10. It should be noted that just as it is possible to methylate selectively the C_1 position, so the methoxy group may be removed selectively (X).

The six-membered ring structures are termed *pyranose* forms by analogy with the six-membered heterocycle pyran. They have a shape similar to that

269

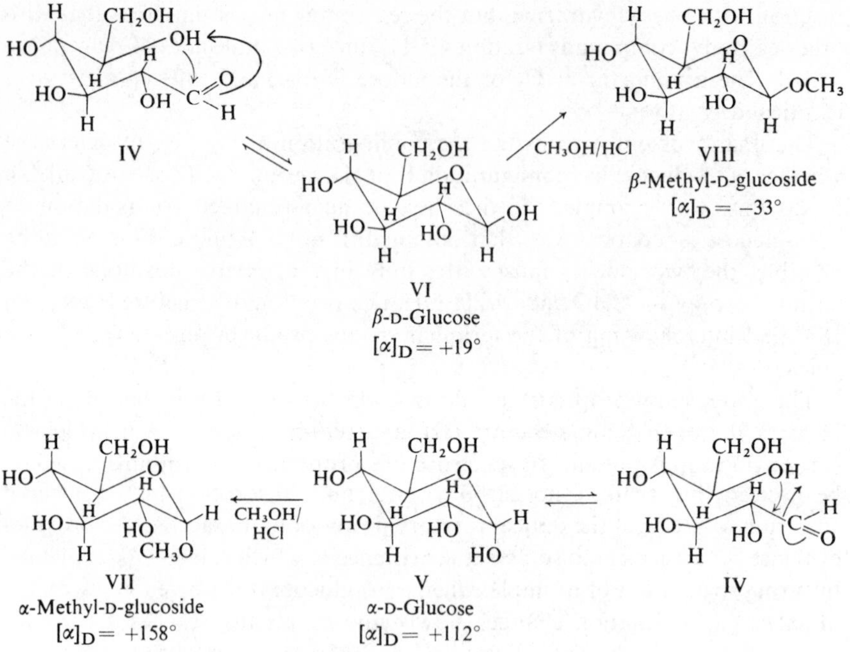

Fig. 7.9 Mutarotation of D-glucose and the formation of α- and β-methyl-D-glucosides

of cyclohexane (section 2.11). In the stable *chair* conformations, it will be noticed that the hydroxyl groups are, for the most part, equatorial (except at C_1 in α-D-glucose). It is also possible under special conditions to isolate derivatives of five-membered ring forms. These rings are planar and are termed *furanose* forms by analogy with the five-membered heterocycle furan. Again, two anomeric forms are found, for example α- and β-glucofuranose. In aqueous solution, the four cyclic forms and the open-chain form exist in equilibrium where α- and β-glucopyranose predominate.

The aldohexoses D(+)-mannose and D(+)-galactose both occur predominantly in the pyranose ring form. D-Mannose has opposite configuration to D-glucose at C_2 and D-galactose has opposite configuration at C_4. Aldopentoses may also exist in both pyranose and furanose forms. In the former, there are no carbon atoms outside the ring. There are two aldopentoses of outstanding biological interest, D(−)-ribose and D(−)-deoxyribose. D-Ribose is found as part of the structure of some coenzymes and also in ribonucleic acids. In both these, it is present in the furanose ring form. D-Deoxyribose occurs in deoxyribonucleic acids also in the furanose form.

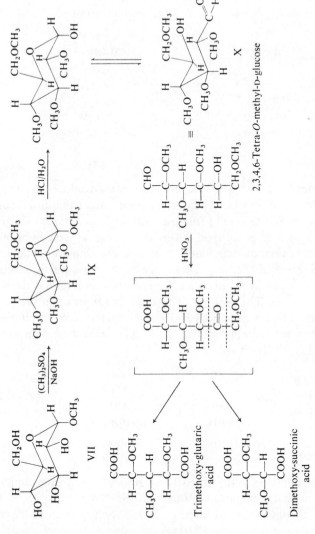

Fig 7.10 Proof of the pyranose ring structure of α-methyl-D-glucoside by methylation studies

271

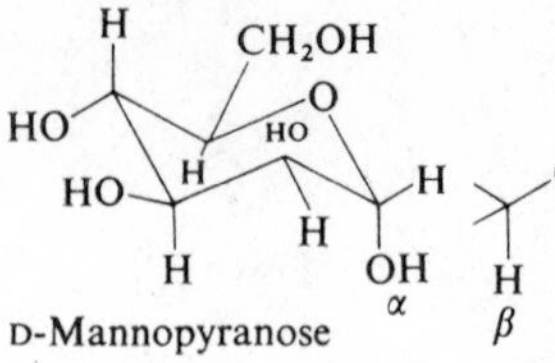

D-Mannopyranose

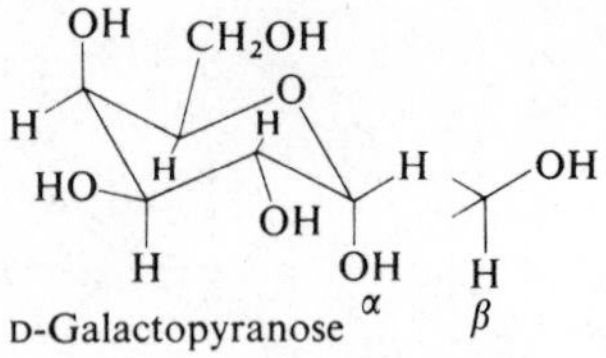

D-Galactopyranose

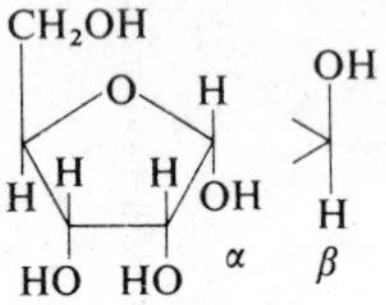

D-Ribofuranose

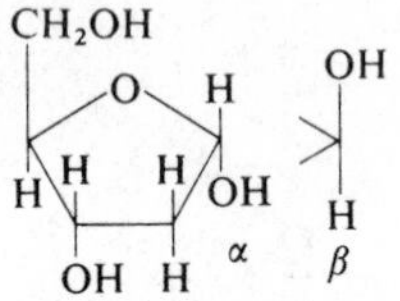

D-Deoxyribofuranose

Ketoses

There are fewer ketoses which occur naturally than aldoses, but they are often essential intermediates in metabolic processes rather than food sources. The most common ketose is D(−)-fructose. Although fructose is oxidized by most oxidizing agents, it is not oxidized by mild reagents such as bromine water. Furthermore, when oxidation does occur, the reaction product contains fewer carbon atoms than fructose. This suggests the presence of a ketone group rather than an aldehyde, albeit a more reactive group than is normally found in simple ketones. The position of this functional group in the carbon chain is determined by reaction with HCN and conversion to the branched-chain carboxylic acid, α-methyl-hexoic acid (XI), indicating that the carbonyl group is at C_2 (XII).

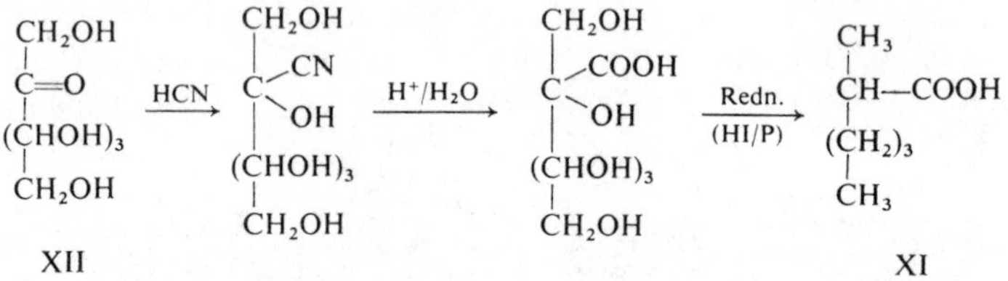

The determination of the stereochemical formula is greatly simplified by the observation that glucose and fructose form the same osazone (Fig. 7.8). Through this observation it is clear that the configuration at the three asymmetric centres of D-fructose (XIII) is the same as the corresponding centres in D-glucose.

Ketoses exhibit mutarotation. In D-fructose, for example, an equilibrium exists in solution in which pyranose and furanose forms are present. The furanose forms (XIV and XV) are found in fructose derivatives, for example, sucrose.

272

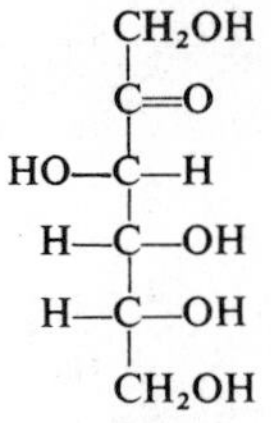

CH$_2$OH
C=O
HO—C—H
H—C—OH
H—C—OH
CH$_2$OH

XIII

D(−)-Fructose
(open-chain)

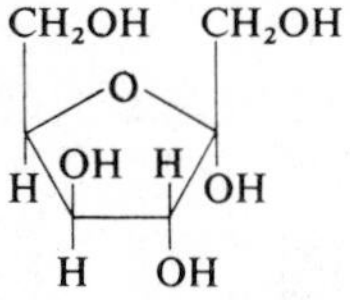

CH$_2$OH CH$_2$OH
O
H OH H OH
H OH

XIV

α-D-Fructofuranose

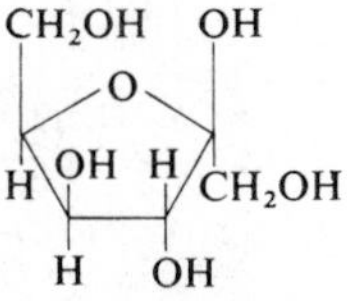

CH$_2$OH OH
O
H OH H CH$_2$OH
H OH

XV

β-D-Fructofuranose

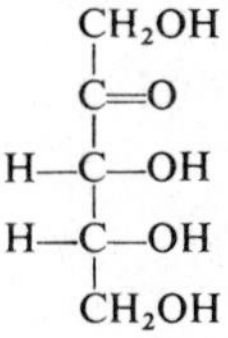

CH$_2$OH
C=O
H—C—OH
H—C—OH
CH$_2$OH

D-Ribulose

CH$_2$OH
C=O
HO—C—H
H—C—OH
CH$_2$OH

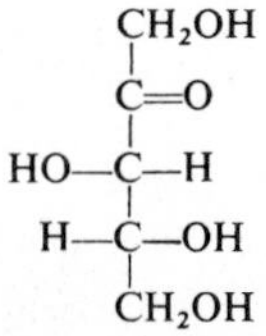

D-Xylulose

Two ketopentoses, found as intermediates in metabolic processes, are D-ribulose and D-xylulose. Like D-fructose, these ketoses have the carbonyl group at C$_2$ (open-chain structure).

7.3.2 Nitrogen-containing monosaccharides and vitamin C

The two most common nitrogen-containing monosaccharide derivatives are the *nucleosides*, where the C$_1$ of a pentose is joined to a nitrogen atom of a heterocyclic base (section 7.4.1) and the *amino-sugars*. All naturally occurring amino-sugars are hexoses and the amino-group replaces the hydroxyl group at C$_2$. Amino-sugars and their derivatives occur widely in polysaccharides and also as components of some antibiotics, glycolipids, and glycoproteins.

D-Glucosamine, found in polysaccharides such as chitin, has an identical structure to D-glucose with an —NH$_2$ replacing the equatorial —OH at C$_2$. An *N*-methylated-L-glucosamine residue is found in streptomycin (XVI) (I = streptose, II = *N*-methyl-L-glucosamine and III = streptidine). D-Galactosamine is found in the polysaccharide chondroitin. Once again, the C$_2$ —OH is replaced by —NH$_2$. Neuraminic acid is the most common amino-sugar derivative occurring in certain animal tissues, such as the brain. Neuraminic acid (XVII; X = H) is usually found as the *N*-acetyl derivative (XVII; X = —COCH$_3$) which is known as a sialic acid and occurs in glycolipids (section 7.2.3) and glycoproteins (section 8.4.6).

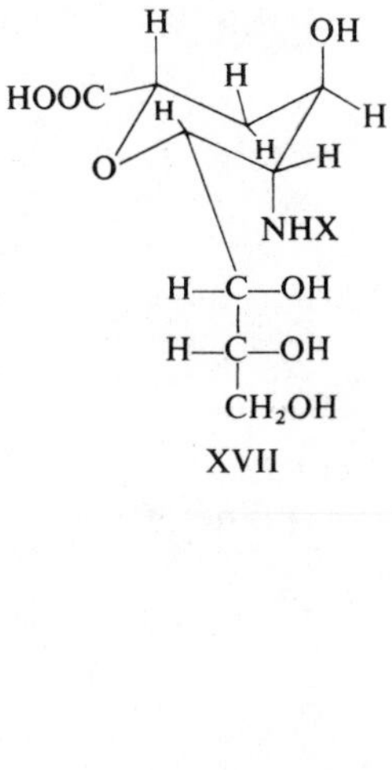

H OH
HOOC
H
H H
O H H
NHX
H—C—OH
H—C—OH
CH$_2$OH

XVII

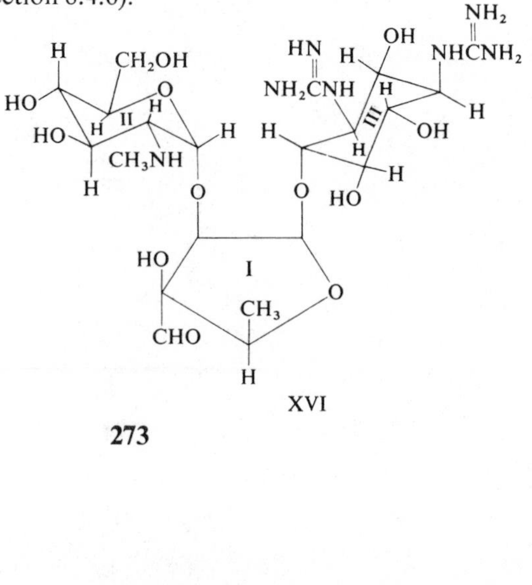

H CH$_2$OH
HO
O
HO H H H
CH$_3$NH
H
O
HO
I
CH$_3$
CHO
H

NH$_2$
OH
HN H NHCNH$_2$
NH$_2$CNH H
H H
OH
H
HO
H
O HO

XVI

273

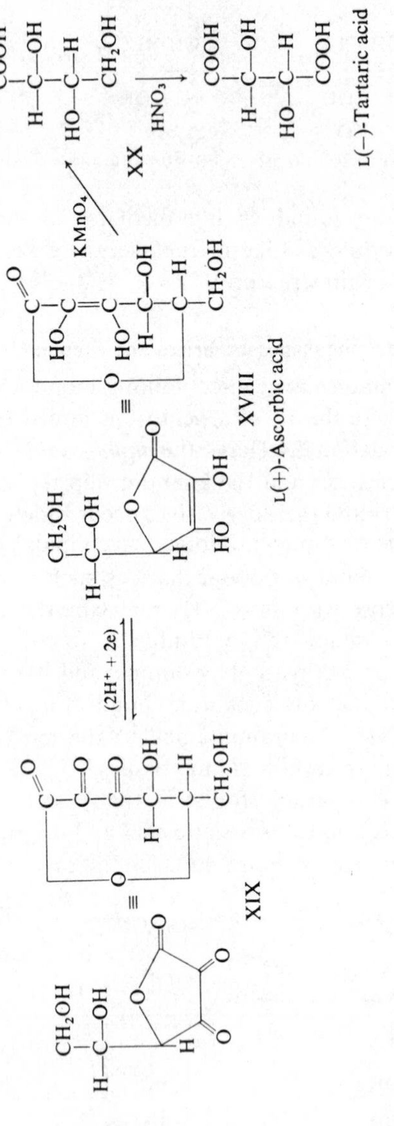

KMnO$_4$

HNO$_3$

(2H$^+$ + 2e)

XVIII

L(+)-Ascorbic acid

XIX

XX

L(−)-Tartaric acid

COOH
H—C—OH
HO—C—H
CH$_2$OH

COOH
H—C—OH
HO—C—H
COOH

CH$_2$OH
H—C—OH
CH$_2$OH

274

Vitamin C, known also by the chemical name L(+)-ascorbic acid, is widely distributed in both animal and plant tissues. Deficiency of this vitamin leads to a condition known as scurvy. This deficiency disease is confined to a relatively small group of primates which include Man; other animals presumably have the ability to synthesize their vitamin C requirements. The crystalline vitamin was first isolated from plant sources, and in subsequent degradation studies shown to have many of the structural features of a carbohydrate. It has an acidic reaction and a much greater reducing power than a typical monosaccharide. The acidity is due to an *enol-group* (XVIII) and a monosodium salt may be prepared. The reversible interconversion of ascorbic and dehydroascorbic (XIX) acids occurs in living organisms. But *in vitro* the oxidation process is the most prominent.

The configuration at C_5 in ascorbic acid is L, since it may be degraded to L-threonic acid (XX) with potassium permanganate and on further oxidation to L(−)-tartaric acid. The structure of ascorbic acid was confirmed by many syntheses, some of which have been used commercially.

7.3.3 The structural investigation of disaccharides

There are four common disaccharides, namely (+)-maltose (malt-sugar), (+)-cellobiose (the structural unit of cellulose), (+)-lactose (milk-sugar) and (+)-sucrose (cane or beet sugar). The first stage of the structural determination is to identify the two component monosaccharides. The glycosidic bond is broken by acid hydrolysis (Fig. 7.11). During this reaction, the ring size of the monosaccharides can change, since mutarotation will occur. Therefore, conclusions regarding ring size or configuration at the reducing carbon atoms in the original disaccharide cannot be drawn. The composition of the

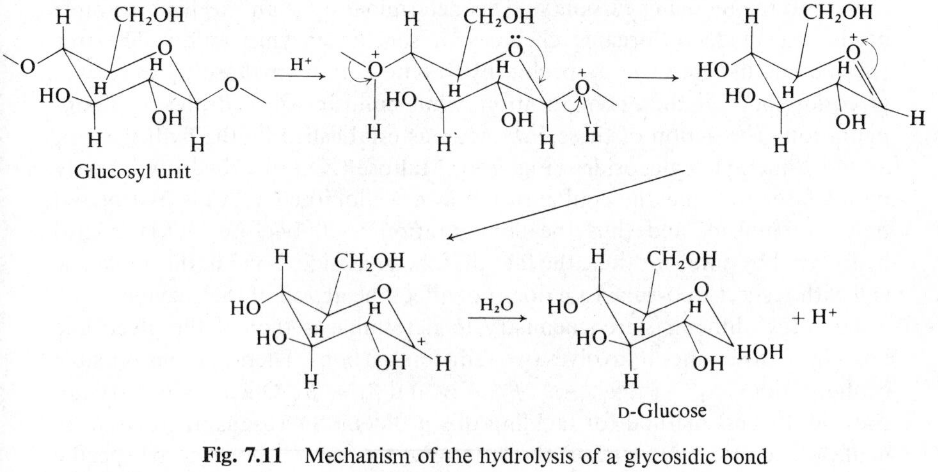

Glucosyl unit

D-Glucose

Fig. 7.11 Mechanism of the hydrolysis of a glycosidic bond

275

hydrolysate is deduced by the preparation of derivatives such as osazones or by chromatography. It is found that (+)-maltose and (+)-cellobiose contain only D-glucose, (+)-lactose contains D-glucose and D-galactose and (+)-sucrose contains D-glucose and D-fructose.

The second part of the structural investigation is to determine the position of the glycosidic bond and the size of the rings in the component mono-saccharides. The glycosidic bond involves at least one of the reducing carbon atoms. Hence, if the disaccharide shows reducing properties, the second reducing carbon is free and not involved in the glycosidic bond; such is the case with maltose, cellobiose and lactose. Sucrose, however, is non-reducing, and thus the glycosidic bond is from C_1 of the glucose residue to C_2 of the fructose residue.

In the case of (+)-lactose, it is necessary to determine which of the two components bears the reducing carbon atom. This can be done either by the preparation and hydrolysis of lactosazone (XXII), or by the oxidation of the reducing carbon to lactobionic acid (XXIII), followed by hydrolysis. In both cases D-galactose is recovered, and thus the glycosidic bond is at C_1 of this residue. The position of the glycosidic bond on the reducing glucose residue is determined by methylation studies on lactobionic acid. This compound is fully methylated and then hydrolysed, and the acidic component derived from the glucose residue is isolated. The position of the free hydroxyl group is then identified through oxidation. The acidic component is 2,3,5,6-tetra-O-methyl-D-gluconic acid, and these reactions are summarized in Fig. 7.12. Thus, the glycosidic bond in lactose is C_1 galactose to C_4 glucose (XXI). By a similar series of reactions, it can be shown that both maltose and cellobiose are joined C_1 to C_4. Methylation studies are also used to determine the size of the ring in the two components—for aldohexoses these are pyranose.

Finally, the configuration of the glycosidic bond must be determined with respect to the reducing carbon(s). This determination is an excellent example of the use made by organic chemists of specific enzyme action. The two enzymes used here have a specific hydrolytic action; maltase hydrolyses a glycosidic bond in an α configuration, while emulsin will hydrolyse a β configuration. The action of these enzymes was established by the hydrolysis of α- and β-methyl-D-glucosides (Fig. 7.9). Maltose (XXIV) is hydrolysed only by maltase, and thus the configuration is α. Cellobiose (XXV) is hydrolysed only by emulsin, and thus the configuration is β. Lactose (XXI) is also hydrolysed by emulsin; thus, the fact that the glycosidic bond in this molecule is β with respect to D-galactose does not affect the action of the enzyme.

The most difficult stereochemistry to determine is that of the glycosidic bond in sucrose, since it involves two reducing carbons. There are four possible configurations: $\alpha_1 \rightarrow \alpha_2$, $\alpha_1 \rightarrow \beta_2$, $\beta_1 \rightarrow \alpha_2$ and $\beta_1 \rightarrow \beta_2$. Once again, enzymes provide the best method for tackling this problem. Sucrose is hydrolysed by maltase and also by invertase; the latter enzyme can be shown to be specific

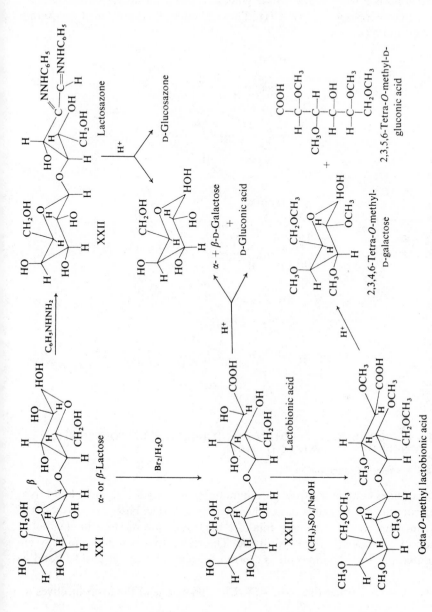

Fig. 7.12 Methods for the structural determination of (+)-lactose

for the hydrolysis of β-methyl fructofuranoside. This suggests that the glyco-sidic bond is α with respect to the glucose component and β with respect to the fructose component (XXVI). This structure was confirmed by X-ray studies and by synthesis.

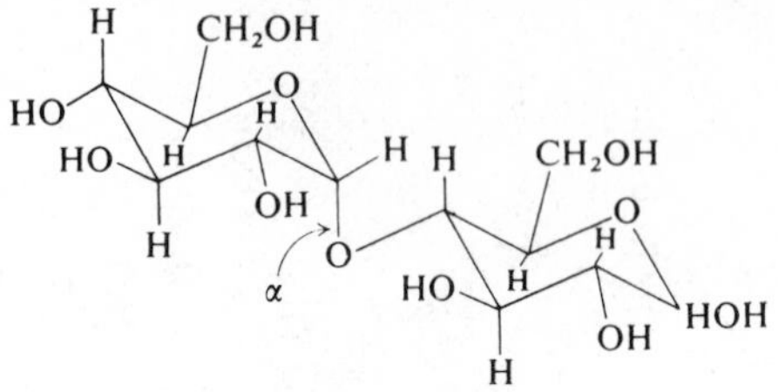

XXIV

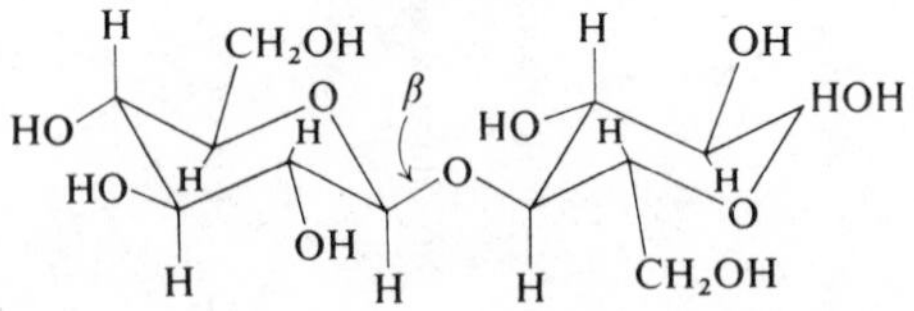

XXV

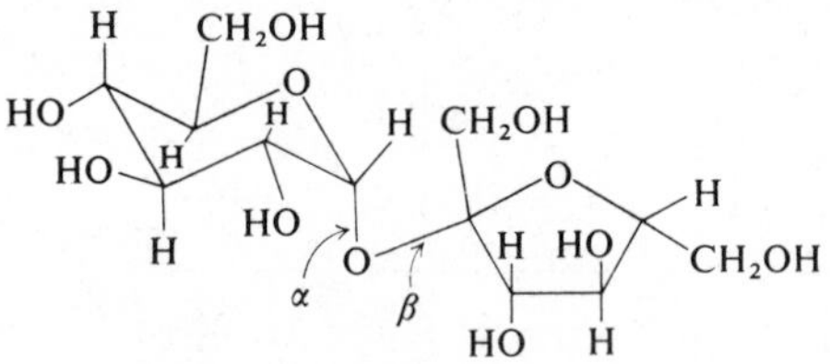

XXVI

7.4 NUCLEOSIDES, NUCLEOTIDES, AND NUCLEOTIDE COENZYMES (INCLUDING B-GROUP VITAMINS)

7.4.1 Nucleosides and nucleotides

Nucleosides contain a carbohydrate moiety joined by a glycosidic bond to a heterocyclic nitrogeneous base. The usual heterocyclic bases are purines and pyrimidines. The two components of a nucleoside are released in equimolar proportions when they are hydrolysed. The ease with which the bond between the two parts of the molecule is cleaved suggests that the glycosidic bond is

$$-\overset{|}{N}-\overset{|}{C}-O- \quad \text{rather than} \quad -\overset{|}{C}-\overset{|}{C}-O-.$$ Thus, one of the first objectives in

the structural determination is to establish precisely which ring nitrogen atom is involved in the glycosidic bond. This was not fully established until the total synthesis of the nucleosides had been accomplished. It was shown that, in the purine nucleosides, N_9 was involved in the glycosidic bond, and in the pyrimidine nucleosides the bond was at N_1. Nucleosides are found as structural units in nucleic acids and certain coenzymes. In nucleic acids, nucleoside units are found with one of two carbohydrate residues: D-ribose and D-deoxyribose (section 7.3.1). The position of the glycosidic bond at the pentose residue is easily shown to be at C_1, since all the natural nucleosides are non-reducing. The pentose ring was shown by methylation studies to be furanose. Another structural feature which was established only in the total synthesis was the stereochemistry of the glycosidic bond, and this was shown to be β.

The principal heterocyclic bases present in nucleosides are shown in Fig. 7.13. There are tautomeric forms of some of the purine and pyrimidine bases. Guanine, for example, exists mainly as the *lactim* (enol) in water at pH 7,

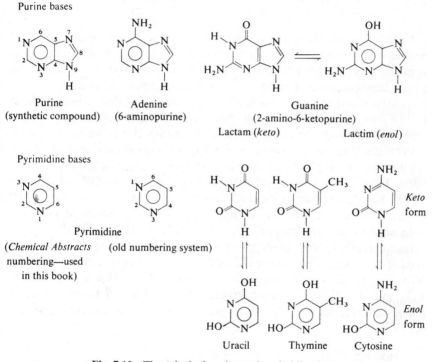

Fig. 7.13 The principal purine and pyrimidine bases

while the *lactam* (keto) form occurs in nucleosides. In cytosine, thymine, and uracil, the keto form predominates in aqueous solution at pH 7 and also occurs in nucleosides.

The two main classes of nucleic acid (see also chapter 8) may be distinguished on the basis that ribonucleic acids (RNA) contain nucleosides of D-ribose, and deoxyribonucleic acids (DNA) contain nucleosides of D-deoxyribose. There are four common ribonucleosides (I): uridine (I; B = uracil, U), cytidine (I; B = cystosine, C), adenosine (I; B = adenine, A) and guanosine (I; B = guanine, G). There are also four main deoxyribonucleosides (II): deoxy-thymidine (II; B = thymine, T), deoxycytidine (II; B = cytosine, C), deoxy-adenosine (II; B = adenine, A) and deoxyguanosine (II; B = guanine, G). The carbon atoms of the carbohydrate residue are designated 1', 2', 3', etc., to distinguish them from the numbers given to the atoms of heterocyclic rings.

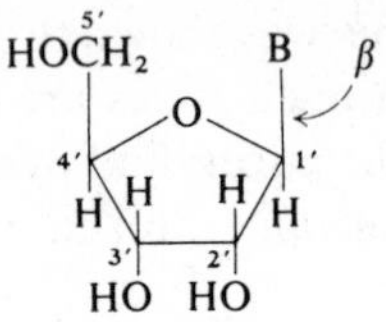

I

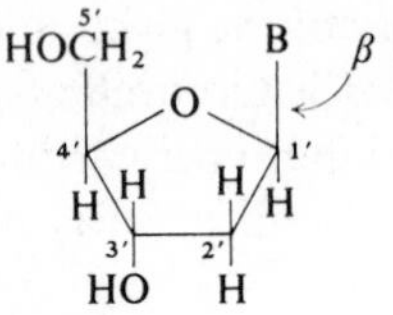

II

Nucleotides are the *monomer* units of nucleic acids (cf. amino acids and proteins). They are the monophosphate esters of nucleosides. It will be apparent that a number of isomeric phosphates may arise: in the case of the ribonucleosides there could be 2'-, 3'- or 5'-phosphates and in the case of the deoxyribonucleosides the 3'- and 5'-phosphates. All of these compounds are known and may arise during hydrolysis of nucleic acids. Although the more common nucleotides have been given trivial names it is more satisfactory to name them after the nucleoside from which they are derived and to indicate the position of the phosphate ester by a number. Thus *muscle adenylic acid* is adenosine-5'-phosphate—AMP (III; B = adenine, X = —OH). The three-letter abbreviations are in common use for the 5'-phosphates, i.e., AMP, GMP, CMP and UMP. The corresponding deoxyribonucleotides are distinguished by the use of 'd', i.e., dAMP, dGMP, dCMP and dTMP.

In addition to these simple phosphates, cyclic phosphates are known. A single type of cyclic phosphate is found for deoxyribonucleotides—the 3',5'- (IV; X = H). Two cyclic ribonucleotides arise—3',5'- (IV; X = —OH) and 2',3'- (V). The former type of structure is found in adenosine-3',5'-cyclic phosphate (cyclic-AMP) which is an activator in enzyme systems (see section 9.3.4).

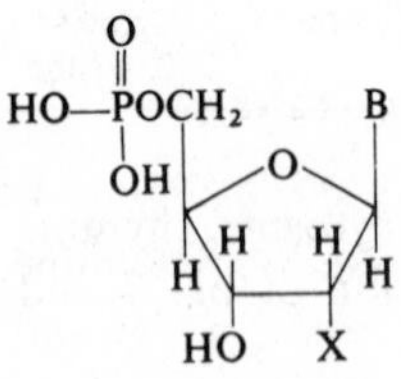

III

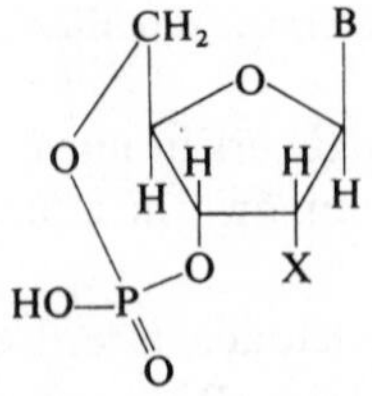

IV

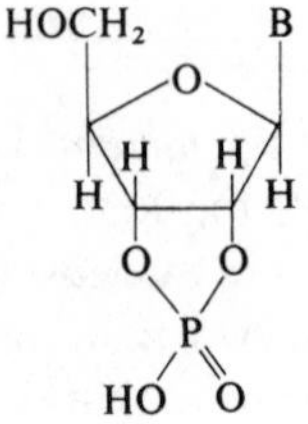

V

Another important group of 5'-nucleotides are the polyphosphates. Adenosine-5'-di- and triphosphates—ADP and ATP (VI and VII) were the first of this group of compounds to be discovered. In recent years, the 5'-di- and triphosphates corresponding to all the commonly occurring ribo- and deoxyribonucleosides have been isolated. ATP and ADP are of special importance in biochemical reactions. They are interconverted by trans-phosphorylation reactions of the type

$$ATP + S \rightleftharpoons ADP + S—H_2PO_4$$

The significance of this type of reaction is considered later (see section 9.2). While some of the other 5'-triphosphates have been shown to carry out transphosphorylation reactions (e.g., GTP), their main biochemical signifi-cance is that they act as reactive intermediates in the biosynthesis of nucleic acids (see section 9.5). ATP is the universal energy carrier of living systems.

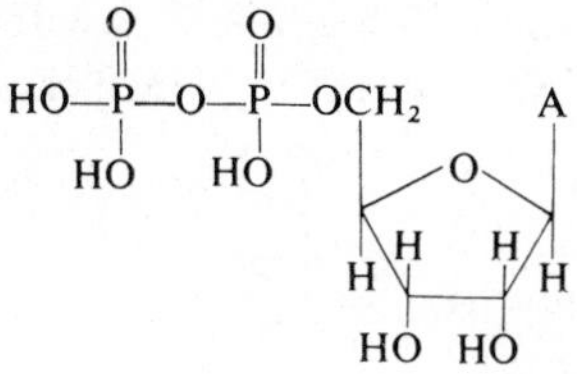

VI 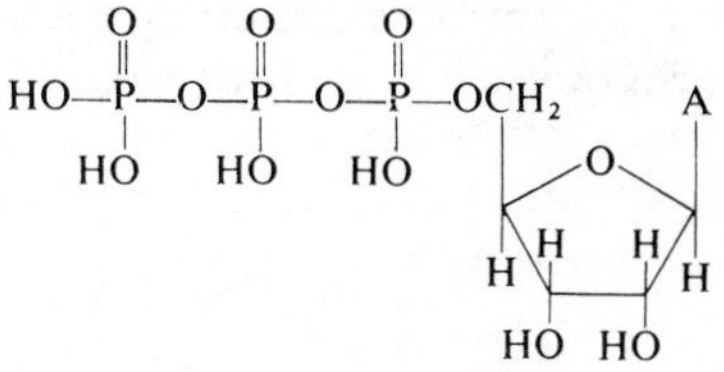   VII

The synthesis of ATP (from ADP) is a method for conserving some of the free energy that is generated in the degradation of carbohydrates and fats. The relatively high free energy of hydrolysis of ATP to ADP ($\Delta G_7^{\theta} \sim -28 \cdot 8$ kJ mole^{-1}) is sometimes used as a measure of the high internal energy of ATP. Structurally, the high energy is attributed to the considerable electrostatic repulsion found in the ionized triphosphate group and lack of dissipation of this charge through delocalization. However, it must be pointed out that ATP participates in biochemistry by phosphorylation rather than by hydrolysis.

7.4.2 Coenzymes containing nucleotide units and other coenzymes related to B-group vitamins

In the compounds considered so far in this chapter, a common feature is that large amounts are taken in in the diet of animals, and that they are used as a source of energy or as components in structural materials. There are also certain compounds, termed *vitamins*, that must be present in the diet, but in very small amounts. This diverse group of compounds is difficult to classify rigidly on the basis of either chemical structure or biological function. They may be broadly divided into two major groups: the water-soluble vitamins described in this section, and the fat-soluble vitamins described in section 7.5.

281

As vitamins have been discovered, they have been given trivial names (often several) and designated by a letter A, B, C, etc. As more compounds were identified, it was necessary to sub-divide most of the lettered groups, i.e., A_1 and A_2, D_2 and D_3, K_1 and K_2. In the large B-group, which contains most of the water-soluble vitamins, both numbers and letters have been used as suffices. The members of the B-group have no structural similarity, but the grouping is justified biochemically in that all the members have been shown to have a catalytic role in biochemistry, being part of coenzyme molecules.

(a) Thiamine (vitamin B_1) and thiamine pyrophosphate Thiamine occurs in all living organisms, usually as its pyrophosphate ester (VIII; $X =$

$$-O-\overset{\displaystyle O}{\overset{\displaystyle \|}{P}}-O-\overset{\displaystyle O}{\overset{\displaystyle \|}{P}}-OH)$$
$$\;\;\;\;\underset{OH}{|}\;\;\;\;\underset{OH}{|}$$

which is a coenzyme. Man requires a daily intake of 1–3 mg, and the deficiency disease is polyneuritis (malfunctioning of the nervous system; this condition is known as *beriberi*). Thiamine is isolated in the form of its chloride hydrochloride (VIII; $X = -OH$) from which the free

VIII

base may be obtained. The two heterocyclic rings are capable of being synthesized only in plants, although certain bacteria may perform a partial synthesis. Thiamine pyrophosphate (previously known as co-carboxylase) is a coenzyme involved in the metabolism of pyruvate and other α-keto acids. It is also involved in certain *transketolase* reactions (section 9.3.2), notably those of the pentose pathway of photosynthesis. Deficiency of this vitamin leads to disruption of carbohydrate metabolism.

(b) The nucleotide 'redox' coenzymes (i) *Nicotinic acid, nicotinamide (vitamin PP) and the pyridine nucleotides* The structurally simple compounds nicotinic acid (IX) and its amide (X) are found to be essential for normal health. Nicotinic acid is in fact the *provitamin* being converted to the amide *in vivo*. Deficiency in humans leads to the condition called pellagra (dermatitis followed by malfunction of digestive, nervous, and brain tissue, and ultimately death). The average daily requirement in Man is 10–20 mg.

IX   X

The biological importance of nicotinamide lies in the fact that it is the functional moiety of two redox coenzymes: nicotinamide adenine dinucleotide, NAD^+ (XI; $R = -OH$), and nicotinamide adenine dinucleotide phosphate, $NAD P^+$ (XI; $R = $ —O—P—OH). NAD^+ was the water-soluble,

$$\overset{O}{\underset{|}{\overset{\|}{\text{—O—P—OH}}}}$$

heat-stable cofactor required in alcoholic fermentation, which was discovered by Harden and Young as long ago as 1906. The crystalline compound, however, was not isolated until 1936. These two coenzymes act in an identical way in a large number of biological reactions. In general NADPH, the reduced form of the coenzyme $NADP^+$, occurs as the hydrogen donor for biosynthesis reactions, notably those of photosynthesis in plants. NAD^+, on the other hand, is found mainly in animal metabolism as a coenzyme for oxidative degradation. The two compounds participate in a large number of reactions in a relatively non-specific manner, but the enzymes (oxidoreductases) with which they act are generally specific for a particular substrate. Probably the most common redox reactions carried out by the two coenzymes are those involving alcohol groups.

$$\text{—CH}_2\text{OH} + \text{NAD}^+ \rightleftharpoons \text{—CHO} + \text{NADH} + \text{H}^+$$

$$\text{>CHOH} + \text{NAD}^+ \rightleftharpoons \text{>C=O} + \text{NADH} + \text{H}^+$$

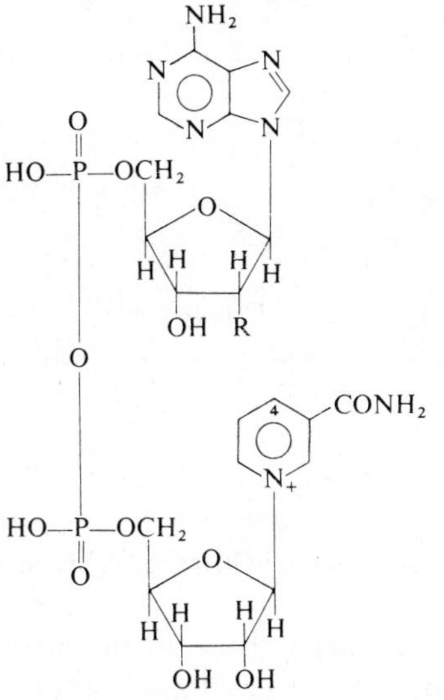

XI

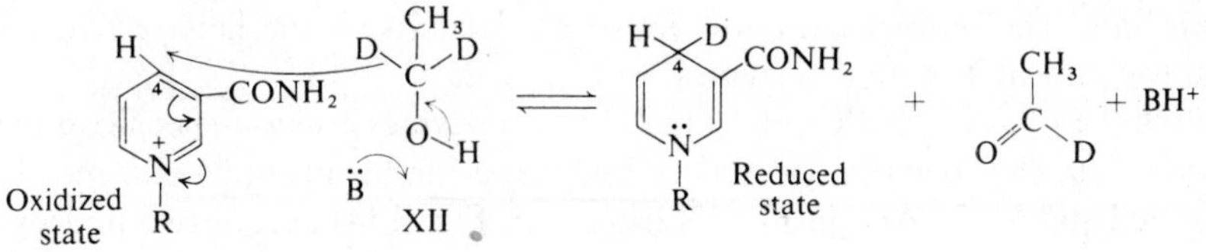

Oxidized state   XII   Reduced state   + BH⁺

The mechanism by which NAD^+ and $NADP^+$ transfer hydrogen has been fully investigated. Isotope studies, with a labelled ethanol substrate (XII), showed that deuterium atoms were transferred directly, as deuteride ions (D^-) to the 4 position of the pyridine ring (see also Fig. 8.25).

The redox process may be followed by changes in the absorption spectrum. NAD^+ has a strong absorption band at 259 nm (mμ) due to the adenine and nicotinamide moieties. NADH, on the other hand, has a slightly weaker band at 259 nm (mμ), due entirely to adenine, and a second absorption band at 338 nm (mμ) due to the dihydronicotinamide moiety. The appearance or disappearance of this latter absorption band may be used to follow redox reactions involving this coenzyme.

(*ii*) *Riboflavin (vitamin B$_2$) and the flavin coenzymes*   Riboflavin has been obtained as a yellow crystalline solid from both plant and animal sources. It may be isolated as its phosphate ester, FMN, or bound, covalently, to protein enzymes (flavoproteins). Man requires 2–3 mg per day, but in some animals it may be synthesized by intestinal bacteria. The deficiency disease is chellosis (cracking of the skin). Riboflavin is the functional part of two important coenzymes, which participate in biological redox reactions. These are flavin mononucleotide, FMN, which is the 5'-monophosphate of riboflavin, and flavin adenine dinucleotide, FAD (Fig. 7.14). These two coenzymes have been

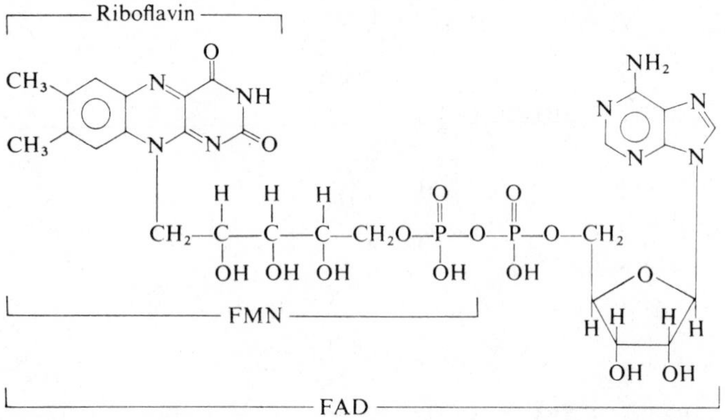

Fig. 7.14   The structural relationship between riboflavin, FMN and FAD

incorrectly named, since the linkage between the base (riboflavin) and the carbohydrate (ribitol) is not a true glycosidic one, as the carbohydrate residue is in a reduced state. Thus FMN is not in fact a *nucleotide* and FAD is a *mononucleotide*. The biological action, however, depends on the heterocyclic part and is identical in both coenzymes.

Like the pyridine nucleotides, the flavin coenzymes are non-specific in their action, but each reaction is catalysed by a specific flavoprotein enzyme. The oxidized states of FAD and FMN (shown in Fig. 7.14) accept two hydrogen atoms to give reduced states $FADH_2$ and $FMNH_2$, the process probably occurring by a free-radical mechanism. The hydrogen atoms are taken up in a stepwise manner and the process may be followed by changes in the absorption spectrum or fluorescence spectrum (Fig. 7.15).

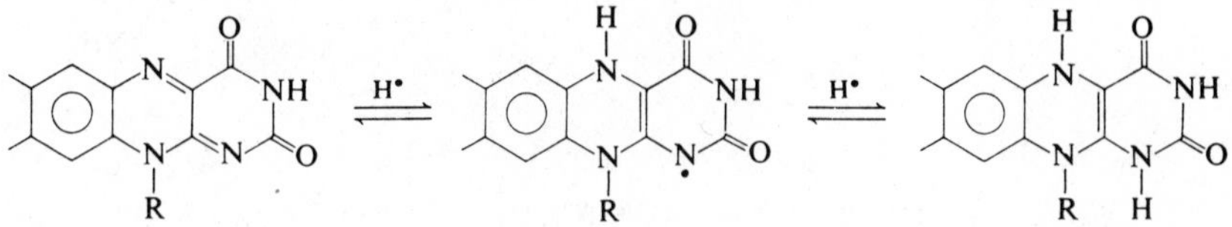

| FAD or FMN (yellow) | Flavin semiquinone | FADH₂ or FMNH₂ (colourless) |

Absorption
bands: 280, 370, 450 nm   280, 370, 450, 590 nm   280, 370 nm

Fig. 7.15 Oxidation and reduction of FMN and FAD

(*iii*) *Pantothenic acid* (*vitamin B₃*), *carnitine* (*vitamin Bₜ*) *and coenzyme A*
Dietary supplies of pantothenic acid do not appear to be necessary in Man, who probably obtains sufficient from intestinal bacterial synthesis. In lower animals, however, deficiency causes various conditions which retard growth and produce dermatitis. Pantothenic acid is a yellow, viscous, optically active oil. It is easily decomposed by acids and bases and is thermolabile. The structure (XIII) shows a single asymmetric carbon atom, and this has been

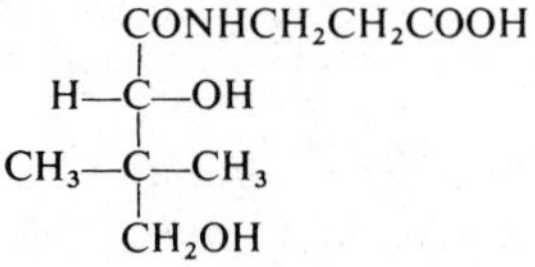

$$CONHCH_2CH_2COOH$$
$$H—C—OH$$
$$CH_3—C—CH_3$$
$$CH_2OH$$
XIII

found to have a D configuration; only this enantiomorph has biological activity. The importance of pantothenic acid is that it is a structural component of coenzyme A.

Carnitine is a widely distributed compound in nature and it had been isolated many years before its function as a coenzyme became known. It is synthesized in most organisms, but it has been observed that it is a necessary factor in the diet of certain insects. Carnitine (XIV) acts as an acetyl transfer

$$OH$$
$$(CH_3)_3\overset{+}{N}—CH_2CH—CH_2COO^-$$
XIV

agent (like coenzyme A) and acts as such in fatty-acid metabolism. It differs from the larger coenzyme A molecule, in that it may transport acetyl groups

285

across mitochondrial membranes. The acetyl group is bound through the β-hydroxyl group, whereas in coenzyme A it is bound as a thiol ester.

In coenzyme A (XV), the pantothenic-acid residue is joined by a peptide bond to β-mercaptoethanolamine (this unit is called D-pantotheine) and via a phosphoester bond to the nucleotide unit.

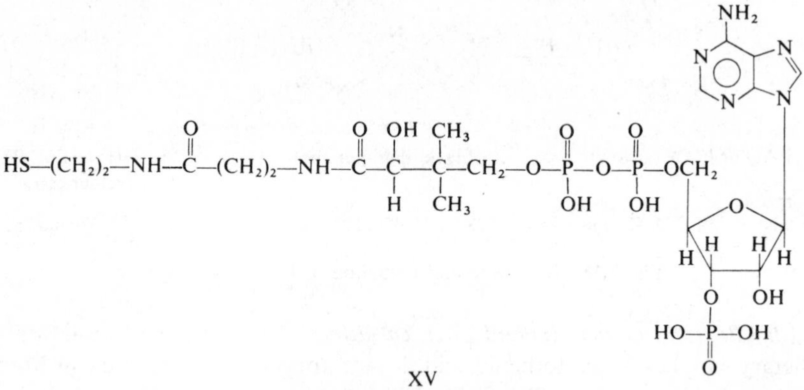

$$HS-(CH_2)_2-NH-\underset{O}{\overset{O}{C}}-(CH_2)_2-NH-\underset{H}{\overset{O}{C}}-\underset{CH_3}{\overset{OH}{C}}-\underset{CH_3}{\overset{CH_3}{C}}-CH_2-O-\underset{OH}{\overset{O}{P}}-O-\underset{OH}{\overset{O}{P}}-OCH_2$$

XV

Coenzyme A has a key role in metabolic processes, where its main function is the transfer of two carbon units in both catabolic and biosynthetic reactions. Foremost among the reactions in which it is involved is the conversion of oxaloacetate to citrate in the TCA cycle (see section 9.2.6). The groups transferred by coenzyme A are attached to the sulphur atom as thiol esters and, for simplicity, the coenzyme is denoted by CoA—SH and its acyl derivatives as CoA—S—$\overset{O}{\overset{\|}{C}}$—R (e.g., CoA—S—$\overset{O}{\overset{\|}{C}}$—CH$_3$).

(iv) *Cyanocobalamin (vitamin B_{12}) and porphyrins* The discovery of vitamin B_{12} arose from experiments in which raw liver was fed to patients suffering from pernicious anaemia. The active material was isolated in the crystalline state in 1948. Although much of the human requirement is met by intestinal bacterial synthesis, Man, unlike other animals, requires an external source estimated at 1 μg per day. Cyanocobalamin is water soluble and crystallizes as dark-red crysrals. The structure (Fig. 7.16) was deduced by a combination of spectral, chemical and the X-ray studies by Hodgkin and her co-workers. One of the main structural features is the presence of the macrocyclic porphyrin ring system which plays an important role in many other molecules of biological importance.

Porphyrins are derived from the parent tetrapyrrole porphin (XVI), the four pyrrole rings are designated I–IV. Natural porphyrins occur in which the hydrogens at positions 1–8 have been replaced by a variety of side chains. The tetrapyrrole system contains conjugated double bonds and this part of the molecule is the chromophore which gives porphyrins their characteristic dark-red colour. It is possible to distinguish the various types of substituent from the absorption spectrum. A very important structural feature is the metal atom, which is sometimes co-ordinated to the tetrapyrrole ring. Metal chelates containing magnesium, iron, zinc, nickel, cobalt, copper and silver are known. Porphyrins are conveniently classified on the basis of the nature of the *side chain*. Uroporphyrins, found in urine, have tetra-acetic and tetra-propionic substituents. Of the four possible isomers, those with two substituents on each pyrrole ring are found in nature (XVII and XVIII; $X = -CH_2CH_2COOH$ and $Y = -CH_2COOH$). The methyl groups found in the coproporphyrins arise from decarboxylation of the acetic substituents (XVII and XVIII; $X = -CH_2CH_2-COOH$ and $Y = -CH_3$). In the same way, the

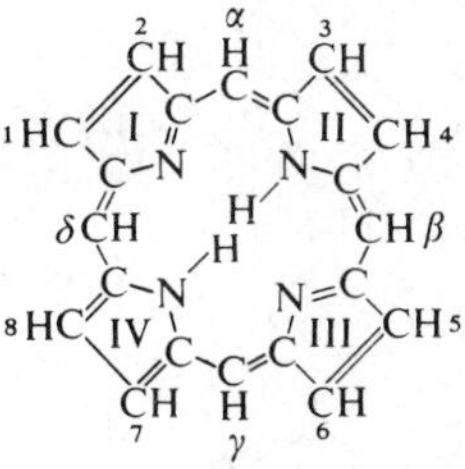

XVI
Porphin

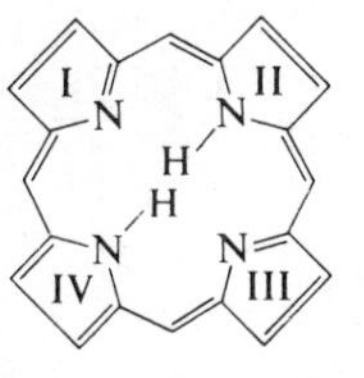

XVI'
Simplified diagram of
porphin ring

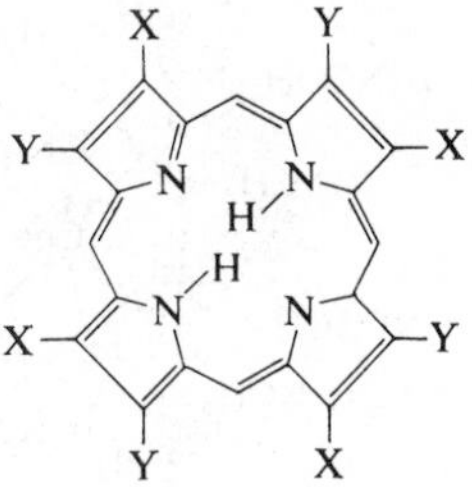

XVII

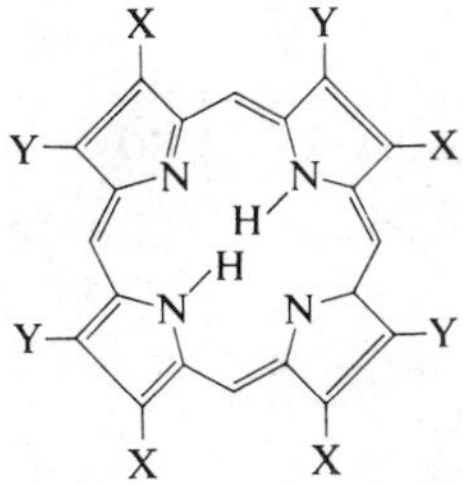

XVIII

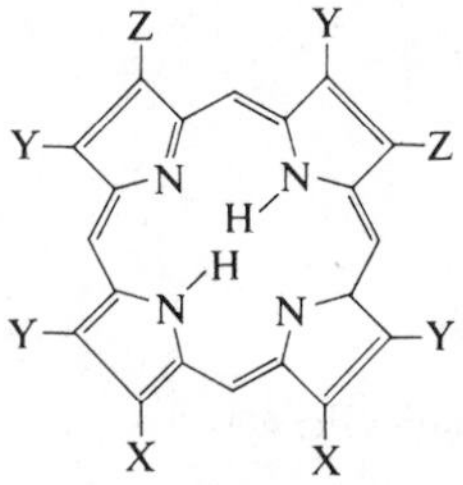

XIX

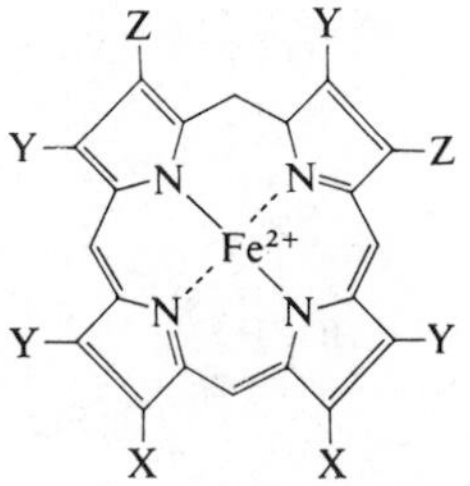

XX

two ethyl substituents of a mesoporphyrin arise through the decarboxylation of two of the propionic substituents of the coproporphyrins (XIX; $X = -CH_2CH_2COOH$, $Y = -CH_3$, $Z = -CH_2CH_3$). Etioporphyrin has four methyl and four ethyl substituents in an arrangement derived from a copro-porphyrin (XVIII; $X = -CH_2CH_3$ and $Y = -CH_3$). Haematoporphyrin has an arrangement of substituents directly related to mesoporphyrin with hydroxy-ethyl groups replacing the ethyl groups (XIX; $X = -CH_2CH_2COOH$, $Y = -CH_3$ and $Z = -CH_2CH_2OH$). Dehydration of the two hydroxy-ethyl substituent produces two vinyl substituents. This protoporphyrin, with a co-ordinated iron atom, occurs in the haem group (XX; $X = -CH_2CH_2COOH$, $Y = -CH_3$ and $Z = -CH=CH_2$). The haem moiety occurs as a prosthetic group in proteins involved in the transfer of oxygen, for example haemoglobin and myoglobin, and in electron transfer for example, the cytochromes.

The magnesium chelate of a modified protophorphyrin is found in the *chlorophylls*. A 7,8-dihydroporphyrin nucleus, now termed a *chlorin*, and a fused cyclopentane ring (V) are present. The complete ring system (I–V) is called a *phaeoporphyrin*. Several types of chlorophyll are known, of which chlorophylls *a* and *b* (Fig. 7.16) have been the most fully investigated. The role of these molecules in the maintenance of life is described later (see section 9.3.2).

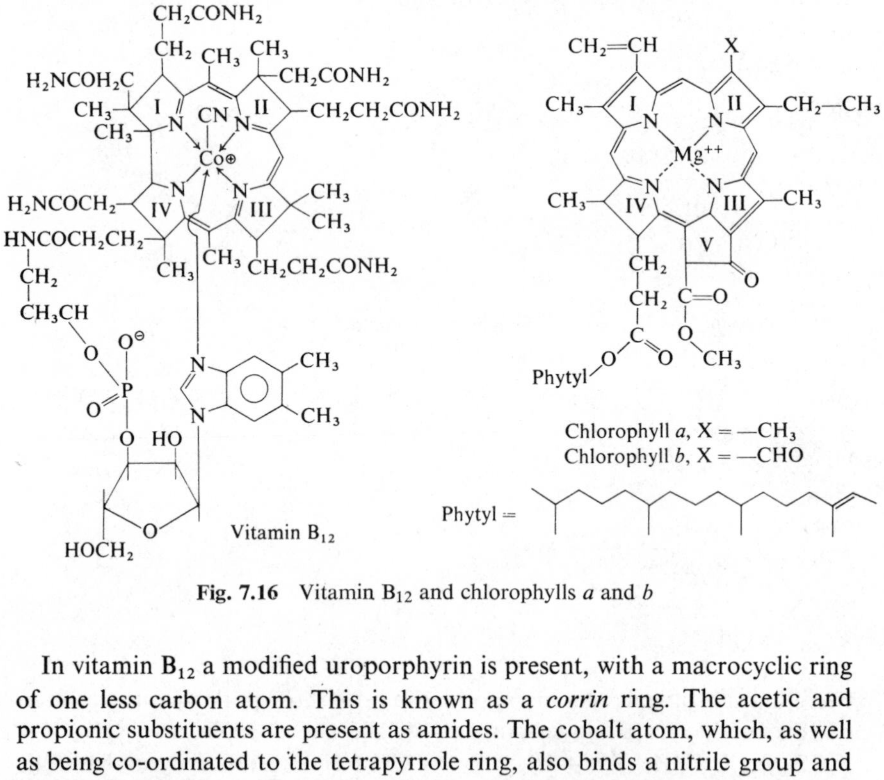

Fig. 7.16   Vitamin B_{12} and chlorophylls *a* and *b*

In vitamin B_{12} a modified uroporphyrin is present, with a macrocyclic ring of one less carbon atom. This is known as a *corrin* ring. The acetic and propionic substituents are present as amides. The cobalt atom, which, as well as being co-ordinated to the tetrapyrrole ring, also binds a nitrile group and the benzimidazole residue. The cobalt atom has a single positive charge, which is balanced by a negative charge on the phosphate residue; the latter is part of an unusual nucleotide residue. The exact biological role of vitamin B_{12} is not fully understood. Pernicious anaemia does not arise through a lack of this vitamin, but rather through a deficiency of an *intrinsic factor* required for absorption of the compound from the intestine. Whatever its role, the outstanding feature of this vitamin is the remarkably small amount required in the diet.

(*v*) *Other nucleotide coenzymes*   Recent studies on the pathways for the biosynthesis of oligo- and polysaccharides have revealed that sugar molecules are present as phosphate esters of uridine, guanosine and other nucleotides. The most fully studied of these compounds have been the uridine diphosphate sugars, particularly those of D-glucose—UDPG (XXI) and of D-galactose—

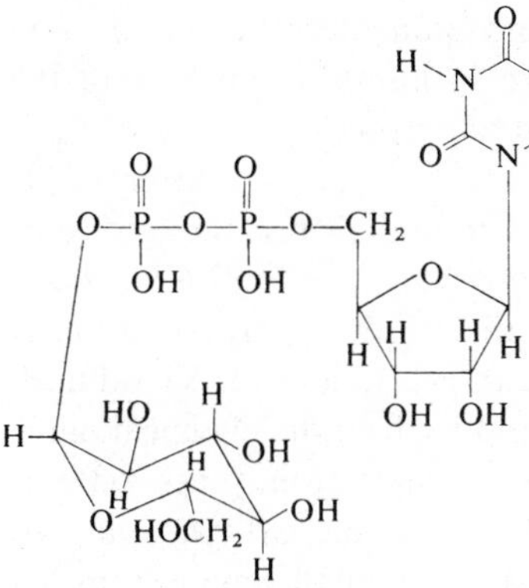

XXI

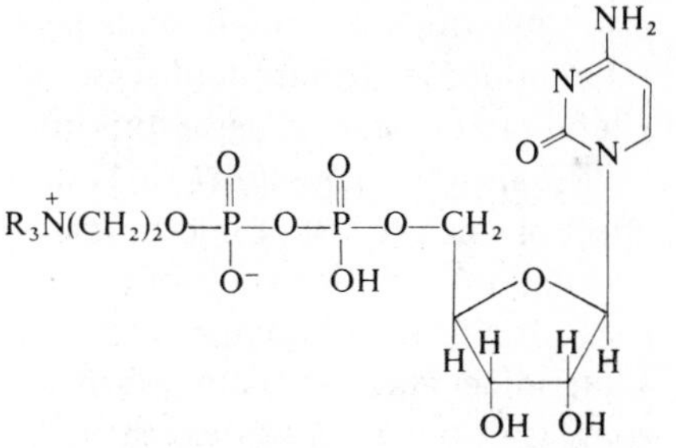

XXII

UDPGal. The sugar molecule is joined at C_1 to the terminal phosphate and the glycosidic bond has an α configuration. The other nucleoside diphosphates known include: GDP-D-mannose, GDP-D-glucose, ADP-D-glucose and TDP-D-glucose.

Cytidine diphosphate coenzymes have been shown to be involved in the biosynthesis of lecithins and other lipids. The structures of CDP-choline (XXII; $R = CH_3$) and CDP-ethanolamine (XXII; $R = H$) have been fully established.

(*vi*) *Other B-group vitamins—pyridoxine, folic acid and biotin*   1. *Pyridoxine* (*vitamin* B_6)   Pyridoxine refers to a group of closely related compounds: pyridoxol (XXIII), pyridoxal (XXIV) and pyridoxamine (XXV) which, in the form of their phosphates, are interconvertible *in vivo*. Pyridoxol was the first

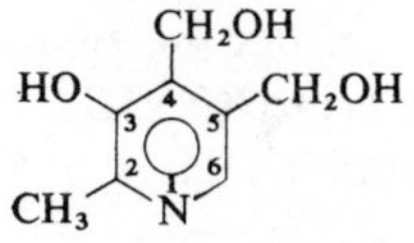

XXIII

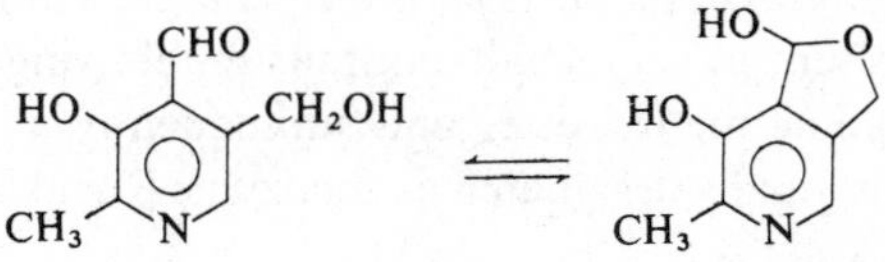

XXIV

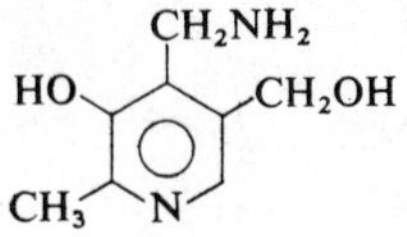

XXV

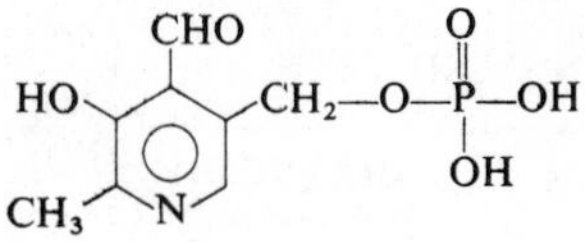

XXVI

289

of these compounds to be characterized and synthesized. Other metabolites were later isolated that proved to be biologically much more effective than pyridoxol. These were the phosphorylated derivatives of pyridoxal (XXVI) and pyridoxamine. These compounds are concerned in the metabolism of amino acids, in particular the interconversion process known as *transamination* (section 9.4.2). Pyridoxal phosphate (XXVI) is also active in a number of other reactions of amino acids such as racemization, decarboxylation and elimination. A deficiency disease is not known in humans, but lack of the vitamin in rats causes dermatitis and retardation of growth.

2. *Folic acid (vitamin B_c)* The early work on this vitamin concerned its effect on the growth of microorganisms. In higher animals it is thought to be essential for the formation of polynuclear erythrocytes. The term *folic acid* is used for a group of compounds which contain the following structural units: a pteridine nucleus, *p*-aminobenzoic acid and L-glutamic acid. Vitamin B_c consists of one each of these structural units, and is given the chemical name pteroylglutamic acid (XXVII; $n = 1$). The factor isolated from yeast contains two extra molecules of L-glutamic acid and is known as pteroyl-γ-L-glutamyl-γ-L-glutamyl-L-glutamic acid (i.e., XXVII, $n = 3$). The peptide linkage is rather unusual in these compounds, in that it is through the glutamic acid side chain and not through the α-carboxyl group.

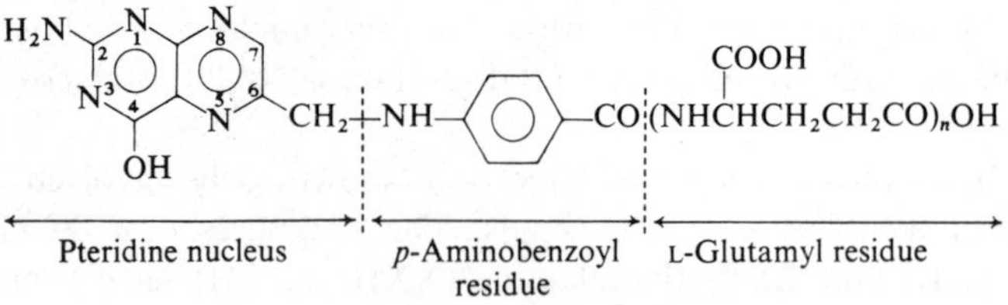

XXVII

Folic acid serves as a coenzyme for transfer of single carbon units at the oxidation level of formaldehyde and formic acid. It is, for example, used in the conversion of glycine to serine and the methylation of ethanolamine to choline.

3. *Biotin (vitamin H)* Biotin is a growth factor which has been shown to be present in very small amounts in all living cells. It was first isolated as the crystalline methyl ester and subsequently as the free acid (XXVIII). Biotin was originally designated as coenzyme R and later as vitamin H; it is, however,

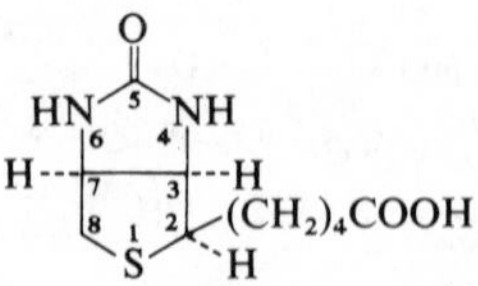

XXVIII 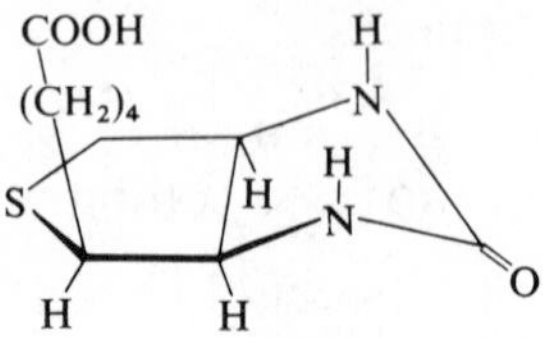   XXVIII'

290

best considered as part of the vitamin B group. A deficiency disease is unknown in Man (cf. pantothenic acid), since it is synthesized by intestinal bacteria. The structure (XXVIII) shows three asymmetric centres (C_2, C_3, and C_7) and the ring junction is *cis* fused. Only (+)-biotin is biologically active and has the stereochemistry shown in XXVIII'. The role of biotin in fatty-acid biosynthesis is described in section 9.3.5.

7.5 FAT-SOLUBLE VITAMINS AND STRUCTURALLY RELATED COMPOUNDS, INCLUDING STEROIDS

Like the water-soluble vitamins (B-group and vitamin C), the fat-soluble group is, structurally, a diverse group of compounds. One member, lipoic acid, should, biologically, be placed in the B-group, since it is an essential growth factor in living systems, and has a well established role as a coenzyme. The *essential fatty acids*, sometimes known as vitamin F, clearly belong to the fat-soluble group (for the structures, see section 7.2.1). The remaining fat-soluble vitamins of groups A, D, E, and K will be described in this section. All of these have been extensively investigated structurally and nutritionally with respect to Man. Whether or not they, like the B-group, are universally essential remains to be proved. With the exception of vitamin A, less is known of the exact biochemical role of these vitamins; although in some cases there is an obvious structural relationship with known coenzymes.

7.5.1 Fat-soluble vitamins: lipoic acid, vitamins A, E and K

(a) Lipoic acid This compound has been demonstrated to be a growth factor in a number of living organisms, although no deficiency disease has been reported in Man. Lipoic acid is a cyclic disulphide of octanoic acid. The molecule possesses a single asymmetric carbon atom and the (+) enantiomorph occurs naturally. Lipoic acid is one of the coenzymes involved in the oxidative decarboxylation of α-keto acids. In this process, reduction of the disulphide bond takes place, to give the dithiol (I), and the oxidized form (II) is regenerated by interaction with enzyme-bound FAD (flavoprotein) (see Fig. 9.4).

(b) Vitamin A (including terpenoids and carotenoids) *Terpenoids and carotenoids* A large number of naturally occurring compounds can be thought of as arising from the combination of isoprene, C_5H_8 (III), units. The terpenes are classified according to the number of these units they contain. Thus a monoterpene ($C_{10}H_{16}$) has two isoprene units; a sesquiterpene ($C_{15}H_{14}$)

291

has three; a diterpene ($C_{20}H_{32}$) has four; a triterpene ($C_{30}H_{48}$) has six, and a tetraterpene ($C_{40}H_{64}$) has eight. Carotenoids are tetraterpenes. The isoprene units are usually joined *head to tail* (IV and IV′) and may cyclize as in simple monocyclic terpenes (V). The latter could also be considered as derivatives of a benzenoid compound—*p*-cymene (VI). Many other cyclic terpenes are

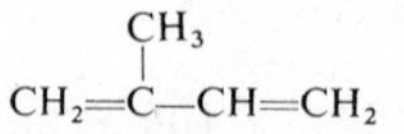

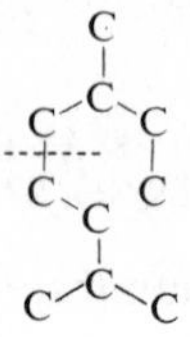

found with more complex ring systems. Natural terpenoids contain functional groups such as —OH, —CHO or $>$CO and are found as components in *essential oils* of plant origin.

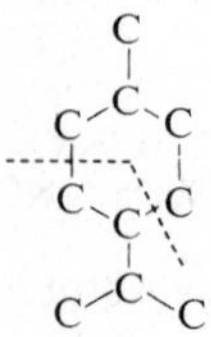

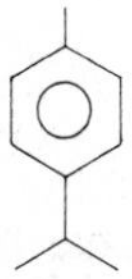

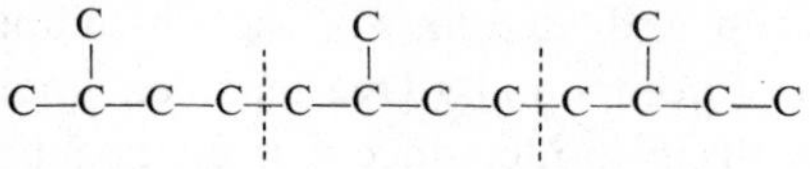

The most common carotenoids are lycopene (VII) and α-, β-, and γ-carotene (VIII, IX and X respectively). These compounds are found as red pigments in plants, for example lycopene in tomatoes and α-, β-, and γ-carotenes in carrots. Of these only β-carotene has all the double bonds in conjugation. The terminal cyclic unit of the carotenes is called an *ionone ring* and the particular one in α-, β-, and γ-carotenes is β-ionone (XI). Some eleven carotenoids, including α-, β-, and γ-carotene, may serve as provitamins for vitamin A, and are the chief dietary source.

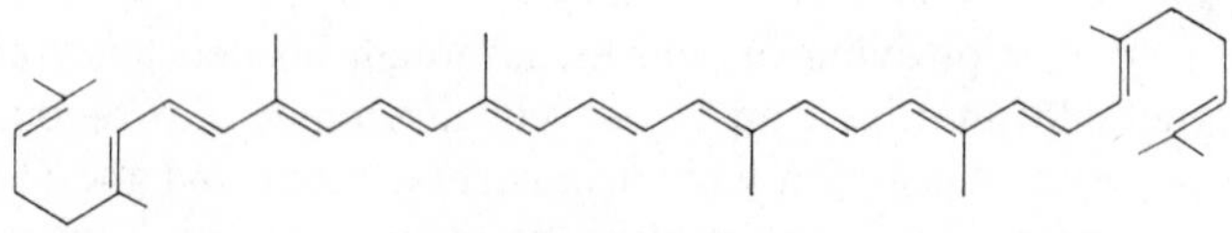

Lycopene—VII
($C_{40}H_{56}$)

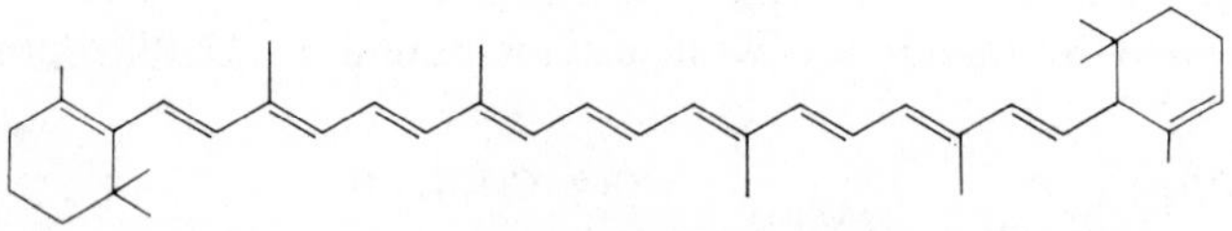

α-Carotene—VIII
($C_{40}H_{56}$)

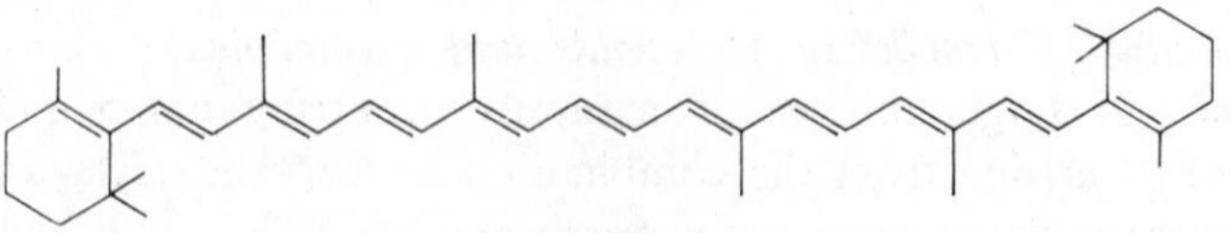

β-Carotene—IX
($C_{40}H_{56}$)

γ-Carotene—X
($C_{40}H_{56}$)

β-Ionone—XI

Vitamin A   Vitamin A is a factor associated with the formation of new cells in tissues and with normal vision. Deficiency gives rise to retarded growth and night blindness. Two compounds have been identified, and are designated vitamin A_1 (retinol), and vitamin A_2 (dehydroretinol). The latter compound has only one-hundredth of the activity of the former. The best direct sources of retinol are fish-liver oils. The structure (XII) of retinol has been confirmed by several syntheses, some of which have been used for commercial production. With five double bonds, there are theoretically thirty-two geometrical

XIII   XII

isomers. However, due to steric hindrance, the number of *cis* configurations is strictly limited. Retinol, like the carotenes, has the all *trans* configuration. Dehydroretinol (XIII) has an extra double bond in the cyclic moiety.

In the biochemistry of vision, the action of light on the light-sensitive pigment *rhodopsin* produces isomerization of the 11-*cis*-retinal component (the aldehyde from retinol). The *all-trans*-retinal dissociates from the protein component, opsin. Reduction of the retinal produces retinol, which in turn isomerizes to the 11-*cis*-retinol. Oxidation of this to the 11-*cis*-retinal and combination with opsin regenerates rhodopsin (Fig. 7.17).

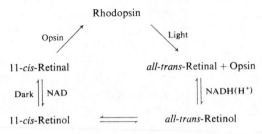

Rhodopsin

Opsin   Light

11-*cis*-Retinal   *all-trans*-Retinal + Opsin

Dark ‖ NAD   ‖ NADH(H^+)

11-*cis*-Retinol   ⇌   *all-trans*-Retinol

Fig. 7.17   Transformations during vision

(c) Vitamin E (the tocopherols)   The parent compound is *tocol* (XIV). The E vitamins have structures related to tocol in which substitution in the bicyclic system occurs and, also, in some cases, unsaturation in the side chain.

Of these compounds, α-tocopherol (5,7,8-trimethyl tocol) is the most widely distributed among animal tissues. The tocopherols are found in various cereal plants of which wheat germ, maize, and rice are important sources for Man. Vitamin E is a factor associated with the normal functioning

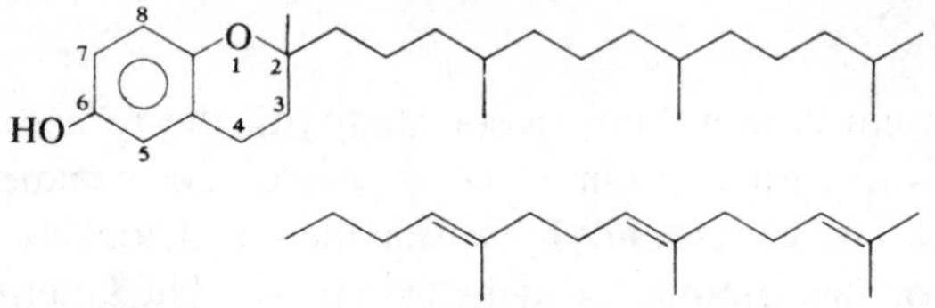

XIV

of the reproductive organs. Experiments in animals have also shown that deficiency results in muscular degeneration. The active part of the molecule lies in the bicyclic ring system, and minor changes can be made in the alkyl side chain provided its length is maintained. When α-tocopherol is fed to vitamin E-deficient animals, it is converted to quinones (XV; $n = 8$ and $n = 9$). Quinones of similar structure occur naturally; for example, plastoquinone (XVI; $n = 9$, $R = -CH_3$) of plant chloroplasts and a group of coenzymes known as the ubiquinones (XVI; $n = 6-10$, $R = -OCH_3$), which occur widely in both plants and animals. These compounds are involved in biological redox reactions. However, the main role of the E vitamins appears to be as cellular antioxidants, where they stabilize certain fats, vitamin A and sulphur-containing amino acids.

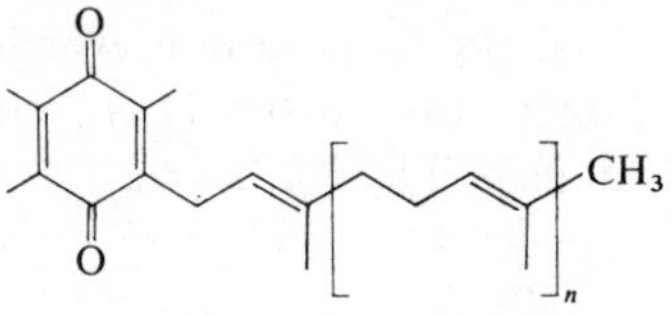

XV

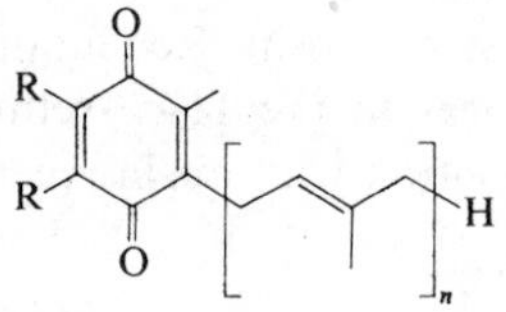

XVI

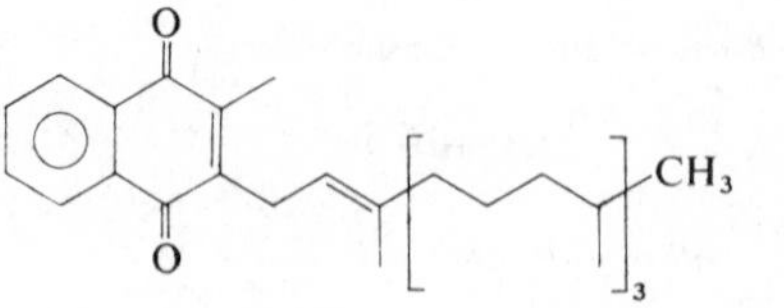

XVII

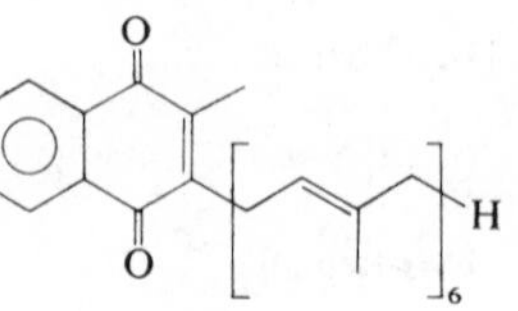

XVIII

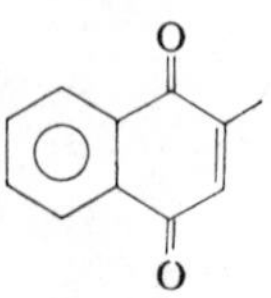

XIX

294

(d) Vitamin K (the quinones) The most fully studied of this group are K_1, phylloquinone (XVII), which occurs in green plants, and K_2, farnoquinone (XVIII), which is found in bacteria. The structural arrangement is not unlike that found in the tocopherols since they contain a bicyclic system, this time containing a *quinone* group and a side chain. In K_1, the side chain is a branched C_{20} chain derived from phytol, and in K_2 an all *trans* terpenoid chain (C_{30}) is present. Several other K vitamins of this latter type are known and are designated according to the length of the terpenoid chain, for example $K_{2(20)}$ and $K_{2(45)}$.

The K vitamins are necessary for normal blood coagulation, and K_1 has been shown to be involved in oxidative phosphorylation. There is also an obvious structural similarity with the ubiquinones (XVI; $n = 6–10$, R = —OCH_3). The most common of the latter group of compounds is that with six isoprene units, i.e., XVI, $n = 6$. The ubiquinones have a key role in the electron-transport system of living organisms (see Fig. 9.8).

One of the most important aspects of the chemistry of quinones is their ability to undergo interconversion to the corresponding *hydroquinone*. Quinones are formed by oxidation of hydroquinones, and the latter may in turn be reduced to quinones. Thus, 1,4-dihydroxy-benzene (the simplest hydroquinone) (XX) is oxidized by ferric ion to *p*-benzoquinone (XXI), which in turn is reduced back by sulphite ion. This process takes place in two stages, each involving the loss of an electron and a proton (hydrogen atom), in which an intermediate free radical—a *semiquinone* (XXII) is formed. Direct evidence for such an intermediate in both this reaction and in biological redox reactions of more complex quinones is obtained from ESR studies. Biological redox reactions of the ubiquinones takes place in the electron-transport system of cell mitochondria (section 9.2.7).

Quinones usually arise from the oxidation of aromatic compounds. Thus *p*-benzoquinone is formed in the dichromate oxidation of aniline and 2-methyl-1,4-naphthoquinone (menadione, XIX) in the oxidation of 2-methyl naphthalene. Menadione is biologically interesting, in that it has proved to be biochemically active being converted to $K_{2(20)}$ *in vivo*.

7.5.2 Steroids

The steroids form a group of naturally occurring compounds which have a common structural feature—a tetracyclic ring system known as the cyclopentanoperhydrophenanthrene ring (XXIII). The component rings are

XXIII   XXIV

designated by letters A, B, C, and D, and the individual carbon atoms by numbers. The structural features by which steroids are distinguished include: the presence of double bonds, the presence of side chains (XXIII; R^1, R^2, R^3) and the presence of oxygen-containing functional groups in both the ring system and the side chains (usually R^3). The side chains R^1 and R^2 are usually methyl groups but there is considerable variation in the structure of the side chain R^3. There are 7 asymmetric centres (C_5, C_8, C_9, C_{10}, C_{13}, C_{14}, and C_{17}), giving a total of 128 (2^7) possible stereoisomers. When certain functional groups are joined to any of the other carbon atoms, further asymmetry arises. Thus the *sterols* which have a hydroxyl group at C_3 could exist as 256 (2^8) possible stereoisomers. Fortunately the number of different configurations encountered in natural steroids is limited, due to a number of common structural features in the ring system. The stereochemistry may be simplified by considering firstly the way in which the rings are fused together (see section 2.11), and secondly the configuration of the substituents at C_{10}, C_{13}, C_{17} and, in the case of a sterol, C_3.

From a consideration of the stereochemistry at the ring junctions, two groups of steroids emerge.

(a) The cholestane series (allo series also known as the 5α series) in which all the ring junctions have a *trans* configuration (XXVa and b).

(b) The coprostane series (normal series also known as the 5β cholestane series) in which the A/B junction is *cis* while those at B/C and C/D have a *trans* configuration (XXVIa and b).

In the conventional structural diagrams (e.g., XXVa and XXVIa) the dotted lines represent atoms or groups projecting below the plane of the rings, and the full lines represent atoms or groups projecting above the plane. A more accurate picture of the shape of steroid molecules is, of course, given by the conformational diagrams (XXVb and XXVIb).

In both series of compounds the methyl groups (conventionally represented by a line rather than —CH_3) at C_{10} and C_{13} are on the same side of the

296

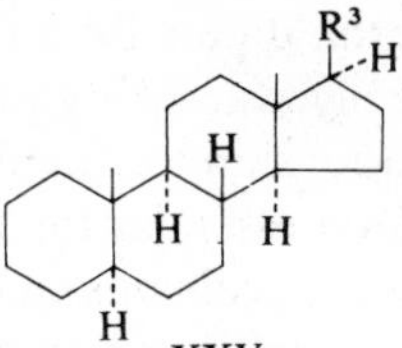

XXVa 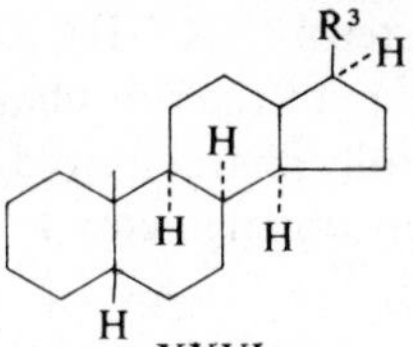   XXVIa

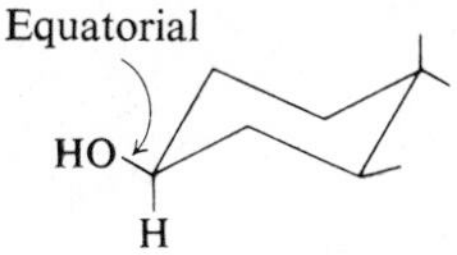

Equatorial

HO

XXVc 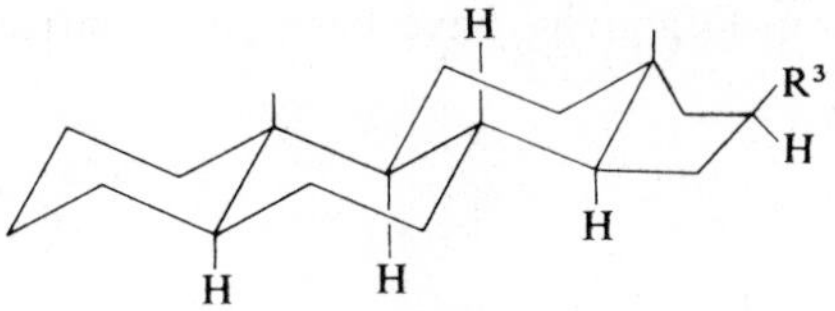   XXVb

Axial

HO

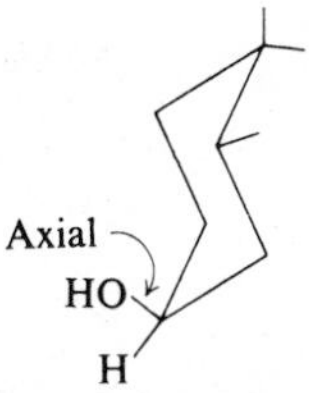

XXVIc 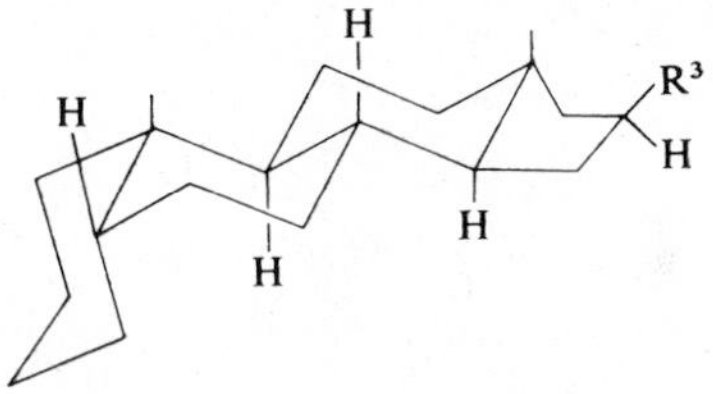   XXVIb

molecule—*cis*—as also is the side chain at C_{17} (R^3). The other configuration of importance is that at C_3. By convention, when a hydroxyl group is present at C_3 and projects above the plane of the ring, i.e., *cis* to the —CH_3 groups, the configuration is designated β. This configuration is found in all natural sterols (XXVc and XXVIc).

(a) Sterols and vitamin D   This group of steroids is characterized by the presence of an —OH group at C_3. The common sterols have an endocyclic double bond, usually at position 5,6, and further unsaturation may be present in the side chain at C_{17} (R^3). The presence of this alkyl side chain distinguishes the sterols from certain of the hormonal steroids which also have an —OH group at C_3. The sterols occur widely in nature, both freely and in combination as esters with long-chain fatty acids. They may be classified on the basis of their origin: thus *zoosterols* arise from animals, *phytosterols* from plants and *mycosterols* from yeasts and fungi. The best known of the sterols, and indeed of the whole steroid family, is cholesterol (XXVII). This is the principal zoosterol and was first isolated from gallstones, which consist almost entirely of cholesterol. It was one of the first steroids to be structurally investigated, and biochemically it can be considered as the precursor of other animal steroids (see section 9.3.6). In common with other steroids, selenium dehydrogenation gives among other products *Diels hydrocarbon*, 3'-methyl-1,2-cyclopentenophenanthrene (XXIV). Further structural investigation involves degradation, interconversion to other steroids and total synthesis.

297

Stigmasterol (XXVIII), a common phytosterol, differs from cholesterol in the structure of the side chain at C_{17} (R^3). The mycosterol ergosterol (XXIX) has been fully characterized, because of its relationship to vitamin D_2.

The nutritional factor known as vitamin D is essential for normal bone formation. The function of this factor is to control calcium and phosphorus metabolism, and deficiency causes *rickets*. Several compounds possessing vitamin-D activity have been characterized; they and their provitamins are

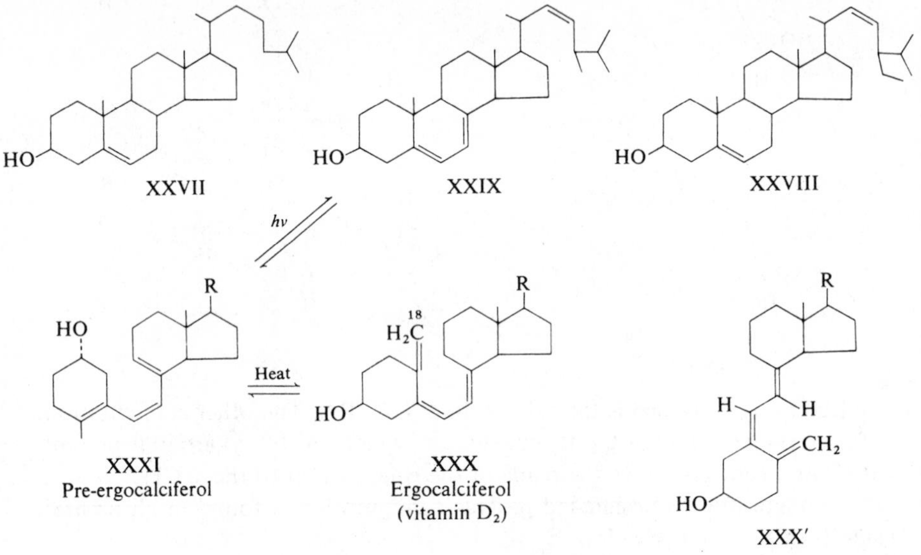

Fig. 7.18 Common sterols and the formation of vitamin D_2

all steroid derivatives. Anti-ricket properties were first discovered in food-stuffs which had been subject to irradiation with ultraviolet light. The most common provitamin which undergoes photochemical decomposition is the mycosterol ergosterol (XXIX). This compound undergoes complex changes when irradiated, and one of the products has anti-ricket activity. This is ergocalciferol (XXX), and it arises by way of the intermediate pre-ergo-calciferol (XXXI).

The structure of ergocalciferol has been investigated by both chemical and physical methods. Unlike a true steroid, this produces no phenanthrene derivatives on selenium dehydrogenation, and the fact that it is the B ring which is absent is revealed by oxidation studies. The presence of four double bonds is established by hydrogenation, and the ultraviolet spectrum shows the presence of a conjugate triene. Three of the double bonds have the same position as in ergosterol itself, and the fourth is at $C_{10}-C_{18}$. X-ray studies have confirmed the structure and shown that the configuration of the central double bonds is *cis*-5,*trans*-7 (**XXX′**).

Irradiation of the sterol 7-dehydrocholesterol (this has the *nucleus* of ergosterol and the side chain of cholesterol) produces a very potent anti-ricket compound. This compound, named cholecalciferol, has been designated vitamin D_3. Cholecalciferol turned out to be identical with the anti-ricket factor isolated from halibut and other fish oils.

(b) The bile acids The bile acids are found in the secretion of the liver known as the bile. These compounds contain the steroid nucleus and have a carboxyl group present at the end of the side chain at C_{17}. They occur naturally in the form of amides of amino acids, notably glycine. The bile acids are present as sodium salts (e.g., **XXXII**; $X = -NHCH_2COO^-\ Na^+$) and their function is to act as emulsifying agents for fats. Structurally, the bile acids are characterized by the presence of —OH groups (often several) all of which have an α configuration, i.e., the —OH group is on the opposite side of the ring to the C_{10} and C_{13} methyl groups and to the C_{17} side chain. Thus, cholic acid is represented by the conventional diagram (**XXXII**; $X = -OH$) or the conformational diagram (**XXXIII**). The four most abundant bile acids occurring in human bile are lithocholic (3α —OH), deoxycholic (3α, 12α di-OH), chenodeoxycholic (3α, 7α di-OH), and cholic (3α, 7α, 12α tri-OH) acids. All these compounds may be correlated with coprostane (**XXVI**) and thus have A/B ring junction *cis* fused.

XXXII   XXXIII

(c) The hormonal steroids Two groups may be distinguished—the sex hormones and the adrenal hormones. The sex hormones, secreted in the gonads (testes in the male and ovaries in the female), are steroids. Three types of sex hormone may be distinguished: androgens, which are male hormones from the testes; gestrogens, which are female hormones from the corpus luteum; and oestrogens, which are female hormones from the ovaries.

The primary male sex hormone, testosterone (**XXXIV**) controls the development of the genitals, and is responsible for secondary sexual characteristics. Two other hormones are found, presumably derived biochemically from testosterone; they are androsterone (**XXXV**) and androstenolone (**XXXVI**). The first of these compounds to be structurally investigated was androsterone

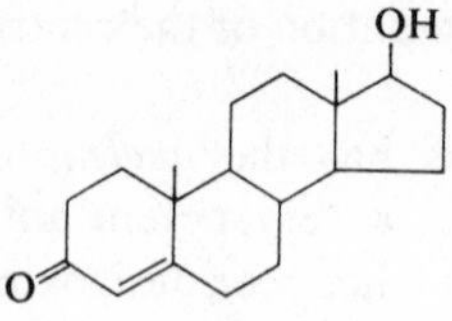

XXXIV 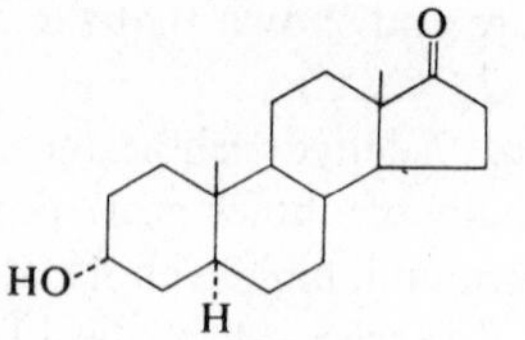   XXXV 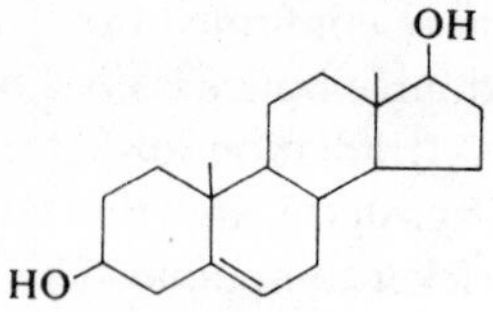   XXXVI

which can be correlated with cholestane (XXVa). Androstenolone and testosterone have been synthesized from cholesterol.

The corpus luteum is a yellow-coloured tissue which forms in the ovary following the release of an ovum. The function is to secrete the gestrogens responsible for the preparation of the uterus for pregnancy and, should conception occur, to maintain the pregnancy and later produce lactation. The principal hormone released for this process is progesterone (XXXVII) which has been isolated from animal ovaries. Pregnolone (XXVIII) has also been isolated from the corpus luteum and may be converted, chemically, to progesterone. Pregnanediol (XXXIX) is the chief excretory product of progesterone.

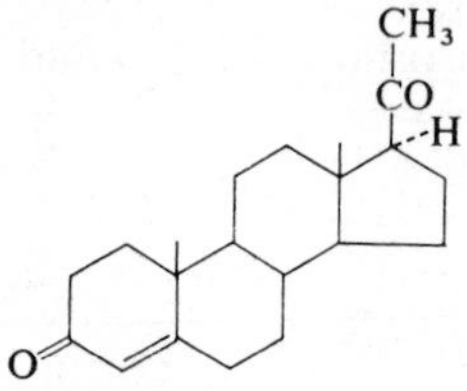

XXXVII 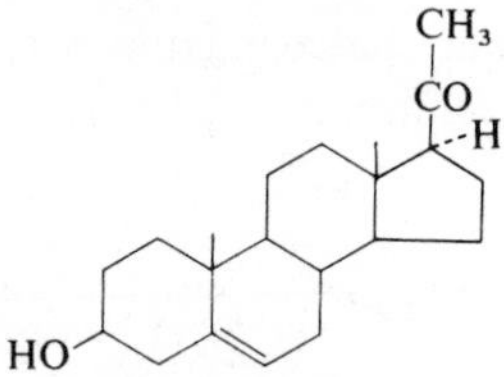   XXXVIII 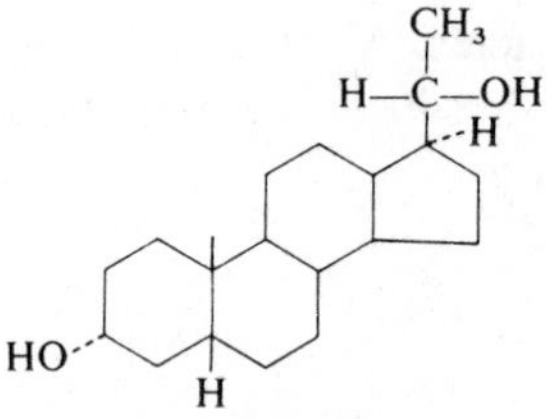   XXXIX

There are three principal female sex hormones, of which oestradiol (XL) is the primary compound, and oestrone (XLI) and oestriol (XLII) are the more abundant but less active hormones. These compounds control the uterine cycle and produce secondary sexual characteristics. An interesting feature

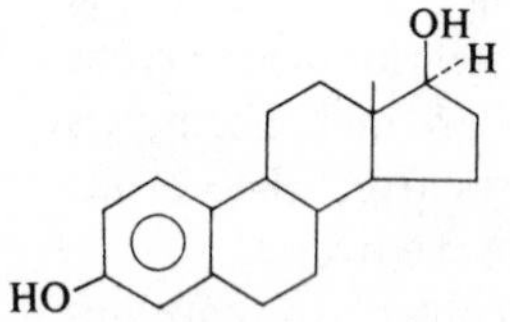

XL 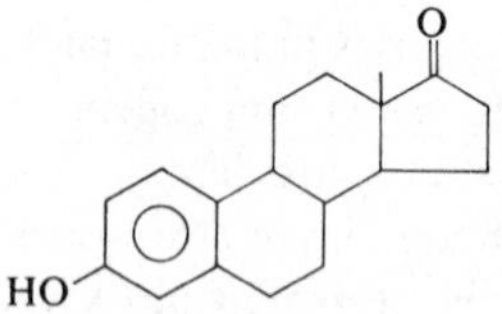   XLI 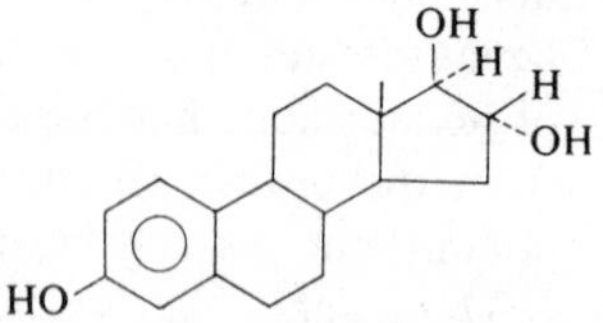   XLII

of their structures is the presence of a benzenoid A ring, and this gives the —OH group at C_3 phenolic character.

300

In the adrenal glands, situated just above the kidneys, two regions may be distinguished: the medulla, which produces adrenalin, and the cortex, which produces steroid hormones. Production of the latter is controlled by the pituitary hormone ACTH (section 8.4.3). At least twenty-eight cortical steroids have been identified and these include many of the sex hormones. Of this large number, seven compounds have emerged as the principal active adrenocortical steroids.

Structurally they may be grouped as follows:

(i) Cortisol (XLIII; R = —OH), its ketone cortisone (XLIII; R = =O), and cortexolone (XLIII; R = H$_2$) all have an α hydroxyl group at C$_{17}$, and differ only in the nature of the substitution at C$_{11}$.

(ii) A corresponding series based on corticosterone (XLIV; R = —OH), 11-dehydrocorticosterone (XLIV; R = =O) and cortexone (XLIV; R = —H$_2$) do not have a 17α —OH group and again differ only in the substitution at C$_{11}$.

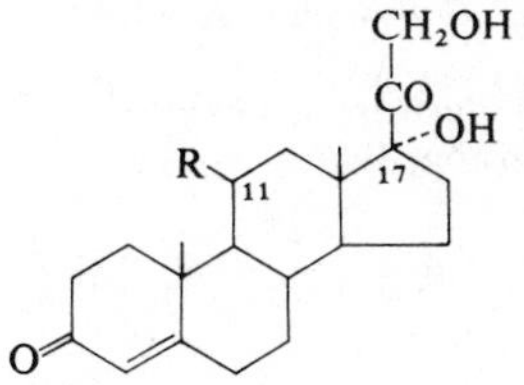

XLIII 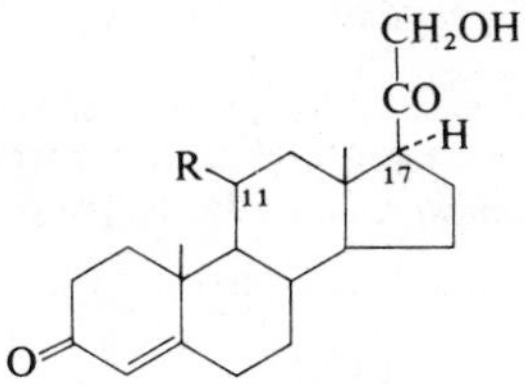   XLIV 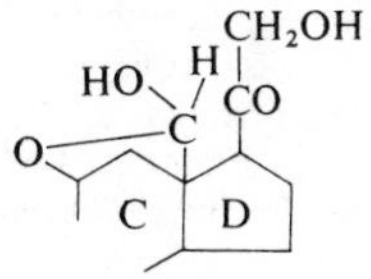   XLVI

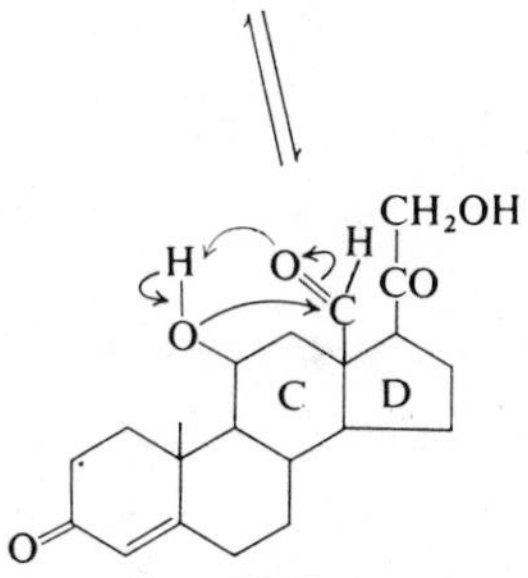

XLV

(iii) The seventh member of the active adrenocortical steroids is aldosterone, which is unusual in that it has an angular aldehyde group. This compound exists in an equilibrium of aldehydo (XLV) and hemi-acetal (XLVI) forms (cf. aldoses).

Biologically, the corticosteroids may be divided into those which are concerned with electrolyte and water balance (cortexolone, cortexone and aldosterone), and those which are important in carbohydrate and protein metabolism (cortisol, cortisone, corticosterone and 11-dehydrocorticosterone).

301

Bibliography

1. I. L. Finar, Vol. 2, *Organic Chemistry*, 5th Edn, Longmans, 1975.
2. H. D. Law, *The Organic Chemistry of Peptides*, Wiley, 1970.
3. M. Bodansky and M. A. Ondetti, *Peptide Synthesis*, Wiley/Interscience, 1966.
4. H. D. Jakubke and H. Jeschkeit, *Amino-acids, Peptides and Proteins—an introduction*, Macmillan, 1975.
5. D. Chapman, *Introduction to Lipids*, McGraw-Hill, 1969.
6. F. D. Gunstone, *An Introduction to the Chemistry and Biochemistry of Fatty Acids and their Glycerides*, 2nd Edn, Chapman and Hall, 1968.
7. M. I. Gurr and A. T. James, *Lipid Biochemistry—an introduction*, 2nd Edn, Chapman and Hall, 1975.
8. P. B. Curtis-Prior, *Prostaglandins*, North-Holland, 1976.
9. R. D. Guthrie and J. Honeyman, *An Introduction to the Chemistry of Carbohydrates*, 4th Edn, Oxford UP, 1974.
10. R. W. Bailey, *Oligosaccharides*, Pergamon, 1964.
11. T. L. V. Ulbricht, *Purines, Pyrimidines, and Nucleotides and the Chemistry of Nucleic Acids*, Commonwealth and International Library, 1964.
12. D. W. Hutchinson, *Nucleotides and Coenzymes*, Methuen, 1965.
13. S. F. Dyke, *The Chemistry of the Vitamins*, Interscience, 1965.
14. T. W. Goodwin, *The Biosynthesis of Vitamins and Related Compounds*, Academic Press, 1963.
15. W. Templeton, *An Introduction to Terpenoids and Steroids*, Butterworths, 1969.
16. L. F. Fieser and M. Fieser, *Steroids*, Holt, Rinehart and Winston, 1959.
17. W. R. Butt, *Hormone Chemistry*, 2nd Edn, Horwood, 1975.

8. The structure and properties of biopolymers

8.1 PHYSICAL PROPERTIES AND STRUCTURAL FEATURES OF BIOPOLYMERS

8.1.1 Macromolecules and colloids

In solutions of small-molecular-weight solutes, the solute is more or less dispersed into separate molecules or ions. Suspensions, on the other hand, contain particles which are observable either by the naked eye or by means of a low-powered microscope. Between these two extremes are systems which are said to be in the *colloidal state*. There are no sharp dividing lines between these three states, but colloids are usually thought of as having particle sizes in the range $0.2\,\mu m$–5 nm ($0.2\,\mu$–5 mμ). Particles slightly outside this size range also have colloidal properties. For example, red cells and platelets are slightly larger than colloids as defined by these dimensions, but they possess electrical charges and undergo electrophoretic migration in an electric field in the same way as colloids. Macromolecules—that is, molecules of high molecular weight —have, in many cases, a molecular size approaching colloidal dimensions, and hence their solutions have properties often similar to those of colloidal dispersions. The macromolecules with which we are concerned in this chapter are polymeric materials which occur naturally, and hence are called *biopolymers*. The term *polymer* defines a molecular structure built up of repeating structural units. These units, called the *monomers*, have similar or even identical structure. A polymer molecule will consist of anything from 100 to several thousands of these monomer units. The number of monomer units per polymer chain is called the *degree of polymerization*.

(a) Some properties of the colloidal state   The material that is dispersed in the colloidal form is called the *disperse phase*. The medium containing the disperse phase is called the *disperse medium*. There are essentially two different types of colloidal systems: *lyophobic colloids* (solvent hating) and *lyophilic colloids* (solvent loving). Their respective properties are best considered separately.

Lyophobic colloids are usually inorganic, and can be made with metallic salts such as hydroxides or even metals themselves. They consist of discrete particles of material suspended in the dispersion medium. In many cases, the particles are too small to be seen by an optical microscope. Their presence is apparent, however, by observing the *Tyndall effect*. This phenomenon is the scattering of light by the particles, and may be observed in the ultramicroscope. A beam of light is directed into the colloid and the scattered light is viewed at right angles (Fig. 8.1).

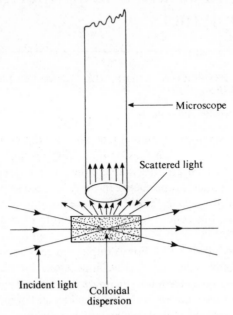

Fig. 8.1   Schematic representation of the Tyndall effect

The amount of light scattered by a colloid (I) depends not only on the wavelength of the light but also on the particle size, and is given by

$$I = \frac{kV^2}{d^2 \lambda^4},$$

where k is a constant involving the difference in refractive indices of the disperse phase and the dispersion medium, V is the volume of a particle, d is the distance from the observer, and λ is the wavelength of the light. The Tyndall effect is the basis of the light-scattering method of molecular-weight determination for macromolecules. The intensity of the light scattered at various angles by polymer molecules in solution is measured. From this, the molecular weight may be deduced (see also section 8.1.2). The intensity of the scattered light is very sensitive to molecular shape, and deductions may be made regarding the overall molecular shape, i.e., spherical, cylindrical, or random.

304

Most lyophobic colloids will pass through the pores of a filter paper. They can be purified by *dialysis*, using a cellophane membrane. The contaminating ions and molecules are small enough to pass through the cellophane, and are washed away while the colloid is retained.

All lyophobic colloids are electrically charged. This arises from the electrical double layer at the particle–liquid interface. Because of this charge, the colloid particles migrate under the influence of an applied electric field. This phenomenon is termed *particle electrophoresis*, and the speed of migration is proportional to a potential at the particle surface known as the *zeta potential*. It is

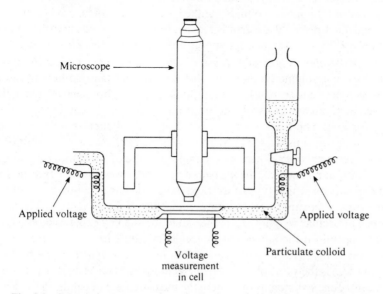

Fig. 8.2 Schematic representation of a horizontal microelectrophoresis cell

possible to observe the electrophoresis of individual particles if they can be seen in an optical microscope (microelectrophoresis, Fig. 8.2).

The effect of added substances upon the magnitude of the zeta potential has important consequences on the stability of colloids. Below a certain value of zeta potential, the particles do not have sufficient electrical charge to keep them apart, and they coagulate in order to reduce their surface area. Electrolytes coagulate colloids; the ion responsible is that of opposite sign to the charge on the surface of the colloid. The coagulating power of an ion is proportional to its valency. The coagulating power of monovalent, divalent and trivalent ions is approximately $1:10:600$.

Lyophilic colloids are not particulate in character and are formed as very viscous solutions which, when cooled, usually form a *gel*. This type of colloid frequently arises with biopolymers. The colloidal material is in an extremely high state of hydration, and this state of hydration is of great importance for their stability. Under the influence of an electric field, the whole colloid migrates. The direction of the migration is dependent on the pH of the system, since changes in pH bring about changes in charge on the colloid. At the isoelectric point the colloid has zero charge and does not migrate, *and* is also perfectly stable.

Addition of electrolyte to a lyophilic colloid does not normally cause coagulation. If, however, very large quantities of electrolyte are added, then dehydration occurs, which leads to coagulation. The stability towards electrolytes is decreased if the lyophilic colloid is partially dehydrated by acetone or ethyl alcohol. Lyophilic colloids, unlike lyophobic colloids, can be dehydrated and hydrated reversibly. For this reason, lyophilic colloids are often referred to as *reversible colloids*, and lyophobic colloids as *irreversible colloids*.

(b) Molecular weight of polymers One of the most important physical constants of a polymer is its molecular weight, and many different methods have been devised for these determinations. The value obtained for the molecular weight of a polymer usually depends upon the experimental method for its measurement. The reason for this is that most polymer samples consist of molecules of various sizes. This feature is termed *polydisperse*, in contrast to a *monodisperse* polymer, where all the molecules are of the same size and structure. Thus, in most cases, the measured molecular weight is an average value, and depends on which type of average the particular experimental method is measuring. There are three important molecular-weight averages. The *number average* molecular weight $(\overline{M}_n)$ is the value obtained by experimental methods which depend on the *number* of molecules present; in other words methods based on colligative properties of solutions. The *weight average* molecular weight $(\overline{M}_w)$ is the value obtained from techniques, such as light scattering and ultracentrifuge sedimentation, where the measurement depends on the mass of the molecules in solution. A third molecular-weight average is obtained from viscosity measurements.

A hypothetical molecular-weight distribution curve is shown in Fig. 8.3 for a polymer sample which is polydisperse with respect to molecular weight. It can be seen that the average values defined above differ considerably for such a sample. The value of $\overline{M}_w$ is approximately twice the value of $\overline{M}_n$. If $\overline{M}_w$ equals $\overline{M}_n$, then the polymer sample is completely homogeneous with respect to molecular weight (monodisperse).

(c) Measurement of number average molecular weights $(\overline{M}_n)$ (*i*) *End-group analysis* In this method, the number of polymer molecules in a known weight of polymer is measured. This is done by estimating the number of functional groups situated at the ends of each polymer chain in the sample. This analysis is usually carried out by a chemical method, such as a titration. If w is the weight of polymer taken, r is the number of reactive groups per molecule, and g is the weight (in grams) of reagent used (of molecular weight q), then

$$\overline{M}_n = \frac{rqw}{g}$$

The upper limit of molecular weight for which this method can be used is about 25 000.

(*ii*) *Thermoelectric method (vapour pressure osmometry)* Commercial instruments are available for this method. Very small quantities of solvent and dilute polymer solution are placed on the tips of thermistors inside a thermostatted container, which is saturated with solvent vapour. The solvent and solution assume, at equilibrium, a small temperature difference ($\sim 10^{-4}$ °C) due to differences in the relative rates of condensation and evaporation. This temperature difference, which is proportional to the weight and

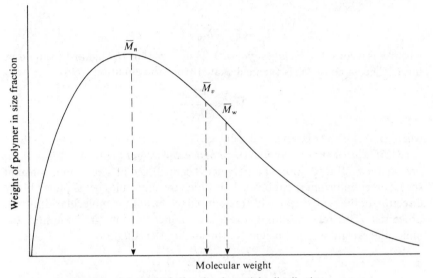

Fig. 8.3 A hypothetical molecular-weight distribution curve

molecular weight of the solute, is measured by a change in resistance in a Wheatstone bridge, of which the thermistors are part. The instrument is calibrated with a compound of known molecular weight, and values up to about 20 000 can be measured.

(*iii*) *Cryoscopy and ebulliometry* Both these methods are a direct application of Raoult's law, and commercial equipment is available for them. For the cryoscopic method,

$$\overline{M}_n = K_f c M_1 / 1000 \Delta T_f$$

where ΔT_f is the depression of the freezing point of the pure solvent, c is the solute concentration in grams per 1000 g of solvent and K_f is the corresponding *cryoscopic constant*.

A similar equation is used in the ebullioscopic method, with ΔT_b, the elevation of the boiling point, and K_b, the ebullioscopic constant. The upper limit for both methods is a molecular weight of about 20 000.

(*iv*) *Osmotic-pressure measurement* This method is suitable for high number average molecular weights (up to 2×10^6) and a number of commercial instruments are available. For an ideal solution, the osmotic pressure (Π) of a polymer solution would be given by

$$\frac{\Pi}{RTc} = \frac{1}{\overline{M}_n}$$

where c is the polymer concentration, T is the temperature and R is the gas constant. For the non-ideal polymer solutions the equation takes the form

$$\frac{\Pi}{RTc} = \frac{1}{\overline{M}_n} + Ac$$

where A is a constant (*virial coefficient*). Thus, a plot of Π/c against c should be linear. The value of $\overline{M}_n$ is then calculated from the equation

$$\overline{M}_n = \frac{RT}{(\Pi/c)_0}$$

where $(\Pi/c)_0$ is the extrapolated value of Π/c at zero concentration ($c = 0$).

(d) Measurement of weight average molecular weight ($\overline{M}_w$) (*i*) *Ultracentrifuge method* If a solution of a polymer is centrifuged at a very high constant speed, an equilibrium is established, in which the molecules being pulled in the direction of the centrifugal field are opposed by the normal molecular-diffusion processes. The relationship between the concentration gradient and the molecular weight at equilibrium is expressed in the equation

$$\overline{M}_w = \frac{2RT \ln(c_2/c_1)}{w^2(1 - Vd)(x_2^2 - x_1^2)}$$

where c_1 and c_2 are the concentrations of polymer at distances x_1 and x_2 from the axis of rotation, V is the partial specific volume of the solute, d is the density of the solvent, and w is the angular velocity of rotation. The concentration gradient is usually measured by a refractive-index method, or by interferometry.

An alternative approach is to carry out measurements during the pre-equilibrium period, and measure the *rate* of sedimentation by means of the sedimentation coefficient (s). This is the velocity of the solute molecules divided by the centrifugal field:

$$s = \frac{dx/dt}{w^2 x} = \frac{1}{w^2} \frac{d(\ln x)}{dt} = \frac{2 \cdot 303}{w^2} \frac{d(\log x)}{dt}$$

The coefficient s (measured in seconds) may be obtained as the gradient of the graph of log of the distance of a solute band from the centre of rotation as a function of time. The rate of sedimentation for a given class of polymer is proportional to molecular weight, and thus s is related to molecular weight. A convenient unit for the sedimentation coefficient is the Svedberg (S) and $1\,S$ equals $10^{-13}\,s$. It is now common practice with certain biopolymers to quote their S-value as a measure of molecular size; thus $4S$ RNA's are transfer-RNAs with molecular weights in the range 25 000–30 000.

(*ii*) *Light-scattering method*   The principle of this method has already been described in connection with the Tyndall effect of colloids. The intensity of the light scattered by a polymer solution is expressed in terms of the *Rayleigh ratio* (R):

$$R_\theta = r^2\,I_r/I_0$$

where I_r is the intensity of the scattered light at angle θ and distance r, and I_0 is the intensity of the monochromatic incident beam. The relationship between R_{90} (the Rayleigh ratio at $90°$ to the incident beam) and $\overline{M}_w$ is given in the equation

$$\frac{Kc}{R_{90}} = \frac{1}{\overline{M}_w} + 2Ac$$

where K is a constant, c is the polymer concentration, and A is the virial coefficient. A graph of Kc/R_{90} against c has an intercept at $c = 0$ of $1/\overline{M}_w$.

(*e*) **Measurement of viscosity average molecular weight**   The measurement of polymer molecular weight by the viscosity method is by far the most convenient practical method. It is based upon the empirical *Mark–Houwink* equation

$$[\eta] = K(\overline{M}_v)^a$$

The intrinsic viscosity (limiting viscosity number, $[\eta]$) is obtained as the intercept of a graph of η_{sp}/c or $\log\eta_{sp}/c$ against c, where the specific viscosity η_{sp} is $(\eta_s - \eta_0)/\eta_0$, and η_s and η_0 are the solution and solvent viscosities respectively. When the value of $[\eta]$ has been obtained, the value of $\overline{M}_v$ for the polymer is calculated from the Mark–Houwink equation.

8.1.2   General structural features of biopolymers

Polymers may be classified into three broad groups. The first of these are the biopolymers of which the three principal members—polysaccharides, proteins, and nucleic acids—are the subject of this chapter. The second group consists of certain chemically modified natural polymers of great commercial important such as cellulose acetate fibres. The third group are the totally synthetic polymers, and include such well known materials as polyethylene, polyvinyl chloride, polystyrene, nylon, and terylene.

A further point of classification is to distinguish a polymer consisting of a single monomer unit, such as cellulose, composed of D-glucose residues or polyvinyl chloride made from vinyl chloride from a polymer containing a number of monomer units, such as proteins composed of α-amino acids. The first type of polymer is termed a homopolymer, and the second type a heteropolymer.

The vast majority of polymer samples are polydisperse, and this is always true of synthetic polymers, polysaccharides and modified polysaccharides. In the case of soluble proteins and some nucleic acids, however, it is possible by careful fractionation and purification to obtain completely homogeneous material and to determine the complete structure. Before a detailed account is given of the structure of the biopolymers, it is convenient to describe the general structural features common to all of them. For this purpose, the structural organization can be considered at two broad levels: the arrangement of the covalent bonds in the molecule and the three-dimensional structure. The former is referred to as the *primary structure*.

(a) Primary structure of biopolymers   In common with other polymers, the covalent bond structure is based on a linear arrangement of monomer units. The monomer unit in polysaccharides is a monosaccharide; both homo- and heteropolysaccharides are known. Those made up of D-glucose residues are the most abundant—cellulose, starch and glycogen. The monosaccharides are joined by glycosidic bonds in long linear chains, the C_1 of the monosaccharide (for an aldose) is always involved, and in the common polysaccharides the bond is $1 \rightarrow 4$. The stereochemistry of the glycosidic bond is of some importance in determining the conformation of the chain. In cellulose, the glycosidic bonds are $\beta(1 \rightarrow 4)$ and in the amylose fraction of starch they are $\alpha(1 \rightarrow 4)$ (Fig. 8.4). Each linear polysaccharide chain has a *reducing end group* and a *non-reducing end group*.

The amino-acid residues in proteins are linked by peptide bonds (see section 7.1), and the resulting polymer chain is known as a *polypeptide chain*. The average protein contains about twenty different monomer units, and the term *sequence* is used to define the order of the amino acids in a chain. This sequence is of fundamental importance in determining the three-dimensional structure of the molecule, and hence the biochemical properties. Sequence determination is one of the major tasks during the primary structure determination of a protein. Figure 8.8 shows the sequence of the 153 amino-acid residues in the single polypeptide chain of the protein myoglobin; notice that each residue is designated by its three-letter abbreviation (see Table 7.1). In this case, the polypeptide chain has an amino and carboxyl terminus, although in many cases these end groups are chemically modified—for example, a terminal amide group may be present rather than a carboxyl.

The monomer units of nucleic acids are the nucleotides, which are joined together by phosphodiester bonds to give a *polynucleotide chain*. Since there

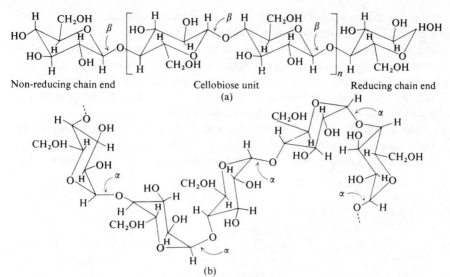

Fig. 8.4 Linear polysaccharide chains: (a) $\beta(1 \to 4)$-linked D-glucose residues of cellulose; (b) part of an amylose chain $\alpha(1 \to 4)$-linked D-glucose residues

are two distinct types of nucleotide (section 7.4.1), two types of polynucleotide chain arise. A chain consisting of ribonucleotides is found in ribonucleic acids (RNA) and chains of deoxyribonucleotides in deoxyribonucleic acids (DNA) (Fig. 8.5). Each type of chain has a 5'-phosphate terminus and a 3'-hydroxyl

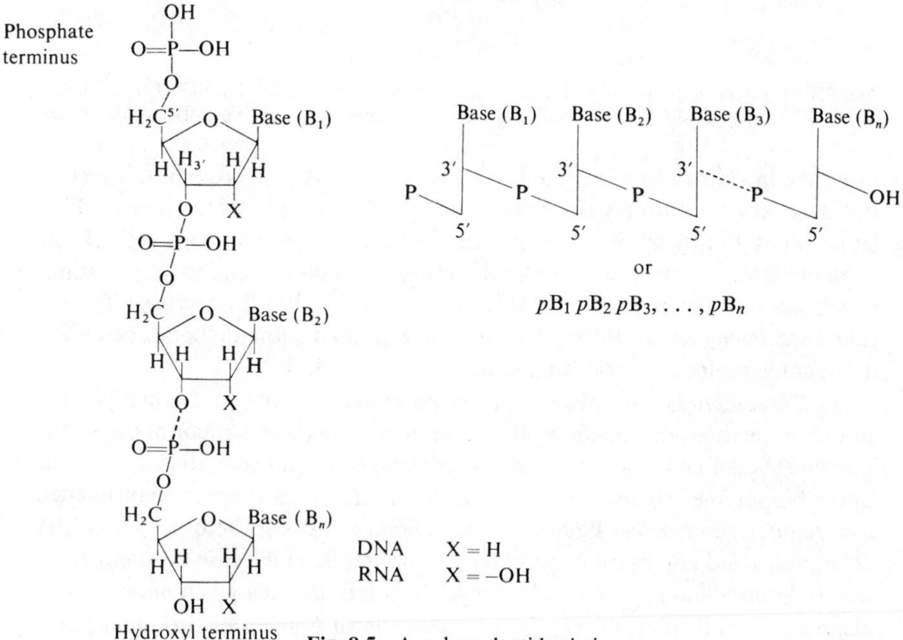

Phosphate terminus

OH
|
O=P—OH
|
O

$H_2C^{5'}$ ⎯O⎯ Base (B_1)

H $H_{3'}$ H/H

O   X

O=P—OH
|
O

H_2C ⎯O⎯ Base (B_2)

H\H H/H

O   X

O=P—OH
|
O

H_2C ⎯O⎯ Base (B_n)

H\H H/H

OH   X

Hydroxyl terminus

Base (B_1)   Base (B_2)   Base (B_3)   Base (B_n)

$3'$ $3'$ $3'$
P   P   P ⋯⋯⋯ P   OH
$5'$ $5'$ $5'$ $5'$

or

$p B_1 \, p B_2 \, p B_3, \ldots, p B_n$

DNA   X = H
RNA   X = —OH

Fig. 8.5 A polynucleotide chain

311

terminus. Since both DNA and RNA are heteropolymers, the problem of sequence arises in the determination of primary structure. In polynucleotide chains the sequence relates ultimately to the nature of the base moiety attached to the pentose residue in each monomer unit, i.e., the order B_1, B_2, B_3, ..., B_n (Fig. 8.5). Sequence determination in this field has advanced greatly in the last few years. Sequences of some 50 transfer-RNAs are now known as well as a viral-RNA (MS 2) and a viral-DNA (ϕ X174).

The structure of the polymeric chains in polysaccharides and proteins may be further complicated by the presence of covalent bonds which join together different chains (*inter-chain cross links*) or join together different parts of the

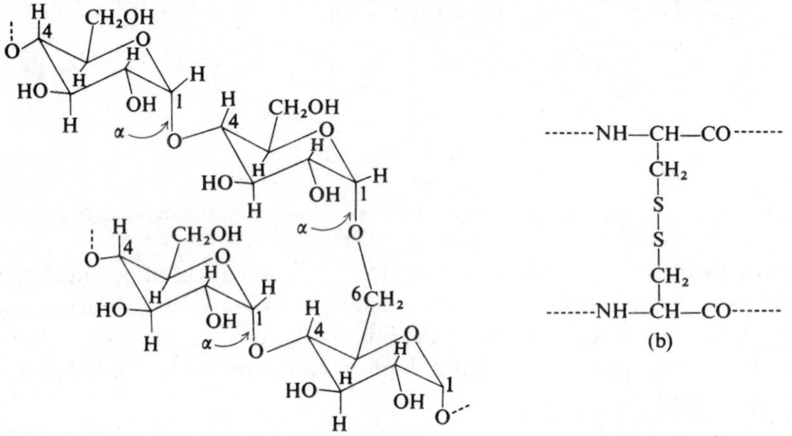

Fig. 8.6 (a) Part of an amylopectin molecule showing the cross linking of $\alpha(1 \to 4)$ chains by an $\alpha(1 \to 6)$ glycosidic bond. (b) A cystine residue cross linking two polypeptide chains

same chain (*intra-chain cross links*). The former type of cross link arises in polysaccharides through the formation of $\alpha(1 \to 6)$ glycosidic bonds. This situation is found in the amylopectin fraction of starch [Fig. 8.6(a)]. In proteins, both types of cross link may occur through the amino acid cystine, which can participate in two peptide bonds [Fig. 8.6(b).] Such cross links are called *disulphide bonds*. Both inter- and intra-chain disulphide bonds can arise in the same molecule, for example, in insulin (Fig. 8.7).

(b) Three-dimensional structure of biopolymers   Owing to the complexity found in the three-dimensional structure, further levels of structural organization must be defined. The secondary structure describes the spatial conformation of the biopolymer chain; this may be *ordered*, in that its shape may be likened to a regular geometrical figure, for example, a helix. On the other hand, the chain may bend and twist, apparently at random, in which case the conformation is described as *disordered*. It should be noted that in a given molecule the disordered conformation may be reproducible in a given environment, and

this allows the conformation to be determined. Ordered helical conformations are found in all three biopolymers. The stereochemistry of the glycosidic bond in amylose (Fig. 8.4) allows the chain to twist in a helical conformation in contrast to the linear conformation found in cellulose. The helical conformation is a common feature of a polypeptide chain; for example, in myoglobin about 70 per cent of the chain is in a helical conformation [Fig. 8.8(c)]. Probably the most well known of all helical conformations is that found in DNA. In this case, two polynucleotide chains are hydrogen bonded together and wound in

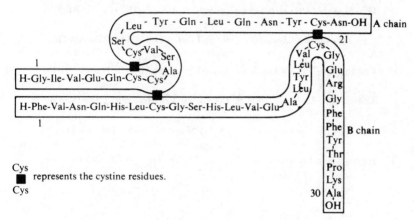

Fig. 8.7   The primary structure of bovine insulin

the form of a *double-stranded helix*; both linear and cyclic examples of this are found in nature (Fig. 8.9).

Since in most biopolymer molecules a completely ordered secondary structure, as exemplified in DNA, is rarely found, it is necessary to consider the overall shape of the molecule. This is described in the *tertiary structure*. When a molecule has a completely helical and linear conformation it has an overall rod-like shape; this is found in the case of certain insoluble proteins as well as DNA molecules. In other cases, regions of ordered structure are interspersed with regions of disordered conformation and the whole molecule assumes a compact often spherical tertiary structure. Figure 8.8(b) shows the complex tertiary structure of myoglobin and that of α-chymotrypsin in Fig. 8.40.

In some large macromolecules a further level of structural organization must be defined, this is the *quaternary structure*. It arises in molecules built up of *sub-units*, each of which is already a macromolecule. The quaternary structure describes the arrangement of these sub-units with respect to each other. This situation is common in the larger proteins and in some of the largest macromolecules known—the viruses (Fig. 8.10).

H-Val-Leu-Ser-Glu-Gly-Glu-Trp-Gln-Leu-Val-Leu-His-Val-Tyr-Ala-Lys-Val-
1 10

Glu-Ala-Asp-Val-Ala-Gly-His-Gly-Gln- Asp-Ile-Leu-Ile-Arg-Leu-Phe-Lys-
20 30

Ser-His-Pro-Glu-Thr-Leu-Glu-Lys-Phe-Asp-Arg-Phe-Lys-His-Leu-Lys-Thr-
40 50

Glu-Ala-Glu-Met-Lys-Ala-Ser-Glu-Asp-Leu-Lys-Gly-His-His-Glu-Ala-Glu-
60

Leu- Thr-Ala-Leu-Gly-Ala-Ile-Leu-Lys-Lys-Lys-Gly-His-His-Glu-Ala-Glu-
70 80

Leu-Lys-Pro-Leu-Ala-Gln-Ser-His-Ala-Thr-Lys-His-Lys-Ile-Pro-Ile-Lys-Tyr-
90 100

Leu-Glu-Phe-Ile-Ser-Glu-Ala-Ile-Ile-His-Val- Leu-His-Ser-Arg-His-Pro-Gly-
110 120

Asn-Phe-Gly-Ala-Asp-Ala-Gln-Gly-Ala-Met-Asn-Lys-Ala-Leu-Glu-Leu-Phe-
130

Arg-Lys-Asp-Ile- Ala-Ala-Lys-Tyr-Lys-Glu-Leu-Gly-Tyr-Gln-Gly-OH
140 150 153

(a)

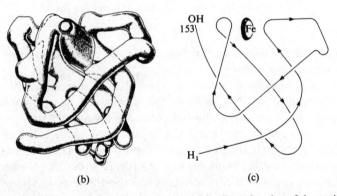

(b)   (c)

Fig. 8.8 (a) The primary structure of whale myoglobin. (b) A drawing of the tertiary structure of whale myoglobin. (c) A diagram showing the course of the polypeptide chain (straight
sections are α-helix) (by permission of J. C. Kendrew, 1960, and the editor of *Nature*)

314

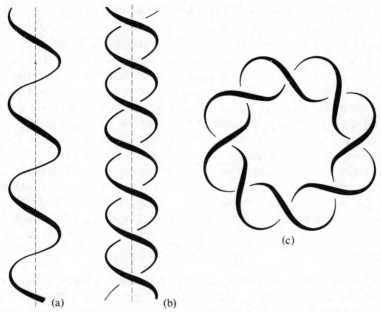

Fig. 8.9   Helical structures found in nature: (a) right-handed single-chain helix; (b) right-handed double-chain helix; (c) cyclic double-chain helix

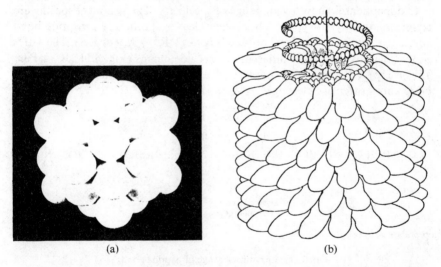

Fig. 8.10   (a) A model of a particle of turnip yellow virus showing the arrangement of protein sub-units. Each sub-unit is spherical and consists of 191 amino acids (by permission of H. L. Nixon and A. J. Gibbs, 1960, and the editor of *The Journal of Molecular Biology*). (b) A drawing of a section of tobacco mosaic virus. The central spiral is the position occupied by an RNA molecule and is surrounded by protein sub-units. Each sub-unit consists of 157 amino acids (by permission of A. Klug and D. L. P. Caspar, 1960, and the editor of *Advances in Virus Research*)

315

(c) Enzymic fragmentation of biopolymers   The basic process here is one of hydrolysis, where the enzyme catalyses the 'addition of water' across the covalent bond linking the monomer units (a single exception is the phosphorolysis process that takes place with polysaccharides—see section 9.2.2). The hydrolysis reactions are important, both from the point of view of structural investigation and also as processes that occur during biopolymer degradation *in vivo*. The enzymes that carry out the hydrolysis of biopolymers are generally specific with regard to the linkage they act on: thus, enzymes catalysing hydrolysis of polysaccharides (the polysaccharidases), act on glycosidic bonds, those hydrolysing polypeptides (the peptidases) act on amide bonds and those hydrolysing polynucleotides (the nucleases) act on phosphodiester bonds. Two basic types of action may be distinguished: firstly, *exo-action*, where the enzyme acts at a chain end and removes the monomer units in a stepwise manner, and secondly, *endo-action*, where the enzyme acts at specific linkages within the molecule.

Peptidases

Two types of exopeptidase occur: one type which acts at the N-terminal end (e.g. leucine aminopeptidase), and another which acts at the C-terminal end (e.g., carboxypeptidases A, B and C). In both cases, the rate of cleavage of the terminal peptide bond depends on the nature of the terminal side-chain group.

Endopeptidases show a wide range of specificity. The two most specific are trypsin and α-chymotrypsin. The former cleaves specifically a peptide bond adjacent to an arginyl or lysyl residue (Fig. 8.11; R^x = Arg or Lys). The latter cleaves mainly at linkages adjacent to aryl side chains (Fig. 8.11; R^x = Phe, Tyr or Trp). Other endopeptidases, such as pepsin, are much less specific and bring about extensive cleavage.

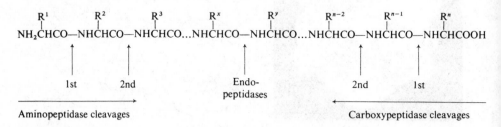

Fig. 8.11   Enzymic cleavage of peptide bonds

Nucleases

Two broad groups occur: those hydrolysing DNA are called deoxyribonucleases, and those hydrolysing RNA are the ribonucleases. The latter type will be used as examples. The phosphodiester bond can be attacked in two possible

316

ways. Attack at *site 1* leads to the formation of a terminal 3′ —OH group. While attack at *site 2* will produce a terminal 3′ phosphate group.

$$\begin{array}{c}
\text{O—CH}_2\text{ O} \quad \text{B}' \\
\text{H} \quad \text{H} \quad \text{H} \\
\text{O} \quad \text{X} \\
\text{-O—P=O} \\
\text{O—CH}_2\text{ O} \quad \text{B}'' \\
\text{H} \quad \text{H} \quad \text{H} \\
\text{O} \quad \text{X}
\end{array}$$

Site 1
Site 2

Two types of exonuclease are found: those which act at *site 2* adjacent to a 5′ terminal —CH_2OH group (e.g. spleen phosphodiesterase), and those which act at *site 1* adjacent to a 3′ terminal —OH group (e.g., snake venom phosphodiesterase). It should be noted that a terminal phosphate group prevents reaction by an exonuclease; such a terminal group may be removed by the action of a phosphomonoesterase (e.g., alkaline phosphatase).

Endonucleases act at site 2 and show high specificity. Pancreatic ribonuclease cleaves a phosphodiester bond adjacent to a pyrimidine base (Fig. 8.12, B^x = U or C); takadiastase ribonuclease T_1 acts in a similar way at guanine (Fig. 8.12, B^x = G) and takadiastase ribonuclease T_2 acts at adenine (Fig. 8.12, B^x = A).

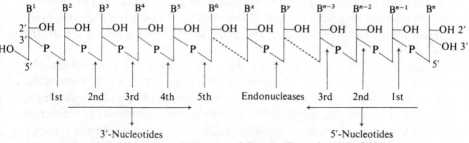

Fig. 8.12 Enzymic cleavage of phosphodiester bonds in RNA

Polysaccharidases

There are two common enzymes in this group that are found in living organisms: endo or α-amylase and exo or β-amylase; both are specific for α(1→4) glucosidic bonds. Exo-amylase acts in a stepwise manner from a non-reducing chain-end, releasing maltose units, while endo-amylase operates at most α(1→4) bonds causing general fragmentation. It is important to note that while the action of exo-amylase would be stopped at an α(1→6) cross link, endo-amylase can operate on either side of such a point.

317

8.2.1 The nature of enzyme-catalysed reactions

The role of enzymes as the catalysts of biochemical reactions has already been referred to in many places in this book. In the previous section, it was pointed out that they have become invaluable tools with which the organic chemist can investigate the complex structure of biopolymers. Proteolytic enzymes are even used to investigate the structures of other enzymes! It is therefore appropriate at this point in the book to collect together and summarize the more important aspects of the properties of enzymes and their mode of action as catalysts.

The basic structural feature of all enzymes is that they are proteins, with molecular weights ranging from 10 000 to 500 000. It is obvious that the structures of these molecules are very complex, and detailed molecular structures are known in only a very few cases. However, in general, we may say that enzyme molecules are approximately spherical in shape, rather than rod-like. Furthermore, all the fundamental theories of enzyme action were discovered long before any of the structural details of enzymes were known, and most of these theories were based on kinetic investigations of enzyme-catalysed reactions.

One of the earliest and certainly the most perceptive of the theories of enzyme action was proposed by Fischer in 1894. He proposed that the substrate on which the enzyme acted as catalyst fitted into a cavity in its surface rather as a key fits into a lock (Fig. 8.13). Since the enzyme catalyses the reaction of only a small part of the substrate, there are only a few groups in the enzyme involved in the catalytic process. That part of the enzyme which is involved in the binding of the substrate in the cavity and in the subsequent reaction is termed the *active site*.

Apart from efficiency, probably the most important feature of enzymic catalysis is the high degree of specificity shown by an enzyme for a substrate. The vast majority of enzymes catalyse a reaction on one particular substrate. Fischer explained this specificity by reasoning that compounds of a different shape from the substrate do not fit into the 'lock', and thus do not undergo reaction. This explanation of specificity is still broadly acceptable today and has been amended only recently. Koshland (in 1963) proposed that the *fit* between the enzyme and the substrate is not between two rigid surfaces, but that the substrate induces a conformational change in the enzyme molecule, bringing about the correct alignment of groups between the enzyme and the substrate (Fig. 8.14).

The high degree of specificity of an enzyme for its substrate enabled the early investigators to obtain meaningful kinetic data, despite the impurity of the enzyme preparations that they had to use. Michaelis and Menten (in 1913) formulated a rate expression based upon observed kinetic results. This

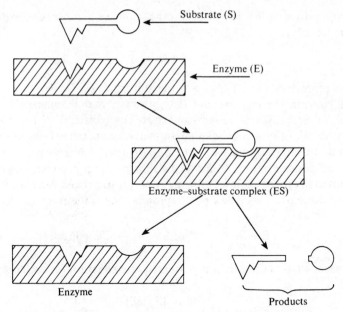

Fig. 8.13   Fischer 'lock and key' mechanism of enzyme action

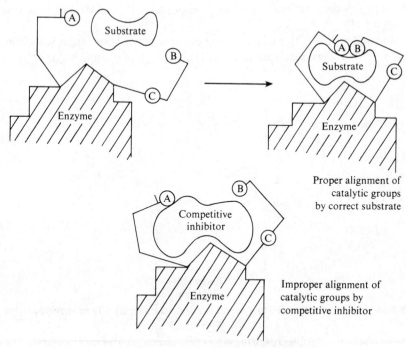

Fig. 8.14   Koshland 'induced fit' mechanism

expression provided direct evidence for the sequence of processes envisaged by Fischer; namely,

$$E + S \rightleftharpoons ES \rightarrow E + P$$

where E represents the enzyme, S is the substrate, ES represents a complex formed between the enzyme and the substrate, and P represents reaction product. In most cases the enzyme–substrate complex (ES) is likely to consist of one molecule of substrate bound to the active site of the enzyme molecule.

The rates of enzyme-catalysed reactions are usually directly proportional to the enzyme concentration. As far as the substrate is concerned, however, the rate is often first order at low substrate concentrations and zero order at high substrate concentrations. The kinetic representation of the above mechanism is[1]

$$E + S \underset{k_{-1}}{\overset{k_{+1}}{\rightleftharpoons}} ES \xrightarrow{k_{+2}} E + P$$

It can be shown that the Michaelis–Menten rate equation for such a scheme is

$$\text{Rate of reaction } (V) = \frac{k_{+2}[E_T][S]}{K_m + [S]} \tag{8.1}$$

where $[E_T]$ is the total enzyme concentration, and K_m, the *Michaelis constant*, is equal to $(k_{-1} + k_{+2})/k_{+1}$.

A typical graph of rate as a function of substrate concentration is shown in Fig. 8.15. It will be seen that the rate V tends to a maximum value (V_{max}) at

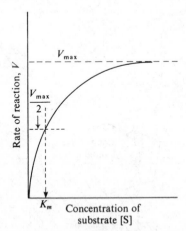

Fig. 8.15 Rate of reaction as a function of substrate concentration in an enzyme-catalysed reaction

[1] The plus sign in the subscript of the value of k indicates that it applies to a forward reaction, whereas a minus sign indicates a reverse reaction.

high substrate concentrations. The Michaelis–Menten equation can also be written in the form

$$V = \frac{V_{max}[S]}{K_m + [S]} \tag{8.2}$$

which shows that K_m can also be defined by the equation

$$K_m = [S] \left(\frac{V_{max}}{V} - 1 \right) \tag{8.3}$$

Thus, when V equals $V_{max}/2$ then K_m is equal to [S].

A preferred method of obtaining K_m is to invert eq. (8.2):

$$\frac{1}{V} = \frac{K_m + [S]}{V_{max}[S]} = \frac{1}{V_{max}} + \frac{K_m}{V_{max}[S]} \tag{8.4}$$

This is known as the Lineweaver–Burk equation. A plot of $1/V$ against $1/[S]$ (Fig. 8.16) is linear, having intercepts of $1/V_{max}$ and $-1/K_m$ and a slope of K_m/V_{max}. The value of K_m can be determined from this graph, and is used as a measure of enzyme activity. It has the dimensions of concentration (moles/litre).

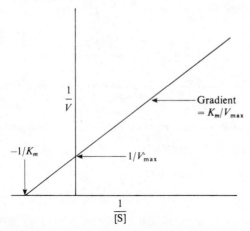

Fig. 8.16 Lineweaver–Burk plot to determine K_m (Michaelis constant)

The fact that at high levels of substrate concentration the rate of reaction remains almost constant (Fig. 8.15) is easily explained on the basis that there is initially a rapid formation of the enzyme–substrate complex which then passes through a transition state and then dissociates into products and enzyme (Fig. 8.17). Thus, once all the available enzyme molecules have combined with substrate molecules, further reaction of substrate must await the regeneration of enzyme molecules in the dissociation to enzyme and product.

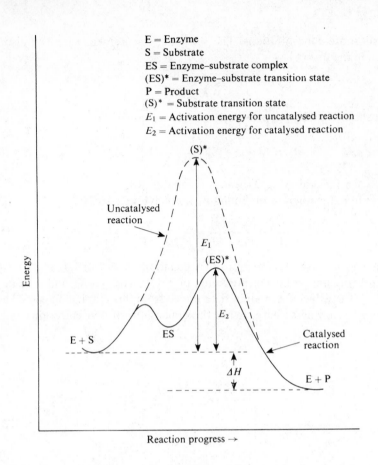

E = Enzyme
S = Substrate
ES = Enzyme–substrate complex
(ES)* = Enzyme–substrate transition state
P = Product
(S)* = Substrate transition state
E_1 = Activation energy for uncatalysed reaction
E_2 = Activation energy for catalysed reaction

Fig. 8.17 Comparison of potential-energy diagrams for uncatalysed and enzyme-catalysed reaction

Enzyme inhibition

While most enzymes possess a high degree of specificity with regard to a particular substrate, it is possible for molecules which have similar size and structure to the substrate to interfere or *inhibit* the enzyme-catalysed reaction. These *inhibitors* achieve this effect by competition with the substrate at the active site of the enzyme. This effect, known as *competitive inhibition*, while being undesirable *in vivo*, can often be used to some advantage for *in vitro* kinetic studies, for it can give information concerning the structure and size of the active site of the enzyme.

Inhibition of an enzyme can also be brought about by reagents which bind strongly (ionically or covalently) with reactive groups of the active site. These compounds generally bear no structural similarity to the substrate and unlike competitive inhibition is usually irreversible. It is referred to as *non-competitive inhibition*. Such compounds are often reagents, which are capable of reacting covalently with functional groups such as hydroxyl (—OH), thiol (—SH) and amino (—NH$_2$ or $>$NH). Non-competitive inhibition may also occur when anions interact with a cation which is associated with the active site. Examples of such anions include CN$^-$, F$^-$, S^{2-} and oxalate ion, which inhibit enzymes containing the cations Fe^{3+}, Mg^{2+}, Cu^{2+}, and Ca^{2+}, respectively.

The two types of enzyme inhibition can be clearly distinguished by the study of the effect of substrate concentration on rate and the determination of the K_m value. In the presence of competitive inhibitor, the K_m value is greater than that obtained with enzyme and substrate alone. When a non-competitive inhibitor is present, the same K_m is obtained as for the enzyme–substrate system alone, but the rate at any particular substrate concentration is reduced, leading to a lower V_{max}. In both cases, these differences are apparent in the simple plot of rate versus substrate concentration and in the corresponding Lineweaver–Burk plot (double reciprocal plot) (Fig. 8.18).

Competitive inhibitors operate by forming a complex with the enzyme in competition with the substrate. An association constant (K_i) may be defined for the formation of the inhibitor–enzyme complex:

$$ E + I \; \underset{k'_{-1}}{\overset{k'_{+1}}{\rightleftharpoons}} \; E—I $$

where

$$ K_i = \frac{k'_{+1}}{k'_{-1}} $$

In comparison

$$ K_m = \frac{k_{-1} + k_{+2}}{k_{+1}} $$

(see previous section) and since $k_{-1} >>> k_{+2}$ then

$$ K_m \sim \frac{k_{-1}}{k_{+1}} $$

Hence K_m approximates to the dissociation constant of the enzyme–substrate complex.

In applying the Michaelis–Menton equation (8.2) to the competitive inhibitor situation, it can be shown that the K_m value is increased by the factor $(1+1/K_i)$:

$$ V = \frac{V_{max} \, [S]}{K_m(1+1/K_i) + [S]} \tag{8.5} $$

When eq. (8.5) is inverted it becomes:

$$1/V = \frac{K_m(1 + 1/K_i)}{V_{max}} \frac{1}{[S]} + \frac{1}{V_{max}}$$

(8.6)

A comparison between eq. (8.4) and eq. (8.6) shows that in the plot of $1/V$ versus $1/[S]$ the 'y' axis intercept ($1/V_{max}$) is the same whether a competitive inhibitor is present or not. The 'x' axis intercept on the other hand is different [Fig. 8.18(a)] and from it a value of $K_m(1+1/K_i)$ may be calculated.

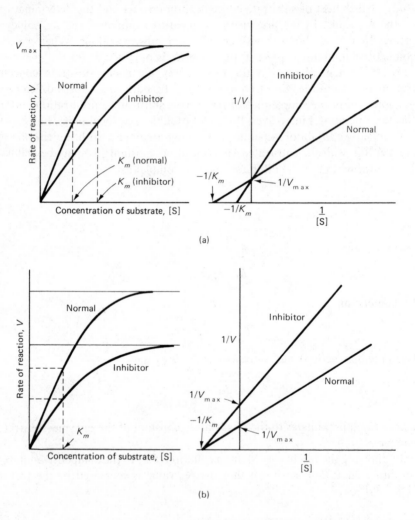

Fig. 8.18 (a) Kinetic analysis of competitive inhibition of enzyme catalysis. (b) Kinetic analysis of non-competitive inhibition of enzyme catalysis

324

Alternatively, the same information may be obtained from the slope of the double reciprocal plot:

$$\text{Slope} = \frac{K_m(1 + 1/K_i)}{V_{max}}$$

If the value of K_m is known for the uninhibited reaction then K_i can be calculated; like K_m it has the units of concentration (moles/litre.)

Allosteric inhibition and activation

It is relevant at this point to mention another type of inhibition process which operates as a control mechanism in metabolism, that is allosteric inhibition. This phenomenon was first observed in biosynthesis pathways where it was found that certain end-products were capable of regulating the rate of their own synthesis. This control is exerted by the end-product having the ability to act as a 'competitive' inhibitor for an enzyme required in an early stage of the pathway [often the first stage—Fig. 8.19(a)]. One well established example of this process is that in the synthesis of cytidine triphosphate (CTP). The initial stage in the synthesis of this compound is the reaction between carbamyl phosphate (amidophosphate) and aspartate. The enzyme required for this reaction—aspartate transcarbamylase (ATC*ase*)—is inhibited by CTP. There is clearly no structural similarity between either of the two substrates and CTP, and thus normal competitive inhibition at the substrate active-site by CTP would appear unlikely. Enzymes of this type are called *allosteric*

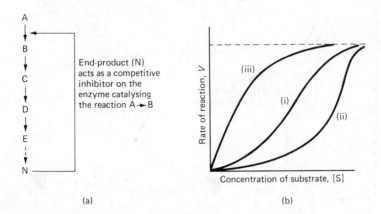

Fig. 8.19 (a) The general mechanism of allosteric inhibition in a biosynthetic pathway. (b) Kinetic analysis of an allosteric enzyme in the presence of:
   (i) Substrate(s) only,
   (ii) Inhibitor and substrate(s),
   (iii) Activator and substrate(s)

325

enzymes and they may be clearly distinguished from other enzymes by kinetic measurements.

When rate versus substrate concentration plots are examined, the normal hyperbolic curve (Fig. 8.15) is replaced by a sigmoid curve and this is accentuated in the presence of the allosteric inhibitor [Fig. 8.19(b)]. The activity of allosteric enzymes can be increased by certain metabolites—activators; for example, in the case of ATC*ase*, ATP has an activating affect. In the presence of activator, the normal hyperbolic curve is obtained in the rate versus substrate concentration plot. It is clear from these kinetic measurements

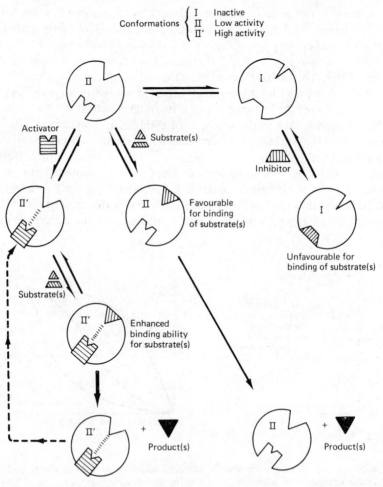

Fig. 8.20 Schematic representation of interactions of an allosteric enzyme (e.g., ATC*ase* where substrates are carbamyl phosphate and aspartate; inhibitor is CTP and activator is ATP)

[Fig. 8.19(b)] that high rates of reaction at low substrate concentration levels only take place in the presence of activator, and the reaction rates are very low in the presence of inhibitor even at quite high substrate levels.

Many allosteric enzymes have now been identified not only in biosynthetic pathways but also in catabolic processes. A number of these are described in section 9.3.4. The mode of action of allosteric enzymes conforms to that predicted in the allosteric theory of Monod and his co-workers. The allosteric enzyme has a flexible molecular conformation and can exist in at least two stable conformations in equilibrium. One of these is *inactive* with respect to the substrate active-site and this form binds the inhibitor. This causes the equilibrium to change in favour of the inactive conformation. In the second conformation, the substrate active-site is *active* and can bind substrate and catalyse the reaction on it. If the allosteric enzyme is subject to activation by a third species, the binding of this, in the inhibitor site, increases the amount of enzyme in the 'active' conformation. These changes are illustrated diagram-matically in Fig. 8.20.

Effect of pH and temperature on enzyme activity

The rates of enzyme-catalysed reactions are often fairly sensitive towards changes in pH. There is, for most enzymes, a range of pH values outside which the enzyme will not function. Within this range of pH (normally pH 5 to 9) there is invariably an optimum value of pH at which the enzyme has maximum efficiency in catalysing the reaction. The pH of the medium may influence enzyme reactions in several possible ways:

(a) ionization of the enzyme, particularly at the active-site,
(b) ionization of the substrate or a co-reagent such as a coenzyme,
(c) interference with the equilibrium between the activated enzyme and its inactive precursor.

In most kinetic investigations, the latter two contributions may be ignored and only the effect of pH on the ionization of groups within the enzyme is important. At extremes of pH, gross disruption of the enzyme structure may occur (denaturation), a process from which it may not be possible to restore the catalytic activity. Figure 8.21 shows a selection of pH versus activity plots; the case of endo-amylase is typical of the normal optimum pH, while the other two show that pH optima can be found at extremes of the pH scale.

At high concentrations of substrate, the enzyme may well be saturated with respect to the substrate. If, under such conditions, V_{max} is found to vary with pH then it must be the rate of decomposition of the enzyme–substrate complex which is being influenced by pH changes rather than the free enzyme. At low substrate concentrations, however, when the enzyme active site is not saturated, then any variation in the rate of reaction at various pH values is controlled by the ionization of the free enzyme. Many active sites contain acidic and basic groups and it is possible to use kinetic data together with values of pK_a and pK_b to identify the particular groups involved. For example, the activity of α-chymotrypsin is influenced by a group which has pK_a of 7, and this turns out to be histidyl residue in the active-site of the enzyme [Fig. 8.24(b)].

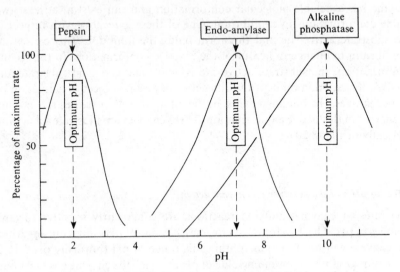

Fig. 8.21 Examples of pH optima for enzyme-catalysed reactions

The effect of temperature upon the rates of enzyme reactions is not simple. While it is relatively easy to measure the overall change in reaction rate as a function of temperature, its interpretation in terms of the various rate constants and also K_m is not always possible. Like most chemical processes, rise in temperature causes increase in reaction rate in enzyme-catalysed reactions. However, at temperatures above about 55°C, denaturation of the enzyme commences and the rate of reaction falls (Fig. 8.22).

The energetic considerations of a simple reaction were described in Fig. 8.17. This shows clearly the role of the enzyme in reducing the activation energy compared with the non-catalysed reaction. The value of the activation energy (E_A') may be obtained by measuring the change in rate with temperature and making use of the Arrhenius equation (see section 3.9.6).

8.2.2 Structural and mechanistic interpretation of enzymic catalysis

The kinetic work described in the previous section stimulated research into a more detailed study of enzyme active sites and the processes that take place

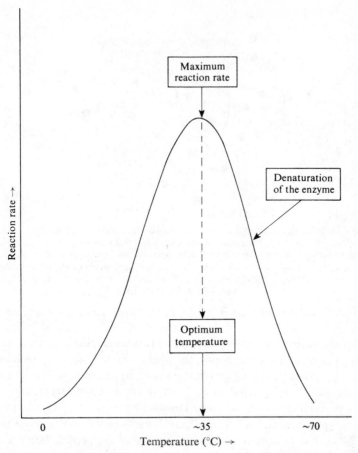

Fig. 8.22 Effect of temperature on the reaction rate of an enzyme-catalysed reaction

in them. In common with ordinary organic reactions, it is one of the objects of modern biochemistry to deduce the structure of enzyme–substrate complexes and their corresponding transition states. The amino acids of the active-site may be divided into those with a binding role and those with a reactive role (Fig. 8.23). The remainder of the protein provides a structural backbone, through which the components of the active site are kept in their correct spatial positions. In fact, in some enzymes, it has been possible to remove substantial parts of the molecule without affecting the catalytic action. A complete description of the enzyme–substrate complex will be achieved only when the full three-dimensional structure of the enzyme is known. This, however, is a long-term objective, since each such determination takes many years. Fortunately, there are other ways in which the amino-acid residues which make up the active site may be identified. Some of the work that has been

329

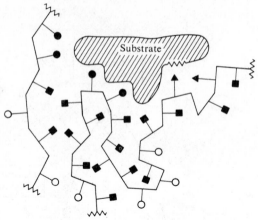

Fig. 8.23 Diagrammatic representation of an active site. Solid circles—contact amino-acid residues whose fit with substrate determines specificity; triangles—catalytic residues acting on substrate bond, indicated by a jagged line; open circles—non-essential residues on the surface; squares—residues whose interaction with each other maintains the three-dimensional structure of the protein (by permission of D. E. Koshland, Jr, 1963, and the editor of *Science*, Vol. 142, p. 1534, 1963.)

carried out on the enzyme α-chymotrypsin will serve to illustrate these techniques.

α-Chymotrypsin is an enzyme that has a fairly wide specificity catalysing the hydrolysis of certain peptide bonds, the hydrolysis of *N*-acyl amino acids and also the hydrolysis of simple carboxylic esters. In common with a number of other enzymes, it is secreted in an inactive form—chymotrypsinogen. The inactive precursors of enzymes are known as *zymogens*. The activation of α-chymotrypsin has been fully studied, and the sequence of reactions is shown in Fig. 8.24(a). The process is started by cleavage of the peptide bond between arginyl and isoleucyl residues (Nos. 15 and 16) by the enzyme trypsin. The π-chymotrypsin formed in this process undergoes self-catalysed changes resulting in the loss of two dipeptides: seryl-arginine (Nos. 14 and 15) and threonyl-asparagine (Nos. 147 and 148).

$$
\begin{array}{c}
\overset{|}{C}{=}O \\
H{-}\overset{|}{C}{-}CH_2OH \\
\overset{|}{N}H \\
\text{Seryl residue}
\end{array}
\;+\;
\begin{array}{c}
F{>}P{<}^{OC_3H_7}_{OC_3H_7} \\
O \\
\text{(DIPF)}
\end{array}
\;\longrightarrow\;
\begin{array}{c}
\overset{|}{C}{=}O \qquad\quad OC_3H_7 \\
H{-}\overset{|}{C}{-}CH_2{-}O{-}\overset{|}{P}{-}OC_3H_7 \\
\overset{|}{N}H \qquad\qquad\; O
\end{array}
$$

$\downarrow$ Hydrolysis

$$
\text{Amino acids} \;+\;
\begin{array}{c}
COO^- \qquad\quad OH \\
H{-}\overset{|}{C}{-}CH_2{-}O{-}\overset{|}{P}{-}OH \\
\overset{|}{N}H_3^+ \qquad\qquad O
\end{array}
$$

Serine phosphate

330

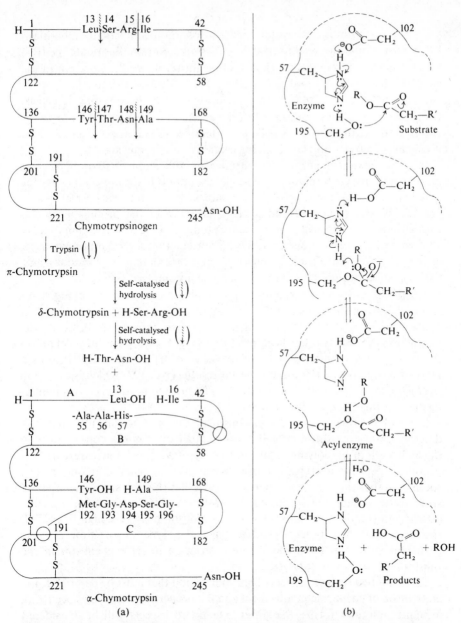

Fig. 8.24 (a) Diagrammatic representation of the process for the activation of α-chymotrypsin (the outline primary structure shown for chymotrypsinogen is based on the sequence studies of Hartley, 1964). (b) A mechanism for the action of α-chymotrypsin, showing the interaction of the histidyl residue (No. 57), the aspartyl residue (No. 102), the seryl residue (No. 195) and the substrate—in this case a carboxylic ester (R′CH₂CO·OR). The attack of the seryl hydroxyl group on the carbonyl carbon atom is promoted by a relay of charge from the aspartyl residue via the histidyl residue. In certain cases the *acyl enzyme* may be isolated.

331

α-Chymotrypsin is irreversibly inactivated (non-competitive inhibition) by a stoichiometric reaction with diisopropylphosphofluoridate (DIPF) which reacts with only *one* of the twenty-eight serine residues present in the enzyme (the serine affected is No. 195). The hydrolysate from the inactive enzyme contains serine phosphate in addition to unchanged serine molecules. On the basis of kinetic studies, a histidyl residue can also be shown to be involved in the active site. This residue is identified as that at position 57, since it may be selectively alkylated, giving total loss of enzymic activity.

Inactivation of the enzyme by chemical modification of two amino-acid residues, far apart in terms of sequence, lends support to the important concept that an active site is made up of a few residues brought into the correct spatial position by the secondary and tertiary structure of the protein molecule. Furthermore, it is possible, by sequence studies, to identify the amino acids adjacent to these *active residues*. It has been found that several other esterases, including trypsin and elastase, contain reactive seryl and histidyl residues, and that sequences around these residues show many similarities.

The three-dimensional structure of an α-chymotrypsin derivative (Fig. 8.40) shows that the histidyl residue (No. 57) and the seryl residue (No. 195) are in fact within 5 Å (50 pm) of each other. A catalytic mechanism based on the interaction of these two has been proposed [Fig. 8.24(b)]. In this mechanism the strong nucleophilic character of the seryl —OH group is explained by a relay of charge from an ionized aspartyl residue (No. 102) which is buried in the *hydrophobic* interior of the molecule. The histidyl residue acts as an intermediate in this charge relay system.

Detailed treatments of the mechanism of catalytic action, like that just described, are now substantiated for a number of enzymes concerned with the hydrolysis of biopolymers, for example, lysoszyme, ribonuclease, carboxypeptidase, pepsin and trypsin. These enzymes are, in general, among the less specific, in that they catalyse a particular reaction (hydrolysis) on a variety of structurally similar macromolecular substrates. The majority of enzymes which catalyse the reactions of cell metabolism possess a high degree of specificity and usually catalyse *one* particular type of reaction on *one* particular substrate. Even the slightest variation in stereochemistry in the substrate prevents any catalytic action.

There are two further aspects of enzymic action that must be described: the mechanism of coenzyme involvement and the properties of enzymes occurring in multi-molecular forms—*isozymes*. These two aspects will be considered with the aid of the enzyme L-lactate dehydrogenase (LDH) which is itself fairly typical of the cellular dehydrogenases: other examples are alcohol dehydrogenase (ADH), glyceraldehyde-3-phosphate dehydrogenase (GAPDH) and malate dehydrogenase (MDH).

All these enzymes require the coenzyme NAD^+ (structure, see section 7.4.2)

332

which becomes reduced to NADH in the oxidation reaction being catalysed. The enzyme is specific for the substrate undergoing oxidation. The reactions are reversible and may be described by the equation:

$$S—H_2 + NAD^+ \xrightleftharpoons{\text{Dehydrogenase}} S + NADH(H^+)$$
(Reduced substrate)   (Oxidized substrate)

For LDH, 'S—H_2' is L(+)-lactate and 'S' is pyruvate (section 9.2.3).

(a) *Mechanism of coenzyme involvement*   LDH and other dehydrogenases may be irreversibly inactivated, through non-competitive inhibition by reagents specific for thiol groups. For example, LDH and GAPDH are inactivated by iodoacetate, in the latter case the whole of glycolysis can be blocked by this inhibition.

$$\left[CH_2—SH + I—CH_2—COO^- \longrightarrow \right[CH_2—CH_2—COO^- + HI$$

(Cysteinyl residue No. 165 in LDH)
(Cysteinyl residue No. 149 in GAPDH)

Now that the full details of the active-site are known for these two enzymes, it appears that in the case of GAPDH the thiol group is involved in binding NAD^+, while in LDH it is not involved in binding either coenzyme nor substrate but its carboxymethylation produces steric hindrance in the active-site.

Direct transfer of hydride ion (H^-) between substrate and NAD^+ takes place in the both oxidation and reduction processes. The hydrogen atom is bound to the 4-position of the nicotinamide ring in oxidation and transferred from it in reduction. There is a difference amongst dehydrogenases in the stereochemistry of this transfer. In LDH, transfer of hydrogen takes place on the amide side of the pyridine ring (face A); while in GAPDH transfer to the side of the ring (face B) opposite the amide group occurs.

On the basis of the three-dimensional structure of LDH (the M_4 isozyme was used), a mechanism has been proposed for the oxidation of L-lactate [Fig. 8.25(a)]. Binding of NAD^+ is the first step and this involves numerous types of non-covalent interaction: hydrophobic binding of the two heterocyclic rings (nicotinamide—face B and adenine), hydrogen bonding of hydroxyl groups and an ionic bond between the ionized pyrophosphate residue and a protonated arginyl residue (No. 101). It is interesting to note that this latter residue moves 13 Å (130 pm) from its position before entry of the coenzyme and provides an excellent example of the 'induced fit' theory. L-Lactate, as an anion, is also bound by a protonated arginyl residue (No. 171). In the oxidation reaction, a histidyl residue (No. 195) acts as proton acceptor (of the alcoholic hydrogen) and this is followed by hydride ion transfer.

333

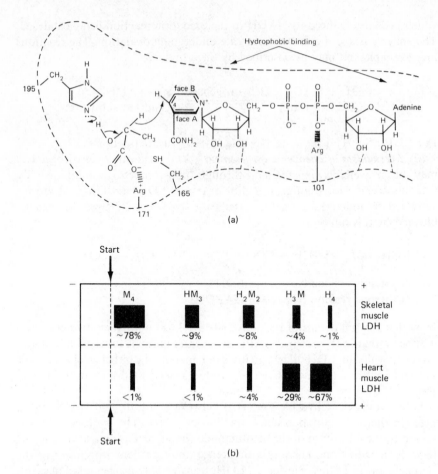

Fig. 8.25 (a) Diagrammatic representation of the active-site of lactate dehydrogenase showing the binding of substrate and coenzyme and the electron movements in the oxidation of lactate. (b) The separation of skeletal and heart muscle lactate dehydrogenase by starch-gel electrophoresis

In reduction of pyruvate this same histidyl residue acts as proton donor and NADH transfers hydride ion.

(b) Isozymes of LDH Isozymes are structurally different forms of an enzyme which *all* catalyse the same reaction albeit at different rates. The proportion of the isozymes present in different tissues may also be quite different. LDH has been the most fully studied of all isozyme systems. Its isozymes may be separated by starch-gel electrophoresis [Fig. 8.25(b)]. Each isozyme has a quaternary structure made up of four sub-units (each with a molecular weight of about 35 000) giving a tetramer of molecular weight

140 000. There are two basic types of sub-unit; the M-type (associated with skeletal muscle LDH) and the H-type (associated with heart muscle LDH). The proportion of each isozyme found in Human tissues is shown in Fig. 8.25(b). The regular difference in electrophoretic mobility reflects a gradation of charge in the different isozymes and this, in turn, reflects a difference in 'chargeable' amino-acid composition. The H_4 isozyme contains relatively more acidic amino acids (Asp and Glu) and less basic (Lys) than the M_4 isozyme.

Although all the isozymes of LDH catalyse the same reaction, the manner in which they do it is different. The M_4 isozyme, which predominates in muscle, is ideally suited to the conversion of pyruvate to lactate (this enables glycolysis to continue under anaerobic conditions—section 9.2.3). Kinetic studies show that this isozyme is *not* inhibited by high pyruvate levels and also the ability to 'turnover' pyruvate molecules at a high rate. On the other hand, the H_4 isozyme, occurring in heart muscle, has a much lower activity and is inhibited at high pyruvate levels. The conversion of pyruvate to lactate is not required in an aerobic situation and the H_4 isozyme probably functions to convert lactate back to pyruvate to undergo aerobic oxidation.

8.2.3 Nomenclature and classification of enzymes

The isolation and characterization of enzymes during the first part of this century followed a pattern analogous to that of organic compounds a hundred years earlier, and in doing so gave rise to a large number of trivial names. Many of these are still in common usage; for example, the proteolytic enzymes trypsin, α-chymotrypsin and pepsin are always likely to be known by these names. In more recent times enzymes have been designated by the suffix '-ase', preceded by a term which indicates either the general nature of the substrate, the actual name of the substrate, the type of reaction catalysed or a combination of these facets. Thus, for example, urease catalyses the hydrolysis of urea, ribonuclease the hydrolysis of RNA, lactate dehydrogenase the oxidation (or dehydrogenation) of lactate.

The most comprehensive system for the classification and nomenclature of enzymes was devised by the Commission on Enzymes of the International Union of Biochemistry.† In this classification, enzymes are divided into six groups.

1. Oxidoreductases, which catalyse oxidation and reduction reactions.
2. Transferases, which catalyse group transfer reactions.
3. Hydrolyases, which catalyse hydrolytic reactions.
4. Lyases, which catalyse the addition of groups to double bonds.
5. Isomerases, which catalyse isomerizations.

† *Enzyme Nomenclature, Recommendations of the 1964 International Union of Biochemistry,* Elsevier, 1972, second edition.

335

6. Ligases or synthetases, which catalyse the formation of a bond between two molecules, for example, a C—C bond. The process is usually accompanied by the cleavage of a nucleoside triphosphate (ATP).

Each broad group is then divided into sub-groups on the basis of the nature of the particular reaction the enzyme catalyses. In this classification it is possible to give every enzyme a unique designation by means of four numbers. For example, sub-group 1.1 consists of oxidoreductases acting on alcohols; 1.1.1 consists of those oxidoreductases acting on alcohols which require the participation of NAD^+ or $NADP^+$ as coenzymes. Some common enzymes of sub-group 1.1.1 are 1.1.1.1, alcohol dehydrogenase, 1.1.1.27, lactate dehydrogenase, and 1.1.1.37, malate dehydrogenase.

Some of the sub-groups for the hydrolases (Group 3) are as follows. 3.1 are hydrolases acting on ester bonds, 3.1.1 are those acting on carboxylic ester bonds, and 3.1.2 are those acting on thiol ester bonds; 3.2 are hydrolases acting on glycosidic bonds (this sub-group includes the amylases); 3.4 are hydrolases acting on peptide bonds; sub-division is achieved by considering the mode of action. Thus, for example, the endopeptidases are sub-group 3.4.4, pepsin is 3.4.4.1, trypsin is 3.4.4.4. In some of the metabolic pathway diagrams given in chapter 9, the I.U.B. numbers of the enzymes are shown.

This method of classification allows for the complete specification of every enzyme, and based on this, a systematic name can be devised; thus, lactate dehydrogenase is L-lactate:NAD oxidoreductase. However, as in the nomenclature of organic compounds, trivial names for enzymes are likely to persist, particularly those which give a good guide as to the action of the enzyme.

8.3 POLYSACCHARIDES

8.3.1 Structural investigation

Polysaccharides are widely distributed in nature and perform diverse functions in living organisms. Two basic functions may be distinguished. Firstly, polysaccharides are involved in the maintenance of cell structure—these are found mainly in plants and lower organisms. Secondly, polysaccharides are involved in the nutritional requirements of the organism—these are found in all types of living system. The latter group are sometimes termed the storage polysaccharides. From the point of view of molecular structure, it is possible to divide polysaccharides into homo- and heteropolymers. The former contain only one type of sugar molecule, while the latter contain two or more. Unfortunately, there is no correlation between the two systems of classification, and in this section the polysaccharides described are divided on the basis of their biological function.

The structural determination procedure follows the pattern used for oligosaccharides (section 7.3.3). The component monosaccharide(s) have to be identified after complete hydrolysis of the polymer by acid (Fig. 7.11). A few polysaccharides are found to be polymers of *uronic acids* rather than aldoses and ketoses. The ring size of the components and the position and stereo-chemistry of the glycosidic bond have to be determined. Linear and branched chain structures must be distinguished. Partial hydrolysis either by acid or enzymes often affords information regarding the position and stereochemistry of the glycosidic bond. Thus, the isolation of cellobiose (XXV, section 7.3.3) from cellulose (Fig. 8.4) provides evidence that the glycosidic bonds are $\beta(1\rightarrow4)$. Two chemical techniques have been used in the structural analysis of every polysaccharide; these are methylation studies and periodate oxidation. Both techniques have already been described in connection with the structural analysis of disaccharides, and similar procedures are used on the macro-molecules.

The complete methylation of a polysaccharide is a lengthy process, and re-peated treatment with dimethyl sulphate in sodium hydroxide solution is necess-ary. After complete methylation of all the free —OH groups, the methylated polysaccharide is hydrolysed by acid and the methylated components separated and analysed. Gas–liquid chromatography has proved a particularly valuable modern method for examining these hydrolysates. From the quantitative analysis, a great deal of information about the structure of the polysaccharide may be obtained. For example, when cellulose is treated in this way, one major product, 2,3,6-tri-O-methyl-D-glucose (I), and one minor product, 2,3,4,6-tetra-O-methyl-D-glucose (II), are formed. The interpretation of this is that cellulose consists of linear $1\rightarrow4$ linked chains in which inner residues have three —OH groups which are methylated, while the residues at the chain ends have four —OH groups. (In this interpretation, a pyranose ring structure for each glucose residue is assumed.) It should be noted that during the acidic hydrolysis the O-methyl group at C_1 of the reducing chain end is lost to form the

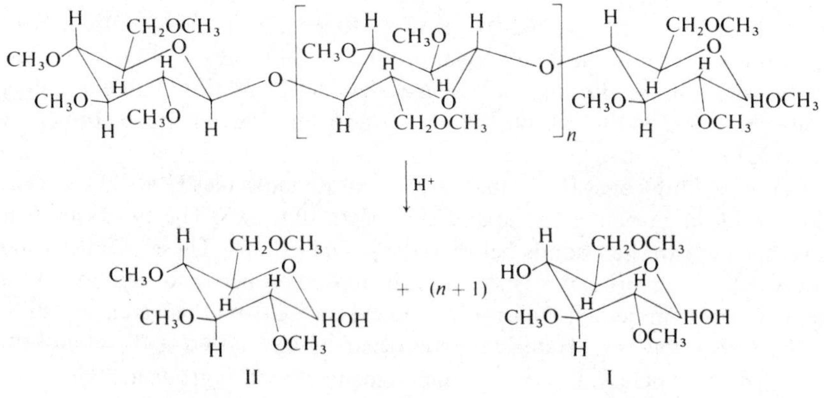

Fig. 8.26 Methylation of a linear polysaccharide chain (cellulose)

337

trimethylated derivative (cf. methylation studies on D-glucose, section 7.3.1). The tetramethylated derivative coming only from the non-reducing chain end provides a direct measure of the number of chains, and hence may be used as a *chemical method* of molecular-weight determination. Unfortunately, it is impossible to completely methylate a polysaccharide without causing some degradation, and hence the values obtained in this way must be regarded as minimum values.

The periodate technique provides similar information. In a linear arrangement like that shown in Fig. 8.26, three molecules of formic acid are formed per chain. One molecule comes from the non-reducing chain end and two from the reducing chain end. Less degradation occurs during the periodate reaction and thus molecular weight values obtained by estimation of formic acid provide a quick, reliable method. The inner residues too are oxidized by periodate but since there are only *two* adjacent —OH groups (C_2 and C_3) each residue is converted to a dialdehyde. This, of course, is further evidence of the presence of $1 \rightarrow 4$ glycosidic linkages and the pyranose ring structure.

8.3.2 Structural polysaccharides

(*a*) *Cellulose* This is the most abundant organic material on earth, making up 30–90 per cent of all the carbon of vegetation. It is the main constituent of cell walls of plants, where it acts as a supporting structure. Ruminants are able to utilize cellulose as a food.

The covalent structure of this important substance has already been considered (Fig. 8.4). Several different forms of cellulose are known, which differ widely in molecular weight. These forms may be distinguished on the basis of solubility. α-Cellulose, which has the highest molecular weight, is insoluble in aqueous sodium hydroxide and water; β-cellulose is soluble in aqueous sodium hydroxide but insoluble in water and γ-cellulose, the lowest-molecular-weight form, is soluble in both. One of the best solvents for cellulose is cuprammonium hydroxide, in which it dissolves to give a viscous solution. Such solutions are used in the commercial production of some cellulose fibres, and also as solutions for viscosity molecular-weight determination. Values obtained range from 300 000 to 500 000, while those from ultracentrifuge studies are even higher.

Cellulose fibre consists of bundles of cellulose molecules (100–200) packed side by side and oriented in the direction of the fibre axis. The chains are held together by hydrogen bonds between the —OH groups. These bundles show as crystalline regions in X-ray studies. The tensile properties of cellulose fibre, on which its commercial importance depends, arise from this arrangement.

(*b*) *Hemicelluloses* Hemicelluloses occur in association with cellulose in the cell walls of plants. The most common members of this group are the xylans. These materials give on complete hydrolysis D-xylose. Methylation gives

2,3-di-$\bar{O}$-methyl-D-xylose as the main product, indicating $1\rightarrow4$ glycosidic linkages and a pyranose ring structure. Wood pulp, the raw material for the paper industry, contains cellulose, hemicelluloses and lignin. The wood xylan pentose units are believed to be joined in chains of 20–40 units by $\beta(1\rightarrow4)$ linkages and cross linking between the chains may occur by $1\rightarrow3$ glycosidic bonds. Lignin is not a polysaccharide, but is a polymer of coniferyl alcohol (III). It is removed from wood pulp by sodium bisulphite solution.

Xylans from plants such as wheat also contain L-arabinose units. These are present as non-reducing chain end residues since 2,3,5-tri-O-methyl-L-arabinose is formed during methylation studies. Mannans and glucomannans are found in association with xylans. The mannans of vegetable ivory, for example, contain D-mannopyranose units linked $\beta(1\rightarrow4)$. Glucomannans are found in softwoods and are linear chains of D-glucose and D-mannose units arranged in a random manner.

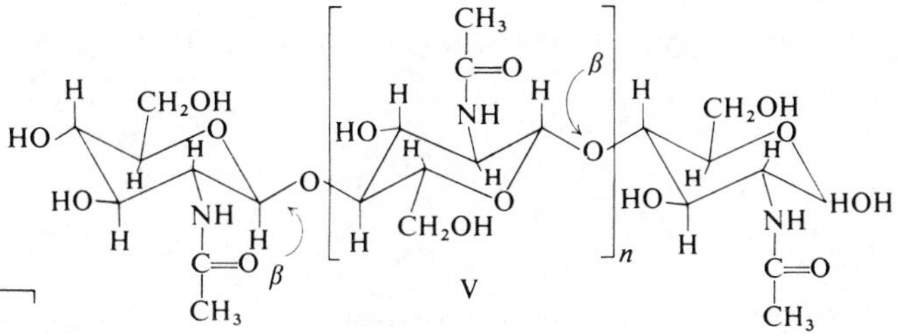

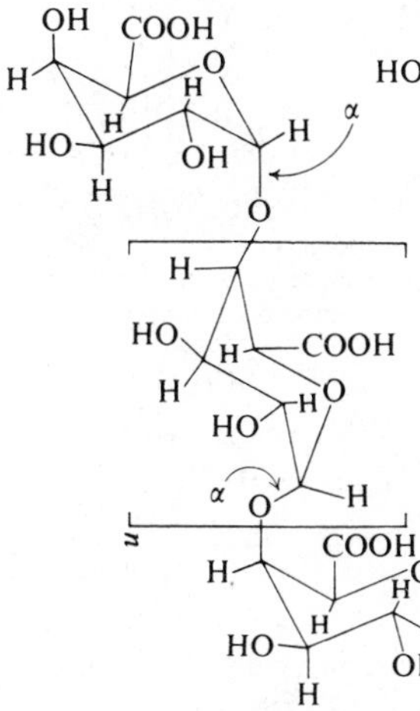

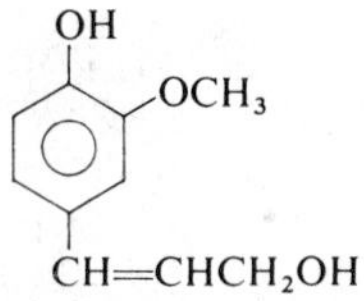

(c) Pectic substances This is a group of heterogeneous polysaccharides which occur in higher plants, for example, citrus and other fruit. The biological role of these materials is that of an intercellular adhesive. The main component of this group is poly-D-galacturonic acid (IV) in which the chain is formed through $\alpha(1\rightarrow4)$ linkages. The carboxyl groups may be partially esterified with methyl groups and the various pectic substances may be distinguished on the basis of the relative number of ester groups present.

(d) Mucopolysaccharides Structural polysaccharides are found in certain animal tissues. The muco- or aminopolysaccharides occur in the connective tissues like cartilage and tendon, and also in mucous secretion. Structurally,

the simplest member of this group is chitin (V), which is found in the shells of arthropods such as crabs and oysters. Chitin, like cellulose, has a linear arrangement of monomer units joined by $\beta(1 \to 4)$ linkages. The monomer unit is, however, the *N*-acetyl derivative of D-glucosamine (see section 7.3.2). A disaccharide, chitobiose, may be isolated from a chitin hydrolysate. This molecule has a structure identical with cellobiose apart from the —NH$_2$ group at C$_2$.

In higher animals mucopolysaccharides have a more complex structure, since they contain two monomer units. The common structural feature is that a disaccharide unit is present, in which a *uronic acid* is glycosidically bound to the 3-position of an acetylated amino sugar. These disaccharide residues (Fig. 8.27) are present in the mucopolysaccharides joined $1 \to 4$ to give linear molecules. Connective tissues contain five of these polymers: chondroitin, the chondroitin sulphates (A, B and C) and hyaluronic acid. The composition

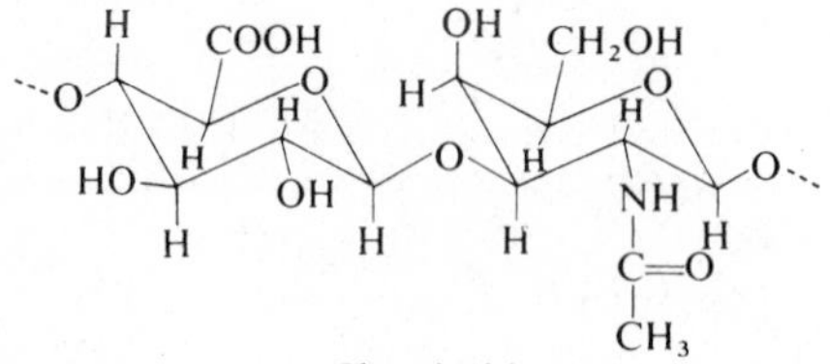

Chondroitin
(D-Glucuronate + *N*-acetyl-D-galactosamine)

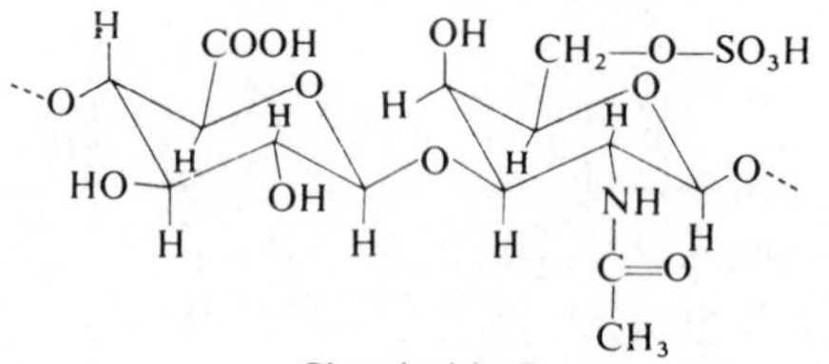

Chondroitin C
(D-Glucuronate + *N*-acetyl-D-galactosamine-6-sulphate)

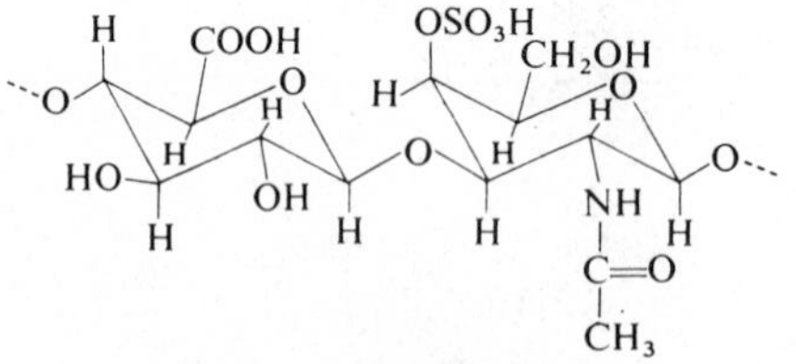

Chondroitin A
(D-Glucuronate + *N*-acetyl-D-galactosamine-4-sulphate)

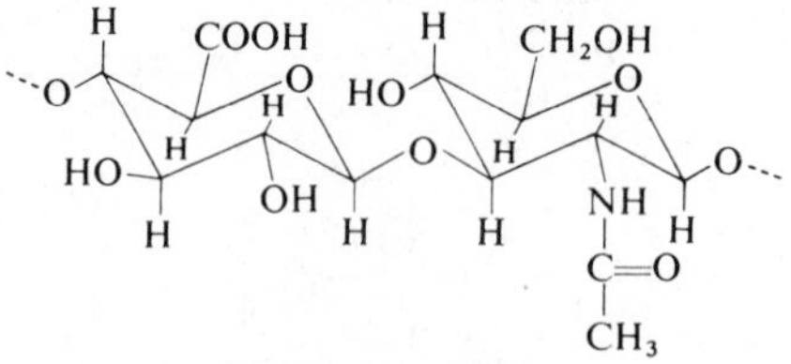

Hyaluronic acid
(D-Glucuronate + *N*-acetyl-D-glucosamine)

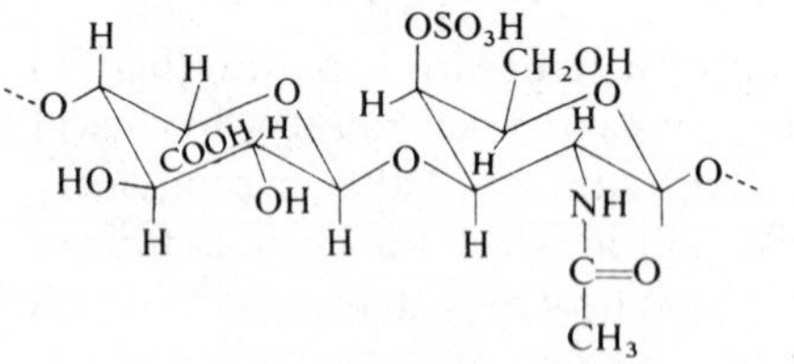

Chondroitin B
(L-Iduronate + *N*-acetyl-D-galactosamine-4-sulphate)

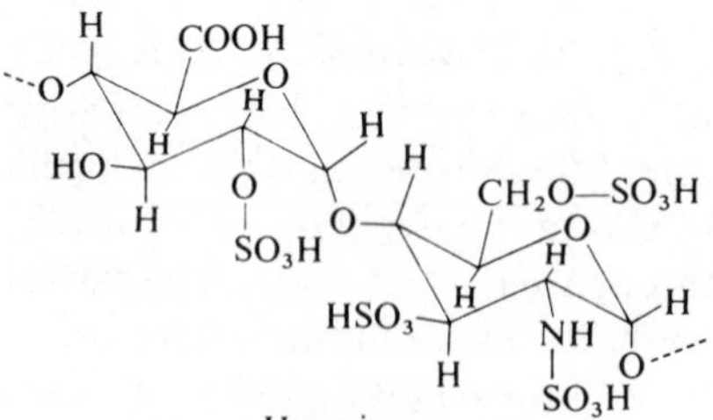

Heparin
(2-*O*-Sulphonyl-glucuronate + *N*-sulphonyl-D-glucosamine-6,3-*O*-disulphate)

Fig. 8.27 Structural units in mucopolysaccharides

340

of these is shown in Fig. 8.27. The presence of the carboxylic group and, in the case of the chondroitin sulphates, of the sulphate groups, gives rise to acidic properties. Heparin, which acts as an anti-coagulant in blood clotting, has a similar structure. It consists of a repeating disaccharide unit made up of a sulphate ester of glucosamine N-sulphate and a sulphate ester of glucuronic acid.

(e) *Bacterial cell wall polysaccharides* (*Mureins*)   Bacteria are unicellular organisms surrounded by a mechanically strong cell wall and an inner membrane, the latter resembling the cell membrane of a multi-cellular organism. The composition and structure of the outer cell wall is of great interest in bacteriology since it is this that responds to Gram's stain, is penetrated during attack by bacteriophages and whose biosynthesis is disrupted during the action of certain antibiotics. The principal materials of the cell wall are conjugate polysaccharides, where the non-carbohydrate part may be poly-peptide, lipid or phosphate groupings. The most abundant polymers are the mureins (also known as peptidoglycan) and are found in all bacteria. Other polymeric materials include teichoic acids (found in gram-positive bacteria) and lipopolysaccharides (found in gram-negative bacteria).

(i) *Mureins*   The polymeric backbone in these complex materials is a repeating   disaccharide: N-acetyl-D-glucosamine-N-acetylmuramic   acid joined $\beta(1 \rightarrow 4)$ (cf. glucose units in cellulose). Muramic acid is the 3-O ether of D-glucosamine and lactic acid [Fig. 8.28(b)]. It is the glycosidic bond between these amino-sugar derivatives that is broken in the enzymic action of lysozyme following a bacteriophage infestation. Projecting from the carboxyl function of the lactyl residue are tetrapeptide chains of specific sequence. Variation in the composition of the peptide chains arises in different species of bacteria; for example, *Staphylococci* have the sequence: L-Ala-D-Glu-L-Lys-D-Ala while *Esch. coli* and gram-negative bacteria contain diaminopimelic acid (DAP) instead of the L-lysine residue. The peptide chains are cross-linked from the carboxyl terminus at the D-alanine residue to the side-chain amino group (either L-Lys or DAP) of another chain either directly or by means of a pentaglycyl peptide. These two methods of cross-linking afford another structural feature which varies from one species of bacteria to another. For example, in *Esch. coli* direct linking occurs while in *Staph. aureus* a penta-glycyl bridge is found (Fig. 8.28).

The pathway of the biosynthesis of this complex structure has been eluci-dated mainly as a result of the observation that several antibiotics inhibit the development of bacterial cell walls. Briefly, a pentapeptide chain is assembled on muramic acid residues while the latter is joined to the coenzyme·UDP (cf. biosynthesis of nutritional polysaccharides, see sections 9.3.2 and 9.3.3). The first three amino acids are added in a stepwise manner and then the dipeptide—D-Ala-D-Ala—is joined. (The synthesis of this dipeptide is inhibited by antibiotics, for example, D-*cyclo*serine). N-acetyl-D-glucosamine

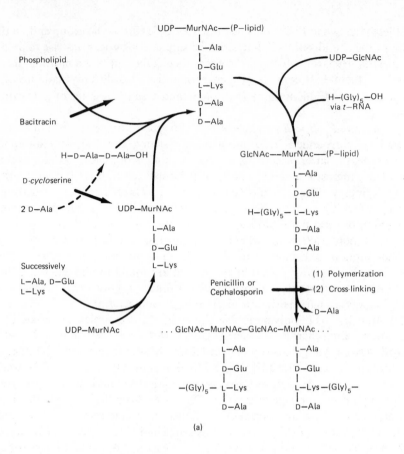

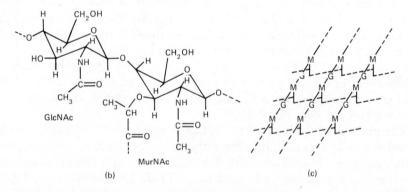

Fig. 8.28 (a) Outline of the biosynthesis of murein as it occurs in *Staph. aureus*. (b) Detailed structure of the repeating disaccharide unit of a murein. (c) General layout of a cross-linked murein. M and MurNAc = *N*-acetylmuramic acid; G and GlcNAc = *N*-Acetyl-D-glucosamine

$n = 1$ Polyglycerol phosphate
$n = 3$ Polyribitol phosphate

(a)

Poly(glycerol phosphate *N*-acetylglucosamine phosphate)

(b)

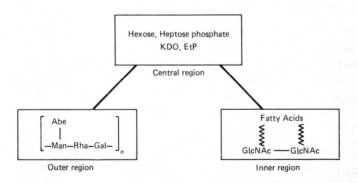

Man = D-Mannose
Rha = L-Rhamnose (6-deoxy-L-mannose)
Gal = D-Galactose
Abe = D-Abequose (3,6-dideoxy-D-galactose)

KDO = 2-Keto-3-deoxyoctanoate
EtP = Ethanolamine phosphate
GlcNAc = *N*-Acetyl-D-glucosamine

(c)

Fig. 8.29 Bacterial cell wall polymers. (a, b) Teichoic acids, (c) lipopolysaccharides

343

residues are added followed by pentaglycyl peptide to complete the 'monomer' unit. Formation of the polysaccharide chain then takes place followed in the final stage of cross-linking of the peptide chains with the elimination of the terminal D-alanyl residue. It appears that penicillins and cephalosporins inhibit this final stage, while other antibiotics inhibit other stages in this biosynthesis pathway as indicated in Fig. 8.28(a).

The second major component of gram-positive bacterial cell walls are polymers called *Teichoic* acids. These are water-soluble polymeric carbohydrate phosphate derivatives where the inter-monomer bond is a phosphodiester linkage similar to that found in nucleic acids. The simplest of these materials are homopolymers: polyglycerol phosphate and polyribitol phosphate [Fig. 8.29(a)]. More complex teichoic acids have a repeating 'disaccharide' unit: for example, polyglycerol phosphate *N*-acetyl-D-glucosamine phosphate with a D-alanyl residue esterified to the hexose [Fig. 8.29(b)]. The teichoic acids are covalently bonded to the mureins in the bacterial cell wall.

In gram-negative bacteria, the murein content can be as low as 5 per cent and the major component is lipopolysaccharide. Only an outline structure of this material is currently known. Three regions may be distinguished: an outer region made up of a repeating tetrasaccharide, a central region composed of hexose sugars, heptose phosphate, 2-keto-3-deoxyoctanoate and ethanolamine; the inner region consists of a disaccharide to which long-chain fatty acids are esterified [Fig. 8.29(c)].

8.3.3 Nutritional polysaccharides

Many living organisms store carbohydrate in the form of polysaccharide. In plants, the polymeric carbohydrate is usually starch, although in a few species it is inulin. Animals, which tend to use fat as a reserve foodstuff, store carbohydrate to a lesser extent. However, significant amounts of the polysaccharide glycogen are found in liver and muscle tissue. The storage of carbohydrate in a polymeric form offers two main advantages:

(i) The molecules are almost insoluble.
(ii) The few dissolved molecules give solutions of low osmolarity, and the low solubility ensures a constant concentration while allowing wide variation in the mass of storage carbohydrate.

(a) Starch As well as being the most abundant nutritional (storage) carbohydrate of plants, starch is also the primary source of carbohydrate for animals. In plants, starch is stored in the roots and tubers, as in potato, and in seeds, as in cereals. Starch forms a lyophilic colloid in water. The two components, amylose and amylopectin, may be separated on the basis of solubility. Amylose is precipitated from an aqueous solution by *n*-butanol and represents

about 20 per cent of the starch. The amylopectin fraction (~80 per cent) may then be recovered from the solution.

The amylose fraction may be easily distinguished, since it is this part of starch which gives rise to the characteristic blue-violet coloration with iodine. The structure was determined by a method very similar to that described for cellulose. Methylation studies give 2,3,6-tri-O-methyl-D-glucose as the main product with about 0·3–0·5 per cent of the 2,3,4,6-tetra-methylated derivative, indicating a linear (1→4) arrangement. Maltose may be isolated from the enzymic or partial acid hydrolysates, and this indicates that the glycosidic bonds have an α configuration. The molecular-weight value based on methylation studies is ~35 000 (200 glucosyl units); physical methods give considerably greater values with as many as 4000 units per chain (MW ~700 000).

Molecular-weight determination by physical methods shows that amylopectin molecules are larger than those of the amylose fraction. On the other hand, methylation studies show that there is one non-reducing chain end-group for every 23–27 glucosyl units (based on the isolation of ~4 per cent 2,3,4,6-tetra-O-methyl-D-glucose). These data are explained by the presence of a highly branched structure. About 5 per cent of 2,3-di-O-methyl-D-glucose is present in the hydrolysate, and these residues come from points of chain branching [Fig. 8.6(a)]. The major component in the methylated hydrolysate (~91 per cent) is once again the 2,3,6-tri-O-methyl-D-glucose, showing that most of the residues are joined by 1→4 glucosidic bonds. The stereochemistry of these bonds is α, since partial hydrolysis affords maltose. Another disaccharide, isomaltose (6-O-α-D-glucopyranosyl-D-glucose), has also been isolated, and this indicates that the chain branching occurs by $\alpha(1→6)$ glycosidic bonds. Recent studies have shown that there may also be a small number of $\alpha(1→3)$ linkages.

The molecular structure of a branched chain polysaccharide such as amylopectin is best described by a simplified diagram [Fig. 8.30(a)]. This structure, known as the *bush structure*, contains three different types of $\alpha(1→4)$ linked chain.

(i) 'A-Type' chain, which is attached to only one other chain by an $\alpha(1→6)$ linkage from the reducing carbon (C_1) to a residue in a B chain.

(ii) 'B-Type' chain, which has its terminal reducing carbon atoms attached by an $\alpha(1→6)$ linkage to another B chain or to a C chain, i.e., a B chain is linked to at least two other chains. There are approximately equal numbers of A and B chains.

(iii) 'C-Type' chain has only B chains joined to it through their reducing carbon atoms. It is the only chain in the molecule which possesses a 'free' reducing carbon. No matter how highly branched the molecule there is only one C chain.

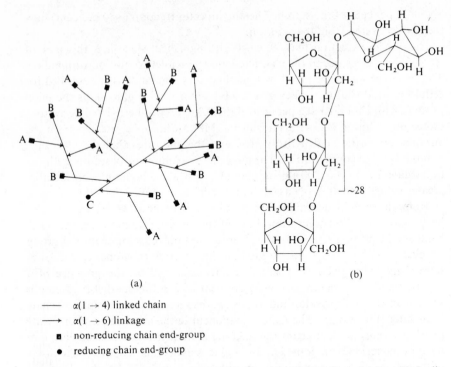

———	α(1 → 4) linked chain
——→	α(1 → 6) linkage
■	non-reducing chain end-group
●	reducing chain end-group

Fig. 8.30 (a) Diagrammatic representation of a branched polysaccharide. (b) Inulin

(b) Glycogen This is the common nutritional carbohydrate reserve material of animals. Like starch, it is easily hydrolysed and some degradation during isolation and purification is inevitable. Nevertheless, molecular-weight values as high as 400×10^6 have been reported, and there is evidence of considerable heterogeneity in glycogen samples. The molecular arrangement based on D-glucose as monomer is very similar to that of amylopectin. The structure is even more highly branched than in amylopectin, with only 10–16 glucose residues for each non-reducing chain end-group. About 9 per cent of 2,3,4,6-tetra-*O*-methyl-D-glucose is formed during methylation studies, twice that of amylopectin, and thus there must be twice the amount of chain branching. It is estimated that branching occurs at every 3rd–5th residue.

(c) Inulin This is a nutrient polysaccharide that replaces starch in the roots of certain plants. Particularly good sources are the tubers of dahlia and the taproots of dandelion. Inulin is quite soluble in water due to the relatively low molecular weight (~5000). The principal sugar formed in the complete hydrolysis is D-fructose, but small amounts of D-glucose are also present. Methylation studies give 3,4,6-tri-*O*-methyl-D-fructose as the main product with about 3·7 per cent 1,3,4,6-tetra-methylated derivative. The amount of the latter

346

compound indicates only about 30 units per chain, which must be linear since no dimethylated derivative arises. The D-fructose residues are joined by $1 \rightarrow 2$ linkages and the stereochemistry is β. The fructose units are present in the furanose form. At each reducing chain end-group is a single D-glucose molecule joined C_1 to C_2 of the terminal D-fructose residue. Thus, in fact, there is no reducing carbon present in an inulin molecule (cf. sucrose).

8.4 POLYPEPTIDES AND PROTEINS

8.4.1 Classification

The terms polypeptide and protein refer to two groups of compounds, composed of α-amino acids that may be distinguished on the basis of molecular size and structure. The term polypeptide refers to the smaller naturally occurring molecules of this type with molecular weights below 10 000, although this figure is somewhat arbitrary. The remaining amino-acid-containing molecules are classed as proteins. The molecular-weight range of these molecules is enormous, ranging from 10 000 to several million. Such a range of molecular size, coupled with differences in composition and arrangement of the component amino acids, makes possible an almost infinite number of proteins, each with unique properties. Although some general properties and structural features emerge (section 8.1.2), each protein must be considered in its own right as a distinct molecular species.

The usual method of protein classification was devised as long ago as 1907. Today, this classification is not completely satisfactory, for it is done on the basis of solubility rather than structure. However, it will be some time before sufficient detailed structures have been elucidated in order to see whether a more satisfactory system emerges. Proteins are first divided into two broad groups on the basis of their structural components:

(a) Simple proteins which contain only α-amino acids as structural components.
(b) Conjugate proteins which contain other components:
    (i) lipoproteins which contain a lipid component,
    (ii) glyco- or muco-proteins which contain a carbohydrate component,
    (iii) phosphoproteins which contain a phosphate residue,
    (iv) chromoproteins which contain a coloured pigment,
    (v) nucleoproteins where the protein is attached to another macromolecule—a nucleic acid.

In most cases, it is possible to obtain the protein free from these other structural components, and then to classify it on the basis of solubility. Again there are two broad groups, those proteins which are relatively soluble in aqueous media and those which are not. The *soluble* group includes the albumins and the globulins found in animals, the glutelins and the prolamines found in plants, and the protamines and histones which make up the protein of nucleo-protein. The *insoluble* proteins or scleroproteins, often referred to as fibrous proteins because of their shape, are insoluble in all common solvents. Several groups may be distinguished, including the keratins of hair and skin, the collagens of connective tissue and the elastins of ligaments.

8.4.2 Structural determination—primary structure

The structural investigation of a polypeptide or protein falls conveniently into two stages. Firstly, there is the primary structure determination, which is carried out by chemical and enzymic reactions in solution. Secondly, there is the determination of the three-dimensional structure, for which the principal method is X-ray diffraction studies on the crystalline protein. In both determin-ations, the protein used must be in a high state of purity. The primary structure determination can be divided into a number of stages, the first of which is the purification.

(a) Purity The isolation and purification of a soluble protein is often as great a problem as the subsequent structural determination. The integrity of the three-dimensional structure and the biological activity of soluble proteins depends on the operation of weak bonding forces which are easily disrupted by extremes of pH, heat, or by the presence of organic solvents. These may cause the *denaturation* of the protein, and while denatured samples may contain an intact primary structure, they are of no use in the three-dimensional structure studies.

A crude sample of the protein is obtained by precipitation near the isoelectric point. The sample is freed from salts by dialysis or gel filtration. In some cases, proteins become denatured on complete removal of the ionic environment. Fractionation of the crude sample is carried out by chromatographic methods —ion exchange and gel filtration being the most commonly used—after which the purified sample is isolated by freeze drying.

It has been found possible to crystallize some proteins, but even this is not a complete guarantee of homogeneity. A thorough check for traces of other closely related proteins is necessary before the structural determination starts. Methods used for assessing purity of a protein include electrophoresis, counter-current distribution, and ultracentrifuge studies. The latter method also pro-vides a value for the molecular weight of the protein. The molecular weight is determined by several methods in order to demonstrate whether the true value of the basic structural unit is being obtained or whether it is that of an *associ-ated system* of several units. It is always necessary to compare the molecular-weight values obtained by physical methods with that calculated from the amino-acid content. This latter value represents the minimum molecular weight.

348

Insoluble proteins are much more easily purified. Non-protein materials can be removed by extraction, but any attempt to dissolve the protein leads to denaturation. In this case, covalent bonds are broken, and consequently very little can be discovered about the primary structure. The structure of insoluble proteins has been determined mainly by means of X-ray studies on the native material.

(b) Amino-acid composition The total hydrolysis of the protein is first carried out. Acid hydrolysis (6 M HCl, 110°C) is the most common procedure. Alkaline hydrolysis (1 M Ba(OH)$_2$, 110°C) is also used but leads to more reaction in the amino-acid side chains. Enzymic hydrolysis by non-specific peptidases, such as pronase, is also used.

The amino acids in the hydrolysate are most efficiently separated by ion-exchange chromatography, and this procedure is the basis of the commercial *amino-acid analyser* (section 6.1.4). In these separations, the relative amount of each amino acid present can be estimated, and hence an *empirical formula* in terms of the amino acids of the protein can be deduced. For example, a hydrolysate of the enzyme ribonuclease gave the following analysis:

$$Asp_{16}, Thr_{10}, Ser_{15}, Pro_5, Glu_{12}, Gly_3, Ala_{12}, Val_9, Cys_8, Met_4,$$

$$Ile_3, Leu_2, Tyr_6, Phe_3, Amide(NH_3)_{17}, Lys_{10}, His_4, Arg_4$$

This analysis gave a total of 126 residues, compared with 124 found in the subsequent structural work.

This analysis is used not only on the intact protein but also on the various fragments that arise during the primary structure determination. In this way, a continuous check is possible to ensure that the sum of the amino acids in a series of fragments is the same as that in the intact molecule.

(c) End-group determination There are numerous methods available for identifying the N-terminal amino acid of a polypeptide chain. The three most commonly used are summarized in Fig. 8.31. The Sanger and dansyl methods are directly comparable, in that the complete hydrolysis of the whole molecule has to be carried out before the N-terminal residue can be identified. The more recently developed dansyl procedure has the advantage that the TLC identification of the amino-acid derivatives is 100 times more sensitive than in the Sanger method. As little as 10^{-9} mole of a dansyl amino acid can be detected! In the Edman method, the N-terminal amino acid is removed, and identified as the *thiohydantoin*, leaving the remainder of the polypeptide chain intact. This has become the standard procedure for chemical-sequence determination.

The chemical methods devised for the determination of the C-terminal amino acid are less satisfactory. Nevertheless, it is desirable for this determination to be attempted in order that a particular chain may be conclusively identified. The two chemical methods that have been most used are the hydrazinolysis technique in which all the residues apart from the C-terminal one are converted

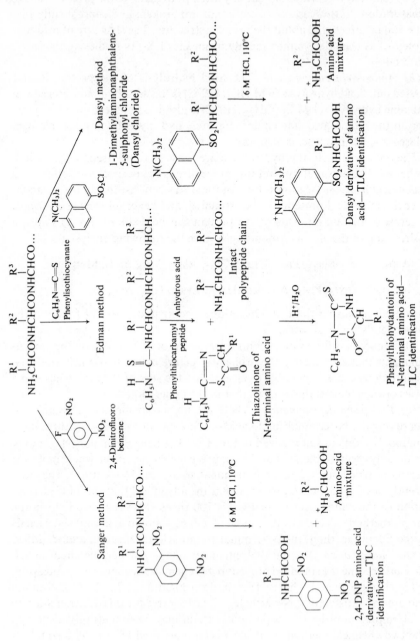

Fig. 8.31 Methods for N-terminal end-group analysis

350

to acyl-hydrazides (section 7.1.1), and the reduction of an esterified C-terminal residue to an amino-alcohol residue. In the subsequent hydrolysis, the amino alcohol is released. Use has also been made of exopeptidases for both amino and carboxyl end-group determination (section 8.1.2).

(d) Disulphide bond cleavage This must be carried out before sequence determination is started. The disulphide bonds are broken either by oxidation or reduction. Oxidation with performic acid produces chain(s) containing cysteic acid residues. Peptide bonds are not normally affected by the reagent and only a few changes occur in the amino-acid side chains. Cysteic acid residues are stable and their presence assists the separation of the oxidation mixture by ion-exchange methods. Disulphide bonds may be reduced to dithiols by a variety of reagents including sodium borohydride. Alternatively, the same reaction may be achieved by *disulphide exchange* with thiols such as mercapto-ethanol. The thiol groups have to be protected from atmospheric oxidation. These procedures are summarized in Fig. 8.32.

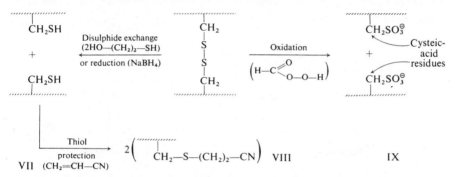

Fig. 8.32 Methods for the chemical cleavage of disulphide bonds

(e) Sequence determination Following disulphide bond cleavage, the mixture of polypeptide chains (assuming the original protein consisted of chains joined by disulphide bonds) is separated and each chain is characterized by end-group determination. Whether or not any further fragmentation of the chains is necessary depends largely on their size. By means of the Edman procedure, it is possible to remove the amino acids in a stepwise manner from a chain sixty residues long. This is a major advance since, in previous structure determination, a chain had to be fragmented into small units each consisting of only a few residues. An automatic instrument has been devised to carry out the series of reactions (Fig. 8.31). Fifteen residues are removed from a polypeptide in 24 hr. With a loss of only 2 per cent at each stage of the cycle, only 0·25 moles of a protein containing sixty residues is needed. This procedure will greatly increase the number of sequence determinations carried out, and this in turn will lead to a great increase in the number of primary structures elucidated.

Thus, in the future, the emphasis will be on fragmentation methods which will produce, reliably, a small number of large fragments on which the Edman method may be applied.

There are both enzymic and chemical methods available for the specific fragmentation of a chain. The enzymic methods use endopeptidases, and two of these—trypsin and α-chymotrypsin—are particularly useful since they have a very specific action (section 8.1.2). Cyanogen bromide (BrCN) cleaves a chain specifically at a methionyl residue. This reagent is useful in obtaining large fragments, since methionine occurs infrequently in the average polypeptide chain. Oxidation with *N*-bromosuccinimide cleaves a chain at tyrosyl and tryptophyl residues (the latter selectively when low concentrations of reagent are used).

By the use of two or more of these methods, it is possible to obtain a different series of fragments from the same chain. Sequence determination is performed on each fragment and certain *overlapping sequences* are revealed which show how the fragments are joined together in the original molecule. This procedure is illustrated in Fig. 8.33.

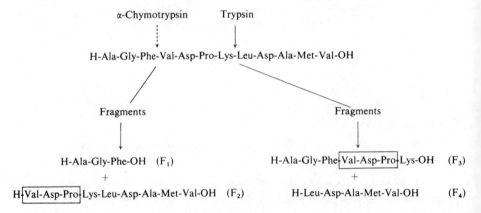

Fig. 8.33 Fragmentation of a dodecapeptide by α-chymotrypsin and trypsin. The sequence -Val-Asp-Pro- is found as part of the large fragments F_2 and F_3 and shows how these two fragments 'overlap' in the original peptide

The final problem to be solved is to determine the position of the disulphide bonds. Enzymic fragmentation of the original molecule produces peptides joined together by disulphide bonds. Sequence determination on these reveals sequences which coincide with those already found in the constituent chains around the cysteine residues. In the next few sections, examples will be seen of the complete primary structures for a number of polypeptides and proteins. These structures were determined using the methods described in this section.

8.4.3 Polypeptide hormones

Some of the most important advances in this field of study in the last decade have been achieved as a result of the discovery that a number of mammalian hormones are relatively low-molecular-weight polypeptides. These molecules do not have the structural complexity of proteins, and thus the primary structures have been easily determined and many have been synthesized. From molecular fragments obtained during the degradation and the synthesis, it has been possible to study structure–function relationships.

These hormones are products of the endocrine (ductless) glands and are secreted by these directly into the blood stream. It is still not exactly clear how they act when they reach their target organ. One theory is that they make up part of the active site of an enzyme system; another is that they affect the permeability of cells in the target organ and thus exert a control over the metabolism. Because of their important physiological action, these hormones have been the subject of extensive pharmacological studies. These studies generally take the form of the preparation of synthetic analogues, in which the position and nature of the amino-acid residues is changed. By the preparation of a large number of these analogues, much information regarding structure–function relationships may be obtained.

(a) Pituitary hormones A number of polypeptide hormones from this gland have been characterized, including the growth, luteinizing, follicle-stimulating, thyroid-stimulating and adrenocorticotrophic hormones. In addition, the octapeptides, oxytocin and vasopressin, have been isolated from the posterior pituitary. There is a considerable difference in molecular size within this group of hormones. They range from relatively small molecules like oxytocin X (MW = 1006) to molecules of protein size such as thyroid-stimulating hormone (MW = ~30 000).

(i) Oxytocin and vasopressin These hormones produce three well recognized effects; increase in blood pressure (pressor activity), contraction of the uterus (oxytocic effect) coupled with milk ejection and an antidiuretic effect.

X   XI   XII

H-Cys-Tyr-Ile-Gln-Asn-Cys-Pro-Leu-GlyNH$_2$
  1   2   3   4   5   6   7   8   9

H-Cys-Tyr-Phe-Gln-Asn-Cys-Pro-Lys-GlyNH$_2$
  1   2   3   4   5   6   7   8   9

H-Cys-Tyr-Phe-Gln-Asn-Cys-Pro-Arg-GlyNH$_2$
  1   2   3   4   5   6   7   8   9

353

The isolation of these two hormones was achieved by du Vigneaud. The amino-acid sequences were determined and the primary structures confirmed by synthesis. The two forms of vasopressin (XI and XII) differ only in one amino acid (at position 8). The arginine variety occurs in many species including Man, whilst lysine-vasopressin has been found in pigs. Due to the similarity of structure there is considerable overlap of physiological action by the hormones, but pressor activity is strongest in the vasopressins.

It is pertinent to mention here some other polypeptides which, like the vasopressins, show powerful pressor activity. They are angiotensin (XIII), bradykinin (XIV; X = H), kallidin (XIV; X = H-Lys-), eledoisin (XV), and phyalaemin (XVI). The first three of these compounds are of mammalian origin, being produced from inert plasma protein by enzymic action. Brady-kinin and kallidin are very similar in both structure and physiological action. Eledoisin and phyalaemin are isolated from *lower* animals.

H-Asp-Arg-Val-Tyr-Ile-His-Pro-Phe-OH	XIII
X-Arg-Pro-Pro-Gly-Phe-Ser-Pro-Phe-Arg-OH	XIV
Glp-Pro-Ser-Lys-Asp-Ala-Phe-Ile-Gly-Leu-MetNH$_2$	XV
Glp-Ala-Asp-Pro-Asn-Lys-Phe-Tyr-Gly-Leu-MetNH$_2$	XVI

$$Glp = \begin{array}{c} CO-(CH_2)_2 \\ | \qquad\quad | \\ NH-CH-CO- \end{array}$$

(ii) Adrenocorticotrophin (ACTH) ACTH controls the growth of the adrenal cortex and influences the production of corticosteroids. It also possesses a number of extra adrenal effects which include melanophore-stimulation activity. This arises from the structural similarity of part of the ACTH molecule to α-MSH (α-MSH has the sequence 1–13 and is the *N*-acetyl *C*-amide). The structure of ACTH has been determined, and the structure (Fig. 8.34) confirmed by synthesis. During the degradation and synthesis studies, it became apparent that the full range of biological activity resides in the fragment 1–24. The fragment 1–13 shows a small but detectable amount of adrenal activity, and thus may be considered to be the *functional* part of the molecule. The portion 14–24 is concerned with binding the molecule to its target. The steady increase in activity as the amino acids are added to the 1–13 fragment is shown in Fig. 8.34. Another interesting feature is that the species variation in amino-acid sequence is confined to a very small part of the molecule (25–33), i.e., the *active* part is always the same.

(b) Gastro-intestinal hormones A number of polypeptide hormones have been found in the organs and secretions of the gastro-intestinal tract. The best known of these is insulin, which is secreted by the β cells of the pancreas. Insulin is involved in the control of carbohydrate metabolism, and when the

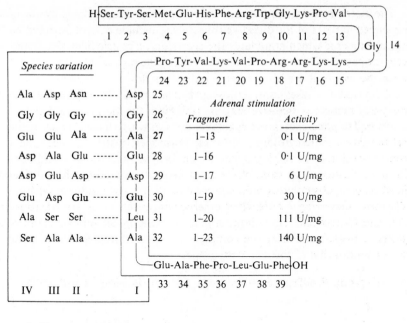

I   Pig
II Human
III Bovine
IV Sheep

Fig. 8.34 Structure–function relationships in the corticotrophins

supply is deficient, the amount of sugar in the blood increases (hyperglycaemia). The exact role of insulin in this process has still not been completely ascertained. The structure of insulin was described in section 8.1.2 (Fig. 8.7). The total synthesis has been accomplished, but only by the formation of the disulphide bonds in a random oxidation. This produced a complex mixture from which a small amount of active material was isolated.

Glucagon was first isolated from insulin preparations and later shown to be secreted by the α cells of the pancreas. Glucagon acts to raise the blood-sugar level by controlling the release of glucose from glycogen in the liver. This action explains the transitory period of hyperglycaemia following the injection of insulin containing glucagon. The hormone has a single chain of twenty-nine amino acids and has the sequence

H-His-Ser-Gln-Gly-Thr-Phe-Thr-Ser-Asp-Tyr-Ser-Lys-Tyr-Leu-Asp ⌐

HO-Thr-Asn-Met-Leu-Tyr-Gln-Val-Phe-Asp-Gln-Ala-Arg-Arg-Ser ⌐

355

The secretory activities of certain digestive glands are regulated by hormones produced in parts of the digestive tract. These include gastrin, secreted by the antral mucosa, which stimulates the secretion of gastric acid (HCl) and the enzyme pepsin. Two hormones are secreted by the region of the upper intestine near the mucosal glands; secretin induces a flow of pancreatic juice and cholescytokinin causes contraction and evacuation of the gall bladder and the release of numerous digestive enzymes (this latter function had been previously attributed to pancreozymin, a substance now known to have a structure identical to that of cholescytokinin). Of these hormones, gastrin has been the most fully studied. It has a single polypeptide chain of seventeen amino acids, ending in an amide group . In most species, two gastrins are present which differ only in whether an *O*-sulphate group is present on the tyrosyl residue at position 12. The most interesting feature which emerged during chemical investigation was that the C-terminal tetrapeptide amide, present in all known mammalian gastrins, possesses almost the complete range of gastric activities at about 80 per cent of that of the whole molecule.

$$\text{Glp-Gly-Pro-Trp-Leu-(Glu)-}_5\text{Ala-Tyr-Gly-Trp-Met-Asp-PheNH}_2$$

1   12   17

Human gastrin I

Polypeptide hormone precursors and their releasing factors

Several of the polypeptide hormones described in this section are synthesized *in vivo* as part of larger molecules from which the biologically active hormones are later produced. For example, the two polypeptide chains of insulin (Fig. 8.7) arise from the single polypeptide chain of proinsulin (Fig. 8.35). Similarly, precursor-ACTH ('big'-ACTH) is converted into ACTH by the action of trypsin. The two species of gastrin, found in most mammalian

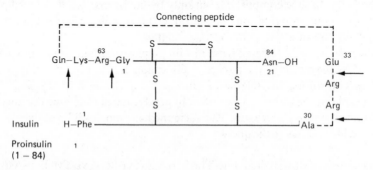

Fig. 8.35 A diagrammatic representation of proinsulin showing its relationship to hormonal insulin (→ possible sites for removal of 'connecting peptide' by trypsin-type action)

species, arise from two precursors ('big'-gastrins) containing a further seventeen amino acids at the N-terminus.

At least ten polypeptides of relatively small molecular size have been identified which act as regulators for the release of polypeptide hormones from pituitary gland. The origin of these is the hypothalamus and they appear to be secreted by hypothalamic nerve fibres and pass via the portal system to the pituitary. These *hypothalamic regulating factors* either stimulate the pituitary to produce specific hormones or inhibit their release. The factors so far identified are listed in Table 8.1 together with some examples of their structure.

Table 8.1 Hypothalamic releasing factors

Name of hormone/releasing factor	Abbr.
1. *Stimulators*	
Corticotrophin (ACTH) releasing factor	CRF
Follicle-stimulating hormone (FSH) releasing factor	FRF
Growth hormone (GH) releasing factor	GRF
Luteinizing hormone (LH) releasing factor	LRF
Melanocyte-stimulating hormone (MSH) releasing factor	MRF
Prolactin releasing factor	PRF
Thyroid-stimulating hormone (TSH) releasing factor	TRF
2. *Inhibitors*	
Growth hormone release-inhibiting factor	GH-RIF
Melanocyte-stimulating hormone release-inhibiting factor	MRIF
Prolactin release-inhibiting factor	PIF

Glp-His-ProNH$_2$ Glp-His-Trp-Ser-Tyr-Gly-Leu-Arg-Pro-GlyNH$_2$

   TRF   LRF   Glu

H-Pro-Leu-GlyNH$_2$ H-Val-His-Leu-Ser-Ala-Glu-Glu-Lys   or   Ala-OH

   MRF   GRF   Gln

8.4.4 Polypeptide antibiotics

Polypeptide molecules with antibiotic properties are found to have a number of unusual structural features. In the first place, uncommon amino acids may be present; these are either the D-enantiomorph of a common amino acid or an amino acid with an unusual side chain. The second feature is the presence of cyclic structures. Unlike the ring systems of oxytocin or insulin, these do not involve S—S bonds, but arise through condensation of terminal amino and

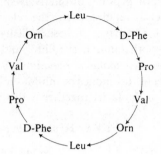

$$\text{Val} \rightarrow \text{Orn} \rightarrow \text{Leu} \rightarrow \text{D-Phe} \rightarrow \text{Pro} \rightarrow \text{Val} \rightarrow \text{Orn} \rightarrow \text{Leu} \rightarrow \text{D-Phe} \rightarrow \text{Pro}$$

Gramicidin S

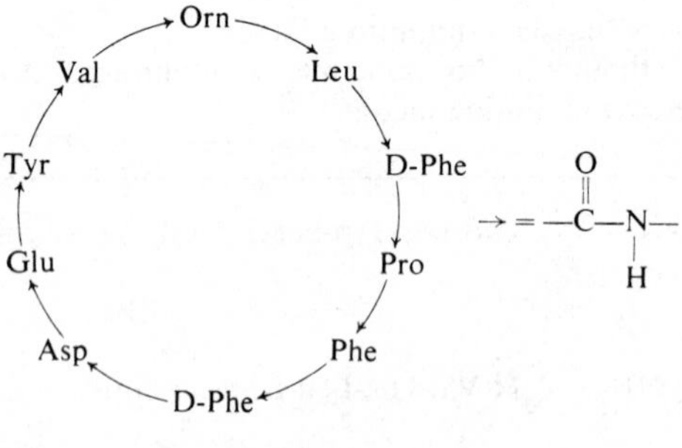

$\rightarrow = \quad \overset{\displaystyle O}{\underset{\displaystyle H}{-C-N-}}$

$$\text{Val} \rightarrow \text{Orn} \rightarrow \text{Leu} \rightarrow \text{D-Phe} \rightarrow \text{Pro} \rightarrow \text{Phe} \rightarrow \text{D-Phe} \rightarrow \text{Asn} \rightarrow \text{Gln} \rightarrow \text{Tyr}$$

Tyrocidin A

358

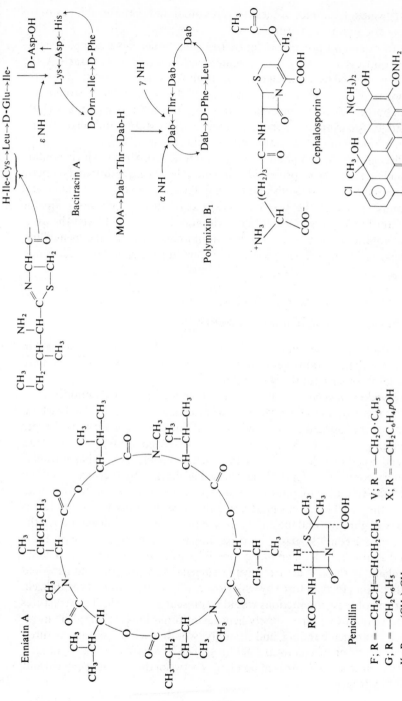

Fig. 8.36 Structures of some antibiotics

359

carboxyl groups. Examples of these features are found in the antibiotics of the tyrocidine and gramicidin groups.

The bacitracin and polymixin antibiotics have rather more complex structures with both cyclic and linear polypeptide chains present. In bacitracin A, the linear chain is joined by a side-chain amide group (ε NH) to a lysyl residue of the cyclic moiety. Furthermore, there is no free thiol group, and a thiazoline ring is formed by the isoleucine and cysteine residues. The polymixins contain a fatty acid residue, for example, 6-methyloctanoic acid (MOA) and also the uncommon amino acid L-α,γ-diaminobutyric acid (Dab).

Another group of compounds with antibiotic properties which contain amino acids are the cyclodepsipeptides or peptolides. These compounds contain both amino and hydroxy acids and the ring system is made up of amide and ester bonds. Some of the best characterized of these compounds are the enniatin antibiotics. The polypeptide antibiotics have not achieved the same pharmacological importance of other antibiotics such as the penicillins, cephalosporins, tetracyclines, or streptomycins (for the structure, see section 7.3.2).

8.4.5   The three-dimensional structure of proteins

The importance of three-dimensional structure has already been mentioned in connection with the action of enzymes (section 8.2). Here we will consider more fully the levels of structural organization.

(a) Secondary structure   X-ray studies on amides and small peptides show that the atoms around the peptide bond lie in a plane, i.e., the carbonyl carbon, nitrogen and the four atoms attached to them (Fig. 8.37). The carbon–nitrogen bond length is shorter than that for a normal C—N bond in, for example, an amine, and this shows that the C—N bond in a polypeptide chain has considerable double-bond character ($\sim$50 per cent). The double-bond character allows for a definite spatial configuration, and this has been shown to be *trans* with respect to the α carbon atoms joined on either side. Another important fact is that this configuration and the dimensions of the chain do not depend upon the structure of side chain R. Based on these fundamental facts, Pauling (in 1951) proposed a number of theoretically possible ordered structures for a polypeptide chain. In these structures it was assumed that hydrogen bonding would be the chief non-covalent force by which the conformation would be stabilized, and as many of these interactions would be present as possible. The structures proposed were of two types: firstly helical conformations stabilized by intramolecular hydrogen bonding, and secondly two-dimensional sheet structures, in which a number of chains are held together by intermolecular hydrogen bonds. In each case, the hydrogen bonding is between the carbonyl oxygen and the imino hydrogen.

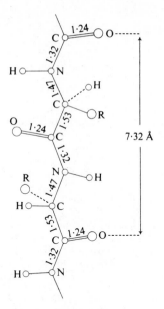

Fig. 8.37 The dimensions of an extended *trans* polypeptide chain

Of the many different helical conformations possible, one conformation emerged as the most likely, and is known as the α-*helix*. Each amino-acid residue is in an exactly equivalent spatial position, and is hydrogen-bonded to residues five positions back and five positions forward in the chain (except at the chain ends; Fig. 8.38). Of the two possible senses for a helical conformation, the right-handed helix is preferred theoretically. Since the α-helical conformation was first proposed, evidence has been accumulating that it is the most common type of ordered secondary structure. The direct evidence has come from X-ray studies on both soluble and insoluble proteins, and indirect evidence from the results of the numerous solution measurements of protein conformation (section 6.2.8). The helical conformation is prominent in the secondary structure of myoglobin, but in certain enzymes whose structures are known very little helix is present.

In the sheet structures, the chain is in a more extended conformation. Of the two theoretical conformations, the one with the N-termini and C-termini oriented in alternate directions is found in nature, and is called the *anti-parallel pleated sheet* (Fig. 8.39). There is evidence that this conformation occurs in insoluble proteins (e.g., silk fibroin) but only to a limited extent in soluble proteins.

The stability and extent of ordered secondary structure in the soluble proteins are features of great importance in biochemistry. Whether or not a helical conformation occurs depends in the first instance on the primary

361

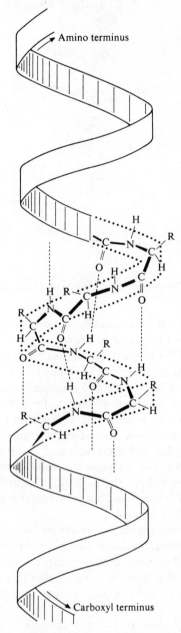

Fig. 8.38 A diagrammatic representation of the α-helix

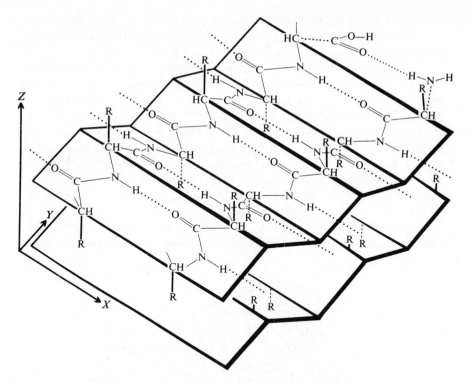

Fig. 8.39 A diagrammatic representation of the anti-parallel pleatéd sheet

structure. For example, the presence of a proline residue disrupts a helical conformation. Also, in soluble proteins, there is competition for hydrogen bonding with water molecules. This effect is reduced by a compact tertiary structure.

(b) Tertiary structure The tertiary structure in describing the overall spatial arrangement of the polypeptide chain (or chains) gives an exact account, in most small and medium-sized proteins, of molecular shape. The detailed determination of this shape has been carried out for so few proteins that generalizations are, at the moment, not possible. In the case of soluble proteins, it seems likely that the overall shape is globular, the chain folding and bending so that the molecule appears as a compact sphere. Although a number of solution techniques can be used to determine the general shape of a protein, only X-ray studies on the crystalline solid give a direct method for the exact location in space of each amino-acid residue. The resolution now possible in this technique allows many of the amino-acid side chains to be distinguished, and thus determination of the primary structure is also achieved. However, the technique required for X-ray studies of this type is so specialized that

there are few institutions capable of undertaking such work. Each determination takes many years to carry out, and at the moment the detailed three-dimensional structure of only a few proteins is known.

The structures of several enzymes have now been completely determined, and the full three-dimensional structure is known. **Figure 8.40** shows the results of one such determination—a derivative of α-chymotrypsin. Other determinations have included lysozyme (1965) and ribonuclease (1967). In all cases, there is very much less ordered helical structure than was found in the myoglobin molecule. While lysozyme and ribonuclease contain a single polypeptide chain containing 129 and 124 residues respectively, each involving four disulphide bonds, α-chymotrypsin consists of three chains joined by disulphide bonds **(Fig. 8.40)**. In the three structures, a compact tertiary structure is observed.

Many more such investigations are at present in progress. A very fundamental question has still to be answered: is the structure so determined on the

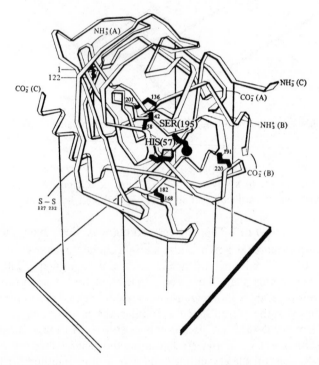

Fig. 8.40 The three-dimensional structure of tosyl-chymotrypsin (tosyl group at seryl residue 195) at 2 Å resolution (by permission of D. M. Blow, 1968, and the editor of *Journal of Molecular Biology*). The three chains (A, B, and C) are joined by disulphide bonds: A—B, 1—122; B—C, 136—201. Other intrachain disulphide bonds are 42—58, 168—182 and 192—221. See also Fig. 8.24(a).

crystalline protein identical or even similar to that in aqueous solution, where the biological properties are exerted? It should be noted that the crystals used in X-ray studies contain water, sometimes as much as 50 per cent, and thus the polypeptide chain is probably in a very similar environment to that in aqueous solution.

(c) Quaternary structure Most large and even some medium-sized proteins exist as an association of sub-units. These sub-units are parts of the protein which can be disrupted by reagents which do not break covalent bonds. Thus, two chains joined by disulphide bonds would not be described as sub-units. Each sub-unit, of course, has a primary, secondary and tertiary structure, although two or more sub-units in a given protein may be identical. The haemoglobin molecule is made up of four sub-units (two α chains and two β chains). X-ray studies have shown that each sub-unit is very similar to a myoglobin molecule. Each chain binds a haeme group and there are minor differences in folding between the α and β chains, which depend on differences in primary structure. The chains fit together in an approximately tetrahedral arrangement in the quaternary structure of haemoglobin.

(d) Insoluble proteins Many of the structural proteins occur in the form of fibres. The fibres are made up of bundles of *fibrils* which are packed together in a parallel arrangement. The fibrils of some of the more common structural proteins have been examined by X-ray diffraction.

The keratins are structural proteins of wool, hair, nails, claws, and hooves. Their secondary structure is variable; hair and wool appear to contain α-helical regions and bundles of these helices twist together to give *super-helices*. On stretching, rearrangement to a pleated sheet conformation (β-keratin) occurs. There is a high degree of cross linking of the chains by S—S bonds, making these materials very insoluble.

Collagen, a structural protein found in teeth, skin, bone, tendon and cartilage, has an unusual amino-acid composition. Large amounts of glycine, proline and hydroxyproline are present, so the normal type of helical conformation cannot arise. X-ray studies have shown that three polypeptide chains twist together to give a unique helical conformation.

Muscle proteins have attracted a great deal of attention, since through a detailed study of their structure it may be possible to explain the mechano-chemical reaction of muscular contraction. Muscle tissue contains about 20 per cent protein and, since 40 per cent of the mammalian body is muscle, muscle protein represents a large proportion of body protein. The two proteins present are myosin (MW ~500 000) and actin (MW ~70 000). These have an overall rod-like shape, and their polypeptide chains are completely helical.

(e) Forces involved in the maintenance of three-dimensional structure Both covalent and non-covalent forces are involved in stabilizing the three-dimensional structure of a protein. The most prominent covalent force is the S—S bond, whose position is determined not only by the position of the cystine

365

residues but also by the way in which the chain folds. This is the strongest force, and thus is of great importance in maintaining tertiary structure. A stable three-dimensional structure can, of course, arise without S—S bonds, e.g., myoglobin. The folding of the chain is caused by numerous types of non-covalent interaction, and most, if not all, types may occur in a given protein. However, they have very different degrees of importance.

All proteins contain amino acids with non-polar (alkyl or aryl) side chains and the proportion of these is usually in the region of 20–40 per cent. The conformation adopted by the parts of the chain containing these side chains is such that as many of them as possible group together to form a *non-polar environment* to the exclusion of water. The force between the side chains and water molecules is called hydrophobic or apolar bonding. The quantitative calculation of the strength of this form of interaction is difficult, but it appears to be of the same order of magnitude as a hydrogen bond. The main contribu-

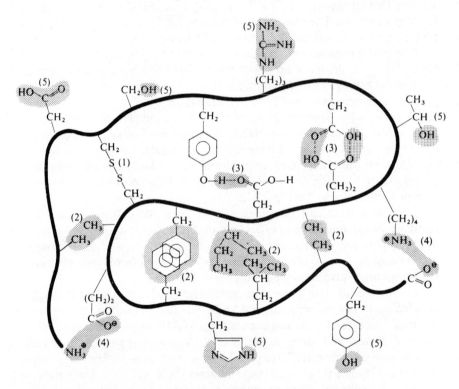

Fig. 8.41 A diagrammatic summary of the stabilization of tertiary structure in a protein (adapted from Anfinsen, 1959). (1) disulphide bonds (S—S); (2) hydrophobic bonding (e.g., Ile-Leu; Ala-Ala; Phe-Phe); (3) side-chain hydrogen bonding (e.g., Tyr-Asp; Asp-Glu); (4) salt linkages (e.g., Asp-CO_2^-; Lys-$\overset{+}{N}H_3$); (5) polar group interaction with water on the surface (e.g., Asp, Ser, Arg, Thr, His and Tyr)

tion to its strength comes from the change in the structure of water. An increase in entropy occurs, since the association of non-polar groups within the interior of the protein molecule allows the water molecules of hydration to revert to their normal less-ordered structure.

Polar interactions are also possible, but there is evidence that they are of much less importance than the non-polar forces. Hydrogen bonding may take place between polar side chains. A few *salt-linkages* may also be present; these are formed by interaction of protonated basic side chains (Arg, Lys or His) with ionized side chains (Asp, Glu or Tyr). X-ray studies on soluble proteins have revealed that the vast majority of polar side chains are directed outwards from the surface of the molecule, and thereby assist in making the molecule soluble, rather than binding together different parts of the chain. It is possible that salt linkages may be of more importance in the aggregation of sub-units. The forces involved in the maintenance of tertiary structure are summarized in Fig. 8.41 (See also section 5.6.2).

Denaturation is, initially, the breaking up of the three-dimensional structure. If the process can be achieved by breaking the non-covalent bonds, then reversible denaturation is possible. If, on the other hand, disulphide bonds are broken, then the change is irreversible. Denaturation can be brought about by variation of temperature and pH, and by the action of denaturing agents such as urea or detergents. Since the stabilization of tertiary structure is dependent on non-polar interactions, denaturation can be brought about very efficiently by the action of solvents such as acetone or dioxan. These solvents weaken the hydrophobic bonds by producing a non-polar environment.

8.4.6 Glycoproteins

Apart from nucleoproteins, discussed in the next section, glycoproteins probably represent the most important group of conjugate proteins. These molecules contain as prosthetic group(s) one or more hetero-oligosaccharide moieties covalently attached to the amino-acid side-chain groups of a polypeptide chain. The oligosaccharide chains are usually branched and contain a relatively low number of monosaccharide residues. The total carbohydrate content is extremely variable ranging from 1 per cent in ovalbumin to 85 per cent in 'blood group' glycoproteins. Even in glycoproteins with a high carbohydrate content, the prosthetic groups are present as many short oligosaccharide chains rather than a few long ones. As in simple proteins, a wide range of molecular weight is found ranging from ribonuclease B with a value of 14 700 to ovine submaxillary mucin with a value of about 1×10^6. Glycoproteins have been found in both vertebrates and invertebrates, and, more recently in green plants and fungi. The most fully studied, structurally, have been the plasma glycoproteins and certain hormonal glycopeptides such as Human chorionic gonadotrophin (HCG) and follicle-stimulating hormone (FSH).

The variety of monosaccharide units known to be present in the carbo-hydrate moieties of glycoprotein is quite small (about nine) as compared with the total number of monosaccharides found in Nature (about 100). The commonly occurring monosaccharides of glycoproteins include D-galactose, D-mannose, L-fucose, L-arabinose, D-xylose and D-glucose; also present are the derivatives N-acetyl-D-glucosamine, N-acetyl-D-galactosamine and sialic acids of which N-acetyl-neuraminic acid is the most prominent (structure, see section 7.3.2). In spite of this small number of structural components, the number of ways in which they can be bonded to one another is very large. While two different amino acids can form only two different dipeptides, eleven isomeric disaccharides can arise from the combination of two identical hexose molecules. The number of isomers rises rapidly with the introduction of different hexoses, thus a trisaccharide made up of three different hexoses could give rise to 1056 structures, whereas three different amino acids can form only six tripeptides. The number of possible isomers of the carbohydrate moiety of α_1-acid glycoprotein based on composition alone has been esti-mated to be 10^{24}, which reduces to 6×10^6 once the sequence is known [Fig. 8.42(a)]. This large number of possible isomers arise from the many different positions and stereochemistry of glycosidic bonds in hetero-oligosaccharides.

Another feature which adds to the difficulties of defining accurately the structures of glycoproteins is the problem of 'microheterogeneity'. In a particular organism, every molecule of a particular 'simple' protein is identi-cal. Consequently, when it is isolated, purified and analysed, the ratio of the component amino acids is integral (see section 8.4.2). But, when a similar type of analysis is carried out on monosaccharides of a glycoprotein, it is found that the ratio is non-integral. For example, in ovalbumin the ratio of D-mannose to N-acetyl-D-glucosamine is 5·5:4. These non-integral ratios arise because the structure and composition of the oligosaccharide chains vary from molecule to molecule owing to the mechanism of their biosyn-thesis. In the biosynthesis of a glycoprotein, the polypeptide chain is first assembled at a ribosome in a carefully controlled manner that ensures a reproducible sequence of amino acids (see section 9.5.3). The carbohydrate residues are then added, in the Golgi region, each addition requiring a separate enzymic reaction. No rigid template is present for this latter process and hence there is opportunity for structural variation. This mechanism also permits the extensive chain branching found in the oligosaccharide moieties.

There are a number of types of bonding by which the prosthetic groups of glycoproteins are attached to the polypeptide chain; the most common being through an asparaginyl side-chain [Fig. 8.42(b)]. Others include a normal O–glycosidic bond between C_1 of a monosaccharide and the hydroxyl function of a seryl or threonyl residue or an S-glycosidic bond with a cysteinyl residue.

The complete structural determination of a glycoprotein is clearly a formidable task and, at the moment, very limited information on these molecules is available. A probable structure of the five oligosaccharide moieties of α_1-acid glycoprotein (also known as orosomucoid), a plasma protein of molecular weight 44 000, is shown in Fig. 8.42(a).

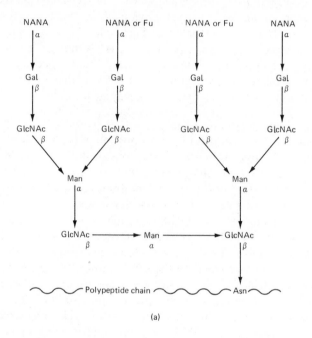

(a)

Asn = Asparaginyl
Man = D-Mannose
GlcNAc = N-Acetyl-D-glucosamine
Gal = D-Galactose
NANA = N-Acetyl-neuraminic acid
      (a sialic acid)
Fu = L-Fucose (6-Deoxy-L-galactose)

(b)

Fig. 8.42 (a) The probable sequence of monosaccharides in an oligosaccharide moiety of Human α_1-acid glycoprotein. (The stereochemistry with respect to the reducing carbon atom is shown but the exact position of attachment at the non-reducing carbon is not known). (b) The structure of the carbohydrate–amino acid linkage found in α_1-acid glycoprotein

369

8.5.1 Introduction

The nucleic acids are macromolecules concerned in some of the most essential functions of living organisms. They provide the material for the storage and transmission of genetic information, and are present in all cells. Cell nucleic acid is of two kinds: deoxyribonucleic acid (DNA) and ribonucleic acid (RNA). In most organisms, the most obvious difference between these is in molecular size. DNA molecules have very high molecular-weight values, indeed they are among the largest molecules known; RNA molecular-weight values are generally much lower. There are also more subtle differences in composition and molecular architecture, which will be described later. From the point of view of biological function, DNA and RNA may again be clearly distinguished. In most organisms, DNA is the material in which genetic information is stored, and by which it is conveyed from one generation of cells to the next. RNA, on the other hand, is responsible for the transmission of the genetic instructions, and controls the means by which the instructions are utilized in the biosynthesis of protein. These aspects are considered in more detail in section 9.5. It should be noted that in some lower organisms, notably viruses, DNA is not present, and RNA takes on the role as the basic genetic material.

Apart from certain viruses, DNA is found in all living organisms. In *prokaryotes*, where there is no organized nucleus, the DNA is distributed throughout the organism. This situation is found in organisms such as bacteria and blue-green algae. In *eukaryotes* the DNA is found in the cell nuclei in the form of nucleoprotein. In some eukaryotes, DNA occurs in other cell organelles such as the chloroplasts of higher plants, and also in cell mitochondria. Nucleoprotein is complex material where there is an electrostatically bound association between anionic DNA molecules and cationic protein. In the prokaryotes, DNA does not occur bound to protein.

The common source of DNA is from the nucleoprotein of cell nuclei. The DNA is isolated after the protein has been denatured, usually by phenol. Pure DNA is formed as a white fibrous solid which, although it is insoluble in pure water, dissolves in salt solutions. DNA preparations are fractionated by centrifuging on a caesium chloride gradient.

RNA is generally isolated from the cell cytoplasm and is freed from protein by denaturation of the latter. RNA samples must also be freed from other water-soluble compounds, such as polysaccharides. RNA preparations may be fractionated analytically by electrophoresis, and preparatively by gel filtration or counter-current distribution. Gel filtration is used to obtain a separation between the different types of RNA, and counter-current distribution to fractionate molecular species within each group. This latter technique has been particularly successful with the separation of transfer RNA's.

8.5.2 Deoxyribonucleic acid (DNA)

The DNA from most cell nuclei is polydisperse. Several thousand different DNA molecules of molecular weight about 10^9 are found in the chromosomes of eukaryotic cells. Homogeneous samples of DNA are found in viruses and bacteria, where the DNA is usually present as single DNA molecules of high molecular weight. In *Esch. coli* the chromosome is a single DNA molecule of molecular weight 3×10^9 and is 1mm long. The smallest homogeneous DNA is that of bacteriophage ϕX174; this has a molecular weight of $1\cdot7 \times 10^6$ and consists of a single (circular) polynucleotide chain of 5375 deoxynucleotides. The sequence of this molecule has recently been determined by Sanger and his co-workers and this represents one of the most important advances of structural organic chemistry and of biochemistry in recent years. Since the structure of the nine proteins of this virus are known, we have a direct check on the structural relationship between an organism's genome and the products arising from it.

Prior to this structural determination, it had been difficult to envisage the complete structural determination of a molecule as large as DNA and studies had concentrated on the broad structural arrangement. X-ray studies by Wilkins showed that DNA molecules were rod-like and the polydeoxyribonucleotide chains were in a helical conformation. Unlike polypeptide molecules, in which a single chain has a helical conformation, most DNA molecules have two chains wound helically and held together by hydrogen bonds between the bases. This structure was predicted theoretically in 1953 by Watson and Crick, and its implications regarding the molecular basis of genetics laid one of the foundation stones in the field of molecular biology. The main structural features of the DNA *double helix* are shown in Fig. 8.43. The two polynucleotide chains are in an anti-parallel arrangement (cf. the polypeptide chains in the pleated sheet conformation; Fig. 8.39). The hydrogen bonds which hold the two chains together lie in the centre of the helix and are formed in a highly specific manner between the bases. Purine and pyrimidine bases have very different spatial requirements; and so that the helix is not distorted, each hydrogen-bonded base pair in the centre of the helix must consist of one purine and one pyrimidine base. The arrangement is, in fact, even more precise than this, in that adenine forms hydrogen bonds most satisfactorily with thymine rather than cytosine; while guanine forms hydrogen bonds most satisfactorily with cytosine rather than thymine. The most conclusive evidence for this specific *base pairing* comes from the quantitative analysis of the different bases present in a DNA hydrolysate, which was carried out by Chargaff. Some typical values are shown in Table 8.2.

Both DNA and RNA exist as polyanionic molecules due to the ionization of the phosphate groups of each monomer unit. Polymeric cations or polyamines are present as counterions; the type of cation being different in the different

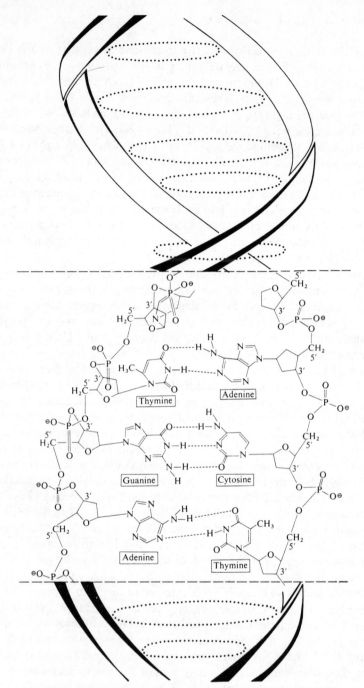

Fig. 8.43 A diagrammatic representation of the DNA double helix

Table 8.2 Base composition in DNA's

Source of DNA	Base proportions (mole per cent)				$\dfrac{A+G}{C+T}$ i.e., $\dfrac{\text{Purine}}{\text{Pyrimidine}}$
	A	T	G	C	
Man (thymus)	30·9	29·4	19·9	19·8	$\dfrac{50 \cdot 8}{49 \cdot 2} = 1 \cdot 03$
Bovine (thymus)	28·0	28·0	22·0	21·0	$\dfrac{50 \cdot 0}{49 \cdot 0} = 1 \cdot 02$
Wheat germ	27·3	27·1	22·7	22·8	$\dfrac{50 \cdot 0}{49 \cdot 9} = 1 \cdot 00$
Yeast	31·3	32·9	18·7	17·1	$\dfrac{50 \cdot 0}{50 \cdot 0} = 1 \cdot 00$
Esch. coli	24·7	23·6	26·0	25·7	$\dfrac{50 \cdot 7}{49 \cdot 3} = 1 \cdot 03$

types of living organism. In animal and plant nuclei, DNA occurs in association with histones which are low molecular weight (10 000–20 000) proteins. Histones are rich in either lysyl or arginyl residues and contain little or no sulphur-containing amino acids. In fish sperm cells, protamines (molecular weight 5000) are present which resemble the arginine-rich histones. The nucleic acid of lower forms of life has simple polyamines associated with it; for example, spermine in bacteria and spermidine or bis-(3-aminopropyl)-amine in DNA-containing viruses.

$$\overset{+}{H_3N}-(CH_2)_3-\overset{\overset{\displaystyle H}{|}}{\underset{\underset{\displaystyle H}{|}}{N}}\!\!\overset{+}{}-(CH_2)_4-\overset{\overset{\displaystyle H}{|}}{\underset{\underset{\displaystyle H}{|}}{N}}\!\!\overset{+}{}-(CH_2)_3-\overset{+}{NH_3}$$

Spermine

$$\overset{+}{H_3N}-(CH_2)_n-\overset{\overset{\displaystyle H}{|}}{\underset{\underset{\displaystyle H}{|}}{N}}\!\!\overset{+}{}-(CH_2)_m-\overset{+}{NH_3}$$

Spermidine ($n = 3$, $m = 4$)

Bis-(3-aminopropyl)-amine ($n = 3$, $m = 3$)

Sequence determination for DNA ($\phi X174$ DNA)

A few years ago, the complete sequence determination of even the smallest DNA molecule in Nature would have been considered an impossible task. This situation was changed by the development of new methods: the use of *restriction endonucleases* to produce defined DNA fragments and new methods of sequencing these fragments. Restriction endonucleases are endodeoxyribonucleases (section 8.1.2) that 'recognize' specific nucleotide sequences in DNA and cleave the molecule only at these points. These enzymes have been isolated in many microorganisms. The first characterized came from *Esch. coli*; for example, EcoRI-G⏐AATTC and EcoRII-⏐CCTGG. The use of one (HpaI) from *Haemophilus parainfluenzae* in the fragmentation of $\phi X174$ DNA is shown in Fig. 8.44(a); this cleaves the molecule at the following sequence:

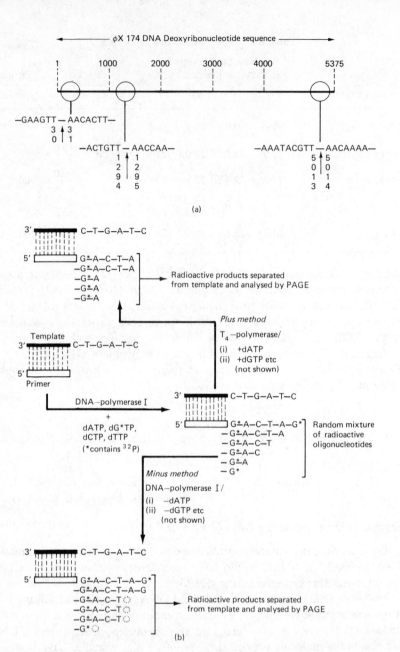

Fig. 8.44 Recent methods of DNA sequence determination. (a) A diagrammatic representation of the fragmentation of φX174 by HpaI restriction endonuclease (from F. Sanger, 1977). (b) A diagrammatic representation of the 'plus' and 'minus' sequence method (from F. Sanger, 1974). (Only six nucleotides are sequenced in this model; in practice the sequence of up to 150 may be achieved.)

GTT↓AAC. In the primary structure determination of ϕX174 DNA, several such enzymes were used to produce a series of well defined and *overlapping* fragments. The action and use of these enzymes is directly equivalent to the use made of trypsin and chymotrypsin in polypeptide fragmentation (section 8.4.2). A further use for fragments produced by restriction endonucleases is as *primers* for the *in vitro* synthesis of DNA chains (see below).

Many ingenious methods have been devised for sequencing fragments from DNA molecules; probably the most rapid and successful, at the moment, is the 'plus' and 'minus' method of Sanger's group. DNA-polymerase I (section 9.5.1) is first used to extend a *primer* oligonucleotide hydrogen-bonded to a *template* DNA whose sequence is being determined. In the presence of the four deoxyribonucleotide triphosphates, one of which contains the radio-active label ^{32}P, a *copy* is made of most of the template molecule [Fig. 8.44(b)]. Since the synthesis of the new radioactive chain proceeds at different rates in different molecules, a 'random mixture' of products is obtained. This mixture is analysed in *two* ways.

(*i*) *The minus method*   The mixture, still hydrogen-bonded to template, is re-incubated with DNA-polymerase I in the presence of three triphosphates. DNA synthesis takes place up to a point in each chain where the absence of the missing triphosphate stops the polymerization. Four such reactions are performed with each triphosphate in turn missing. In each case, the newly synthesized, radioactive chains are separated from template and analysed by electrophoresis. This procedure is shown in Fig. 8.44(b), where the missing triphosphate is dATP ('−A'). From the analysis of the reaction products, the positions of all 'A' residues are located; likewise those of G, C and T, from reactions omitting dGTP, dCTP and dTTP, may be located.

(*ii*) *The plus method*   A different DNA-polymerase is used here; that from bacteriophage T_4-infected *Esch. coli* (T_4-polymerase). This enzyme degrades, by exonuclease action, a DNA molecule from its 3′ terminus, but stops at a residue whose corresponding triphosphate is present in the reaction mixture. This method is applied to the 'random mixture' of radioactive oligonucleo-tides. Samples are incubated with T_4-polymerase and each triphosphate in turn and the products analysed by electrophoresis. For example, when dATP ('+A') is present radioactive chains arise all terminating in A [Fig. 8.44(b)].

When the analysis of all eight radioactive oligonucleotide mixtures has been performed, it is possible to deduce the sequence of the chain synthesized by DNA-polymerase which will be complementary to that of the template DNA whose sequence is being determined. By means of this procedure, deoxy-nucleotide fragments of up 150 residues may be sequenced in a matter of days thus making possible the complete primary structure determination of DNA.

8.5.3 Ribonucleic acids (RNA)

The most fully studied of the RNA molecules are those found in cell cytoplasm. Between 10–20 per cent of cell RNA, however, is found in the nucleolus of the cell nucleus. This organelle may be the site of the synthesis of some of the cytoplasmic RNA. At least three distinct types of RNA are found in the cytoplasm of eukaryotes.

(a) Ribosomal RNA (r-RNA) This is the most abundant RNA, making up as much as 80 per cent of the total cell RNA. It is located in the cytoplasmic particles called ribosomes. The RNA of ribosomes can be fractionated into different molecular-weight ranges in an ultracentrifuge (Fig. 8.46).

(b) Transfer RNA (t-RNA) This is also known as soluble RNA (s-RNA). It is the smallest molecular species of RNA (MW ∼25 000) and is found dissolved in the cytoplasm. It makes up about 15 per cent of the total cell RNA.

(c) Messenger RNA (m-RNA) This material occurs in small amounts (∼5 per cent) and has only a transitory life in the cell. The molecular weight is variable, and is directly related to the size of the polypeptide for which it carries the sequence instructions.

A fourth type of RNA is found in certain viruses (viral RNA). The RNA here is of high molecular weight (∼1 or 2×10^6) and is usually present as a single molecule. Viral RNA assumes the biological role of DNA in these viruses, that is the carrier of genetic information.

Of these species of RNA, the t-RNAs have been the subject of extensive primary structure determination in the last 15 years. It is possible to fractionate a mixture of soluble RNA molecules into homogeneous molecular species. The species so isolated are characterized by their ability to accept and transfer a specific amino acid. These molecules are made up of a linear chain of about 80 ribonucleotide units, and so for sequence studies, they are comparable to the larger polypeptide hormones or small proteins such as insulin, lysozyme or ribonuclease.

Sequence determination in these molecules follows a similar pattern to that used for proteins. Determination of the nucleotide composition precedes the fragmentation, and is used throughout the structural investigation in the same way as amino-acid analysis is used during primary structure studies in proteins. Ribonucleic acid molecules are most satisfactorily hydrolysed by alkali (1 M NaOH) (Fig. 8.45). The mixture of nucleotides in the hydrolysate is separated on an ion-exchange column and the concentration of each species is determined by ultraviolet spectroscopy. In this way, an empirical composition in terms of the nucleotide units may be determined.

Fragmentation of a polynucleotide chain is carried out by endonucleases, and sequence determination on the fragments by exonucleases (see section 8.1.2). Great use of the *overlapping sequence* technique is made in deducing the sequence in large fragments. The first complete t-RNA sequence determination

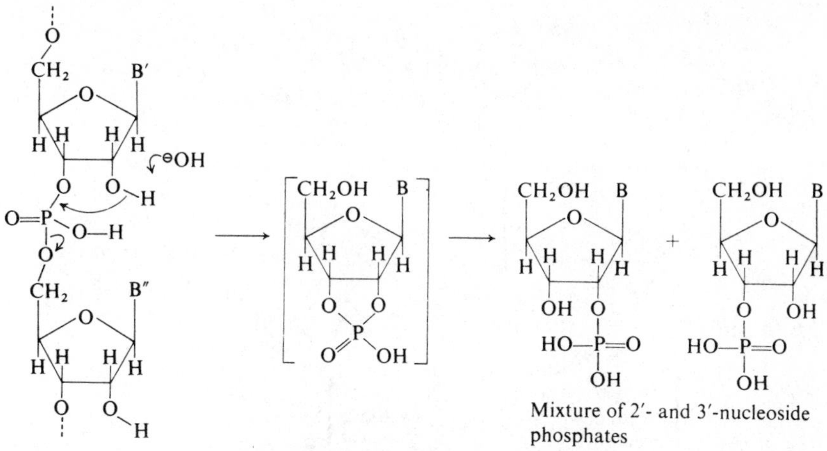

Fig. 8.45 Alkaline hydrolysis of RNA

Mixture of 2'- and 3'-nucleoside phosphates

—that of alanine t-RNA—was completed in 1964, and was an achievement to be compared with that of the determination of the primary structure of insulin a decade earlier. The structural determination had to be undertaken on a small amount of material (~350 mg). The structure of this molecule is shown in Fig. 8.47(b). One of the interesting features is that as well as the usual four nucleotide units, a number of uncommon ones are also present in small amounts. The presence of these greatly assisted the sequence studies, since they acted as 'landmarks' in the various fragments. The presence of these uncommon bases is now found to be a feature of t-RNAs. They arise from reactions taking place after the RNA is synthesized *in vivo* and do not arise from unusual nucleotides.

Achievements in the complete sequence determination of other types of RNA have been more limited owing to their greater molecular size. Ribosomes are made up of r-RNA and *basic* proteins; the r-RNA may be fractionated into three different homogeneous species with widely different molecular weights (Fig. 8.46). The smallest of these, the 5S RNA, from *Esch. coli* contains 120 ribonucleotides and the sequence of this was determined by Sanger's group. Sequences comprising about 95 per cent of the 16S r-RNA of *Esch. coli* are now known.

The largest RNA so far sequenced is that of the viral-RNA of bacteriophage MS 2. It consists of a single polynucleotide chain of 3569 residues (Fig. 8.49). Like the sequencing of the DNA of ϕX174, this represents another major milestone, since again the primary structures of the viral proteins are also known. The intact MS 2 virus particle consists of one RNA, one *maturation* protein, a component necessary for the functional integrity of the virus particle, and 180 *coat* proteins; thus the complete primary structure of the virus (MW~$3\cdot6 \times 10^6$) is known!

377

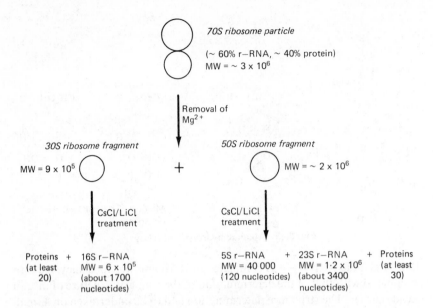

Fig. 8.46 Fragmentation of *Esch. coli* ribosomes. About 50 different proteins have so far been identified ranging in molecular weight from 10 000 to 50 000. Ribosomes from eukaryotic cells are slightly larger—80S—and fragment to give particles of 32S and 50S and a comparable range of constituents

The methods used in the sequence determinations of r-RNA and viral-RNA follow directly from Holley's original procedure: namely, enzymic fragmentation with endoribonucleases, separation, and sequence studies with exoribonucleases. The speed with which these studies may be performed have been greatly increased by the use of the ionophoresis method for separating and identifying the oligoribonucleotide fragments.

The three-dimensional structure of RNA molecules has been the subject of much theoretical speculation. The first type of structure proposed for t-RNA was the *hairpin-loop* structure [Fig. 8.47(a)], in which the single polyribonucleotide chain is folded back on itself and wound in a helical manner with stabilization by hydrogen bonding between specific base pairs. This structure requires a base composition as strict as that found in DNA, and also a sequence of bases that will provide maximum hydrogen bonding. The sequence studies, however, are not consistent with this model. A more complex *clover leaf* structure has been proposed for t-RNA molecules [Fig. 8.47(b) and Fig. 8.48(a)]. In this structure, several regions of hydrogen-bonded helical chain arise, interspersed with *loop* regions. In the loop regions, there is no hydrogen bonding between bases. One of these loop regions provides the

378

anticodon, which interacts with m-RNA during protein biosynthesis (section 9.5.3). It has been found possible to fit every t-RNA primary structure so far determined into this type of model, so that a general picture of the layout of a t-RNA molecule has emerged [Fig. 8.48(a)]. The first X-ray diffraction analyses of a crystalline t-RNA (t-RNA^{Phe} from yeast) were completed in 1974. These largely confirm the existence of the *clover leaf* type of con-

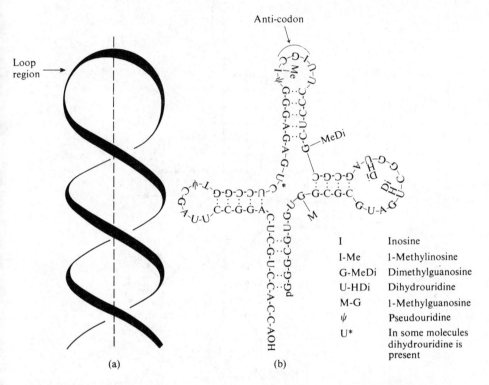

(a)   (b)

I	Inosine
I-Me	1-Methylinosine
G-MeDi	Dimethylguanosine
U-HDi	Dihydrouridine
M-G	1-Methylguanosine
ψ	Pseudouridine
U*	In some molecules dihydrouridine is present

Fig. 8.47 (a) Hairpin-loop structure for a single-chain RNA molecule which is likely to arise in r-RNA. (b) Diagrammatic representation of the base sequence of alanine-transfer RNA, showing a likely folded conformation stabilized by hydrogen bonds between specific base pairs (by permission of R. W. Holley, 1964, and the editor of *Science*, Vol. 147, p. 1464, 1965)

formation, at least in the solid state. A few additional hydrogen-bonded interactions were observed which had not been predicted in the theoretical model [Fig. 8.48(b)].

On the basis of sequence studies, *clover leaf*-type diagrams have been proposed for r-RNAs and also for the viral-RNA of bacteriophage MS 2 [Fig. 8.49(b)]. In general, a higher percentage of the polynucleotide chain is in a helical conformation than in a t-RNA.

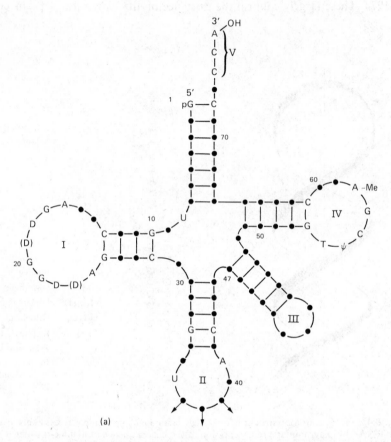

(a)

Fig. 8.48 (a) General structure of t-RNA. Loop I—8–10 nucleotides, containing the uncommon base dihydrouracil (D). Loop II—7 nucleotides, the *anti-codon* loop. Loop and 'arm' III—this is not always present, contains a maximum of 13 nucleotides (as shown). Loop IV—7 nucleotides, contains the sequence 'T-ψ-C'. Region V—these 3 nucleotides are added after *in vivo* synthesis. 3′ Terminus is used for the specific amino-acid attachment

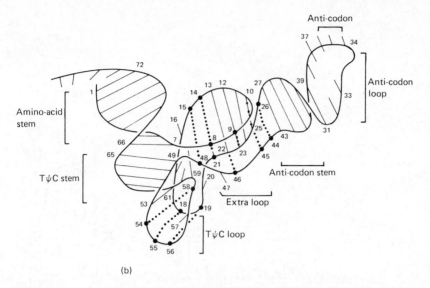

(b)

Fig. 8.48 (b) A schematic diagram of the chain folding and tertiary interactions between bases in yeast t-RNA^Phe. The ribose-phosphate backbone is shown as a continuous line. Base pairs in the double helical stems are represented by long light lines and non-paired bases by shorter lines. Base pairs additional to those in the clover leaf formula are represented by dotted lines (by permission of A. Klug, 1975, and the editor of *Proc. Nat. Acad. Sci. USA,* Vol. 72, No. 11, p. 4415, 1975)

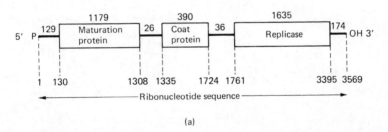

(a)

Fig. 8.49 The RNA genome of bacteriophage MS 2. (a) Genetic arrangement of MS 2 RNA. The three *gene* regions are separated by regions of *non-translated* nucleotides. The entire nucleotide sequence is known, part of it is shown in (b). (b) The nucleotide sequence of the *replicase* gene of MS 2 RNA. The termination codon (UAA) of *coat protein* gene is followed by 36 non-translated nucleotides and the initiation codon (AUG) of replicase gene. The 547 codons (1635 nucleotides) of the gene are followed by 174 non-translated nucleotides at the 3' hydroxyl terminus. While the nucleotide sequence is well defined, the *clover leaf*-type conformation is tentative. (By permission of W. Friers, 1976, and the editor of *Nature*, Vol. 260, p. 502, 1976)

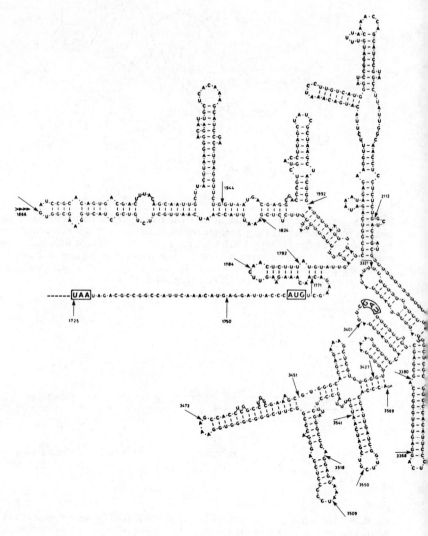

Fig. 8.49 (b)

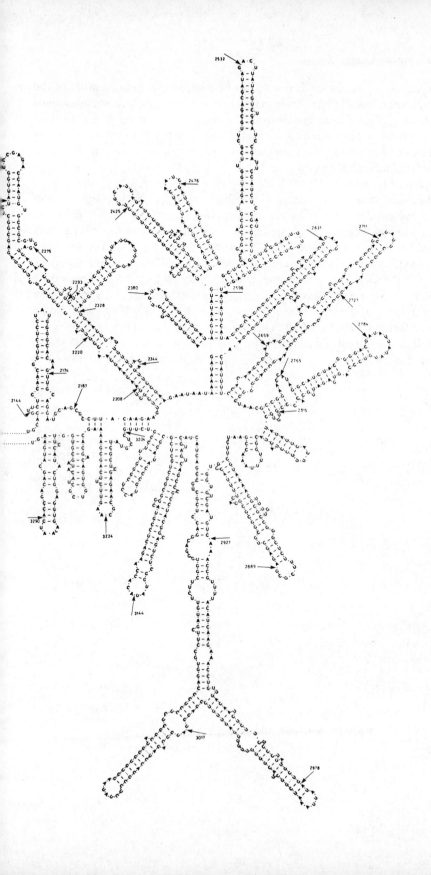

8.5.4 Polynucleotide synthesis

This section on nucleic acids would not be complete without mention of the great progress that has been made in the chemical synthesis of these compounds for use in biological experiments. It is now possible to join together both ribo- and deoxyribonucleotides by 3′—5′ phosphodiester bonds in an unambiguous manner. In both cases, the stepwise synthesis is limited to about five or so structural units, and larger molecules are prepared by joining the small oligo-nucleotides together.

The initial objective in the case of the ribonucleotides was the preparation of triribonucleotides. This work has been carried out mainly by Khorana and his co-workers, and was stimulated by the fact that triribonucleotides can pro-duce a similar effect to an m-RNA molecule in binding specific t-RNA mole-cules at ribosomes. If the sequence of bases of the triribonucleotide is known, and also the identity of the amino acid attached to the t-RNA, a method is available for the determination of the *genetic code* (see section 9.5.2). There are sixty-four possible triribonucleotides derived from the four main mono-ribonucleotides (AMP, GMP, CMP and UMP) and the synthesis of all sixty-four was completed in 1966. The general synthesis scheme used is shown in Fig. 8.50. It must be emphasized that these small molecules in no way act as

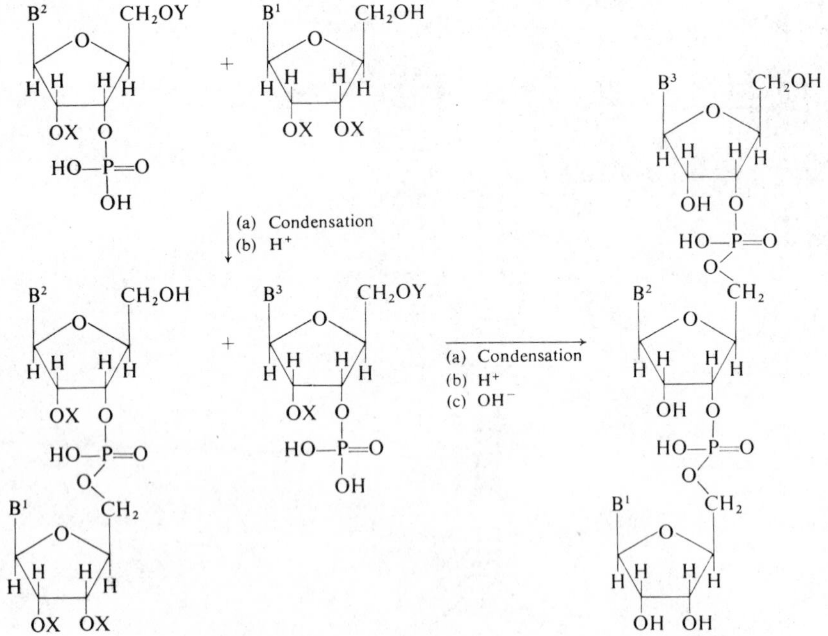

Fig. 8.50 Scheme for the synthesis of triribonucleotides

an m-RNA molecule in stimulating the synthesis of a polypeptide chain. This role is, however, performed by synthetic polymers of repeating mono-, di- or triribonucleotide sequences. These synthetic materials have also been used in the determination of the genetic code.

Many of the problems that arise in the synthesis of triribonucleotides have their counterpart in polypeptide synthesis (section 7.1.2). The most satisfactory method for the specific synthesis of the 3′—5′ interribonucleotide bond is that which involves the condensation (by a carbodi-imide) of a protected ribonucleoside-3′-phosphate (I) with a protected ribonucleoside (II) bearing the free 5′ —OH group. The most satisfactory protecting groups for the 2′ —OH (and the 3′ —OH in II) groups are acetyl or benzoyl groups (X in Fig. 8.50). These groups are also used to protect amino groups of the bases. At the end of the synthesis, the acetyl or benzoyl groups are removed by mild alkaline hydrolysis. The 5′ —OH group of the nucleotide component (I) is protected by a trityl $[(C_6H_5)_3C—]$ or substituted trityl group (i.e., Y in Fig. 8.50) which may be selectively removed by mild acidic hydrolysis. This facet allows for extension of the polyribonucleotide chain.

The objective of deoxyribonucleotide syntheses also largely pioneered by Khorana, has been much greater, namely the chemical synthesis of a model DNA molecule (a *gene*). The determination of the sequence of alanine t-RNA in 1964 provided the stimulus for this major undertaking. A DNA molecule was conceived in which one chain would have identical base sequence with this t-RNA and one chain would be complementary to it (allowing for the replacement of uracil with thymine and for the minor bases). The synthesis of each chain was carried out by

(a) the stepwise synthesis of small deoxyribonucleotides (three, four, and five units) by similar procedures to those in Fig. 8.50, and
(b) the joining of these into larger sections of up to twenty units.

These larger sections were then joined up making use of a *polynucleotide ligase* (this type of enzyme, discovered in 1967, joins together a 3′ terminal —OH to a 5′ terminal phosphate). Before the ligase action was used, sections of each of the *two* deoxyribonucleotide chains were hydrogen bonded together to form a DNA-like molecule on which the enzyme could act (Fig. 8.51). The complete synthesis of this, the first man-made gene, consisting of seventy-seven units in each chain, was finished in 1970. Unfortunately, this synthetic DNA molecule proved to be biologically inactive since it lacked the *promoter* and *terminator* regions of the gene. Furthermore, it was not then known that t-RNA molecules were produced in a larger precursor form, cf. polypeptide hormones, from which the biologically active t-RNA is formed. On the basis of the structure of the tyrosine precursor t-RNA of *Esch. coli*, another gene synthesis was started. The sequence of a DNA chain, complementary to the RNA, was

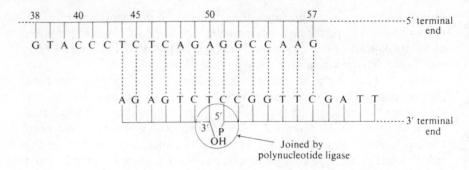

Fig. 8.51 The assembly of a central section of Khorana's model DNA of the t-RNA[Ala] gene (two fragments of seven and eleven units are hydrogen bonded to the twenty-unit section—residues 38–57—and joined by a polynucleotide ligase)

deduced and then the DNA chain complementary to the first. This double-stranded DNA molecule of 126 nucleotides was synthesized and was then used to deduce the sequence of promoter and terminator regions. Once these sequences were known, the whole molecule of length 207 nucleotides was made (Fig. 9.35) and it proved to be biologically active.

Bibliography

1. D. J. Shaw, *Introduction to Colloid and Surface Chemistry*, Butterworths, 1970.
2. A. G. Walton and J. Blackwell, *Biopolymers*, Academic Press, 1973.
3. H. I. Bolker, *Natural and Synthetic Polymers*, Marcel Dekker, 1974.
4. D. W. Jones, *Introduction to the Spectroscopy of Biological Polymers*, Academic Press, 1976.
5. A. Williams, *Introduction to the Chemistry of Enzyme Action*, McGraw-Hill, 1969.
6. W. Ferdinand, *The Enzyme Molecule*, Wiley, 1976.
7. J. H. Wilkinson, *Isozymes*, 2nd Edn, Chapman and Hall, 1970.
8. M. Dixon and E. C. Webb, *Enzymes*, 2nd Edn, Longmans, 1964.
9. *Enzyme Nomenclature*, 2nd Edn, Elsevier, 1973.
10. G. O. Aspinall, *Polysaccharides*, Pergamon, 1970.
11. J. L. Bailey, *Techniques in Protein Chemistry*, Elsevier, 1967.
12. D. T. Elmore, *Peptides and Proteins*, Cambridge UP, 1968.
13. F. Haurowitz, *The Chemistry and Function of Proteins*, Academic Press, 1963.
14. R. M. Evans, *The Chemistry of the Antibiotics used in Medicine*, Pergamon, 1965.
15. T. L. V. Ulbricht, *Introduction to Nucleic Acids and Related Products*, Oldbourne, 1966.
16. J. N. Davidson, *The Biochemistry of the Nucleic Acids*, 8th Edn, Chapman and Hall, 1976.
17. G. G. Brownlee, *Determination of Sequences in RNA*, North-Holland, 1972.

9. Chemical reactions in living organisms

9.1 METABOLIC PROCESSES

The chemical compounds in a living cell are in a constant state of change. A very large number of different reactions are occurring within the cell at any given moment, and the sum of these reactions is referred to as the cell's *metabolism*. These chemical reactions take place in a series of well regulated stages, and it is convenient to group the stages together to give a *metabolic pathway* for a particular compound.

In the past, there was a great reluctance to accept the idea that the activities of a living organism could be explained in chemical terms, mainly because so little was known of the structures of the components within a cell. It will be obvious from the content of the preceding chapters that a great deal of progress has been made in our understanding of the structures of the complex molecules of cells. This progress has been matched by equal advances in our understanding of the metabolic activity in cells. In this chapter, some of the more important and universal metabolic processes will be outlined.

A study of cell metabolism can be conveniently divided into two major processes: in the first place, there are those which are concerned with the breakdown of materials and the release of energy, and these are known as *catabolic processes*. Secondly, there are those processes by which materials are synthesized in the cell, and these are known as *anabolic* or *biosynthesis processes*. The division of metabolic processes in this way, while providing a useful classification for the student, must not be regarded as being rigid. Many of the intermediates produced in catabolic processes are used as intermediates in biosynthesis pathways. Thus, catabolic processes cannot be solely viewed in terms of the efficiency with which they release energy. The principal chemical pathways are now known for the catabolism and biosynthesis of almost all the important chemical compounds of the cell.

A common feature in all the diversity of metabolic processes is the efficiency with which they take place, and one should bear in mind the mild conditions of temperature and the neutrality of solution. Each stage of a metabolic pathway is catalysed by an enzyme, and this aspect of biochemistry is now receiving great attention. This interest stems in part from the fact that the complete structure of several enzymes is now known. In these cases it is possible to write a detailed mechanism for the whole process, explaining how the chemical changes in the substrate are brought about by interaction with certain functional groups in the active site of the enzyme (Fig. 8.24). In other cases, where the full structure of the enzyme is not known, considerable information may still be available regarding the structure of the active site and the processes taking place there.

In many metabolic reactions, it has been found that another co-factor is required in addition to the enzyme and substrate. These compounds have been termed coenzymes, and the structures of some of the most common have been described in chapter 7. Coenzymes, while possessing relatively complex structures, are very much smaller in molecular size than the protein enzyme molecules. Once again, as soon as the structure of a coenzyme became known, it was possible to explain their action in purely chemical terms. The transition state (Fig. 8.25a) in the case of a reaction involving a coenzyme is more complex, and consists of enzyme, coenzyme and substrate. The coenzyme acts as a reagent in the chemical process and becomes chemically changed. The enzyme provides the site for the reaction. Nevertheless, the coenzyme, like the enzyme, is present in only catalytic amounts, and an efficient process is always available for the regeneration of the coenzyme to its original state. Coenzymes are specific for a particular type of reaction—for example, oxidation or reduction —and relatively non-specific with respect to substrate. The specificity with regard to the latter is due to the enzyme.

Thus, much is now known not only about metabolic pathways in their entirety but also about the way in which individual stages take place. Much more, however, has yet to be discovered about the way in which the diverse chemical reactions of a cell are integrated with one another and how they are controlled; at the moment, only some general principles of this aspect of metabolism are known. Much of our knowledge of the way in which metabolism is controlled and regulated has come from a study of microorganisms— in particular, bacteria. These unicellular organisms are free from the complications that are present in higher organisms, due to interaction between cells. Two basic mechanisms have emerged; the first is control of enzymic activity through *allosteric inhibition* and *activation*. The second is regulation of the amount of enzyme produced, and this aspect is considered in section 9.5.

It has been one of the aims of this book to lead the reader to the stage where the reactions in a metabolic pathway are comprehensible in purely chemical terms, and in order to illustrate this a few of the universal metabolic pathways have been selected for discussion. These illustrate both catabolic and biosynthetic processes.

9.2 ENERGY PRODUCTION IN LIVING ORGANISMS THROUGH CARBOHYDRATE AND FAT CATABOLISM

9.2.1 Introduction

Carbohydrate catabolism occupies a central position in all metabolism, for it is by this process that a large part of the immediate energy requirements of the organism is supplied. As we have seen in chapter 8, a large proportion of the carbohydrate which occurs in nature serves as structural material. These carbohydrates are relatively inert, but under certain circumstances they can be broken down by microorganisms, and are then available as foodstuffs. Of much more importance from the point of view of catabolism in most plants and animals, for the supply of energy, are the *nutritional polysaccharides*: starch in plants and glycogen in animals. In special cases, oligosaccharides may also serve as major sources of carbohydrate. Lactose in milk and sucrose in certain plants are examples of this latter type of compound.

By comparison with carbohydrates, there is a much wider variety of structure found in lipids (see section 7.2). However, from the point of view of energy production, the most important lipids are the triglycerides (fats). These are particularly important in mammalian metabolism, and they constitute as much as 10 per cent of body weight. Large amounts of triglyceride are also found in certain plants, and particularly in their seed oils. The triglycerides in animals make up the principal *energy-storage materials*, and the average animal can store almost unlimited amounts of fat in this form. This has certain advantages over carbohydrate storage. Triglycerides are insoluble in aqueous tissue media, and thus do not disturb the osmolarity. Furthermore, they are richer in carbon and hydrogen than carbohydrates, so that there is more oxidizable material in a given weight of fat than in the same weight of carbohydrate. For example, 1 g of a typical fat has a heat of combustion of $-39 \cdot 0$ kJ ($-9 \cdot 3$ kcal), while the corresponding value for 1 g of carbohydrate is $-17 \cdot 6$ kJ ($-4 \cdot 2$ kcal).

The carbohydrates which are broken down in living systems to provide energy are for the most part made up of glucosyl units, and thus the catabolism of these units will be a principal topic of this section. This process operates either in the presence of oxygen (aerobically) or in the absence of oxygen (anaerobically). The object of catabolism is to release the free energy available in a glucosyl unit or in the hydrocarbon chains of fatty acids in a form the organism can use. Adenosine triphosphate (ATP) is the universal energy carrier, and in this section the formation of this compound and its relationship to the breakdown of carbohydrates and fats will be described. The further the breakdown proceeds, the greater is the energy available. The maximum amount of energy available can be obtained from thermochemical experiments, for example:

$$\text{(a)} \quad C_6H_{12}O_6 + 6O_2 \rightarrow 6CO_2 + 6H_2O \text{ (l)}$$

$$\Delta H^{\ominus} = -2815 \text{ kJ } (-673 \text{ kcal}); \Delta G^{\ominus} = -2871 \text{ kJ } (-686 \text{ kcal})$$

$$\text{(b)} \quad CH_3(CH_2)_{14}COOH + 23O_2 \rightarrow 16CO_2 + 16H_2O \text{ (l)}$$

$$\Delta H^{\ominus} = -10\,020 \text{ kJ } (-2398 \text{ kcal}); \Delta G^{\ominus} = -9780 \text{ kJ } (-2340 \text{ kcal}).$$

A cell, of course, would be unable to take up this energy if it were released in a single reaction, and in any case not all the free energy released is *trapped* in ATP molecules, some is available as heat.

There is considerable unity among living organisms in the principal reactions whereby carbohydrates and fats are degraded. In carbohydrate catabolism, the extent of the degradation varies. When the aerobic process occurs, as it does in animals, the complete breakdown to carbon dioxide and water takes place, and this represents the pathway which yields the maximum energy. In lower forms of life, which have to operate anaerobically, the degradation produces end products which still contain a large part of the free energy. For example, yeast produces ethanol:

$$C_6H_{12}O_6 \rightarrow 2C_2H_5OH + 2CO_2$$

$$2C_2H_5OH + 6O_2 \rightarrow 4CO_2 + 6H_2O \quad \Delta H^\oplus = -2736 \text{ kJ } (-653 \cdot 4 \text{ kcal});$$

$$\Delta G^\oplus = -2649 \text{ kJ } (-633 \cdot 6 \text{ kcal}).$$

9.2.2 Formation and degradation of the glucosyl unit to pyruvate

(a) *Formation of the glucosyl unit*   The glucose derivative which undergoes degradation is glucose-6-phosphate, and this arises either from polysaccharide or oligosaccharide sources. In both processes, cleavage of glycosidic bonds must take place. There are two types of enzymic reaction which do this: hydrolysis and phosphorolysis.

Glycosidic bonds are hydrolysed by the action of hydrolases (Fig. 9.1) with the addition of water across the bonds. The digestion of starch by Man and other animals involves this process. The enzymes available for this are the polysaccharidases (section 8.1.2), where the substrate has a high molecular weight, and the glycosidases, which catalyse the hydrolysis of low-molecular-weight substrates (oligosaccharides). Endo-amylase is found in animals and is present in the saliva and pancreas secretions, where it promotes the breakdown of starch. Exo-amylase, on the other hand, occurs mainly in plants, where it also catalyses the breakdown of starch.

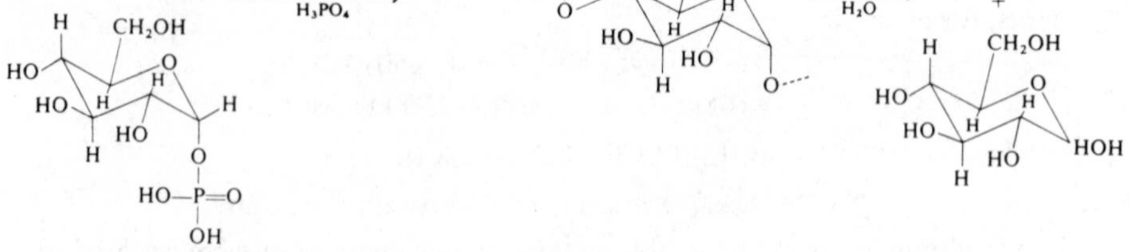

Fig. 9.1   Hydrolysis and phosphorolysis of a glycosidic bond

Several of the common glycosidases have already been mentioned in connection with their use in the structural analysis of oligosaccharides (see section 7.3.3). Glycosidases are present during digestion to complete the hydrolysis begun by the polysaccharidases. The enzyme maltase catalyses the hydrolysis of maltose. Oligo $\alpha(1 \rightarrow 6)$ glycosidase, which is also secreted by the intestinal mucosa, cleaves the $\alpha(1 \rightarrow 6)$ linkages in the fragments formed at chain-branch points. Other glycosidases that are of importance in animal digestion and also occur widely in microorganisms are: lactase, a $\beta(1 \rightarrow 4)$ galactosidase which catalyses the hydrolysis of lactose, and sucrase, an α-glucosidase which hydrolyses sucrose.

Phosphorolysis of glycosidic bonds is catalysed by phosphorylases. The products of these reactions are monosaccharide-1-phosphates, for example glucose-1-phosphate. While this is a reversible reaction, it must be emphasized that it does not represent a pathway for polysaccharide biosynthesis, but only for degradation (see section 9.3.4).

Since glucose-6-phosphate is the starting point for *further* catabolism, glucose produced in the hydrolysis reactions must be phosphorylated. Furthermore, processes must be available for the conversion of other monosaccharides into this key metabolite, and some of these processes are included in Fig. 9.2. Conversion of monosaccharides to their phosphate esters takes place through a process called phosphorylation, and involves transfer of a terminal phosphate group from ATP to the monosaccharide. Direct transfer to the —OH group at position 6 of a hexose takes place. The reaction is catalysed by a hexokinase. The hexokinases are a relatively non-specific group of enzymes, and catalyse a variety of hexose phosphorylations, including D-fructose, D-galactose and D-mannose. Magnesium ion is essential as a co-factor, and probably assists in binding ATP to the enzyme. Phosphorylations have a high negative free-energy value, and can be considered as irreversible.

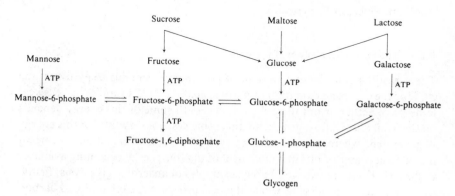

Fig. 9.2 Hydrolysis of disaccharides, phosphorylations and isomerizations

391

(b) Degradation of a glucosyl unit to pyruvate The principal route for the degradation of a glucosyl unit formed from poly- or oligosaccharides is known as the *Embden–Meyerhof–Parnas* pathway. This was originally deduced for the *fermentation process* but has since been shown to be a universal process with a variation of the final stages depending on the organism in which it occurs. For the purposes of this section, the stages from glucose-6-phosphate to pyruvate are discussed. An outline of the pathway is shown in Fig. 9.3, together with the enzyme involved in each stage. Many of the stages in this pathway have been studied in detail and suggestions regarding the mechanism of the catalytic action of the enzymes have been put forward. In this short section, however, it is possible only to point out a few of the more important aspects of the reactions:

(i) Any glucose-1-phosphate present (from phosphorolysis) isomerizes to glucose-6-phosphate. The latter isomerizes to fructose-6-phosphate, which in turn is phosphorylated at the expense of ATP. Phosphorylation reactions are virtually irreversible and this reaction drives the equilibrium in the direction of the degradation.

(ii) The cleavage of fructose-1,6-diphosphate by aldolase is a reversible reaction, and it is further complicated by the fact that the two products are themselves involved in a reversible interconversion. The equilibrium in the latter reaction lies well over in the direction of dihydroxyacetone monophosphate.

(iii) The oxidation of glyceraldehyde-3-phosphate by NAD^+ is a complex process in which an intermediate phosphate ester is established at the *oxidized carbon*, which then phosphorylates ADP.

(iv) The reversible isomerization of 3-phosphoglycerate to 2-phosphoglycerate is a reaction very similar to that between the two glucose phosphates. Dehydration of 2-phosphoglycerate produces an intermediate phosphate ester group which is of sufficient reactivity to phosphorylate ADP. The resulting 'enol' tautomerizes to pyruvate.

9.2.3 The further catabolism of pyruvate

There is still a considerable amount of free energy available in pyruvate; the $\Delta G^\ominus$ for the complete oxidation of pyruvic acid is -1141 kJ mole^{-1} (-273 kcal mole^{-1}). Whether or not the cell gains access to some of this energy depends on the availability of oxygen. In an anaerobic system, very little of this energy is generated, whereas in an aerobic system, complete oxidation to carbon dioxide and water results in a great deal of the free energy becoming available to the cell. There are two well known examples of anaerobic glycolysis: firstly, the fermentation process in which the end products are ethanol and carbon dioxide, and secondly the formation of lactate. The latter process takes place

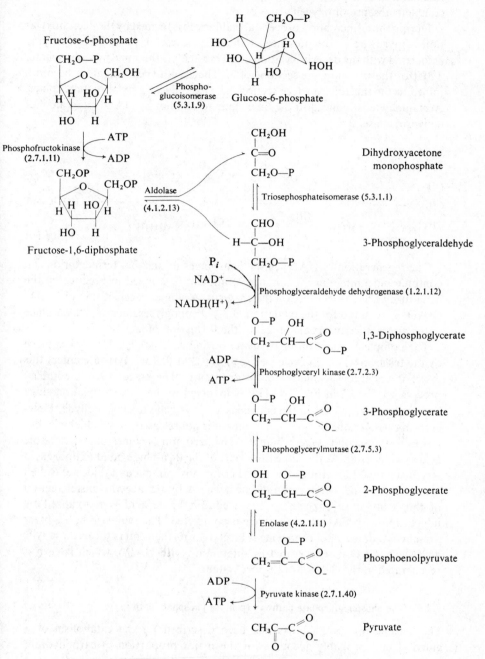

Fig. 9.3 The glycolysis pathway (Embden–Meyerhof–Parnas pathway)

in animal muscle and also in microorganisms which live in a limited or even complete absence of oxygen.

During the fermentation process, acetaldehyde is formed by the decarboxylation of pyruvate in the presence of the enzyme carboxylase. The coenzyme associated with the decarboxylation of α-keto acids is thiamine pyrophosphate, TPP (for the structure, see section 7.4.2). The carbonyl carbon atom becomes joined to the thiazole ring (see section 4.5.1) and decarboxylation takes place. Acetaldehyde is reduced in the final stage to ethanol by NADH and alcohol dehydrogenase.

The regeneration of NAD^+ in the final stages means that fermentation can continue indefinitely in the absence of air, but is stopped in practice by the denaturing effect of ethanol on the enzymes. A similar regeneration of NAD^+ (NAD^+ is required for the oxidation of 3-phosphoglyceraldehyde) takes place in the alternative anaerobic process—the formation of lactate.

The complete oxidation of pyruvate during aerobic glycolysis takes place by the tricarboxylic acid cycle (see section 9.2.6). Before pyruvate enters this cycle, it undergoes oxidative decarboxylation. The stages in this complex process are shown in Fig. 9.4. TPP is involved in the decarboxylation stage in a similar way to that in the conversion of pyruvate to acetaldehyde. However, in this case, the two-carbon fragment is not released as acetaldehyde, but passes to the second stage, where it is oxidized and becomes bound to lipoic acid as a thioester. At the same time, part of the disulphide bond of lipoic acid is reduced to a thiol group. The acetyl group now present as a thioester is then transferred to the —SH group of coenzyme A by the acetyl-transfer section of this multi-stage enzyme system. Reduced lipoic acid is re-oxidized by interaction with FAD, and the cycle is completed. The two-carbon fragment present as a thioester of coenzyme A (acetyl-CoA) then enters the tricarboxylic acid cycle. FAD is regenerated by interaction with NAD^+, which in turn is regenerated in the electron-transport system.

9.2.4 The phosphogluconate pathway (pentose phosphate pathway)

The aerobic process that has just been described for the catabolism of a glucosyl unit probably accounts for the major proportion of carbohydrate oxidized in most organisms. There are, however, alternative processes, one of

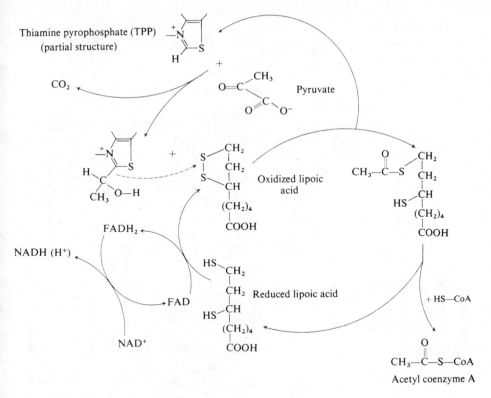

Thiamine pyrophosphate (TPP)
(partial structure)

CO₂

Pyruvate

Oxidized lipoic acid

FADH₂

NADH (H⁺)

FAD

Reduced lipoic acid

NAD⁺

+ HS—CoA

$CH_3-C-S-CoA$

Acetyl coenzyme A

Fig. 9.4   The oxidative decarboxylation of pyruvate

which, the phosphogluconate pathway, occurs widely. It has been estimated that 30 per cent of the glucosyl units may be catabolized by this route in micro-organisms and animal tissues, and in liver tissue the figure may be as high as 50 per cent. The reactions involved in this pathway are shown in Fig. 9.5. A feature of this scheme is that if the glucosyl units are produced through phosphorolysis (i.e., glucose-1-phosphate), then no ATP is required for the catabolism. Thus these reactions could occur in preference to glycolysis in cells with a low ATP concentration. Furthermore, it will be noticed that no ATP is produced directly in the cycle. On the other hand, each cycle produces two molecules of reduced coenzyme (NADPH) which, on oxidation, in the electron-transport system, yields ATP. Alternatively, the reduced coenzyme molecules may be utilized in biosynthesis.

In this cycle of reactions, a hexose molecule is converted to a pentose molecule through the decarboxylation of 3-keto-6-phosphogluconate. This compound has not, in fact, been isolated as a stable intermediate; it is, of

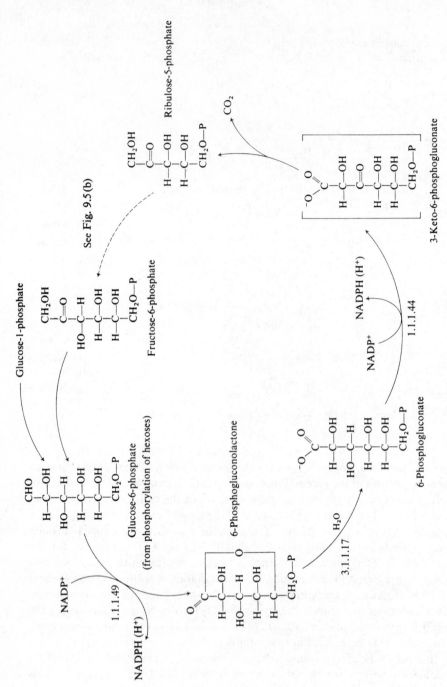

Fig. 9.5 (a) The phosphogluconate pathway

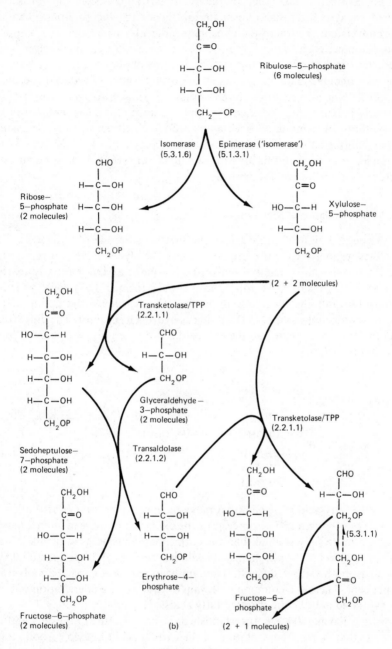

Fig. 9.5 (b) The interconversion of pentose to hexose sugars in the phosphogluconate pathway

397

course, a β-keto acid. Some of the pentose (ribulose-5-phosphate) is converted back to fructose-6-phosphate and hence to glucose-6-phosphate. In this conversion, *five* fructose-6-phosphate molecules arise from *six* ribulose-5-phosphate molecules [Fig. 9.5(b)]. This sequence of reactions involves intermediates similar to those of the pentose pathway of photosynthesis (Fig. 9.10). The phosphogluconate pathway is an important source of reduced coenzyme (NADPH) which is required in biosynthesis processes. Another aspect of the pathway is that it may be used to supply pentose molecules required in the biosynthesis of compounds such as nucleotide coenzymes and nucleic acids. Other intermediates in the pathway serve as precursors in biosynthesis; for example, certain organisms have the facility of converting 6-phosphogluconolactone to ascorbic acid (vitamin C).

9.2.5 The oxidation of triglycerides

In the degradation of triglycerides the first stage is one of hydrolysis. The enzymes responsible for this are the lipases. The glycerol which is released in the hydrolysis can be catabolized through a pathway linking it with carbohydrate catabolism. Glycerol-1-phosphate is formed by phosphorylation with ATP, and this is followed by the selective dehydrogenation of the secondary alcohol group, NAD^+ acting as hydrogen acceptor. The dihydroxyacetone monophosphate can then be oxidized by the normal glycolysis route (see section 9.2.2).

$$
\begin{array}{l}
CH_2O{-}\overset{\overset{O}{\|}}{C}{-}R \\
CH{-}O{-}\overset{\overset{O}{\|}}{C}{-}R \\
CH_2O{-}\overset{\overset{O}{\|}}{C}{-}R
\end{array}
\xrightarrow[H_2O]{Lipase}
\begin{array}{l}
CH_2OH \\
CHOH \\
CH_2OH \\
+ \\
3RCOOH
\end{array}
\xrightarrow[ATP \quad ADP]{}
\begin{array}{l}
CH_2OH \\
CHOH \\
CH_2O{-}P
\end{array}
\xrightarrow[NAD^+ \quad NADH\,(H^+)]{}
\begin{array}{l}
CH_2OH \\
C{=}O \\
CH_2O{-}P
\end{array}
$$

It is the fatty-acid molecules that make the more important contribution to the energy production. The process for the oxidation of these in animal tissues has been more fully studied than the corresponding process in plants. Mammalian fatty acids consist mainly of palmitic acid (C_{16}) 27 per cent and the C_{18} acids, both saturated (stearic) and unsaturated (oleic), make up a further 60 per cent. There is a common pathway for the stepwise degradation of both the saturated and the unsaturated fatty acids.

As long ago as 1904, Knoop established the basic feature of the degradation process; that is, the fragmentation of the carbon chain by two carbon atoms at a time. This became known as the *β-oxidation* theory, since Knoop concluded that the oxidation occurred at the carbon atom β to the carboxyl group. The full details of the process were discovered during the investigation of the role of coenzyme A in metabolism. The sequence of reactions for the removal of a two-carbon fragment is shown in Fig. 9.6.

The sequence of reactions starts with the formation of the fatty-acid ester of coenzyme A, a complex reaction in which a molecule of ATP is required.

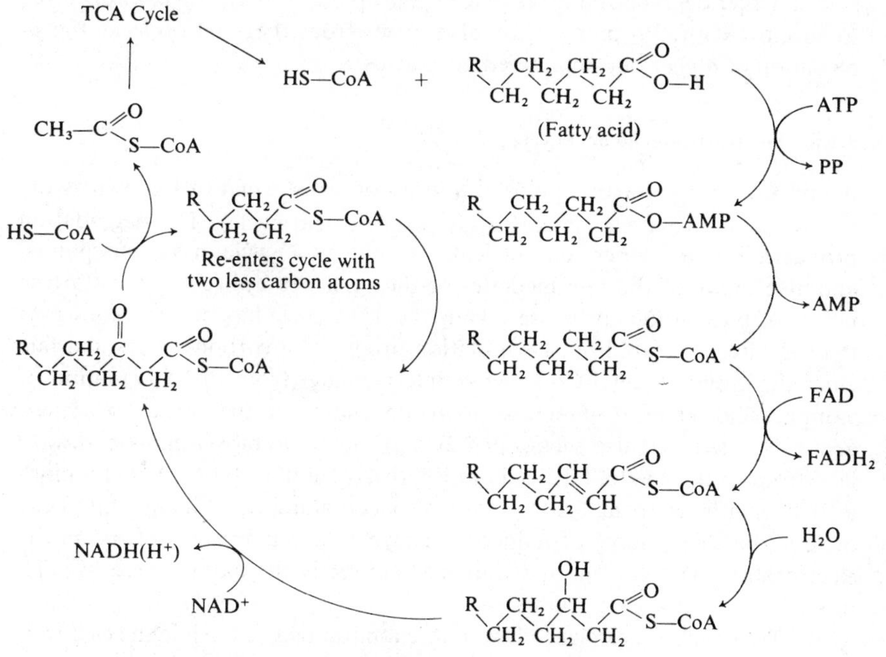

TCA Cycle

HS—CoA

CH_3—C $\diagup$ O, S—CoA

HS—CoA

R CH$_2$ C $\diagup$ O, S—CoA — CH$_2$ CH$_2$
Re-enters cycle with two less carbon atoms

O
R CH$_2$ C C $\diagup$ O, S—CoA — CH$_2$ CH$_2$ CH$_2$

NADH(H$^+$)

NAD$^+$

R CH$_2$ CH$_2$ C $\diagup$ O, O—H — CH$_2$ CH$_2$ CH$_2$
(Fatty acid)

ATP

PP

R CH$_2$ CH$_2$ C $\diagup$ O, O—AMP — CH$_2$ CH$_2$ CH$_2$

AMP

R CH$_2$ CH$_2$ C $\diagup$ O, S—CoA — CH$_2$ CH$_2$ CH$_2$

FAD

FADH$_2$

R CH$_2$ CH C $\diagup$ O, S—CoA — CH$_2$ CH$_2$ CH

H$_2$O

OH
R CH$_2$ CH C $\diagup$ O, S—CoA — CH$_2$ CH$_2$ CH$_2$

Fig. 9.6 β-Oxidation of fatty acids

Thereafter, the complete degradation takes place with no further demand for ATP. In the second stage, dehydrogenation with FAD as hydrogen acceptor introduces a double bond adjacent to the thio-ester group. The double bond is then hydroxylated to give a β-hydroxy thio-ester. Further oxidation yields a β-keto thio-ester; this time NAD$^+$ acts as hydrogen acceptor. Cleavage of the carbon chain takes place in the next stage, and at the *same time* a new thio-ester bond with coenzyme A is formed at the β carbon atom. The two-carbon fragment is released as acetyl-CoA and then undergoes complete oxidation in the TCA cycle. Repetition of the cycle results in the degradation of the entire fatty acid into acetyl-CoA molecules.

It is possible to accommodate unsaturated acids in this scheme, provided the double bond occurs in a position such that it may be hydroxylated directly. It is interesting to note that the Δ^9 bond of oleic acid is not so positioned.

Before oleic acid can be completely catabolized by β-oxidation, the double bond must either migrate or be hydrogenated.

Although the vast majority of fatty acids catabolized in nature are even-numbered, there are some species where odd-numbered fatty acids make up a large part of those available. Many of the intestinal microorganisms that are capable of degrading cellulose in the gut of herbivores produce propionic acid. Further degradation takes place via propionyl-CoA, which is converted to succinyl-CoA. Propionyl-CoA also arises from the final cycle of the β-oxidation of higher odd-numbered fatty acids.

9.2.6 The tricarboxylic acid cycle

Acetyl-CoA is the starting point of a series of transformations known as the tricarboxylic acid cycle (Krebs' cycle or citric-acid cycle). The degradation products of many other cell nutrients can enter the cycle at various points, and also many of the intermediates of the cycle are utilized as the starting points of biosynthesis processes. Thus the TCA cycle has become known as the *hub* of cell metabolism. Degradation products of carbohydrates and fats enter the cycle as acetyl-CoA; while intermediates from the degradation of α-amino acids enter at numerous points depending on the particular amino-acid side chain (see also section 9.4.2). Carbohydrate biosynthesis pathways lead from oxaloacetate, fatty-acid biosynthesis from acetyl-CoA and amino-acid biosynthesis from oxaloacetate or α-ketoglutarate. Finally, the TCA cycle is the chief source of reduced coenzymes which are re-oxidized in the electron-transport system, and thus it is indirectly the main source of ATP in a cell.

The TCA cycle takes place in the mitochondria of a cell, while the electron-transport system takes place simultaneously in the membrane structure. The stages of the TCA cycle are summarized in Fig. 9.7. The carboxylic acids are present as anions which interact with basic groups on the enzymes.

(i) The entry of acetyl-CoA into the cycle is controlled by an enzyme which catalyses the condensation of the acetyl group with oxaloacetate to produce citrate. This is a modified *aldol condensation* (see section 4.5.4). At the same time the thio-ester group is hydrolysed, releasing coenzyme A.

(ii) After the isomerization of citrate to isocitrate the first oxidation occurs, NAD^+ acting as hydrogen acceptor. A β-keto acid—oxalosuccinate—is produced as an unstable intermediate, and spontaneously decarboxylates, to give α-ketoglutarate.

(iii) α-Ketoglutarate undergoes oxidative decarboxylation by a process similar to that already described for pyruvate (see section 9.2.3). The intermediate succinyl-CoA is hydrolysed to succinate. This reaction is coupled to the synthesis of GTP, which in turn phosphorylates ADP.

(iv) Dehydrogenation of succinate with FAD produces fumarate (cf. dehydrogenation in β-oxidation). Fumarate is then hydroxylated to malate. In the final oxidation of the cycle, malate is converted back to oxaloacetate.

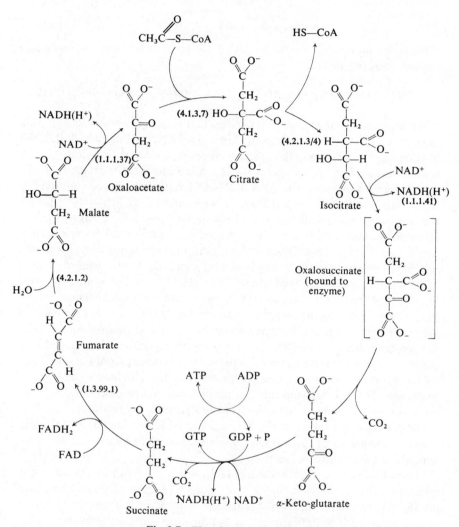

Fig. 9.7 The tricarboxylic acid cycle

9.2.7 The respiratory chain and the production of ATP

The basis of biological oxidation has already been described (see section 4.10.1 and section 5.4.5). The ultimate oxidizing agent of aerobic systems is molecular oxygen, and this acts by taking up four electrons [eq. (9.1)]. These electrons arise in the re-oxidation of the coenzymes reduced during the catabolism of carbohydrate and fat. In the presence of protons, water is formed [eq. (9.2)].

$$O_2 + 4e^- \rightarrow 2O^{2-} \tag{9.1}$$

$$O_2 + 4e^- + 4H^+ \rightarrow 2H_2O \tag{9.2}$$

This, of course, is analogous to the formation of water from hydrogen and oxygen gases [eq. (9.3)].

$$2H_2 + O_2 \rightarrow 2H_2O \text{ (l) } \Delta G^\ominus = -238 \text{ kJ mole}^{-1} (-57 \text{ kcal mole}^{-1}) \tag{9.3}$$

We have seen in the preceding sections that the usual biological oxidizing agent is NAD^+, and this leads to the formation of NADH in the cell. It is the NADH that is oxidized, though not directly, by oxygen, and there is a comparable amount of free energy made available to that shown for eq. (9.3). The potential difference of the $NAD^+/NADH$ system compared with oxygen is 1·14 V [corresponding to a $\Delta G^\ominus$ of -219 kJ mole^{-1} $(-52$ kcal mole$^{-1})$]. This is a very large amount of energy to become available in one stage of a biochemical process, and it is in fact released in a number of discrete stages. These stages make up a series of biological redox reactions known as the *respiratory chain*, and is an example of a biological electron-transport system.

These biological oxidations usually take place in the mitochondria membranes, and processes like the TCA cycle and fatty-acid oxidation are enzymically linked to the respiratory chain. The three major components of the respiratory chain are the pyridine nucleotide linked dehydrogenases, the flavoproteins and the cytochromes. These electron carriers are arranged in a chain of increasing redox potential, with electrons flowing from the substrates via the pyridine nucleotides and flavoproteins to the cytochromes and finally to oxygen. The link between the flavoprotein and cytochrome sections is via quinones, for example, ubiquinone (for the structure, see section 7.5.1). This reaction sequence is shown in Fig. 9.8, together with the redox potential scale. Many of the details of this complex system have still to be worked out, particularly in the cytochrome section.

Most of the free energy made available is trapped at *three* points in the respiratory chain, and is used in the synthesis of ATP from ADP and phosphate ion (P_i). Again the details of the reactions involved in this phosphorylation process have yet to be fully elucidated, but the quantitative relationship is well established. That is, for every electron pair passed through the complete electron-transport system shown in Fig. 9.8, *three* molecules of ATP are synthesized. It is on this basis that the general equation for the respiratory chain reactions may be written

$$NADH + H^+ + 3P_i + 3ADP + \tfrac{1}{2}O_2 \longrightarrow NAD^+ + 4H_2O + 3ATP$$

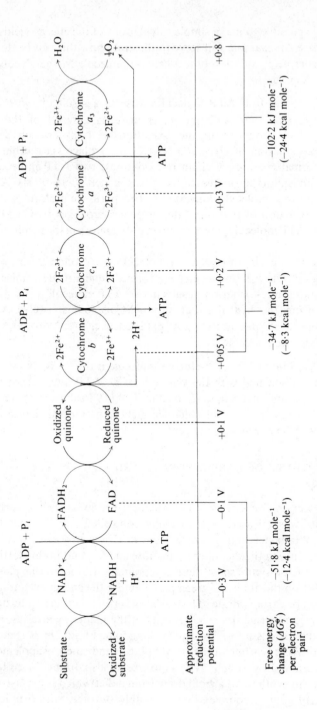

Fig. 9.8 The electron-transport system of the respiratory chain

The loss of electrons in the oxidation process results in the release of free energy, the amount of which is related to the change in redox potential by the equation:

$$\Delta G_7^{\ominus\prime} = -nF\,\Delta E_7^{\ominus\prime}$$

where n is the number of electrons transferred, F is a faraday and $\Delta E_7^{\ominus\prime}$ is the difference in the standard redox potentials of the reacting carriers.

[1] The loss of electrons in the oxidation process results in the release of free energy, the amount of which is related to the change in redox potential by the equation:

403

Furthermore, it is possible to make simple calculations of the energy yields of catabolic processes. An example will serve to illustrate how this can be done.

Consider the complete oxidation of a D-glucose molecule by the glycolysis pathway and TCA cycle.

(a) During glycolysis: four ATP molecules arise as a result of *substrate-linked* phosphorylation; four ATP molecules arise as a result of the re-oxidation of NADH produced in the oxidation of D-glyceraldehyde-3-phosphate (the re-oxidation of *glycolytic* NADH takes place via a different pathway from normal respiratory chain re-oxidation); two ATP molecules are used up in phosphorylation reactions, giving a nett yield of six ATP molecules per D-glucose molecule converted to two pyruvate molecules. The oxidative decarboxylation of two pyruvate molecules produces two NADH molecules, and six ATP molecules are formed on re-oxidation in the respiratory chain.

(b) During the TCA cycle: three NADH molecules are produced per cycle, and on re-oxidation nine ATP molecules are formed; one $FADH_2$ molecule is produced and this, on re-oxidation, results in two ATP molecules; one ATP molecule arises from the hydrolysis of succinyl-CoA. Thus, twelve ATP molecules are produced per acetyl-CoA oxidized, i.e. twenty-four ATP molecules per D-glucose molecule.

Thus, the total yield of ATP per D-glucose molecule is thirty-six. Now, the free-energy change associated with the synthesis of an ATP molecule at the concentration level found in a cell is $+37 \cdot 6$ kJ mole^{-1} ($+9$ kcal mole^{-1}). Thus, $36 \times +37 \cdot 6$ kJ of energy from a molecule of D-glucose is trapped; hence the efficiency is $(1360/2871) \times 100 = 47$ per cent.

9.3 THE BIOSYNTHESIS OF CARBOHYDRATE AND LIPID

9.3.1 Introduction

In the previous section, we saw how the chemical energy stored in carbohydrates and fats was released in a carefully controlled way so that the organism could obtain maximum benefit from it. These processes rely, of course, on the presence in the diet of carbohydrate and fat, and in this section we shall examine the biosynthesis of these compounds. All life on this planet depends ultimately on the ability of green plants to use the energy of sunlight in the biosynthesis of carbohydrate. This carbohydrate is then used not only to meet the energy and structural requirements of the plants themselves, but also as the principal foodstuff of the animal kingdom. Lipids, in particular fats, are formed from carbohydrate metabolites, and these supplement carbohydrate as an energy source. The converse is also found in certain organisms which can synthesize carbohydrate from a diet which is exclusively lipid. There are, of course, complex lipids, notably steroids, with a unique

404

physiological role, and the biosynthesis of these starts from metabolites common to carbohydrates and fats. The various sources of carbon and energy found in living organisms are summarized in Table 9.1, together with selected examples of particular groups of organism. Since the process of primary importance in the maintenance of all life is that associated with the fixation of CO_2 by photoautotrophes, using the energy source of sunlight, only this will be considered in detail.

Table 9.1   Classification of living organisms in terms of carbon source and energy source

Carbon sources

		Inorganic	Organic
Energy source	Radiative	*Photoautotrophes* CO_2 as carbon source. Sunlight as energy source. Examples: Eukaryotic algae, prokaryotic blue-green algae, higher plants and photosynthetic sulphur, containing purple and green bacteria	*Photoheterotrophes* Organic compounds as carbon source such as fatty acids, pyruvate and dicarboxylic acids. Sunlight as energy source. Examples: Photosynthetic purple non-sulphur-containing bacteria
	Chemical	*Chemoautotrophes* CO_2 as carbon source. Energy by oxidation of reduced inorganic sources such as: NH_3, NO_2^-, Fe^{2+}, H_2S, S, $S_2O_3^{2-}$, H_2. Examples: Bacteria such as hydrogen, nitrifying, sulphur oxidizing and iron bacteria	*Chemoheterotrophes* Wide variety of carbon sources, but principally carbohydrate and fat. Energy is obtained through degradation of these carbon sources (section 9.2). Examples: Protozoa such as amoeba, metazoa — multi-cellular animals including Man—fungi and bacteria

9.3.2   The biosynthesis of carbohydrates in green plants

The biosynthesis of carbohydrate takes place by a series of physical and chemical processes which enables atmospheric carbon dioxide to be converted by the energy of sunlight to carbohydrate. These processes may conveniently be divided into two parts:

(a) Photosynthesis. This is the term used to describe the process in which simple sugars (monosaccharides) are formed from carbon dioxide.

(b) Oligo- and polysaccharide biosynthesis. The simple sugars formed during photosynthesis are converted to larger molecules. Oligosaccharides such as sucrose are formed, but more often it is the polysaccharides such as cellulose and starch. Glycogen formation also occurs in animal tissue, and the process has certain similarities with the biosynthesis of branched-chain polysaccharides in plants.

(a) Photosynthesis The overall process of photosynthesis may be described by the equation which is the reverse of the oxidation of a glucose molecule:

$$6CO_2 + 6H_2O \text{ (l)} \rightarrow C_6H_{12}O_6 + 6O_2$$
$$\Delta G^\ominus = +2871 \text{ kJ mole}^{-1} (+686 \text{ kcal mole}^{-1})$$

The positive $\Delta G^\ominus$ value implies that this cannot be a spontaneous process, and much free energy is required. It has been shown by isotope-labelling studies that the molecular oxygen evolved during photosynthesis comes from water, while the oxygen of the carbon dioxide enters the carbohydrate.

$$6C^{16}O_2 + 6H_2^{18}O \rightarrow C_6H_{12}^{16}O_6 + 6^{18}O_2$$
$$6C^{18}O_2 + 6H_2^{16}O \rightarrow C_6H_{12}^{18}O_6 + 6^{16}O_2$$

Photosynthesis is made up of two well defined processes. In the first place there are the *dark reactions*. These form a series of enzyme-catalysed reactions which lead to the formation of hexose phosphates, for example, fructose-6-phosphate. The *dark reactions* are so named because they continue for a time after sunlight illumination has ceased. Secondly, there are the *light reactions*, where the energy available in sunlight is trapped by the plant and converted to a form of energy the cell can use, namely ATP. Furthermore, a study of photosynthesis shows that it is a reduction process in which reduced coenzymes, such as NADPH, are formed and used up. The *light reactions* provide a process for the regeneration of reduced coenzymes. The *dark reactions* will be described first in order to ascertain the exact energy requirements of photosynthesis.

(i) The dark reactions This sequence of reactions was elucidated by Calvin, using isotopic-labelling techniques. Suspensions of *Chlorella*, a green alga, were exposed to short periods of illumination in the presence of $^{14}CO_2/^{12}CO_2$. Samples were removed and, after the enzymes had been denatured by ethanol, the metabolites were separated chromatographically and detected by auto-radiography. Labelled carbon atoms (^{14}C) were found to be present at position 1 in 3-phosphoglycerate; after a longer illumination, the C_3 and C_4 positions of hexoses contained ^{14}C.

Calvin proposed that the carbon dioxide acceptor is ribulose-1,5-diphosphate in its *enol* form. An unstable intermediate is formed, which is cleaved enzymically to give two molecules of 3-phosphoglycerate. The 3-phosphoglycerate is next phosphorylated at the expense of ATP and then reduced to 3-phosphoglyceraldehyde, NADPH acting as hydrogen donor. The major

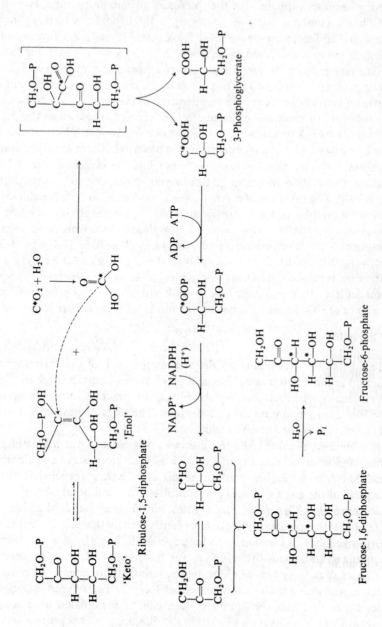

Fig. 9.9 Chemical reactions in the fixation of carbon dioxide

407

part of the 3-phosphoglyceraldehyde so formed isomerizes to dihydroxy-acetone monophosphate. In the presence of aldolase these two triose phosphates combine to give fructose-1,6-diphosphate, which is in turn hydrolysed to fructose-6-phosphate. These latter stages are a reversal of the glycolysis process described in section 9.2.2. The way in which the hexoses become labelled with ^{14}C (C^*) supports this sequence of reactions (see Fig. 9.9).

The process as described in Fig. 9.9 is at the moment incomplete, since no provision has been made for the regeneration of the ribulose-1,5-diphosphate. The sequence of reactions by which this is achieved is known as the pentose pathway. This is a reversible series of transfer and isomerization reactions by which hexoses and pentoses become interconverted. There are three transfer reactions. Two are *transketolase* reactions (T-K 1 and T-K 2, Fig. 9.10), in which a two-carbon fragment is transferred; the coenzyme responsible for this is TPP. The third transfer reaction is a condensation between dihydroxy-acetone monophosphate (isomerized from 3-phosphoglyceraldehyde) and erythrose-4-phosphate. The pentoses—xylulose-5-phosphate and ribose-5-phosphate—can both isomerize to ribulose-5-phosphate (I-1 and I-2 respectively, Fig. 9.10). Ribulose-5-phosphate is phosphorylated by ATP to regenerate ribulose-1,5-diphosphate. In order to obtain the energy require-ments of the dark reactions, the overall equation for the fixation of six molecules of CO_2 by six molecules of ribulose-1,5-diphosphate is derived:

$$6CO_2 + 6H_2O + 18ATP + 12NADPH \rightarrow$$
$$1(\text{fructose-6-P}) + 12NADP^+ + 18ADP + 17P_i$$

This equation is obtained on the assumption that all the carbon dioxide taken up is converted to a hexose, and takes into account the regeneration of six molecules of ribulose-1,5-diphosphate. In practice, other compounds arise, for example, amino acids and lipids. The yield of hexose is normally only a fraction of the possible yield.

(*ii*) *The light reactions*   Photosynthesis takes place in the leaves of green plants, and in unicellular organisms such as blue-green algae and photosyn-thetic bacteria. In higher plants, the pigment system responsible for the 'trapping' of the energy of sunlight is localized into cell organelles of definite structure called *chloroplasts*. Prokaryotes, on the other hand, like blue-green algae, have the pigment system dispersed through the cell in a relatively unorganized way. It was shown as long ago as 1937 by Hill that the chemical reaction brought about by radiation was basically a reduction process, and that in an *in vitro* system of chloroplasts, illumination caused the reduction of ferric ion with simultaneous release of oxygen. The oxygen comes from water molecules, and the light reactions can be formulated as a separate process in which no fixation of carbon dioxide occurs. This process includes the photolysis of water, and is known as the *Hill reaction*:

$$A + H_2O \xrightarrow{\ hv\ } AH_2 + \tfrac{1}{2}O_2$$

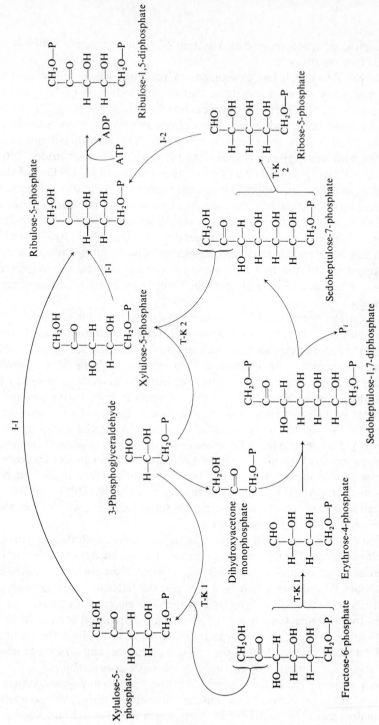

Fig. 9.10 The pentose pathway of photosynthesis

This simple equation represents a system of great complexity which is still under extensive study.

It is possible to suggest a sequence of reactions which fulfils the basic requirements of the light reactions, that is the production of ATP and the regeneration of NADPH. This process involves the *photosynthetic pigments*, the most important of which are chlorophylls *a* and *b* (for the structures, see section 7.4.2), which are found in all plants. The chlorophyll molecules, together with other pigments (auxiliary pigments), are concentrated within the chloroplasts in small bodies known as *grana*. It is the function of these pigments to collect the radiant energy and transfer it to the site of the photochemical reaction. It is now thought that two separate pigment systems (A and B) are present, and each has its own reaction centre to which the radiant energy is channelled. The reaction centres contain chlorophyll molecules which are closely associated with molecules capable of electron transport. The operation of the two light-trapping systems, designated as pigment systems A and B in Fig. 9.11, have different roles and are best considered separately.

In pigment system A, which contains chlorophyll *a* in the reaction centre, radiant energy of the red region [657 nm (mμ)] causes excitation of an electron. Electron transfer occurs with the formation of a reducing species A^- and an oxidizing species A^+. An electron is then transferred from A^- to oxidized ferredoxin, a nonheme iron protein. The electron may then return to the chlorophyll *a* molecule via an electron-transport system. In the passage of electrons through this electron-transport system, the free energy released is partially conserved by the synthesis of ATP from ADP and inorganic phosphate (P_i). This process for ATP production is called *cyclic photophosphorylation*. An alternative and more common process is the interaction of the reduced ferredoxin molecules, in pairs, with a pyridine nucleotide system. This produces coenzymes (NADPH) from oxidized coenzymes ($NADP^+$). The protons required for this process come from the photolysis of water, which takes place in conjunction with pigment system B.

Pigment system B, which operates at shorter wavelength (higher energy), contains chlorophyll *b* in its reaction centre. Radiant energy brings about the formation of an oxidizing species B^+ by transfer of an electron to form B^-. The species B^+ oxidizes a hydroxyl ion, and the latter decomposes with the formation of molecular oxygen and water. The electron transferred to B^- returns to pigment system A via the *same* chain of electron carriers as those participating in cyclic photophosphorylation. In this way, both the synthesis of ATP and the regeneration of the reduced coenzymes can take place simultaneously. This is referred to as *non-cyclic photophosphorylation*.

The free energy released in the return of the electron to pigment system A via a cytochrome system, and used in the phosphorylation of ATP, is a situation analogous to the electron-transport system found in cell mitochondria,

410

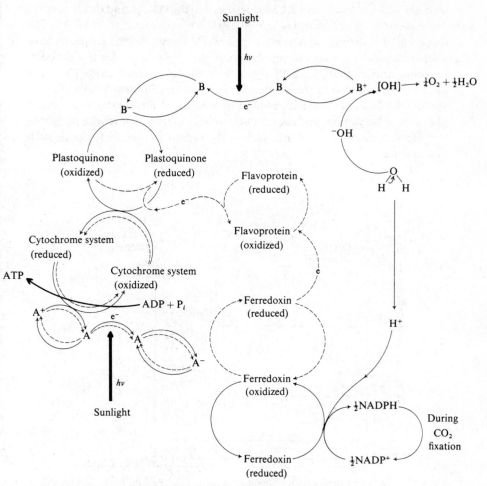

Fig. 9.11 The electron-flow diagram of the light reactions of photosynthesis
– – – – flow of electrons in the cyclic photophosphorylation process.
————— flow of electrons in the non-cyclic photophosphorylation process, where the electron lost in pigment system A is returned via electron transport from pigment system B.

which was described in section 9.2.7. The overall equation for the formation of ATP and NADPH is

$$2H_2O + 2NADP^+ + 2ADP + 2P_i \rightarrow O_2 + 2NADPH + 2H^+ + 2ATP$$

This equation represents only the system found in higher plants. In more lowly organisms, such as bacteria, only parts of the process are accomplished. Bacterial photosynthesis proceeds with no evolution of oxygen. As we have

411

seen, the oxygen results from the oxidation of hydroxyl ion, and this is coupled via non-cyclic photophosphorylation with the reduction of $NADP^+$. The oxidation of hydroxyl ion requires considerable energy, and hence plants have a separate pigment system to supply energy (from blue light) for this purpose. It would appear that the inability of bacteria to produce oxygen in their photosynthesis is due to the absence of this system from their photosynthetic apparatus. Thus, in bacterial photosynthesis, ATP arises only from cyclic photophosphorylation, and the production of NADPH requires the participation of a separate electron donor such as H_2, H_2S or an organic molecule such as succinate.

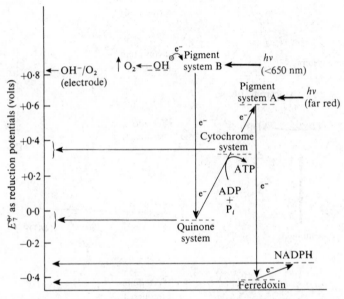

Fig. 9.12 Electrode potentials and simplified electron flow diagram for photosynthesis in higher plants, showing only non-cyclic photosynthetic phosphorylation

The electrode potentials of the well-established participants in the photosynthesis system of higher plants are shown in Fig. 9.12. The electrons required for the reduction of $NADP^+$ must be associated with a sufficiently negative reduction potential; the value of $E_7^{\ominus\prime}$ for $NADP^+$ is -0.32 V, and direct transfer from chlorophyll a does not take place. The discovery of ferredoxin with a remarkably low potential ($E_7^{\ominus\prime} = -0.42$ V) provided the missing link. This compound has the lowest potential of the species in the photosynthesis system, and is the immediate acceptor of an electron from chlorophyll a. The difference in overall potential for the whole process is greater than 1.3 V, which represents an amount of energy considerably in excess of that available

412

from a single quantum of the blue light absorbed by pigment system B. The electrons from both pigment systems flow in the same direction, that is to a more negative potential.

(b) Polysaccharide biosynthesis The hexose phosphates which are formed during photosynthesis isomerize to glucose-1-phosphate. The process for the formation of the polysaccharide in plants then follows a pathway quite similar to that found in mammalian tissues for the synthesis of glycogen. The glucosyl residue becomes attached to a nucleoside diphosphate. In the case of starch biosynthesis it is ADP and in mammalian glycogen biosynthesis it is UDP (for the structure, see section 7.4.2):

$$\text{Glucose-1-phosphate} + \text{BTP} \rightarrow \text{BDPG} + \text{pyrophosphate}$$

where 'BTP' represents the nucleoside triphosphate, e.g., ATP or UTP and 'BDPG' the nucleoside diphosphate glucose, e.g., ADPG or UDPG.

It has been found that small amounts of branched-chain polysaccharide exert a catalytic effect on the polymerization when added to the substrate and synthetase solution. The explanation of the role of a molecule of a poly-saccharide as a *primer* is that the enzyme catalyses the condensation of the nucleoside diphosphate glucose molecules with non-reducing chain end-groups in the primer molecule. The efficiency of the primer is related to the degree of chain branching, and thus a straight-chain polysaccharide, such as amylose, has little *priming* activity. Nevertheless, in the complete absence of primer, an $\alpha(1\rightarrow4)$ amylose-type chain is produced. In order to produce a branched-chain polysaccharide, *branching enzyme* is required. This enzyme catalyses the transfer of short sections of $\alpha(1\rightarrow4)$ linked units from the ends of the newly formed chains to inner glucosyl residues. These sections are then joined by $\alpha(1\rightarrow6)$ linkages. An enzyme—*Q-enzyme*—has been isolated from plants which, by this type of action, converts amylose to amylopectin.

The energy necessary for the formation of the $\alpha(1\rightarrow4)$ glycosidic bonds is supplied directly through the participation of the *high-energy* nucleoside triphosphates (ATP and UTP).

9.3.3 The biosynthesis of carbohydrates in animals

(a) Glucogenesis Animals cannot synthesize carbohydrate from such a simple precursor as carbon dioxide, nevertheless synthesis of hexose sugars takes place, notably in the liver, and these accumulate as glycogen. The principal precursor for this process is lactate formed during anaerobic glycolysis in muscle and transported by the blood to the liver. The pathway whereby lactate is converted back to glucose-6-phosphate is known as gluco-genesis and much of the pathway is common with that of glycolysis (Fig. 9.3). However, two stages arise which are quite different, and these stages represent

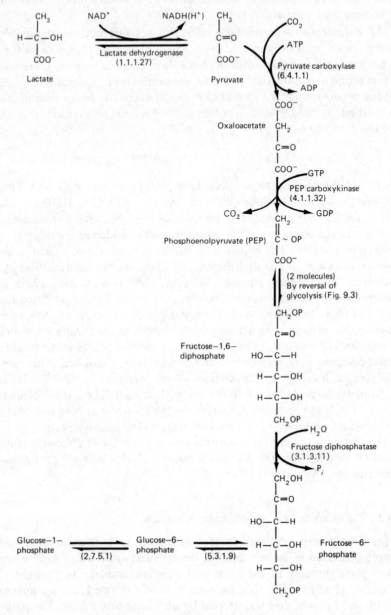

Fig. 9.13 Glucogenesis in mammalian liver

414

control points of the two pathways so that no competition occurs (see section 9.3.4).

Glucogenesis (Fig. 9.13) starts with oxidation of lactate back to pyruvate which is then converted in a two-stage reaction to phosphoenolpyruvate. This conversion is quite different from the corresponding single stage in glycolysis. Carbon dioxide bound to biotin is added to pyruvate (the mechanism of this carboxylation is similar to that shown in Fig. 9.18) to give oxaloacetate which then decarboxylates, with the incorporation of phosphate, to give phosphoenolpyruvate. The energy requirement in the two stages is equivalent to two ATP molecules. From two molecules of phosphoenolpyruvate formed in this way, fructose-1,6-diphosphate is synthesized by reversal of the corresponding reactions of glycolysis. At this point, an irreversible stage in the glycolysis pathway arises and the second distinct stage of glucogenesis takes place. Fructose-6-phosphate is formed by hydrolysis of fructose-1,6-diphosphate with fructose diphosphatase. Isomerization of

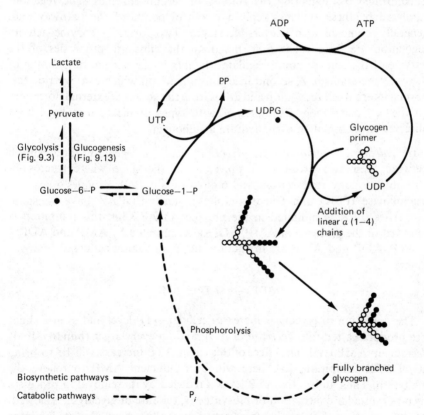

Fig. 9.14 Formation of glycogen after glucogenesis showing relationships with the corresponding catabolic pathways

415

fructose-6-phosphate to glucose-6-phosphate and glucose-1-phosphate then follows.

(b) *Glycogen synthesis* Glycogen is formed from glucose-1-phosphate by a mechanism comparable to the formation of the amylopectin fraction of starch in plants (see section 9.3.2). The donor of the glucosyl residues to 'primer' glycogen is UPDG and these residues are added to the many non-reducing chain-end groups. Linear $\alpha(1-4)$ linked glucose chains are built up and then branching is achieved through the action of amylo-1,6-transglucosidase which transfers sections of the $\alpha(1-4)$ linked chains to the '6' positions of interior glucosyl residues (Fig. 9.14).

9.3.4 Control mechanisms occurring in carbohydrate metabolism

Once the enzymes required in a metabolic pathway have been synthesized and the sequence of reactions is proceeding, the rate of flux along the pathway is controlled by regulating the activity of certain enzymes. The reactions catalysed by these enzymes represent control points of the pathway and, generally, coincide with irreversible stages. Two forms of enzyme activity regulation are found. The first, based on the allosteric properties of the enzyme of the control point, regulates the flux in the normal functioning of the cell's metabolism. A second mechanism is found which can override this normal internal cell regulation and arises from the action of external hormones on the cell membrane. Examples of both types of mechanism have been observed in mammalian carbohydrate metabolism.

(*i*) *Allosteric regulation of glycolysis and glucogenesis* Competition between these two processes is prevented at the stage where fructose-6-phosphate is converted to fructose-1,6-diphosphate. Both enzymes, phosphofructokinase (PFK) and fructose diphosphatase (FDPase) have allosteric properties. PFK is inhibited in the presence of ATP but this inhibition is removed in the presence of AMP. FDPase is inhibited by AMP and ADP.

ATP, ADP and AMP are in equilibrium in a reaction catalysed by myokinase:

$$2ADP \rightleftharpoons ATP + AMP$$

The operation of glycolysis increases cellular ATP level and even a slight rise produces a ten-fold *decrease* in ADP and an even larger (hundred-fold) *decrease* in AMP level. The effect of this slight ATP increase will be to bring about PFK inhibition, for there will be insufficient AMP to relieve the inhibition. Thus, unless the ATP level is reduced by its removal in processes such as muscular contraction or biosynthesis, the rate of glycolysis is slowed. At the same time, FDPase becomes active due to the removal of its inhibitor AMP and glucogenesis can proceed.

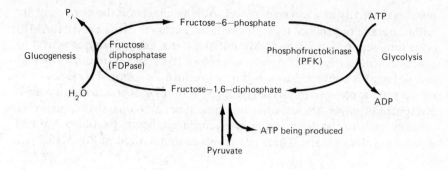

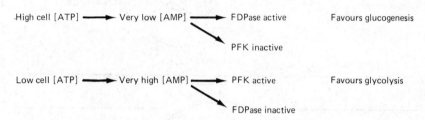

Fig. 9.15 Allosteric regulation of glycolysis and glucogenesis

Conversely, when a slight fall in ATP level occurs, a large increase in AMP is quickly produced and the ATP inhibition of PFK is removed and glycolysis operates to restore the ATP level. The increase in AMP brings about inhibition of FDPase. This sequence of changes is summarized in Fig. 9.15.

(*ii*) *Hormonal regulation of carbohydrate metabolism* The most fully elucidated system of hormonal control of metabolism is the process of glycogen mobilization. Several hormones are involved and their roles may be summarized as follows:

(a) Adrenalin, released from the adrenal medulla, stimulates the breakdown of glycogen to lactate in muscle to produce ATP for contraction and glycogen to glucose-1-phosphate in liver to elevate blood-sugar levels or start glycolysis. A comparable effect arises from noradrenalin in liver but not in muscle.
(b) The polypeptide hormone glucagon (structure, see section 8.4.3) secreted by the α-cells of the pancreas promotes breakdown of glycogen in liver causing a rise in blood-sugar level. On the other hand, the polypeptide hormone insulin secreted by the β-cells of the pancreas lowers blood-sugar levels by increasing the transport of glucose into muscle and inhibiting glucogenesis in liver.

The mechanism of the action of adrenalin is known in some detail and, at the present moment, represents the best example of the interpretation of

417

hormonal activity at a molecular level. Adrenalin acts on the exterior of the cell membrane to produce the 'intra-cellular' hormone cyclic-cAMP (cAMP) (structure, see section 7.4.1). cAMP initiates a sequence of enzyme activating processes within the cell cytoplasm whereby a less active form of phosphorylase (b-form) is converted to a highly active form (a-form). This leads to an increase in the phosphorolysis of glycogen (section 9.2.2) producing glucose-1-phosphate in larger amounts. At the same time, a comparable sequence of changes leads to the deactivation of glycogen synthetase (section 9.3.3) and glycogen synthesis stops. These processes are summarized in Fig. 9.16.

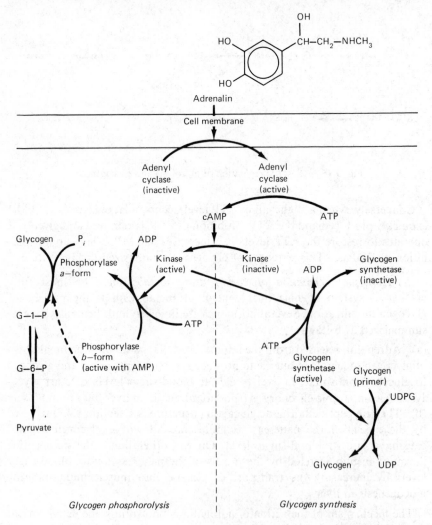

Fig. 9.16 Adrenalin control of glycogen synthesis and phosphorolysis

This hormonal control mechanism overrides the normal control of glycogen phosphorolysis arising from the activity of phosphorylase b. In the absence of adrenalin control, this form of the enzyme is subject to allosteric regulation being active only in the presence of AMP. Thus when cellular ATP level falls, AMP level is high and phosphorolysis of glycogen proceeds to produce glucose-1-phosphate which enters an active glycolysis pathway (PFK is active at high AMP levels). When the ATP level is sufficiently high, AMP level is very low and both phosphorylase b and PFK are inactive.

Since glycolysis could be started from free glucose, a further control point is present in the phosphorylation (by ATP) of the free sugar. The product, glucose-6-phosphate, at high concentration, inhibits hexokinase.

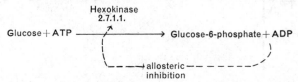

(*iii*) *Control points of carbohydrate metabolism* Both glycolysis and glucogenesis are linked to the TCA cycle and several control points, mainly allosteric in nature, have been identified in this part of metabolism. ATP inhibits the oxidative decarboxylation of pyruvate while acetyl-CoA activates the first reactions of glucogenesis. Thus, in periods of low ATP demand, surplus lactate is channelled via pyruvate into glucogenesis. Two control points arise in the TCA cycle itself. The enzyme, citrate synthetase, which catalyses the entry of acetyl-CoA into the cycle, is inhibited at high ATP levels and, during periods of high ATP level, flux through the cycle is slowed. The second control point involves isocitrate dehydrogenase whose activity is subject to regulation by a number of effectors. ATP and NADH inhibit the activity of this enzyme, while ADP and NAD^+ activate it. This provides a direct link with the electron-transport system since, in periods of ATP sufficiency, NADH level will also be high and there will be no need for TCA cycle or the electron-transport system to be operating at a high rate. On the other hand, in periods of ATP demand, ATP synthesis by the electron-transport system is coupled to reoxidation of NADH; this raises NAD^+ level and TCA cycle becomes active again. The principal allosteric effectors of carbohydrate metabolism are summarized in Fig. 9.17.

9.3.5 The biosynthesis of fatty acids

The biosynthesis of fatty acids has been closely studied owing to their importance in nutrition, and also since they make up part of the structure of most lipids. It is only in recent years that the concept that biosynthesis processes were the exact reverse of the corresponding catabolic processes has

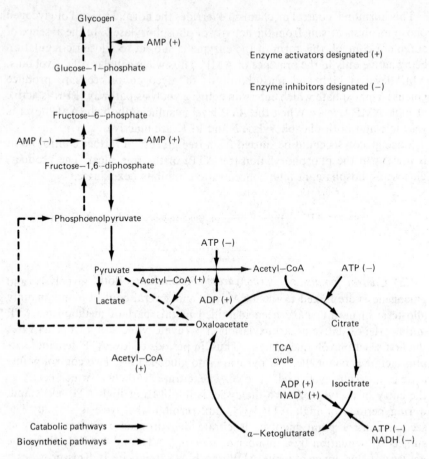

Fig. 9.17 Summary diagram of the principal control points of carbohydrate metabolism

been finally abandoned. This concept arose because of the emphasis placed on reversibility of enzymic reactions, and not enough account was taken of thermodynamic considerations. Thus, as we have just seen, glycogen biosynthesis proceeds by a different route to the reversible phosphorolysis process found in glycogen catabolism. The biosynthesis of fatty acids takes place in both plants and animals by a pathway which is different from the catabolic process—β-oxidation. Nevertheless, the basic feature of the biosynthesis process, like that of the catabolic one, is the use made of *two-carbon units*; this time, it is the stepwise addition of these units. Thus, the vast majority of naturally occurring fatty acids contain an even number of carbon atoms (see Table 7.2).

The donor of the two-carbon unit is malonyl-coenzyme A (malonyl-CoA). This intermediate is formed in a carboxylation reaction with acetyl-CoA. The carbon dioxide donor is an enzyme-bound biotin complex in which the biotin molecule is bound to the enzyme as an amide of a lysyl residue in the latter. Malonyl-CoA produces a more reactive nucleophile than acetyl-CoA (see section 4.7.3) and this favours the biosynthesis process, since the self-condensation of acetyl-CoA is an easily reversible process.

In yeast, the complete synthesis of a long-chain fatty acid is accomplished by a *multi-enzyme complex* which may be isolated as a homogeneous protein of molecular weight $\sim 2 \cdot 3 \times 10^6$. This complex consists of seven different proteins, one for each of the different types of reaction in the biosynthesis process. There appear to be three of each protein, giving a total of twenty-one sub-units of average molecular weight 100 000. Unfortunately, it has not been possible to isolate any of the individual components without denaturation. Thus, studies on the individual stages have been carried out on *Esch. coli*, where the enzymes may be fractionated and characterized. The stages may be summarized as follows. The malonyl residue becomes bound to a thiol group of an enzyme molecule as a thio-ester, and then condenses with an enzyme-bound acetyl group, releasing carbon dioxide. The acetoacetyl unit which is formed remains bound to an enzyme. This sequence of reactions is shown in Fig. 9.18. The acetoacetyl group then undergoes successively hydrogenation, dehydration and a second hydrogenation to give a saturated hydrocarbon (C_4) unit. These latter stages are a reversal of the corresponding stages of β-oxidation (Fig. 9.6). The hydrogen donor in the first hydrogenation is

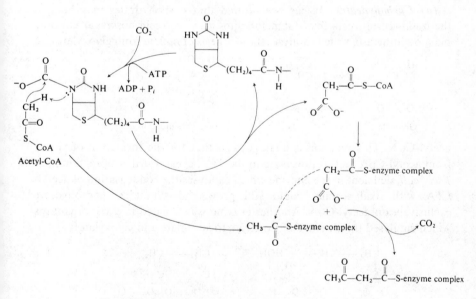

Fig. 9.18 Formation of a C_4 unit in fatty-acid biosynthesis

421

NADPH and in the second $FMNH_2$. The latter is itself produced by the hydrogenation of FMN by NADPH.

The four-carbon unit formed in the first cycle condenses with another malonyl group. The sequence of reactions is repeated to yield a saturated six-carbon unit. Further cycles take place until chains of sixteen or eighteen carbon atoms are formed. The overall equation for the formation of stearic acid, for example, would be:

$$Acetyl\text{-}CoA + 8Malonyl\text{-}CoA + 16NADPH \rightarrow$$
$$CH_3(CH_2)_{16}COOH + 16NADP^+ + 8CO_2 + 9CoA\text{---}SH + 7H_2O$$

The C_{18} unsaturated acids occur widely in living organisms, and oleic acid makes up a large part of animal and plant fat. Certain unsaturated acids, such as linoleic and α-linolenic, cannot be synthesized in animals but are produced in plants. The most general process for the formation of unsaturated acids is by the dehydrogenation of a saturated acid. It has been found that stearic acid is converted to oleic acid. In this process, stearic acid is bound as a thio-ester to a protein carrier and the enzyme catalysing the dehydrogenation requires $NADP^+$ as coenzyme. The reaction is stereospecific, producing only the *cis* isomer. (Dehydrogenation by the pyridine nucleotide coenzymes occurs from one side of the nicotinamide ring.) Oleic acid can be considered as the precursor of the other unsaturated fatty acids.

9.3.6 The biosynthesis of carbohydrate and lipids from acetyl-CoA

(a) Carbohydrates It has been found that carbohydrates may be synthesized in certain cells from fat metabolites. *Esch. coli* cells possess an enzyme, malate synthetase, which catalyses the synthesis of malate from glyoxylate and

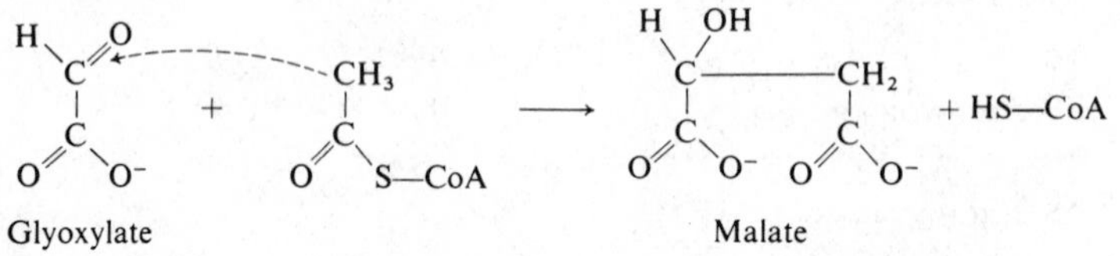

Glyoxylate   Malate

acetyl-CoA. This reaction is analogous to that for the formation of citrate from acetyl-CoA and oxaloacetate in the TCA cycle. Furthermore, a mutant *Esch. coli*, deficient in the enzyme which catalyses the condensation of acetyl-CoA with oxaloacetate, could still grow and synthesize carbohydrate exclusively on acetyl-CoA. Another enzyme was isolated in these organisms which catalysed the cleavage of isocitrate to succinate and glyoxylate:

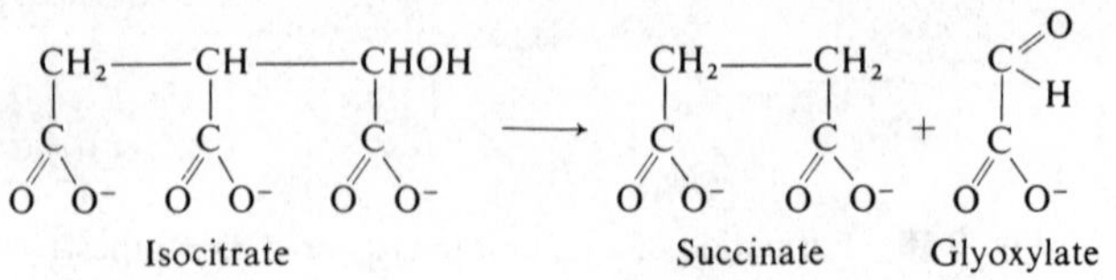

Isocitrate   Succinate   Glyoxylate

422

These discoveries led, in 1957, to a proposal that there was an alternative process to the TCA cycle for the production of oxaloacetate for biosynthesis purposes and which, at the same time, produced succinate to maintain the operation of the TCA cycle. This sequence of reactions is known as the *glyoxylate cycle* (Fig. 9.19). The enzymes required for the cycle have not been found in mammalian tissue, but occur in organisms where acetyl-CoA is the chief source of carbon. There is no pathway known in Man for glucose synthesis at the expense of fatty acid. These organisms, such as plant seedlings and certain microorganisms, use fatty-acid oxidation as a principal energy source. Oxaloacetate is the key intermediate in these organisms for the biosynthesis of carbohydrate via phosphoenolpyruvate, and also for certain amino acids. In mammals, additional supplies of oxaloacetate are supplied from pyruvate by the addition of carbon dioxide from a biotin–enzyme complex (Fig. 9.13).

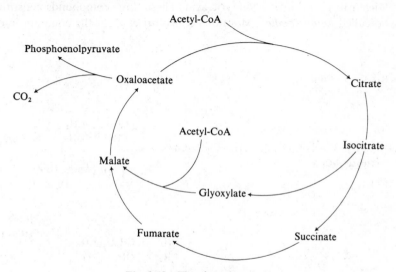

Fig. 9.19 The glyoxylate cycle

(b) Lipids One of the most fruitful studies in the field of biosynthesis in recent years has been that of steroid biosynthesis. It has been shown that, in mammalian tissue, the key steroid is cholesterol, and this compound can be shown, by labelling experiments, to be totally derived from a two-carbon acetyl unit. This long and complex process can be conveniently divided into three stages:

1. Acetyl-CoA to mevalonate.
2. Mevalonate to squalene.
3. Squalene to cholesterol.

(i) *Acetyl-CoA to mevalonate* The formation of mevalonate from acetyl-CoA is closely associated with the process of *ketogenesis*. This process accompanies fatty-acid oxidation and leads to the formation of acetoacetic acid, β-hydroxybutyric acid and acetone. Under normal conditions, the concentration of these is kept low by excretory and biosynthetic processes but, in certain circumstances, the level of these metabolites rises in a condition known as *ketosis*. The basic reaction of ketogenesis is the condensation between two acetyl-CoA molecules to give acetoacetyl-CoA (see section 4.7.3). This reaction releases coenzyme A for use in further fatty-acid oxidation. The reaction is reversible, and the concentration of acetoacetyl-CoA rises when acetyl-CoA is being produced faster than it is being oxidized. When the acetyl-CoA concentration falls, acetoacetyl-CoA is decomposed back to acetyl-CoA.

Acetoacetyl-CoA can be removed by other processes; these include the formation of acetoacetic acid, which either decarboxylates to give acetone or is reduced to give β-hydroxybutyric acid. These three compounds constitute the so-called *ketone bodies*. Mevalonate also arises from the common inter-

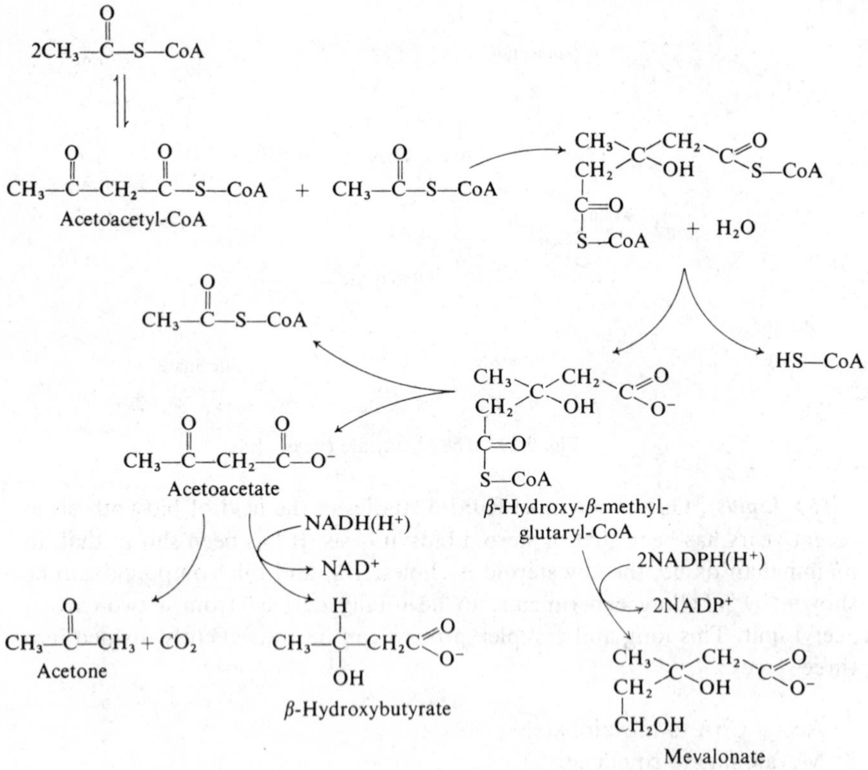

Fig. 9.20 The formation of mevalonate and ketogenesis

424

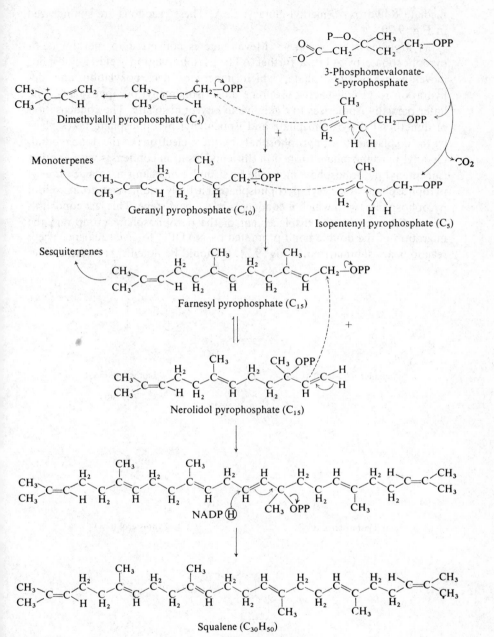

Fig. 9.21 The biosynthesis of squalene

425

mediate β-hydroxy-β-methyl-glutaryl-CoA. These reactions are summarized in Fig. 9.20.

(*ii*) *Mevalonate to squalene*   Mevalonate is converted to mevalonate-5-pyrophosphate by ATP; a further ATP phosphorylation yields 3-phospho-mevalonate-5-pyrophosphate, which undergoes decarboxylation and dehydration to give a reactive isoprene unit—isopentenyl pyrophosphate. The latter partially isomerizes to dimethylallyl pyrophosphate. The condensation of dimethylallyl pyrophosphate and isopentenyl pyrophosphate takes place by the displacement of pyrophosphate by the π-electrons of the double bond. Geranyl pyrophosphate formed in this condensation condenses with another isopentenyl pyrophosphate molecule by a similar mechanism, to give farnesyl pyrophosphate. Farnesyl pyrophosphate partially isomerizes to nerolidol pyrophosphate, with which it condenses in the next stage. This last condensation is followed by the displacement of the pyrophosphate group and the migration of the double bond promoted by NADPH to give squalene. These reactions are summarized in **Fig. 9.21**. It should be noted that intermediates

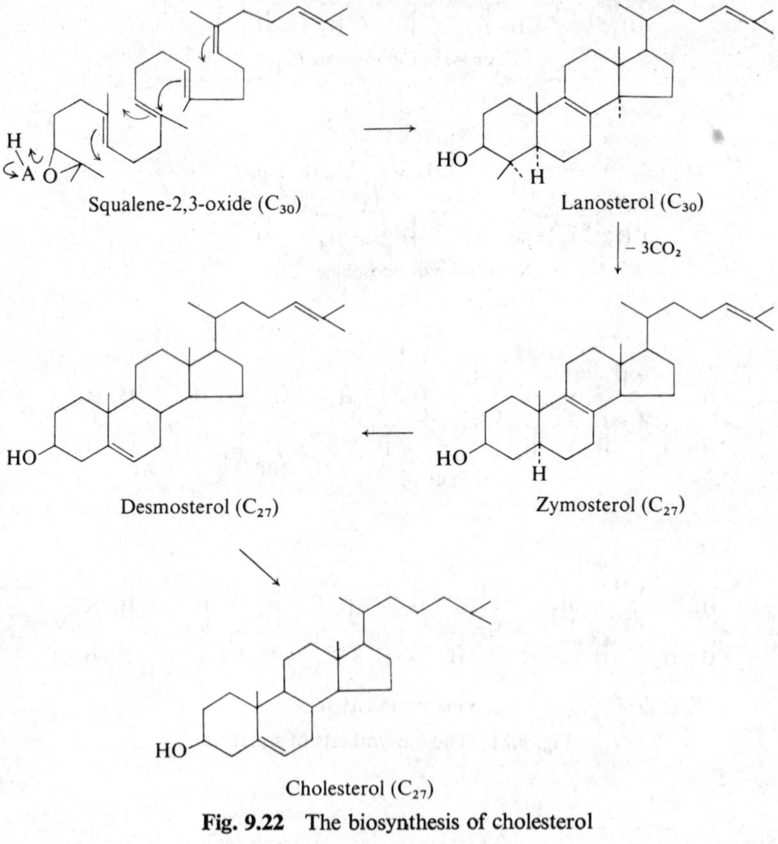

Squalene-2,3-oxide (C_{30})

Lanosterol (C_{30})

$- 3CO_2$

Desmosterol (C_{27})

Zymosterol (C_{27})

Cholesterol (C_{27})

Fig. 9.22   The biosynthesis of cholesterol

426

in this pathway lead, in certain organisms, to the formation of terpenes rather than steroids.

(*iii*) *Squalene to cholesterol*   The full details of this part of the biosynthesis pathway have yet to be elucidated. The cyclization of squalene to lanosterol takes place via squalene-2,3-oxide (Fig. 9.22). During this cyclization two methyl groups migrate to the junction of rings C and D. Three methyl groups are lost in a complex series of oxidation reactions to give zymosterol. The double bond, Δ^8, migrates to position 5 to give desmosterol, and finally the side-chain double bond is hydrogenated to give cholesterol.

Cholesterol occupies a central position in mammalian steroid metabolism. It has been shown that cholesterol may be converted to many of the other steroids. For example, ^{14}C-labelled cholesterol is converted to the bile acids, androgens, oestrogens and the adrenocortical hormones (for structures, see section 7.5.2).

9.4 NITROGEN METABOLISM

9.4.1 Introduction

Unlike the compounds so far considered in this chapter, carbohydrates and fats, the role of the principal nitrogen-containing components of living organisms, nucleic acids and proteins is a structural and functional one rather than a source of energy. Although certain amino acids may be degraded to produce energy, in the case of nucleic acids, it is doubtful whether significant quantities of energy are derived from their catabolism. A common feature of both nucleic acid and protein metabolism is a continuous synthesis and degradation of the molecules. The situation in protein metabolism has been the more fully studied of the two; for example, the biological *half-life* of liver protein in Man is 20–25 days. In nucleic-acid metabolism, the turnover of m-RNA is particularly fast. This rapid turnover of material requires two important types of process; namely, the processes which provide the structural units of the proteins and nucleic acids, and those for the biosynthesis of the macromolecules. In this section, the former processes are described, and in the next section the assembly of the macromolecules will be discussed.

In animals, proteins taken in the diet provide the amino acids for protein biosynthesis, and also the nitrogen for the biosynthesis of other compounds. Dietary proteins are hydrolysed during digestion by the action of various proteolytic enzymes: pepsin (secreted by the stomach), trypsin and chymo-trypsin (secreted by the pancreas—their mode of action is described in section 8.1.2). The large protein molecules are broken down to polypeptides and free amino acids by these endopeptidases, and the degradation process is completed by the action of exopeptidases (carboxypeptidases and amino-peptidases). The whole process is remarkably efficient, and under normal

427

conditions 90–97 per cent of the food protein is hydrolysed. Only *insoluble* proteins such as keratin and collagen are unaffected. The amino acids and small peptides released during hydrolysis are absorbed into the portal circulation from the small intestine; the small peptides are subsequently hydrolysed.

The protein component of nucleoprotein is digested through the action of the proteolytic enzymes. The nucleic acids DNA and RNA are hydrolysed through the action of deoxyribonuclease and ribonuclease respectively. Both enzymes are secreted by the pancreas, and their mode of action has already been described (see section 8.1.2). The oligonucleotides are further degraded by the action of a phosphodiesterase with an exonuclease action secreted by the mucosa of the small intestine. Some further degradation of the nucleotides by phosphatases occurs, to give nucleosides. Both nucleotides and nucleosides are absorbed.

9.4.2 General metabolism of amino acids

Protein nitrogen is the principal source of nitrogen in the animal diet. Traces of inorganic nitrogen are taken in in the form of nitrates, and a small amount of nitrogen may be derived from nucleic-acid components (the intake of nitrogen in plants is considered separately in section 9.4.4). The animal body has practically no facility for storing amino acids, and thus a regular intake of protein is essential and any excess nitrogen is excreted. This has led to the concept that there is a *metabolic pool* of amino groups, estimated at 2 g of nitrogen for an average human, in a state of dynamic equilibrium (Fig. 9.23).

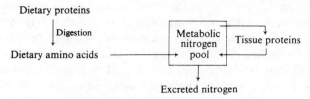

Fig. 9.23 The nitrogen cycle in animals

It is possible to replace the protein of an animal diet completely with pure amino acids. When individual amino acids are eliminated from an otherwise complete diet, it has been found that a particular organism can do without certain of these compounds, but not without others. Members of this latter group are termed *essential amino acids*, and must be present in dietary proteins in order to maintain a sufficient supply for various physiological requirements. Presumably, these amino acids cannot be synthesized to a sufficient extent by the organism. In mammals, eight amino acids are in this class: isoleucine, leucine, lysine, methionine, phenylalanine, threonine, tryptophan and valine. Most animals cannot synthesize the branched hydrocarbon chains required in

428

isoleucine, leucine and valine. The amount of methionine and phenylalanine required varies with the intake of cystine and tyrosine respectively. Arginine and histidine should also be present in the diet, but they can be synthesized at a lower rate than is consistent with optimum growth. It has been shown by labelling experiments, using ^{15}N, that the amino-nitrogen of one particular amino acid may be used in the $-NH_2$ group of certain other amino acids. Through reactions of this type, the *non-essential amino acids* become interconverted.

Apart from the obvious requirement as the structural units for protein biosynthesis, amino acids participate in numerous metabolic processes. In particular, the following processes are found.

1. A process, known as *transamination*, whereby amino acids may be inter-converted through keto acids.
2. Numerous specific processes for the interconversion or degradation of individual amino acids.
3. Oxidative deamination to α-keto acids, a process that is used for the removal of surplus amino nitrogen and as a source of α-keto acids.
4. Decarboxylation to primary amines and carbon dioxide, a process found mainly among microorganisms.

(a) Transamination These reactions may be described by the general equation

α-Amino acid (A) + α-Keto acid (A) ⇌ α-Amino acid (B) + α-Keto acid (B)

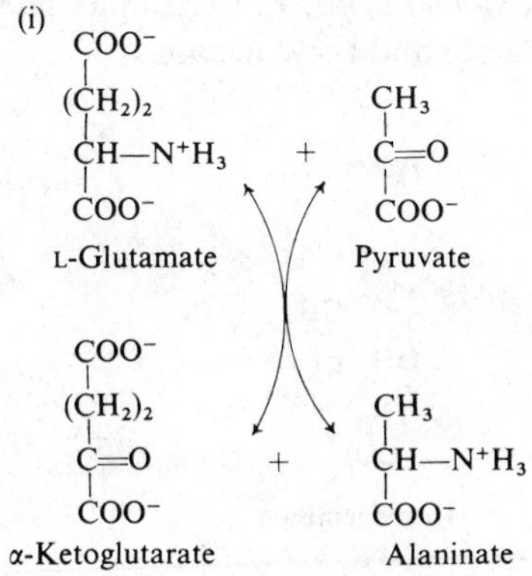

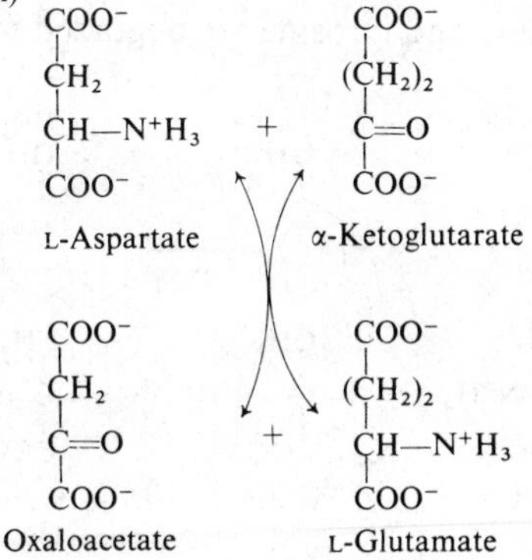

In effect, an amino group is transferred to an α-keto acid (A) from an amino acid (A). A new amino acid (B) is formed, whose side chain is structurally identical to the α-keto acid (A). These reversible reactions are catalysed by a *transaminase* and the coenzyme is pyridoxal phosphate (vitamin B_6). The two most thoroughly studied transaminations in animal tissue are as shown in (i) and (ii). These two reactions are important in so much as the α-keto acids involved are common metabolites and also that aspartate is a key amino acid in the process for nitrogen excretion. The mechanism for a transamination is via the formation of a Schiff's base (see section 4.5.1) with the aldehyde group of pyridoxal phosphate. The coenzyme is converted to pyridoxamine phosphate, which interacts with a keto acid (A), producing amino acid (B).

(b) Specific reactions for individual amino acids The reactions in this group are of two types: there are those by which amino acids are interconverted through changes in the side chain, while maintaining the α-amino and α-carboxyl groups. For example, glycine can arise from serine and threonine;

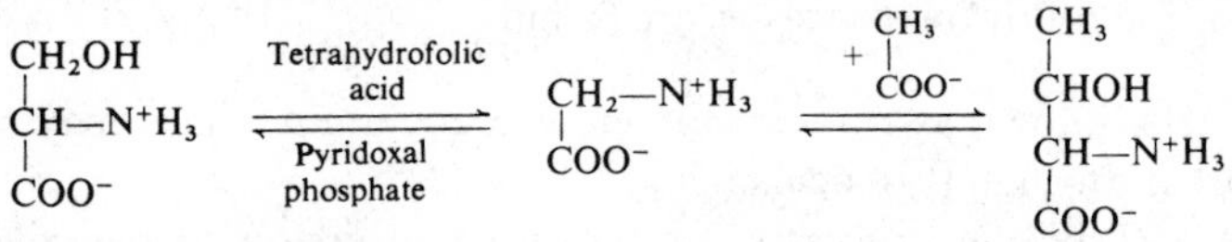

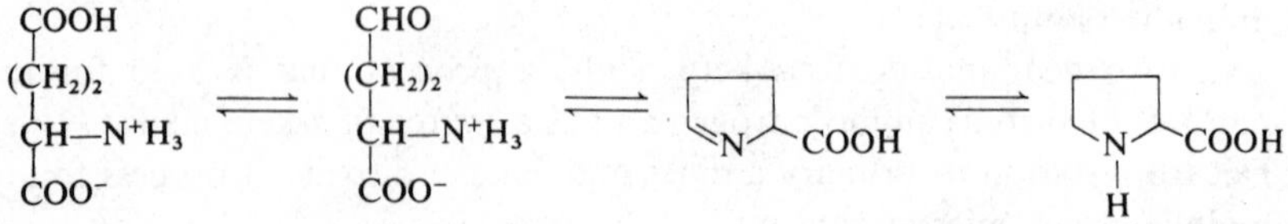

and glutamic acid can be reversibly converted to proline. Secondly, there are degradation processes whereby amino acids are oxidized to provide energy. In these latter reactions two further groups may be distinguished. The majority of amino acids can be degraded to either four carbon dicarboxylic acids or to pyruvate, and thus join a carbohydrate pathway—these are the *glucogenic amino acids*. It will be seen that for aspartate, glutamate and alaninate transamination reactions produce oxaloacetate, α-ketoglutarate and pyruvate directly. In other cases, the pathways are more extensive. On the other hand, isoleucine, leucine, lysine, phenylalanine, and tyrosine, as well as producing carbohydrate metabolites, produce acetoacetate and associated *ketone bodies*. These have been termed *ketogenic amino acids*. For example, phenylalanine and tyrosine are degraded to fumarate and acetoacetate.

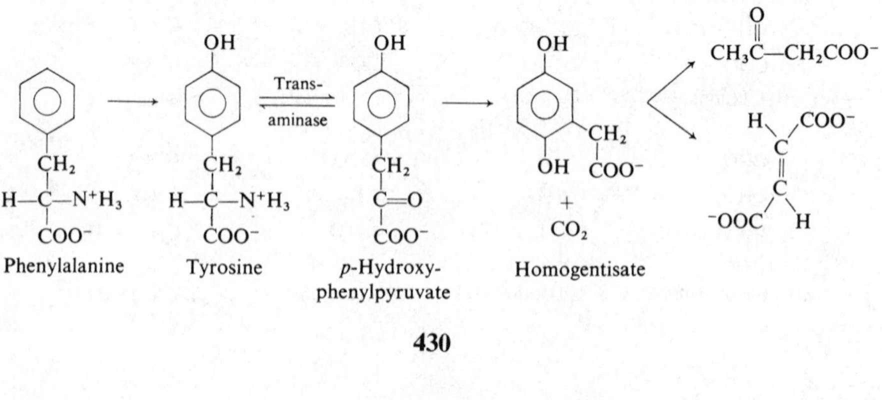

Phenylalanine   Tyrosine   p-Hydroxy-phenylpyruvate   Homogentisate

(c) *Deamination and the excretion of nitrogen*   There are two pathways by which excess nitrogen is removed from the mammalian body. The first is through transamination reactions which yield aspartate, and the second is by oxidative deamination of amino acids. This latter reaction may be described by the general equation

$$^+NH_3CH{-}COO^- + \tfrac{1}{2}O_2 \longrightarrow O{=}\overset{\displaystyle R}{\underset{\displaystyle |}{C}}{-}COO^- + NH_4^+$$

The enzymes which catalyse these reactions are the amino acid oxidases and the coenzyme which takes up the hydrogen is FAD. Examples of both D and L amino acid oxidases are known where two molecules of FAD are present per molecule of enzyme. The oxidized state (FAD—Enz—FAD) is regenerated by direct interaction with molecular oxygen rather than through the electron-transport system. The interaction with molecular oxygen may be

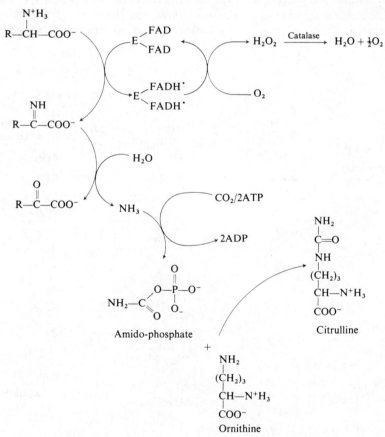

Fig. 9.24   The oxidative deamination of α-amino acids

431

through the *semiquinone* intermediate (•HFAD—Enz—FADH•) which has been shown to be present. The stages in the process are shown in Fig. 9.24. Oxidation of the amino acid produces an *imino acid* which readily hydrolyses to the α-keto acid and ammonia. The ammonia released in deamination is used to synthesize amidophosphate (carbamyl phosphate), which in turn reacts with ornithine to form citrulline. Citrulline is one of the intermediates of the *ornithine cycle*, a metabolic pathway discovered by Krebs for the formation of urea.

The ornithine cycle (see Fig. 9.25) is a cyclic process which, like the TCA cycle, can be considered to start with the *carrier molecule*, in this case the amino acid ornithine. Ornithine is converted to citrulline by the process already described, and is then converted in a two-stage reaction to arginine. The intermediate is arginino-succinate, which is formed in the reaction between citrulline and aspartate. Arginino-succinate is cleaved to give arginine and fumarate, the latter being removed via the TCA cycle. Arginine is hydrolysed by the enzyme arginase to urea and ornithine, and the cycle is complete. The formation of urea is an endergonic process, and the free energy required is

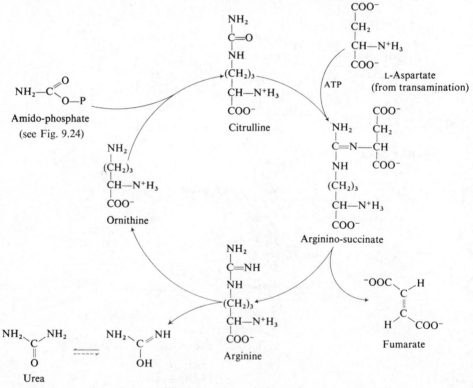

Fig. 9.25 The ornithine cycle

432

supplied by the participation of ATP to the extent of three moles for every mole of urea synthesized.

Apart from the flavin-dependent oxidases which catalyse oxidative deamination, NAD^+ or $NADP^+$ have been found to be required by glutumate dehydrogenase. This enzyme occurs widely in the cells of most tissues and the oxidative deamination of glutamate by this process may serve as a source of NADPH for biosynthesis (i.e., an alternative to the phosphogluconate pathway).

$$
\begin{matrix}
(CH_2)_2COO^- \\
| \\
^+NH_3{-}CH{-}COO^-
\end{matrix}
+ NAD^+ + H_2O
\xrightarrow[\text{dehydrogenase}]{\text{L-glutamate}}
\begin{matrix}
(CH_2)_2COO^- \\
| \\
O{=}C{-}COO^-
\end{matrix}
+ NH_4^+ + NADH(H^+)
$$
$$
\text{or } NADP^+ \qquad\qquad\qquad \text{or } NADPH(H^+)
$$

(d) Decarboxylation Enzymes which catalyse the decarboxylation of α-amino acids have been isolated from microorganisms. It has been shown that the coenzyme for these reactions is pyridoxal phosphate to which the amino acid is joined as a Schiff's base during the decarboxylation (see section 7.1.1):

$$
\begin{matrix}
R \\
| \\
^+NH_3{-}CH{-}COO^-
\end{matrix}
\xrightarrow[\text{phosphate}]{\text{Pyridoxal}}
\begin{matrix}
R \\
| \\
NH_2{-}CH_2
\end{matrix}
+ CO_2
$$

Amino acid decarboxylation occurs in a limited way in mammalian metabolism, nevertheless, the few cases that do arise are of some importance. For example, in brain tissue the highly specific L-glutamate decarboxylase produces γ-amino butyric acid from L-glutamate:

$$
\begin{matrix}
(CH_2)_2COO^- \\
| \\
^+NH_3{-}CH{-}COO^-
\end{matrix}
\xrightarrow[\text{pyridoxal phosphate}]{\text{L-Glutamate decarboxylase}}
\begin{matrix}
(CH_2)_2COO^- \\
| \\
NH_2{-}CH_2
\end{matrix}
+ CO_2
$$

(e) Amino acid metabolism in relation to carbohydrate and fat metabolism Amino acid metabolism represents one of the most complex areas of intermediary metabolism since each amino acid has its own unique pathways for degradation and biosynthesis and, of course, may also participate in the general reactions described in this section. It is possible in this text only to summarize the results of all these reactions in relation to the main pathways of carbohydrate and fat metabolism. Fig. 9.26(a) shows the catabolic fate of the carbon skeleton of the common amino acids. In most cases, the carbon atoms end up in a single intermediate but in a few cases two metabolites arise (e.g., phenylalanine and tyrosine). In the biosynthesis of amino acids, intermediates of carbohydrate and fat metabolism may serve as precursors providing most of the carbon atoms of amino acid [Fig. 9.26(b)].

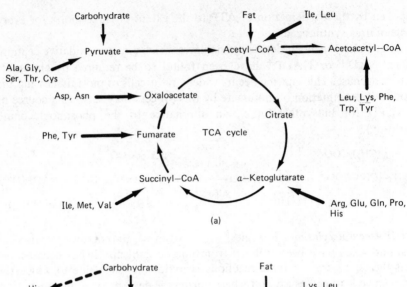

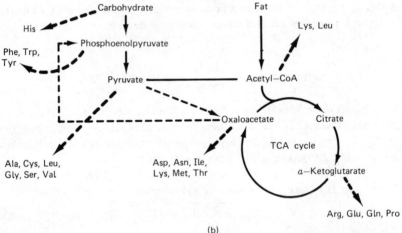

Fig. 9.26 (a) Summary diagram of the catabolic fate of α-amino acid carbon atoms. (b) Summary diagram of the biosynthetic precursors of α-amino acids. (Abbreviations for the α-amino acids are those corresponding to structures given in Table 7.1)

9.4.3 The biosynthesis of pyrimidine and purine bases and the formation of nucleotides

Most species have the ability of synthesizing the purine and pyrimidine bases required as structural components of nucleic acids and nucleotide coenzymes. In only a few cases has it been found that a nutritional supply was needed. The key intermediate in the formation of pyrimidine nucleotides is orotidine-5′-phosphate. Orotic acid is formed in the reaction of aspartate and amido-phosphate followed by cyclization and dehydrogenation. Orotate is joined to a ribosyl unit via phosphoribosyl pyrophosphate (see Fig. 9.27). Orotidine-5'-phosphate formed in the latter reaction is the precursor of the other pyrimidine nucleotides. Decarboxylation yields uridine-5'-phosphate, from which UDP and UTP are formed by phosphorylation with ATP. Cytidine-5'-phosphate is formed by amination of UTP. The conversion of these nucleotides to the corresponding deoxy compounds occurs at the diphosphate stage, i.e., CDP → dCDP.

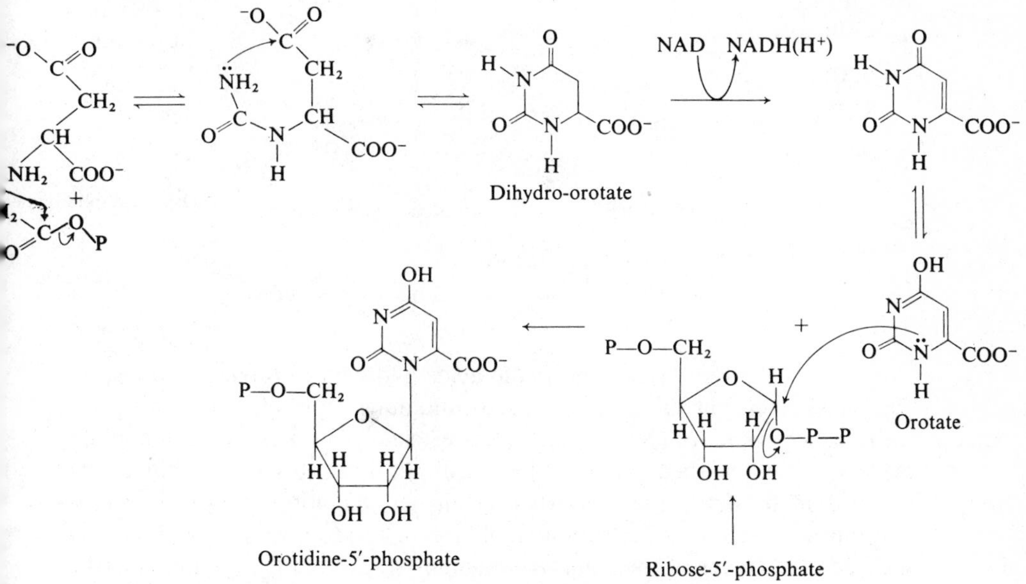

Dihydro-orotate

Orotate

Orotidine-5'-phosphate

Ribose-5'-phosphate

Fig. 9.27 The biosynthesis of pyrimidine nucleotides

A totally different process is found for the formation of purine bases and their nucleotides. In these molecules, the C—N glycosidic bond is formed at the outset of the synthesis. At least six different metabolites contribute atoms in the formation of the purine ring. An outline of the pathway leading to the formation of inosine-5'-phosphate (inosinic acid—IMP) is shown in Fig. 9.28. Adenosine-5'-phosphate arises by the amination of IMP, where the amino donor is aspartate. Guanosine-5'-phosphate arises by the amination of xanthosine-5'-phosphate; the latter is formed by oxidation of IMP.

9.4.4 Assimilation of inorganic nitrogen

The ultimate source of nitrogen to all forms of life is *inorganic*, and the metabolic processes associated with inorganic nitrogen compounds are of fundamental importance to the maintenance of life on this planet. Plants absorb inorganic nitrogen compounds from the soil through their roots and use the

435

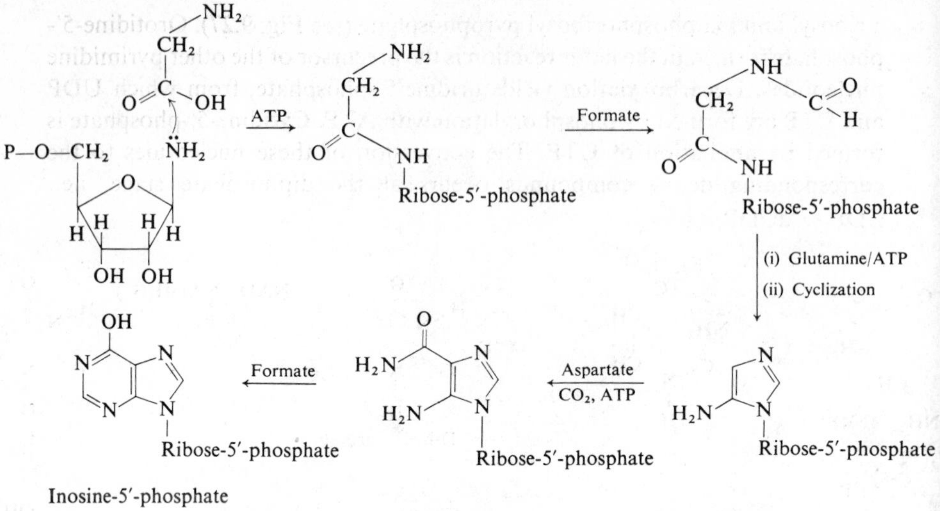

Fig. 9.28 The biosynthesis of purine nucleotides

nitrogen in the biosynthesis of amino acids and hence proteins, and also in the biosynthesis of the other nitrogen-containing molecules. The inorganic salts which serve as nitrogen sources are usually nitrates, but ammonium salts are also absorbed. It should be noted that most of the ammonium salts applied in fertilizers are converted to nitrites and nitrates by soil micro-organisms. The relative ease of assimilation of ammonium salts and nitrates depends on the age of the plant. Ammonium absorption predominates in the early stages of plant growth, and nitrate assimilation at later stages. Some plants can also use elemental nitrogen of the air. This process takes place through symbiotic bacteria in the nodules of the plants' root system. The most common of these symbiotic organisms is *Rhizobium*, a non-photosynthetic bacterium which is responsible for nodule initiation and development. The assimilation of elemental nitrogen is a remarkable example of the power of enzyme catalysis, since the element is particularly stable and inert. These enzyme systems have not yet been fully characterized.

Nitrogen fixation occurs in photosynthetic prokaryotes, such as blue-green algae and some free-living bacteria—for example, *Chlorobium* and *Chromatium*. Non-photosynthetic nitrogen fixation, as well as occurring in symbiotic bacteria, also takes place in free-living bacteria, such as *Azotobacter*, *Beijerinckia* and *Derxia*, and also in soil yeasts, such as *Rhodotorula* and *Saccharomyces*.

Regardless of the source of nitrogen, the first step of the assimilation process is one of reduction to ammonia. Reducing coenzymes are required for this purpose, and in photosynthetic nitrogen-fixing organisms the source of these reduced coenzymes could be the *light reactions* (see section 9.3.2). In non-photosynthetic nitrogen fixation, exogenous reductants are required, and they may also be used in photosynthetic nitrogen fixation as well. Pyruvate has been shown to be a source of reducing power in nitrogen fixation in cell-free extracts of *Clostridium*—a non-photosynthetic free-living bacterium. Molecular hydrogen has been found to stimulate the process in *Chromatium* and also in *Clostridium*. The fixation process in *Chromatium*, like that of blue-green algae, is dependent on a source of radiation, suggesting that photosynthetically reduced coenzymes are necessary in the fixation process.

There is still some controversy regarding the key nitrogen-containing intermediate by which nitrogen becomes incorporated in organic molecules. It now seems likely that ammonia is this key intermediate. However, it is unlikely that ammonium ion exists for any length of time in living cells, since it is a cellular poison. The ammonia formed by reduction of the primary nitrogen sources is quickly assimilated by reaction with organic compounds, notably α-keto acids (i.e., the reverse of oxidative deamination). The most important of such reactions is that where α-ketoglutarate is converted to glutamate:

$$\alpha\text{-Ketoglutarate} + NH_4^+ + NADPH + H^+ \rightarrow \text{Glutamate} + H_2O + NADP^+$$

It will be noted that, as in other biosynthesis processes, NADPH replaces NADH as the hydrogen donor. Other amino acids are then formed by trans-amination. Whether or not all the amino acids are formed will then depend on the availability of the appropriate α-keto acid.

9.5 THE BIOSYNTHESIS OF NUCLEIC ACIDS AND PROTEINS

9.5.1 DNA biosynthesis

Hereditary factors or *genes* were originally defined as biological entities which had the ability to induce characteristics which were identical in each generation. In many species, genes appear to be handed over unchanged from generation to generation, often with millions of progeny in each generation. This requires that genes have the capacity for identical *self-duplication* or *replication*. Sudden changes in hereditary characteristics are not normally found, but mutants can develop and can then be reproduced as faithfully as the original species. One of the major advances in biochemistry in the last twenty years has been the translation of these biological features to a molecular level, and this has given rise to a new branch of science called *molecular biology*. A gene can now be defined at a molecular level, as that part of a DNA molecule which contains the information for the synthesis of one ribonucleic acid chain (section 9.5.2).

This definition arises from the fact that DNA is now known to be the component of the chromosome which is concerned with the storage and transmission of genetic information. Furthermore, a process is known by which this genetic information may be accurately transmitted during cell division and a further process through which DNA can direct and regulate the chemical activity of the cell and hence that of the whole organism. This property is achieved through the control of protein biosynthesis.

One of the most important features of the Watson–Crick structure of DNA (see section 8.5.2) is that it provides a satisfactory mechanism for the molecule to faithfully replicate itself. The genetic information is stored as the sequence of bases and, during replication, this sequence must be preserved and accurately copied. The currently accepted mechanism is that the two chains present in a DNA molecule are parted, and each chain then acts as a template for the synthesis of two new DNA molecules (Fig. 9.29). Provided the base-pair mechanism operates reliably, the two new DNA molecules will be identical with the original ones.

One of the first, and most convincing, demonstrations of this replication mechanism came from an experiment by Meselson and Stahl in 1957. *Esch. coli* bacteria were grown in a medium containing $^{15}NH_4^+$ as the only source of

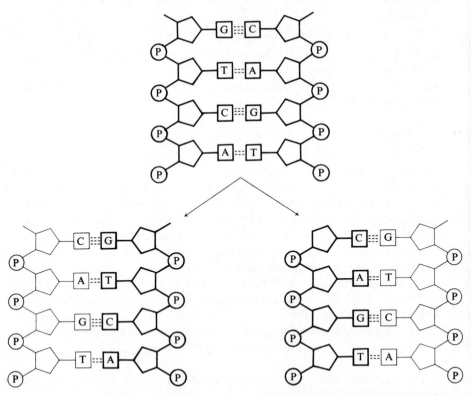

Fig. 9.29 Diagrammatic representation of the replication process for DNA. The faint-lined polynucleotide chains are the newly synthesized chains

nitrogen. In this way, all the nitrogen atoms of the bases in the DNA molecules synthesized became those of the heavy isotope (^{15}N). Such DNA molecules could be distinguished from the natural ones, which contained nearly all the light isotope (^{14}N), by centrifugation on a caesium chloride density gradient. The *Esch. coli* cells containing ^{15}N DNA were next grown on a medium with ^{14}NH$_4^+$ as the source of nitrogen. At the end of the first generation, *hybrid DNA* molecules containing equal parts ^{14}N and ^{15}N were found to be present, a result entirely consistent with the replication mechanism. In the second generation of cells grown on ^{14}NH$_4^+$, both *hybrid* and *light* DNA molecules were present in equal amounts (see Fig. 9.30).

The enzyme which carries out the polymerization of the deoxynucleotide units was first isolated from *Esch. coli*. This enzyme, called DNA polymerase, requires the four deoxynucleoside triphosphates as substrates (dATP, dGTP, dCTP and dTTP). All four must be present for any significant amount of

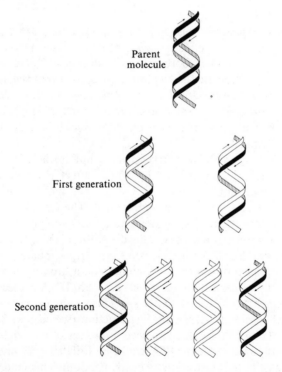

Fig. 9.30 Diagrammatic representation of the Meselson and Stahl experiment. The two strands of the parent molecule, shown in black, contain ^{15}N. In the first generation, each DNA contains ^{15}N in one strand and ^{14}N in the other. In the second generation, two molecules contain ^{14}N and two contain equal amounts of ^{14}N and ^{15}N

439

reaction to occur, as also must be a DNA template molecule. The overall equation of the polymerization is given by:

$$
\begin{array}{c}
n_x\,\text{dATP} \\[4pt]
+ \\[4pt]
n_x\,\text{dTTP} \\[4pt]
+ \\[4pt]
n_y\,\text{dGTP} \\[4pt]
+ \\[4pt]
n_y\,\text{dCTP}
\end{array}
\quad\xrightarrow[\text{Mg}^{2+}]{\text{DNA polymerase}}\quad
\left[
\begin{array}{c}
\text{dAMP} \\
\text{dTMP} \\
\text{dGMP} \\
\text{dCMP}
\end{array}
\right]_{2n_x+2n_y}
\quad + \; 2(n_x+n_y)\,\text{PP}
$$

$$\text{(DNA)}$$

The composition of the new polynucleotide chains is determined entirely by the template and is not influenced by the relative amount of the four deoxyribonucleoside triphosphates. The enzyme shows a specific requirement for Mg^{2+}; when Mn^{2+} is used, for example, ribonucleoside triphosphates can be polymerized.

Mechanism of replication and properties of Esch. coli DNA-polymerase I

The enzyme, isolated from *Esch. coli*, which catalyses DNA biosynthesis has been extensively studied both *in vitro* and *in vivo*. There are significant differences in its action in the two situations. *In vitro*, the rate of DNA formation is much slower, also the DNA template can be single-stranded or even relatively small DNA fragments; furthermore, extensive branching of DNA occurs. Initially, it was not possible to produce biologically active DNA by *in vitro* experiments.

In 1968, Kornberg and his co-workers carried out a series of transformations using *Esch. coli* DNA-polymerase by which direct evidence of the exact nature of the replication process was obtained and moreover, a biologically active DNA molecule was synthesized *in vitro*. The single-stranded circular DNA from bacteriophage ϕX174 was chosen as template (the structure of this molecule has recently been determined—section 8.5.2). In the presence of dATP, dGTP, dCTP and 5-bromodeoxyuridine triphosphate (this compound replaces dTTP and produces a DNA containing a bromine atom instead of the methyl group of each thymine moiety), a new DNA molecule was produced complementary to the ϕX174 DNA. This was an open-chain DNA and was converted to circular-DNA by ligase action (see section 8.5.4). Partial disruption of the two molecules produced a mixture of materials from which the newly synthesized circular-DNA could be isolated (the presence of the bromine atoms allowed separation by centrifugation). This material was now used, in the presence of the polymerase and the appropriate precursors, to synthesize a molecule which proved to be identical to the original ϕX174 DNA. This sequence of transformations (Fig. 9.31) showed that DNA-poly-

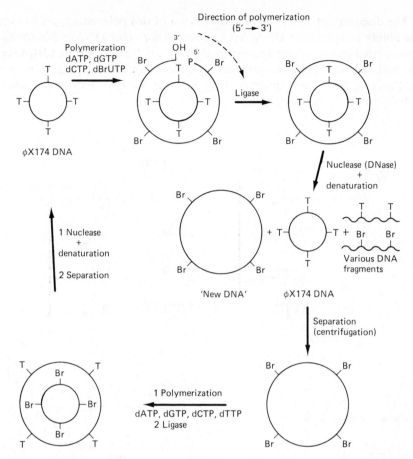

Fig. 9.31 The *in vitro* synthesis of circular-DNA of the bacteriophage φX174 (Kornberg, 1968)

merase had indeed the ability to make an exact copy of template DNA although it lacked ligase capacity.

Another important feature of DNA-polymerase is that, as well as catalysing the formation of a polynucleotide chain, it can also degrade it by exonuclease action (section 8.1.2). It has been shown that this action can take place from either end of the chain, i.e. in $3' \rightarrow 5'$ or $5' \rightarrow 3'$ direction. The function of the $3' \rightarrow 5'$ exonuclease activity is to recognize and remove non-hydrogen-bonded nucleotides, as the 5'-monophosphates, from the 3' terminus. On the other hand, the $5' \rightarrow 3'$ activity is quite different. In this case, as many as ten nucleotides at a time can be removed from the 5' terminus. The purpose of this appears to be the excision of 'mis-matched' nucleotides [Fig. 9.32(a)].

441

The discovery of *Esch. coli* mutants devoid of this polymerase, yet having the ability to synthesize DNA, led to a search for other DNA-polymerases. Two further enzymes have been isolated—DNA-polymerases II and III. Like the well characterized DNA-polymerase I, they both catalyse polynucleotide synthesis in the $5' \rightarrow 3'$ direction [Fig. 9.32(b)] but have only exonuclease activity in the $3' \rightarrow 5'$ direction.

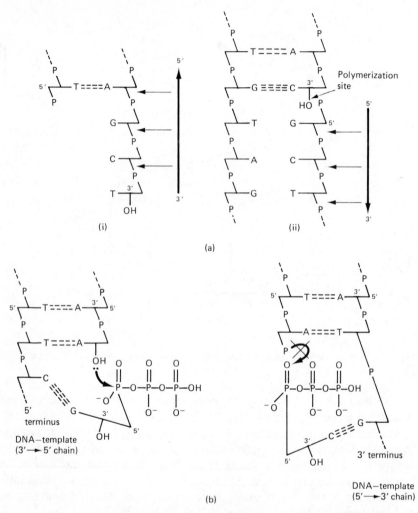

Fig. 9.32 (a) Exonuclease activity of DNA-polymerase. (i) $3' \rightarrow 5'$ Exonuclease action removing non-hydrogen-bonded nucleotides (as 5′-phosphates) from the 3′-terminus. (ii) $5' \rightarrow 3'$ Exonuclease action removing 'mismatched' nucleotides (as 5′-phosphates) from a 5′-terminus (this is the so-called 'repair' action, since it can be followed by polymerization). (b) Mechanism of DNA polymerization. 5′-triphosphates are added to a 3′-hydroxyl terminus in a $5' \rightarrow 3'$ direction using a $3' \rightarrow 5'$ template chain

Kornberg demonstrated clearly the manner in which a single-stranded DNA molecule can be replicated but, when the idea of semi-conservative replication is applied to the double-stranded open-chain molecule, found in eukaryotic cells, a number of problems arise. The major of these is that the direction of replication is known to be 5' → 3' with respect to the chain being synthesized; thus the copying of the 3' → 5' chain of template DNA can be envisaged as proceeding continuously. Nucleophilic attack of the terminal 3' hydroxyl group on the pyrophosphate group of the incoming triphosphate takes place [Fig. 9.32(b)]. However, the other template chain has the wrong 'polarity' for this to be the method of phosphodiester bond formation.

A mechanism has been proposed which overcomes this problem and this is shown diagrammatically in Fig. 9.33. The two strands of part of the DNA molecule separate under the influence of *unwinding protein*. A short *primer* molecule, probably RNA, is established at 3' terminus of template DNA. To the 3' hydroxyl terminus of primer are now added, by DNA polymerase, deoxynucleotides in complementary sequence to the template. After about 1000 nucleotides have been added, the template changes to the 5' → 3' chain and the corresponding number of residues are added. The action of an endonuclease (*nickase*) now cuts the new chain. Further polymerase action takes place on the new 3' terminus after further unwinding. Repetition of

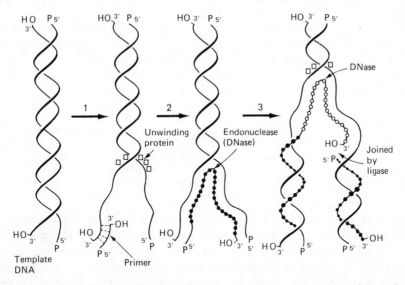

Fig. 9.33 Schematic representation of the possible mechanism of replication of open-chain double-stranded DNA. Stage 1—partial unwinding of template DNA, followed by the synthesis of a short RNA *primer* chain catalysed by transcriptase (section 9.5.2). Stage 2—synthesis of a new DNA chain using DNA-polymerase in the 5' → 3' direction. Stage 3—cleavage of the new chain by an endonuclease ('nickase'), followed by further DNA synthesis
The sections of DNA formed on the 5' → 3' template are joined by ligase action

these processes allows one chain to be formed continuously, while the other is formed in fragments to be joined by ligase action. Eukaryotic DNA-polymerases have been isolated and characterized. The one in liver nuclei is remarkable for its small size (MW = 40 000) compared with *Esch. coli* DNA-polymerase I (MW = 109 000); it also lacks exonuclease activity.

9.5.2 RNA biosynthesis, structure of genes and the genetic code

DNA molecules contain regions for the structural control of both cellular RNA molecules (r-RNA and t-RNA) and cellular protein Control of the latter process is directed by m-RNA, whose synthesis is, in turn, controlled by regions of a DNA molecule. The process through which DNA directs the synthesis of these RNA molecules is called *transcription*. Each region of DNA which is responsible for the formation of an RNA molecule is called a *gene*. Within each gene, three separate regions may be distinguished: promoter, transcription and terminator regions. Of these, only the central—transcription region—gives rise to the RNA molecule (or its precursor). The outer regions ensure the correct starting and finishing positions of the transcription process. Some information is now available on the detailed structure of such gene regions, notably that for the synthesis of *Esch. coli* tyrosine t-RNA precursor gene.

The enzymes responsible for the process of transcription, the DNA-dependent RNA-polymerases (conveniently called *transcriptases*), have been isolated from many different species. They catalyse the reaction:

$$
\begin{array}{c}
n_x\text{ATP} \\
+ \\
n_x\text{UTP} \\
+ \\
n_y\text{GTP} \\
+ \\
n_y\text{CTP}
\end{array}
\quad
\xrightarrow[\text{Mg}^{2+}]{\text{Transcriptase}}
\quad
\left.
\begin{array}{c}
\text{AMP} \\
\text{UMP} \\
\text{GMP} \\
\text{CMP}
\end{array}
\right]_{2n_x+2n_y}
\quad + \quad 2(n_x+n_y)\text{PP}_i
$$

(RNA)

Transcriptases show an absolute requirement for DNA (acting as template) and also require the presence of all four ribonucleoside triphosphates. *In vitro* the transcriptases will use single- or double-stranded DNA as template; in the latter case *both* chains are transcribed, but *in vivo* only *one* chain is transcribed. When different DNA templates are used, a close relationship is always observed between the base composition of template and the RNA produced.

$$
\text{Template}\ \left(\frac{\text{A} + \text{T}}{\text{G} + \text{C}}\right) = \text{RNA produced}\ \left(\frac{\text{A} + \text{U}}{\text{G} + \text{C}}\right)
$$

444

Furthermore, the RNA produced *in vitro* from a given DNA template has the ability to form a stable hydrogen-bonded DNA–RNA hybrid. For this to be possible, the RNA must have a nucleotide sequence complementary to the template RNA.

The transcriptase from *Esch. coli* has been isolated and well characterized; it is much larger than the corresponding DNA-polymerase. While the latter consists of a single polypeptide chain (MW = 109 000), transcriptase has a molecular weight of about 500 000 and has a quaternary structure consisting of five sub-units (2α MW 39 000; 1β MW 155 000; $1\beta'$ MW 165 000 and 1σ MW 95 000). The sub-unit designated σ may be selectively removed leaving an enzyme with transcriptase activity producing heterogeneous RNA. The σ sub-units are associated with the correct location of transcriptase on the DNA template (Fig. 9.34).

A possible mechanism for the action of transcriptase is shown in Fig. 9.34, where one strand of template DNA is being copied. The σ sub-unit of transcriptase 'recognizes' promoter region in such a way that the polymerase action starts only in transcription region. In the active-site of the polymerase about six base-pairs of DNA are parted and ribonucleoside triphosphates are joined sequentially, the base of each pairing with the complementary one on the DNA chain (no primer is necessary here). The direction of polymerization is again $5' \rightarrow 3'$ and stops when the enzyme reaches the end of transcription region. The ρ-factor becomes bound to terminator region and prevents further transcription. This factor has been isolated in the *Esch. coli* system and is a protein of molecular weight about 50 000.

Genes and the genetic code   The outline structure of a gene has already been presented, here we will consider the detailed structure of a gene and the evidence from which it arises. The gene regions of DNA, through transcription, either produce structural RNAs directly or their precursors, in which case there is a simple base-pair relationship between template and product; or m-RNAs are made and from them cellular proteins. In the latter situation, the unambiguous position of twenty or more amino acids must be specified by DNA. The two situations are best considered separately. It should be noted that, in RNA-containing viruses, the single-stranded RNA molecule contains the information for the sequences of the virus's protein components. The structure of one such genome (MS 2 RNA) is known in detail [Fig. 8.49(a)].

(i) Genes coding for structural RNA (r-RNA or t-RNA)   To illustrate this concept, the structural determination of *Esch. coli* tyrosine t-RNA precursor gene will be described. A model of this gene is shown in Fig. 9.35(a). The full nucleotide sequence of the precursor t-RNA molecule and also that of the functional t-RNA molecule is known [Fig. 9.35(b)]. From the nucleotide sequence of the former structure, the sequence of a complementary DNA

445

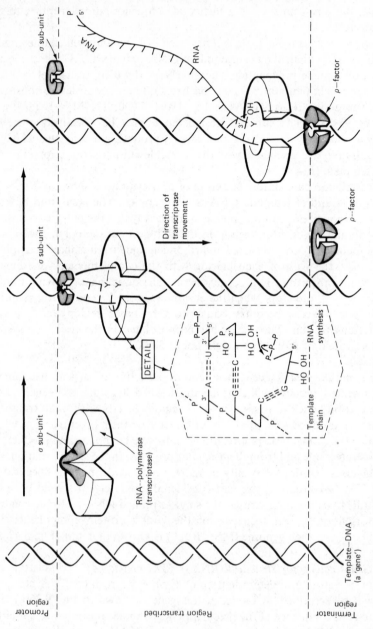

Fig. 9.34 Schematic representation of the mechanism of the action of DNA-dependent RNA-polymerase showing the formation of an RNA molecule in the 5′ → 3′ direction

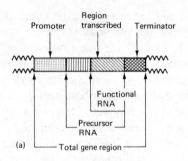

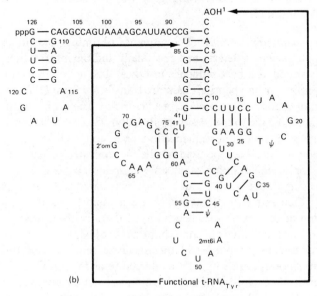

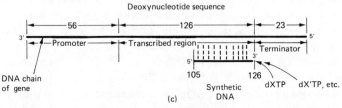

Fig. 9.35 (a) General structure of a gene. (b) Sequence of the precursor of *Esch. coli* tyrosine t-RNA showing its relationship to the functional t-RNA (1 → 85). (The *modified* bases are present only in the functional molecule:

2mt6iA = N^6-isopentenyl-2-methylthioadenine
4tU = 4-thiouracil
ψ = pseudouridine
2′omG = 2-*o*-methylguanosine)

The triphosphate terminal group arises from the mechanism of transcriptase—Fig. 9.34 (From Altman and Smith, 1971). (c) Determination of the deoxynucleotide sequence in the terminator region of the *Esch. coli* tyrosine t-RNA precursor gene (From Khorana, 1975)

chain can be deduced and hence a double-stranded DNA gene. Khorana and his co-workers completed the synthesis of this DNA molecule (section 8.5.4), and then proceeded to identify the nucleotides in promoter and terminator regions. This was done by observing the order of incorporation, by DNA-polymerase, of deoxynucleotides on to a short synthetic DNA chain while the latter is hydrogen-bonded to transcribing region of the gene. A further 23 nucleotides were added to complete terminator region [Fig. 9.35(c)]. A comparable technique produced a sequence of nucleotides (56) in promoter region. This gave a total gene length of 207 nucleotides. When the DNA molecule corresponding to this whole gene was synthesized, it proved to be biologically functional.

(*ii*) *Genes coding for proteins* The sequence of amino acids in a polypeptide chain of a protein is determined genetically and the information for these sequences is stored as a base sequence in DNA. The instructions for the synthesis of a particular polypeptide chain are transferred from DNA to m-RNA by the accurate transcription process just described. The problem still remains of determining how the four bases of m-RNA (A, G, C and U) can dictate, in an unambiguous manner, the sequence in a polypeptide chain when there are at least twenty different amino acids to be incorporated. Clearly, if a single base codes for a single amino acid, only four amino acids can be unambiguously accommodated; if a sequence of two bases code for a particular amino acid, then sixteen (4^2) sequences are available and the positions of sixteen amino acids can be specified. Only if there is a sequence of at least three bases do we have sufficient combinations (4^3 or 64) to code for the amino acids present during protein biosynthesis. These sequences of three bases (strictly three ribonucleotide units) are referred to as *triplets*. One of the great achievements in biochemistry in recent years has been the complete deciphering of the genetic code through the determination of the relationship between a triplet base sequence and the amino acid with which it is associated—*the triplet code*. This has been done mainly through the work of Nirenberg and Khorana and their co-workers. Nirenberg prepared a large number of synthetic m-RNA molecules by enzyme-catalysed polymerization. For example, polymerization of ATP or UTP gave homopolymers with base sequence ...ApApAp... and ...UpUpUp... respectively. When these materials were introduced into a protein biosynthesis system, it was found that polylysine and polyphenylalanine respectively were formed. Hence, it could be deduced that the triplet code for lysine is ApApA, and that for phenylalanine is UpUpU. The polymerization of mixtures of ribonucleoside triphosphates gave heteropolymers which provided further, if often ambiguous, triplet codes. Khorana prepared, by unambiguous chemical synthesis, the sixty-four possible triribonucleotides of general structure XpYpZ (see section 8.5.4). Although these molecules were not of the same order of molecular size as

448

Table 9.2 The genetic code

UUU	} Phe	UCU	}	UAU	} Tyr	UGU	} Cys
UUC		UCC	} Ser	UAC		UGC	
UUA	} Leu	UCA		UAA	*	UGA	*
UUG		UCG	}	UAG	*	UGG	Trp
CUU	}	CCU	}	CAU	} His	CGU	}
CUC	} Leu	CCC	} Pro	CAC		CGC	} Arg
CUA		CCA		CAA	} Gln	CGA	
CUG	}	CCG	}	CAG		CGG	}
AUU	}	ACU	}	AAU	} Asn	AGU	} Ser
AUC	} Ile	ACC	} Thr	AAC		AGC	
AUA		ACA		AAA	} Lys	AGA	} Arg
AUG	Met and Formyl-Met	ACG	}	AAG		AGG	
GUU	}	GCU	}	GAU	} Asp	GGU	}
GUC	} Val	GCC	} Ala	GAC		GGC	} Gly
GUA		GCA		GAA	} Glu	GGA	
GUG	}	GCG	}	GAG		GGG	}

These 'triplets' or codons were determined for *Esch. coli* but appear to be universal. The codons are written in the $5' \rightarrow 3'$ direction. Codons marked * carry the chain termination instruction

m-RNA molecules, nevertheless interaction at a ribosome surface with a specific amino-acid acyl-RNA could be observed. For example, when the following triribonucleotides: ApApA, ApApG, GpApA and ApGpA (all possible components in a heteropolymeric RNA made from an ATP/GTP mixture) were added to a system of ribosomes containing ^{14}C-lysine t-RNA, only ApApA and ApApG stimulated the binding of the labelled amino-acid acyl-RNA to the ribosomes. It was concluded that AAA and AAG only were 'codons' for lysine. By this type of experiment a set of codons for each amino acid were determined (Table 9.2).

It has been found from these studies that the triplet code is *degenerate*— that is, that there is more than one triplet for a particular amino acid. There have also been found to be certain triplets which indicate the termination of a polypeptide chain: UAA, UAG and UGA; and one AUG which initiates the synthesis (see section 9.5.3).

9.5.3 Protein biosynthesis

The mechanism of protein biosynthesis is the most complex process yet studied in living organisms. Most of our knowledge has come from a study of the process as it occurs in microorganisms, particularly *Esch. coli*; but there is every reason to believe that the main features, revealed in the simplest forms of life, are the same in higher organisms. The two fundamental problems that have to be resolved in the process for protein biosynthesis are the processes by which the triplet sequences present in m-RNA are translated accurately into the amino acid sequence; secondly, the process by which the necessary energy is provided for the formation of a peptide bond. This latter process has been shown to require the participation of ATP with which, in the presence of a specific activating enzyme, an amino-acid acyl-derivative (I) is formed. This molecule, still bound to the activating enzyme, interacts with a specific t-RNA molecule. The amino acid becomes bound, at the 3'-hydroxyl group of the terminal adenosine residue, and the enzyme and AMP are released (Fig. 9.36). For each amino acid there appears to be at least one specific t-RNA molecule available, and there is a specific activating enzyme to control both stages of the process.

Four functional sites may be present on a t-RNA molecule [Fig. 8.48(a)]. First, the amino-acid attachment site; this is at the hydroxyl terminus where the nucleotide sequence is invariably CpCpA-OH (Fig. 9.36). These nucleotides are not present in the t-RNA precursor but are added after transcription. The second site is that involved in recognition of the specific amino-acid

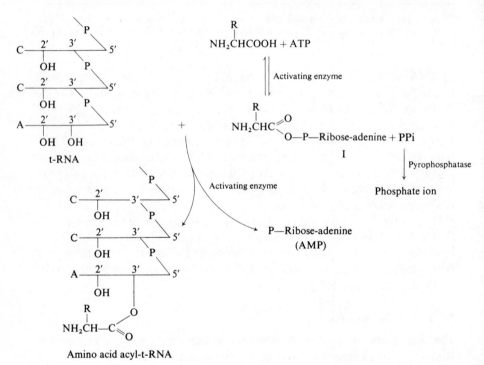

Fig. 9.36 Binding of an α-amino acid to its t-RNA

450

activating-enzyme. This site must involve a sequence of nucleotides which are different in each t-RNA, although this site has not been positively identified, it could be in the region adjacent to the hydroxyl terminus. The third site, also unique to a particular t-RNA, is the *anti-codon* (codon recognizing site). This contains a triplet of non-hydrogen-bonded bases complementary to the codon of m-RNA. These bases lie in the second loop from the phosphate terminus [Fig. 8.48(a)]. Finally, a non-specific fourth site is thought to be present which binds to the 50S ribosome fragment and assists in binding of t-RNA to m-RNA.

The mobilization of the amino acids for protein biosynthesis, as amino acid acyl-t-RNAs, takes place in the cytoplasm. The formation of the polypeptide chain takes place either on the ribosomes of the rough endoplasmic reticulum or in small clusters of isolated cytoplasmic ribosomes (polysomes). The information to define the sequence of amino acids, encoded in a gene of DNA, is brought by m-RNA from the nucleus (in eukaryotic cells)—this process is called *translation*. The two fragments of the ribosome (section 8.5.3) combine together at the phosphate terminus of m-RNA. Two binding sites may be distinguished in the larger of the two ribosome fragments (50S): one which 'accepts' the amino-acid acyl-t-RNA and allows recognition between codon and anti-codon, adjacent to this is the site at which peptide bond formation takes place. Binding of the enzyme peptidyl transferase occurs at the latter site.

The mechanism of polypeptide synthesis shown in Fig. 9.37, was obtained from studies with *Esch. coli in vitro* and is typical of bacterial protein biosynthesis. Many different factors are needed and the exact purpose of some of these is not known with certainty. The initiation codon on m-RNA is AUG and this binds a t-RNA bearing formyl-methionine (t-RNA$_F$) in the acceptor site. Three protein factors have been shown to be needed in setting up the initiation stage (F_1, F_2, F_3—Fig. 9.37). The ribosome moves in a $5' \to 3'$ direction during elongation of the polypeptide chain and this motion, for which GTP is a factor, moves the t-RNA$_F$ to 'peptide site' and the next amino-acid acyl-t-RNA is 'accepted'. Two protein factors (F_4 and F_5—Fig. 9.37) and GTP are needed in the attachment of amino-acid acyl-t-RNAs to the ribosome. Peptide bond formation between the amino acids bound at the ribosome is then catalysed by peptidyl transferase. In this reaction, the t-RNA of the carboxyl component is displaced and leaves the ribosome. Elongation continues by repetition of this sequence of events. The termination codons on m-RNA are known to be UAA, UAG or UGA; when one of these appears at the acceptor site, a protein factor (R—Fig. 9.37) becomes bound and formation of polypeptide ceases.

From this discussion, it is clear that the main features of polypeptide synthesis are known, at least in bacteria. The chain is assembled in an unambiguous stepwise manner from the amino-terminus. The initiation stage so important in ensuring correct reading of the m-RNA message, is well

451

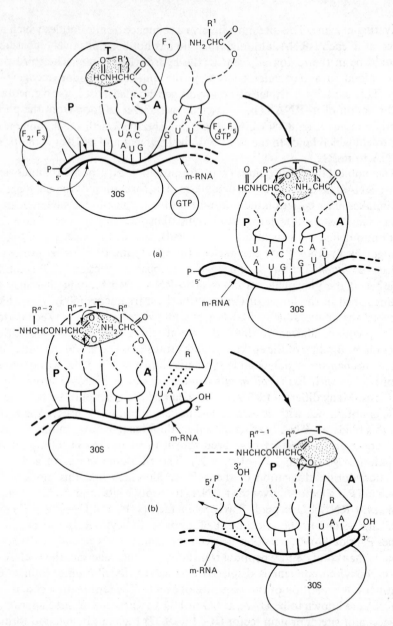

Fig. 9.37 Diagrammatic representation of polypeptide synthesis in bacteria: (a) initiation and elongation, (b) termination. A = 50S ribosome fragment 'acceptor' site. P = 50S ribosome fragment 'peptide bond formation' site. T = 50S ribosome fragment peptidyl transferase binding site. F_1 = initiator factor for t-RNA_F binding. F_2, F_3 = Initiator factors for ribosome/m-RNA binding. F_4, F_5 = Elongation factors for binding other t-RNAs. R = Termination factor. R' = Side-chain of formyl-methionine. R^1 = Side-chain of valine

defined. Methionine appears at the N-terminus of many *Esch. coli* proteins but not all, hence de-formylation must follow polypeptide synthesis and, in many cases, loss of the methionyl residue. Two t-RNAs for methionine are found in *Esch. coli*: one is specific for initiation (t-RNA$_F$) and the second for methionyl residues within the polypeptide chains (t-RNA$_M$). Both respond to the codon AUG. Initiation by this codon, binding t-RNA$_F$, has also been observed in plant chloroplasts and in eukaryotic mitochondrial protein biosynthesis.

Electron microphotographs have shown that several ribosomes become attached to a single m-RNA chain, and at each ribosome a polypeptide chain is synthesized. It appears that the ribosomes move along the m-RNA chain and, as they do so, the polypeptide chain increases in length. This complex system, known as a *polysome system*, is shown in a highly simplified schematic diagram (Fig. 9.38). As the ribosome reaches the end of the m-RNA chain the polypeptide chain is released into the cytoplasm, where it folds into its unique secondary and tertiary structure. The ribosome splits into its two main fragments which are then available to return to the other end of the m-RNA chain and start the operation all over again.

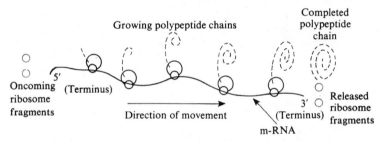

Fig. 9.38 A polysome system

This account of the process of protein biosynthesis is of necessity only an outline of a process on which a great deal of work is currently in progress. It will, however, serve to introduce the topic to the student, and also to provide a basis for the final topic; that is the regulation of enzyme biosynthesis. Through the process of protein biosynthesis just described, we can see how DNA 'directs' the chemical activity of the cell through controlling the sequence, and hence the structure, of polypeptide chains which constitute the enzymes required in the cells' metabolism. In some cases (see, for example, chymotrypsinogen, section 8.2.2), the protein undergoes further structural changes to become the active enzyme. DNA also regulates the production of polypeptides.

Jacob and Monod, on the basis of studies on *Esch. coli*, proposed in 1961 a general process whereby the regulatory role of DNA in protein biosynthesis may be explained. They distinguish two separate functions for the gene regions of DNA. Firstly there is the *operon* region, from which coding of m-RNA molecules associated with enzyme–protein production takes place (designated as regions A, B, C, etc., in Fig. 9.39). Secondly there is a region, known as a *regulator gene*, which codes for an m-RNA which produces a *repressor polypeptide*. This repressor polypeptide can inactivate the operon system by acting on a small part of the operon, the *operator gene* (designated O—Fig. 9.39).

The role of the operator gene is a negative one, in allowing formation of the m-RNAs from the operon, but having the ability to *stop* this transcription when inactivated by the repressor. The action of the repressor can be likened to that of an allosteric enzyme, in that its action may be inhibited by an *inducer*. This latter process allows the synthesis of several functionally related proteins to take place. In examples of this process so far identified, it appears that the inducer may well be a substrate such as a carbohydrate, whose breakdown is required for the release of energy in the organism.

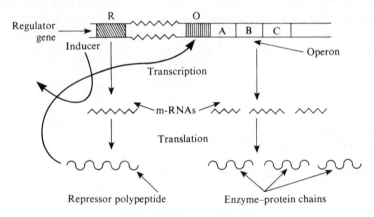

Fig. 9.39 The operon model for the regulation of protein biosynthesis

Since the enunciation of the operon theory, evidence has been produced that the general mechanism is substantially correct, at least for the control of the *lactose system* in *Esch. coli*. It was found that *Esch. coli* only produce a β-galactosidase when a β-galactoside such as lactose is present. On removal of the sugar, production of the enzyme ceases; thus the sugar acts as an *inducer*. In the region of the bacterial chromosome responsible for the lactose system (*lac* region), there are three structural genes (Fig. 9.39: A codes for the β-galactosidase, B codes for a β-galactoside permease—which is involved in transporting the enzyme across the cell wall membrane—and C codes for a transacetylase of unknown function). Much detailed knowledge is now available on structure and properties of the *lac operon*.

This method of regulating metabolic activity is quite different from that due to allosteric inhibition and activation (see sections 8.2.1 and 9.3.4).

Regulator genes control the amount of enzymes produced, while allosteric effects control the activity of the enzymes and in no way control the amount present. Since our knowledge of metabolic pathways is almost complete, it can be expected that in the years to come Biochemists will concentrate on the elucidation of the detailed mechanism of these processes of metabolic control.

Bibliography

1. J. R. Bronk, *Chemical Biology—an introduction to biochemistry*, Collier-MacMillan, 1973.
2. P. Karlson, *Introduction to Modern Biochemistry*, 4th Edn, Academic Press, 1975.
3. H. R. Mahler and E. H. Cordes, *Biological Chemistry*, 2nd Edn, Harper and Row, 1972.
4. S. Dagley and D. E. Nicholson, *An Introduction to Metabolic Pathways*, Blackwell, 1970.
5. A. L. Lehinger, *Biochemistry*, 2nd Edn, Worth, 1976.
6. G. H. Haggis, D. Michie, A. R. Muir, K. B. Roberts and P. M. B. Walker, *Introduction to Molecular Biology*, 2nd Edn, Longmans, 1974.
7. J. Bonner and J. E. Varner, *Plant Biochemistry*, Academic Press, 1965.
8. D. A. Bender, *Amino acid Metabolism*, Wiley, 1975.
9. A. Kornberg, *DNA Synthesis*, Freeman, 1974.
10. V. M. Ingram, *Biosynthesis of Macromolecules*, 2nd Edn, Benjamin, 1972.
11. E. J. DuPraw, *DNA and Chromosomes*, Holt, Rinehart and Winston, 1970.

Index

459

461

463

465

Heat capacity at constant pressure, 74
Heat of combustion, 72
  of selected compounds (table), 73
Heat content, 70
Heat of:
  dilution, 74
  dissociation, 73
  formation, 70
  neutralization, 72
  reaction:
    at constant pressure, 68
    at constant volume, 68
    and enthalpy change, 70
    temperature dependence, 74
    and work in a chemical reaction, 69
  solution, 73
Heisenberg Uncertainty Principle, 6
Helical conformations:
  in biopolymers, 315
  in nucleic acids, 371 ff.
  in polysaccharides, 313
  in proteins, 360 ff.
Helium:
  electronic structure, 4
Helmholtz free energy, 76
Hemi-acetals, 119
Hemicelluloses, 338, 339
  in glucomannans, 339
  in mannans, 339
  in xylans, 339
Henderson–Hasselbalch equation, 192
Henry's Law, 147
Heparin, 340, 341
Hess's Law of Heat Summation, 71
Heterocyclic compounds:
  nomenclature, 46
  reactions of, 116
  structures of, 25, 39
Heteropolymer, 310
Heteropolysaccharide(s), 310, 336
Hexaammino cobaltous ion, 19
Hexacyano cobaltic ion, 19
Hexacyano ferrate ion, 19
Hexokinases, 391, 419
Hill reaction, 408 ff.
Hippuric acid, 251
L-Histidine, 251, 252, 255, 366, 367
Histones, 348, 373
Homogeneous catalysis, 98
Homogenistic acid (Homogenistate), 430
Homologous series, 37, 259
Homolytic cleavage of covalent bonds, 103, 134, 135
Hormonal steroids, 299 ff.
Hund's rule, 4
Hyaluronic acid, 340
Hybridization, 13

Hydrates of carbonyl compounds, 119
Hydration reactions, 123
Hydrazine, 120
Hydrazones, 120
Hydrazinolysis of proteins, 349
Hydrocarbons (see alkanes, alkenes, alkynes and aromatic compounds)
Hydrogen atom, 3
Hydrogen bonding, 26 ff.
  in acetic acid, 27
  in o-chlorophenol, 27
  in nucleic acids, 371 ff.
  in proteins, 360 ff.
  in water, 26
Hydrogenation, catalytic, 122, 123, 260
Hydrogen electrode, 164
Hydrogen molecule, 11
Hydrolases, 335, 336, 390
Hydrophobic bonding in proteins, 332, 334, 366, 367
Hydrogenolysis (see hydrogenation)
Hydrolysis reactions:
  of amides, 132, 133
  of esters, 132
  of glycosidic bonds, 275 ff., 337 ff., 390 ff.
  of nucleic acids, 376, 377
  of proteins, 349
  of salts, 191
Hydriodic acid, 142
Hydroxy acids, 45, 120, 130
Hydroxy aldehydes, 120
β-Hydroxybutyric acid (β-Hydroxybutyrate), 424
Hydroxylamine, 120
α-Hydroxylignoceric acid, 262, 263
Hydroxylation of double bonds, 122
L-Hydroxylysine, 250
β-Hydroxy-β-methyl glutaryl coenzyme-A, 424
α-Hydroxypropionic acid (see lactic acid)
p-Hydroxyphenyl pyruvic acid, 430
L-Hydroxyproline, 250, 365
Hyperfine interaction in ESR, 237
Hyperosmotic solution, 176
Hypertonic solution, 177
Hypoosmotic solution, 176
Hypothalamic releasing factor, 357
Hypsochromic shift, 223

Ideal solutions, 150
D-Idose, 267
L-Iduronic acid, 340
Imidazole, 39
Immunoelectrophoresis, 199
Indole, 39
Induced fit theory, 318, 319, 333

470

471

Pituitary hormones, 353, 354
pK_a and pK_b:
  tables of, 107, 109
Planck's constant, 6
Plasma membrane, 181
Plasmalogens, 260, 262
Plastoquinones, 411
Plateau of radioactive counters, 32
Platelet aggregation, estimation, 234
Pleated sheet structure of proteins, 361,
  363
Plus and minus method, 374, 375
Polarimeter, 49
Polarized light, 49, 241
Polar reactions, 103, 105
Polarography, 173
  applications, 175
  cathode ray, 175
  differential cathode ray, 175
  using Clark oxygen electrode, 176
Polyacrylamide gel electrophoresis (PAGE),
  199
Polyamines, 187
Polyamino acids, 254
Polydisperse, 306, 310
Polyethylene, 309
Polyglycerol phosphate, 343, 344
Polymer(s), 303
  hetero-polymer(s), 310
  homo-polymer(s), 310
Polynucleotide chain, 310
Polypeptide(s), 347 ff.
  antibiotics, 251, 357 ff.
  chain, 250
  hormones, 353 ff.
  hormone precursors, 356, 357
  hormone releasing factors, 357
  synthesis, 251, 255 ff.
Polyprotic acids, 187
Polyribitol phosphate, 343, 344
Polysaccharidase(s), 317, 390
Polysaccharide(s), 266, 317, 336 ff.
  conjugate, 341 ff.
Polysome system, 451, 453
Polyunsaturated fatty acids, 258, 259, 264
Polyvinyl chloride, 309
POPOP (di[2-(5-phenyloxazolyl-)]-benzene),
  33
Porphyrin(s), 286, 287
  coproporphyrin(s), 287
  etioporphyrin(s), 287
  haematoporphyrin(s), 287
  mesoporphyrin(s), 287
  phaeoporphyrin(s), 288
  protoporphyrin(s), 287
  uroporphyrin(s), 287, 288
Positional isomerism, 42

Potassium chloride:
  bonding in, 8
Potassium dichromate:
  oxidation with, 140, 141
Potassium permanganate:
  hydroxylation with, 122, 260
  oxidation with, 140, 141, 275
Potential:
  action (spike), 183
  cardiac, 185
  resting, 184
Potentiometric titrations, 172
PPO (p-terphenyl-2,5-diphenyloxazole), 33
Pregnanediol, 300
Pregnolone, 300
Prephenic aromatase, 127
Primary structure of biopolymers, 310
Progesterone, 300
Projection formula, 50 ff.
Proinsulin, 356
Prokaryotes, 370
Prolactin releasing factor, 357
  release inhibiting factor, 357
Prolamines, 348
L-Proline, 252, 363, 365, 430
Pronase, 349
Propane, 37, 44
Propionaldehyde, 43
Propionic acid, 400
Propionyl coenzyme-A, 400
Proportional counter, 32
Propylene, 121, 123
Prostaglandins, 264, 265
Prosthetic groups of proteins, 287, 367 ff.
Protamines, 348, 373
Protection of functional groups:
  in polynucleotide synthesis, 384 ff.
  in polypeptide synthesis, 255 ff.
Proteins, 347 ff.
  acid–base properties, 189, 190
  amino-acid analysis and composition,
    349
  biosynthesis of, 385, 449 ff.
  catabolism of, 427, 428
  classification, 347
  criteria of purity, 348
  denaturation, 82, 348, 367
  disulphide bonds, 312, 313, 351, 352
  electrophoresis of, 198
  end-group analysis of, 349, 350
  hydrolysis of, 349
  isoelectric point, 190
  in muscle, 365
  non-covalent bonds in, 365 ff.
  optical rotatory power, 243
  primary structure, 310 ff., 348 ff.
  quaternary structure, 313, 365

473

475

476